EVOLUTION AFTER DARWIN

THE UNIVERSITY OF CHICAGO CENTENNIAL

VOLUME I

THE EVOLUTION OF LIFE

SOL TAX, EDITOR

EVOLUTION

AFTER

DARWIN

THE UNIVERSITY OF CHICAGO CENTENNIAL

VOLUME I

THE
EVOLUTION
OF LIFE

ITS ORIGIN,
HISTORY AND FUTURE

THE
UNIVERSITY OF
CHICAGO PRESS

EVOLUTION AFTER DARWIN

THE UNIVERSITY OF CHICAGO CENTENNIAL

VOLUME I

THE EVOLUTION OF LIFE

EDITED BY SOL TAX

VOLUME II

THE EVOLUTION OF MAN

EDITED BY SOL TAX

VOLUME III

ISSUES IN EVOLUTION

EDITED BY SOL TAX AND CHARLES CALLENDER

Library of Congress Catalog Number: 60-10575

The University of Chicago Press, Chicago 37
Cambridge University Press, London, N.W. 1, England
The University of Toronto Press, Toronto 5, Canada

PREFACE

On November 24, 1859, Charles Darwin at last saw in print the manuscript over which he had labored for almost a quarter of a century, the book whose ponderous title has become the familiar *Origin of Species*. The world had been waiting, and in a single day the first edition of 1,500 sold out. One hundred years later, the day was celebrated as marking one of those events that influence the career of man by changing his perspective of himself and his place in the universe.

The University of Chicago in December, 1955, began planning its celebration of the centenary in the most appropriate manner—bringing to bear on the subject of evolution current knowledge from a variety of relevant fields, thus advancing once more our understanding of the world and man.

About fifty scientists were selected during 1956, and their themes were agreed upon; during 1957 and 1958 they developed the papers that are published here. As these were completed, they were exchanged among the authors. Armed with new information and insights, all but five of the authors met at the University on November 22, 1959, to prepare for panel discussions of the issues in evolution; these were held for the public during a five-day Celebration, beginning on the Centennial of the publication date of *Origin of Species*. The discussions were based on the papers that had been prepared and distributed in advance, but were not delivered at the Celebration.

The present volume, *The Evolution of Life*, and its companion volume, *The Evolution of Man*, represent most of the collected University of Chicago Centennial papers. A small group on the relationship between science and spiritual values appears in a third volume, *Issues in Evolution*, which also contains the panel discussions and an index to all three volumes. Collectively, this work is called *Evolution after Darwin*.

Sir Julian Huxley's essay, which opens the present volume, provides an introduction to Charles Darwin and to evolution. Then, after a substantial up-to-date review, from several disciplines, of our knowl-

v

edge of the origin and history of life, the book plunges into an analysis of the processes governing growth and change.

For the selection of scientist-contributors to this first volume, Alfred E. Emerson, Everett C. Olson, and the late Karl P. Schmidt share major responsibility with the editor on behalf of the Darwin Centennial Celebration Committee. The authors themselves are, of course, fully responsible for their respective contributions.

Sol Tax

Chicago
February 1960

CONTENTS

THE EMERGENCE OF DARWINISM   1
  Sir Julian Huxley

ON THE EVIDENCES OF INORGANIC EVOLUTION   23
  Harlow Shapley

THE ORIGIN OF LIFE   39
  Hans Gaffron

VIRUSES AND EVOLUTION   85
  Earl A. Evans, Jr.

THE LAWS OF EVOLUTION   95
  Bernhard Rensch

THE HISTORY OF LIFE   117
  George Gaylord Simpson

EVOLUTION IN PROGRESS   181
  E. B. Ford

THE COMPARATIVE EVOLUTION OF GENETIC SYSTEMS   197
  G. Ledyard Stebbins

THE EVOLUTION OF FLOWERING PLANTS   227
  Daniel I. Axelrod

THE EVOLUTION OF ADAPTATION IN POPULATION SYSTEMS   307
  Alfred E. Emerson

THE EMERGENCE OF EVOLUTIONARY NOVELTIES   349
    Ernst Mayr

EVOLUTIONARY ADAPTATION   381
    C. H. Waddington

EVOLUTION AND ENVIRONMENT   403
    Th. Dobzhansky

PHYSIOLOGICAL GENETICS, ECOLOGY OF POPULATIONS,
    AND NATURAL SELECTION   429
    Sewall Wright

THE ROLE OF POPULATION DYNAMICS IN NATURAL
    SELECTION   477
    A. J. Nicholson

MORPHOLOGY, PALEONTOLOGY, AND EVOLUTION   523
    Everett C. Olson

ECOLOGY AND EVOLUTION   547
    Marston Bates

COMPARATIVE PHYSIOLOGY IN RELATION TO EVOLUTIONARY
    THEORY   569
    C. Ladd Prosser

BEHAVIOUR, SYSTEMATICS, AND NATURAL SELECTION   595
    N. Tinbergen

DARWINISM, MICROBIOLOGY, AND CANCER   615
    G. F. Gause

SIR JULIAN HUXLEY

THE EMERGENCE OF DARWINISM

Today we celebrate the centenary of an outstanding event in the history of science—the birth of Darwinism or evolutionary biology, initiated by the joint contribution of Charles Darwin and Alfred Russel Wallace to The Linnean Society of London, announcing their independent discovery of the principle of natural selection.

I say Darwinism because not only did Darwin have priority in conceiving that evolution must have occurred, and could only have occurred through the mechanism of natural selection, but he also contributed far more than Wallace, or indeed than any other man, to the solution of the problem and the development of the subject. I shall therefore speak almost entirely about Darwin and Darwinism, endeavouring to bring out facts and ideas which illuminate Darwin's unique role in the history of our science.

Charles Darwin has rightly been described as the "Newton of biology": he did more than any single individual before or since to change man's attitude to the phenomena of life and to provide a coherent scientific framework of ideas for biology, in place of an approach in large part compounded of hearsay, myth, and superstition. He ren-

SIR JULIAN HUXLEY is unsurpassed as a biologist and author of imaginative scope, wisdom, and responsibility. During the past half-century he has added to his illustrious name the record of a great many teaching and service posts, including that of Secretary of the London Zoological Society and two years as the first Director-General of UNESCO. His publications are countless, as are the honors he has received, among them the Huxley Memorial Lecture and Medal of the Royal Anthropological Institute and the Darwin Medal of the Royal Society.

The present paper attests to Sir Julian's stature in his field. Originally delivered in London as the Darwin-Wallace Memorial Lecture at the inaugural meeting of the Fifteenth International Congress of Zoology (July, 1958), it also serves an essential function here. In addition to giving a human portrait of the man Darwin and a description of the stimulating times and figures surrounding publication of the *Origin of Species*, Sir Julian defines Darwin's actual contribution to evolutionary theory. By examining aspects of evolution that puzzled Darwin, he traces the emerging concepts as they came under investigation in the century that followed; and in so doing he gives us a sketch of evolution today and a preview of the present centennial series—*"Evolution after Darwin."*

"The Emergence of Darwinism" is also printed in the *Journal of the Linnean Society of London* (Zoology, XLIV, No. 295) and (*Botany*, LVI, No. 365), July, **1958**.

dered evolution inescapable as a fact, comprehensible as a process, all-embracing as a concept.

His industry was prodigious. His published books run to over 8000 printed pages and contain, on my rough estimate, at least 3,000,000 words. His scientific correspondence must have reached similar dimensions, and his contributions to scientific journals comprise well over 400 pages.

The range of subjects with which he dealt, often as an initiator and always magisterially, was equally remarkable. Let us first recall that at the outset of his career he was more of a geologist than a biologist, that his first scientific works, on coral reefs and on the geology of South America, dealt with geological subjects, and that the only professional position he ever occupied was that of Secretary to the Geological Society. Later, he dealt with the taxonomy and biology of that 'difficult' group of animals, the barnacles or Cirripedes, in its entirety; with the principles and practice of classification; with the evidences for evolution; the theories of natural and sexual selection and their implications; the descent of man, including the evolution of his intellectual, moral, and aesthetic faculties; the emotions and their expression in men and animals; geographical distribution, domestication, variation in nature and under domestication, the effects of self- and cross-fertilization (or, as we should now say, in- and out-breeding) and various remarkable adaptations for securing cross-fertilization, the movements of plants, insectivorous plants, and the activities of earthworms.

Not only is he the acknowledged parent of evolutionary biology, but he is also prominent among the founding fathers of the sciences we now call ecology and ethology.

Above all, he was a great naturalist in the proper sense that he was profoundly interested in observing and attempting to comprehend the phenomena of nature, though at the same time he managed to keep abreast of pure scientific advance in the fields which concerned him, such as general botany, embryology, paleontology, biogeography, taxonomy, and comparative anatomy, as well as with the activities both of professionals and amateurs in what we should now call plant and animal breeding.

He had an inborn passion for natural history, which showed itself from early childhood. Later, like most true naturalists, besides being motivated by intellectual interest, he was deeply moved by the wonder and beauty of nature. As a young man, he found an "exquisite delight in fine scenery," [1] and enjoyed exploring wild and strange country.

[1] "Autobiography" in *L. and L.*, I, 101. *Note.*—In the biographical references *L. and L.* denotes *The Life and Letters of Charles Darwin*, edited by F. Darwin (3d

The combination of passionate and deep emotion appears vividly in the notes he made on his first experience of the tropical rain-forest: "Twiners entwining twiners—tresses like hair—beautiful lepidoptera —Silence—hosannah—frog habits like toad—slow jumps." "Sublime devotion the prevalent feeling." And a little later, "Silence well exemplified. . . . Lofty trees, white boles. . . . So gloomy that only shean [sic] of light enters the profound. Tops of the trees enlumined." [2]

I may perhaps note that this last entry was made, not in the remote depths of the great Amazonian forest as one might expect, but close to Rio, at Botofogo, whose beach is now bordered by luxury hotels and crowded with bathing beauties. However, though roads have robbed the forest behind the beach of its primal virginity, it is otherwise untouched, and in its recesses one can still recapture some of Darwin's feelings.

Another characteristic of Darwin was his extraordinary diffidence, coupled with a passion for completeness and a reluctance, so extreme as to appear almost pathological, to publish to the world his ideas on the controversial subject of evolution before he had buttressed his arguments with a body of evidence which would overwhelm opposition by its sheer vastness. It has been suggested that these traits in Darwin's character, and also the constant ill health from which he suffered after his marriage in 1839, were neurotic symptoms springing from unconscious conflict or emotional tension, and that this in its turn was first generated by Darwin's ambivalent attitude to the dominating and domineering figure of his father, Robert Darwin.[3]

While not necessarily accepting this interpretation in its entirety, there seems no doubt that his ill health was in part what psychiatrists now call an escape mechanism, fostered by the devotion of his wife, who became the ideal sick-nurse as Darwin became the ideal patient. His reluctance to commit himself publicly and in print to belief in the mutability of species and in evolution by natural causes sprang ultimately from some unacknowledged inner conflict which was partly rooted in his relations with his father. It was his father who took him away from school early because he thought he was idle and doing no good; who decided first that he should study medicine, and then, when

ed.; 3 vols.; London, 1887); *Origin* denotes *Origin of Species* by Charles Darwin (3d ed.; London, 1872) reprinted with Preface by G. R. de Beer (Oxford University Press, 1956); *Descent of Man* denotes *The Descent of Man and Selection in Relation to Sex* by Charles Darwin (2d ed.; London, 1874; London: J. Murray, 1922); Nora Barlow denotes *The Autobiography of Charles Darwin*, the first complete version, edited and annotated by Nora Barlow (London: Collins, 1958).

[2] *Charles Darwin and the Voyage of the Beagle,* edited by Nora Barlow (Pilot Press, 1945), pp. 162–65.

[3] E.g. *Biology and Human Affairs* (1954), XX, 1; R. Good, *ibid.,* p. 10; *Nora Barlow,* p. 240 ff.

it was clear that Charles disliked the prospect of becoming a physician, sent him to Cambridge to study for the Church, another profession for which he had no inclination or aptitude; and whose strong opposition to Charles accepting the post of naturalist on the *Beagle* nearly robbed the world of its greatest biologist.[4] He clearly deplored Charles' intense (and apparently innate) devotion to nature and natural history, which was manifested in the pursuits of his childhood and youth, from beetle-collecting to shooting and geologizing in the field. Furthermore, his father was a man of decided opinions, very autocratic with his children, and probably hostile to the whole idea of evolution. In his autobiography Charles states that he never heard the idea of evolution favourably mentioned until he had gone as a medical student to Edinburgh: this at least indicates that it was not discussed in the Darwin home. In any case, what could be more symptomatic of a guilt complex than Darwin's confession, in a letter to Hooker early in 1844, that to assert that species are not immutable is "like confessing a murder"![5] If he felt like this, it is little wonder that he kept on putting off the public statement of his views.

Furthermore, the conflict must have been sharpened by his marriage, for his deeply religious wife was opposed to all unorthodox views. In any case, his chronic ill health did not begin until after his marriage.[6]

His extreme diffidence about the merits of his work (clearly another symptom of inner conflict) is illustrated by a letter of 27 August 1859 to his publisher, John Murray, about the "little work"—as he called the *Origin of Species*—which he was then preparing. 'I feel bound [he wrote] for your sake and my own to say in clearest terms that if after looking over part of my MS. you do not think it likely to have a renumerative sale I completely and explicitly free you from your offer.'[7]

It is worthwhile retelling the salient facts of the story. During the voyage of the *Beagle,* probably towards the end of 1835, he had become convinced that species could not be separate immutable creations. In 1837, soon after his return to England, he started a series of notebooks on the "transmutation of species," in the full consciousness that this would imply large-scale evolution and the common ancestry of all organisms, including man. He soon realized the efficacy of selection in creating new varieties of races of domestic animals and plants,

---

[4] *Nora Barlow,* p. 226 ff.

[5] *L. and L.,* vol. II. This was some eight years after he had become personally convinced of the fact!

[6] The two and a quarter years in London before his marriage he records as the most active he ever spent, marked only by occasional spells when he felt unwell ("Autobiography," *L. and L.,* 1, 67).

[7] Quoted by kind permission of John Murray, Ltd., London.

but was unable to see how it could operate in nature. Then, late in 1838 he "happened to read for amusement *Malthus* on *Population.*"— I quote his own revealing phrase—and the idea of natural selection immediately flashed upon him. "Here then" he continued, "I had at last got a theory to which to work." This vivified all his subsequent thinking: for do not let us forget that Darwin combined inductive and deductive method in a remarkable way. He was never interested in facts for their own sake, but only in their relevance to some hypothesis or general principle.[8] But when he had discovered some satisfactory general principle, he proceeded to deduce the most far-reaching conclusions from it. This is particularly evident, as will appear later, with the principle of natural selection; but it is also true of his treatment of uniformitarianism and the principles of continuity, of sexual selection, and of biological adaptation.

This is perhaps the place to stress another aspect of Darwin's mind. Although his laborious patience in the collection and synthesis of factual evidence has rarely been rivalled (he himself called his mind "a kind of machine for grinding general laws out of large collections of facts"[9]), yet sudden intuition was responsible for some of his most important discoveries of principle, notably natural selection and the explanation of biological divergence—a valuable reminder of the fact that imagination as well as hard work is essential for scientific comprehension.

But I must return to my story. In spite of this illuminating discovery, his reluctance to commit himself was such that not until four years later did he "allow himself the satisfaction" (again a revealing phrase) of putting his ideas on paper; and then only by "writing out in pencil a very brief abstract" of his theory and the evidence for it.[10]

Two years later, in 1844, he enlarged this into an "Essay." As a matter of fact, this so-called essay was a sizeable book of 230 pages, covering almost the same ground as the *Origin,* and more than adequate as an exposition of the whole subject.[11] Yet he still procrastinated, and continued to procrastinate for 14 further years. He showed the essay to no one but Lyell and discussed his evolutionary ideas only with him and a few intimate colleagues, notably Hooker. He continued with the interminable collection of facts, until finally, urged on by Lyell and Hooker, he began in 1856 to write a monumental work on the subject.

Here I must pay tribute to Alfred Russel Wallace. I wish I had

[8] See *Nora Barlow,* pp. 157–64.
[9] "Autobiography," *L. and L.,* 1, 101.
[10] *The Foundations of the Origin of Species,* a sketch written in 1842 by Charles Darwin, edited by Francis Darwin (Cambridge University Press, 1909).
[11] Reprinted with Darwin's sketch of 1842, in C. Darwin & A. R. Wallace, *Evolution by Natural Selection,* edited by G. R. de Beer. (Cambridge University Press, 1958).

more space to set forth his great contribution to evolutionary biology. He laid the foundations of zoogeography, and his notable works on the subject—*the Geographical Distribution of Animals* and *Island Life*—can still be read with profit, as can those on tropical natural history in general—*Tropical Nature* and *The Malay Archipelago*. He was the first to make a comprehensive analysis of cryptic adaptations; he contributed materially to the study of mimicry, and originated the theory of warning coloration. He made many original contributions to the species problem, and in 1855 had published a paper, "On the Law which has regulated the Introduction of New Species" (*Ann. May. Nat. Hist.,* 1855, p. 184), which showed that he believed in the evolution of new species from old, and led to Darwin entering into correspondence with him.

But not only was he a great naturalist, not only did he independently discover the principle of natural selection, but by doing so he forced Darwin into publication. If it had not been for Wallace's attack of malarial fever in Ternate and his impulsive temperament, the *Origin of Species* would never have been published in 1859. Ever since 1855, when he had become convinced that evolution had occurred, the question of *how* changes of species could be brought about was constantly in his thoughts, but he never succeeded in thinking the problem out. The fever, by setting him free from his daily routine of practical detail, permitted his roving mind to discover the principle of natural selection (as with Darwin, in a sudden flash of intuition, and also as a result of reading Malthus and Lyell some time previously); and his temperament, the very opposite of Darwin's, led him to write down his ideas that same evening, to elaborate them during the next two days, and then send them straight off to Darwin for his opinion. The first result, after much heart-searching on Darwin's part and the firm intervention of Lyell and Hooker, was the joint announcement of Darwin's and Wallace's views to The Linnean Society of London on 1 July 1858, and their subsequent publication in the Society's Journal. The second and much more important result was the publication of the *Origin of Species*. Strongly pressed by Lyell and Hooker, in September 1858, Darwin started "abstracting" (his own word) his huge incomplete work, and finished the book in just over thirteen months. Although in his autobiography he still called it "only an abstract," he acknowledged that it was "no doubt the chief work of my life," and this is certainly true.

But for Wallace and his fever, Darwin would assuredly not have overcome his resistance to speedy publication, and would have continued working on "the MS. begun on a much larger scale." In 1858 he envisaged its completion "at the soonest" by 1860. But we can be

sure that his inhibitions over coming into the open, which were transmuted into perfectionist dreams of completeness ("I mean to make my
book as perfect as ever I can," he wrote as late as February 1858 [12]),
would have prevented him from publishing for a much longer time—
perhaps five, perhaps even ten years.

He himself said that the book would have been "four or five times
as large as the *Origin*"—which would mean at least 2500 pages, and
over three-quarters of a million words!—and that very few would have
had the patience to read it.[13] It would, indeed, have been almost un-
readable, and the forceful flow of argument, so well manifested in the
Origin, would have been lost in the sands of over-abundant fact.
Biology certainly owes a great deal to Wallace.

Nor must we forget Lyell. He was the chief source of encourage-
ment to Darwin in his evolutionary work after his return to England
and was mainly instrumental in persuading him to publish his ideas
together with Wallace's paper in 1858. We know that his *Principles of
Geology* influenced Wallace more than any other book. Above all, his
great work demonstrating that slow geological change had occurred as
a result of existing physical causes prepared the ground for the idea of
biological evolution by natural means. As T. H. Huxley wrote in 1887,
he was "the chief agent in smoothing the path for Darwin."

Biology also owes a good deal to Darwin's caution, exaggerated
though this was. If Darwin had rushed into print in 1838 with a brief
and bare account of his conclusions, they would have been stillborn.
The idea of evolution needed heavy reinforcement with facts, and the
idea of natural selection had to be thoroughly worked out in all its
implications. Even though the *Essay* of 1844 went a long way towards
satisfying these requirements, its immediate publication would not, I
am sure, have been nearly so effective as was that of the *Origin* 15
years later. This is partly owing to Darwin's enlargement of his evidence and improvement of his argument, but also to the 'pre-adaptation' of opinion of which Dr. Harrison Matthews writes, the increased
interest of biologists in evolution and their increasing readiness to
discuss it, as well as to the appearance on the biological stage of
younger men, like Wallace, Alfred Newton, and especially Huxley,
ready to be persuaded and become forceful champions of the new and
revolutionary ideas.[14] The best time for Darwin to publish was, I would
say, between 1855 and 1860.

[12] *L. and L.,* 2; 110.
[13] "Autobiography," *L. and L.,* I; 88.
[14] Newton was converted by the joint Darwin-Wallace paper of 1858. "Never shall
I forget the impression it made on me," he wrote. "Herein was contained a perfectly
simple solution of all the difficulties that had been troubling me for months past"
(*Nora Barlow,* p. 157). Otherwise the Linnean paper seems to have fallen rather
flat, and it was reserved for the *Origin* in 1859 to produce a major effect.

Above all, delay in publication gave Darwin time to look at every aspect of his enormous subject, to think out its many implications, and to meet all possible objections. The result was extremely impressive, and far more convincing than any brief sketch, however brilliant, or any speculative picture, such as those drawn by Erasmus Darwin and by Lamarck.

The last paragraph of the *Origin* has often been quoted: I quote it here once again, as admirably illustrating this close-reasoned comprehensiveness of Darwin's work.

It is interesting to contemplate a tangled bank, clothed with many plants of many kinds, with birds singing on the bushes, with various insects flitting about, and with worms crawling through the damp earth, and to reflect that these elaborately constructed forms, so different from each other, and dependent upon each other in so complex a manner, have all been produced by laws acting around us. These laws, taken in the largest sense, being Growth with Reproduction; Inheritance which is almost implied by reproduction; Variability from the indirect and direct action of the conditions of life, and from use and disuse; a ratio of increase so high as to lead to a Struggle for Life, and as a consequence to Natural Selection, entailing Divergence of Character and the Extinction of less-improved forms. Thus, from the war of nature, from famine and death, the most exalted object which we are capable of conceiving, namely, the production of the higher animals, directly follows. There is grandeur in this view of life, . . . that, whilst this planet has gone cycling on according to the fixed laws of gravity, from so simple a beginning endless forms most beautiful and most wonderful have been, and are, being evolved.

It is interesting to pursue the question of timing onto a more speculative plane, and ask ourselves what would have happened to Darwin if he had been born a century earlier or a century later. I would guess that if he had been born in 1709 he might well have become a good amateur naturalist, rather after the pattern of his grandfather Erasmus, one who would, perhaps, have indulged in some interesting speculations on natural history, but would not have been likely to make any major discoveries or to exert any important influence on scientific or general thinking. If he had been born in 1909, he might at most, I would hazard, have achieved some eminence as a professional ecologist. In the one case the time was unripe, in the other over-ripe.

Kroeber has demonstrated that the effective manifestation of genius requires not only exceptional individual talent, but depends also on the circumstances and sometimes the accidents of place and period; nowhere is this better illustrated than in the person of Darwin. First of all, the scientific and intellectual atmosphere was propitious. The time was just ripe for the tying together of the facts of geology and biology by the unifying principles of evolution. Then, as a boy and young man, Darwin was able to indulge his early taste for natural history; later, his financial independence enabled him to devote himself entirely to his own chosen work, and his invalidism prevented him from wasting time and energy in a round of social engagements and scientific meetings; as an Englishman, he quickly came into contact with the ideas of Malthus, Lyell, and Hooker, which were so decisive for his thought, and with Huxley, who was so important in spreading his doctrine; above all, he had the luck to go as naturalist on the *Beagle*.

Two circumstances of the voyage seem to have been of outstanding importance. First, he was able to study natural history, in its geological as well as in its biological aspects, on a continental scale, and so to appreciate the overall pattern of the fauna and flora, and also their gradual transitions and modifications of detail in relation to changing conditions of time and place. This forced him to think along broad lines, in terms of continuity and gradual evolutionary change: in a way that would hardly have been possible if he had stayed at home. In similar fashion the small extent but great geological variety of Britain prevented its scientists grasping the general principles of soil science, while the great expanses and broad zonation of the Russian landscape facilitated or even forced their recognition by Soviet pedologists.

The other decisive circumstance was the *Beagle's* visit to the oceanic archipelago of the Galapagos. Oceanic archipelagos are rare natural laboratories, in which enquiring and receptive minds can find a demonstration of evolution and how it operates in practice. Darwin's mind was both enquiring and receptive: it seems clear that his experiences here finally crystallized his thought and convinced him that evolution was a fact.

Here biology must acknowledge its very real debt to Darwin's uncle, Josiah Wedgwood. Robert Darwin's objections to Charles' accepting the post of naturalist on the *Beagle* were so strong (and his influence on his son so powerful) that Charles, though eager to accept, wrote to refuse the offer. And it was only his uncle's intervention that persuaded his father to withdraw his objections.[15]

Robert Darwin seems to have taken a rather poor view of Charles' abilities and character. In fact, however, these must already have been impressive at the age of 22. They impressed Henslow and Sedgwick at Cambridge; the Hydrographer to the Navy, in a letter to Captain Fitzroy, his future commanding officer, speaks of him as 'full of zeal and enterprise and having contemplated a voyage on his own account to South America'; and Captain Fitzroy himself wrote to the Hydrog-

[15] See *Nora Barlow*, p. 226 ff.

rapher on 15 August 1832, that "Mr. Darwin is a very superior young man, and the very best that could have been detailed for the task." [16]

But I must return to my central theme. Whatever the contribution of others, Darwin stands out as the prime author and pre-eminent figure of the biological revolution. Wallace himself fully recognized this. It was he who first called Darwin "the Newton of Natural History" (or biology, as we should say today), and he coined the term *Darwinism* as the title of his own book on evolution. The evidence and the arguments marshaled by Darwin in the *Origin* were decisive in persuading leaders of scientific thought like Huxley and Hooker that evolution had occurred and that it was based on a natural and scientifically intelligible mechanism.

Furthermore, his inhibitions over publication disappeared with the appearance of the *Origin,* and he proceeded to develop various aspects of the subject with remarkable speed and energy. Twenty-two years elapsed between his opening his notebooks on the transmutation of species and the publication of the *Origin,* and fourteen years between the writing of the *Essay* and the appearance of the joint paper with Wallace. In the fourteen years after 1859 he published three truly major works—*The Variation of Animals and Plants under Domestication, The Descent of Man and Selection in Relation to Sex,* and *The Expression of the Emotions in Man and Animals*—and two minor (though still important) ones; and if we take the period of twenty-two years we have to add five more volumes, ending with his last book, the fascinating study of earthworms.[17]

The emergence of Darwinism, I would say, covered the fourteen-year period from 1858 to 1872; and it was in full flower until the 1890's, when Bateson initiated the anti-Darwinian reaction. This in turn lasted for about a quarter of a century, to be succeeded by the present phase of Neo-Darwinism, in which the central Darwinian concept of natural selection has been successfully related to the facts and principles of modern genetics, ecology, and paleontology.

When we biologists take stock of our subject today, we speedily discover the magnitude of Darwin's contribution; we see how much of his thought has become incorporated in the permanent framework of our science, how many of his ideas are still alive and fruitful. In the first place, we build on his demonstration that evolution has taken place, and has taken place by natural means, so that both its course and its mechanism can be further investigated by scientific methods. Then his ideas of continuity and gradual transformation remain basic

---

[16] These two letters I am enabled to quote by the courtesy of the present Hydrographer, Rear-Admiral Collins.

[17] This was the expansion of a paper published 43 years previously.

for evolutionary biology—abrupt changes of large extent, as in poly-ploidy, are exceptional. He stressed the importance of time as a factor in evolution: for selection to produce changes of large extent, time must be forthcoming in enormous quantities—how enormous, we have only recently realized. It is by following out such ideas that evolu-tionary biologists are now calculating the actual rates of evolution in different groups.

The principle of natural selection was Darwin's greatest discovery, and it remains central to all biological thinking. Darwin's tenacious and comprehensive mind insisted on deducing all possible general con-clusions from the principle and on pursuing its implications to the limit. Thus natural selection, he saw, implied that evolutionary change would be gradual and slow. But perhaps his conclusions on biological improvement afford the most remarkable example of his capacity for bold yet careful generalization. Natural selection, he wrote, has as its "ultimate result . . . that each creature tends to become more and more improved in relation to their conditions. This improvement in-evitably leads to the gradual advancement of the organisation of the greater number of living beings throughout the world." [18]

The first sentence refers to small-scale processes and makes intel-ligible the omnipresence of detailed adaptation, or biological fitness, as some modern workers prefer to call it. It also implies the point made explicitly by Darwin elsewhere [19] that natural selection can never pro-duce characters which are solely or primarily useful to another species. The second sentence, referring to long-term evolution, extends the idea of improvement to cover improvement in general organization, and seems to be the first scientifically based argument for the in-evitability of biological progress or evolutionary advance.

He saw the implications of intra-sexual competitive selection in producing masculine weapons, and of inter-sexual allaesthetic selec-tion in generating masculine adornments and displays.[20] In *The Ex-pression of the Emotions* he laid the foundations for the modern science of comparative ethology. The very title of the book illustrates his robust naturalism: he saw clearly that the mental and physical characters of organisms are inseparable, and that emotions and in-telligence must evolve as much as brains and bodily organization. He did not hesitate to extend his argument to cover man's distinctive mental capacities, intellectual, aesthetic, and moral.[21] While subscrib-ing to the view that "the moral sense or conscience constitutes by far

[18] *Origin*, p. 127.
[19] *Ibid.*, p. 87.
[20] See below, pp. 13–14.
[21] *Descent of Man*, 2d ed.; chapters 3–5.

the most important differences between man and lower animals," he considered that it had evolved naturally.[22] I cannot forbear from quoting one characteristic passage:

The following proposition seems to me in a high degree probable—namely that any animal whatever, endowed with well-marked social instincts, the parental and filial affections being here included, would inevitably acquire a moral sense or conscience, as soon as its intellectual powers had become as well, or nearly as well developed, as in man [though, he adds, it might not be identical with ours. And later he states that] the belief in spiritual agencies naturally follows from other mental powers.[23]

It is clear that Darwin had fully grasped the important point that certain characters are what may be called consequential, arising in evolution as a consequence of the prior appearance of some other character, or because correlated with a change brought about by natural selection. Elsewhere Darwin stated this conclusion in general terms: "Owing to the Laws of Correlation, when one part varies or the variations are accumulated through natural selection, other variations, often of the most unexpected nature, will ensue." [24]

Another of Darwin's notable deductive conclusions concerns divergence (or *cladogenesis*, as Rensch has called it). He was the first to realize that natural selection will lead inevitably to evolutionary divergence, both the small-scale divergence of related species, and the large-scale divergence which results in the appearance of distinct and well-defined group-units—genera, families, orders—in a hierarchical arrangement. Through the process of divergence each species exploits the resources of the environment more effectively, so that the large-scale result of divergence in the inhabitants of a region is comparable to the physiological division of labour in an individual body.[25]

Darwin was the first to see the evolutionary explanation of the facts, later subsumed by Haeckel under the head of recapitulation, concerning "the wide difference in many classes between the embryo and the adult animal, and of the close resemblance of the embryos within the same class.[26]

His studies on cross-fertilization, and the mechanisms for securing

---

[22] Mrs. Darwin was very antipathetic to the idea that all human morality has 'grown up by evolution' (see *Emma Darwin*, by Mrs. Lichfield [Privately printed edition; 1904] II, 360) and was anxious to avoid any suspicion that Darwin regarded spiritual beliefs as no 'higher' than their animal origins. She persuaded Francis Darwin to cut out various passages on the subject from the MS. of the autobiography which his father had left for posthumous publication (see *Nora Barlow, passim*, where the excised passages have been restored).

[23] *Descent of Man*, 2d ed.; p. 149; p. 194.

[24] *Origin*, p. 86: see also p. 11; p. 207.

[25] *Ibid.*, p. 116.

[26] "Autobiography," *L. and L.*, I, 86.

it, paved the way for modern work on heterosis or hybrid vigour (and its application in the hybrid corn industry), and for a general theory of breeding systems, such as C. D. Darlington has so successfully propounded. In combination with his exhaustive survey of variation under domestication, they contributed materially to the development of the sciences of plant and animal breeding.

Finally, I must mention his conclusions on the processes by which new and successful types originate. While recognizing the importance of isolation, which we now regard as a necessary prerequisite for the separation of one species into two,[27] he laid greater stress on the numerical abundance of the evolving species and the size of the area occupied by it. Greater abundance gives more chance for favourable variations to occur; greater size and diversity of area leads to more vigorous competition for survival, as well as providing greater opportunities for temporary isolation. All this will promote more rapid evolution, and the successful types will have a greater capacity for dispersal and for further evolutionary differentiation.[28] In this, Darwin anticipated in a remarkable way modern views on the factors underlying the origin, spread, and diversification of new types, new unit-steps in the evolutionary process.[29]

It is also, I think, of interest to examine some of Darwin's errors and omissions in the light of our present knowledge. His theory of sexual selection has been the target for bitter and sometimes violent attack. It is true that he did lump together various kinds of display, notably hostile display against rivals and sexual display to potential mates; and that he ascribed much too great importance to female choice. But he grasped the essential point that striking displays must have a biological significance and must be what we now call *allaesthetic* in character, exerting their effect by stimulating the emotions of another individual via its visual or auditory senses. And he was quite correct in ascribing the evolution of masculine weapons to intra-sexual selection as between competing males.

Strangely enough, though he mentions cases where adornments are equally developed in both sexes, he dismissed the possibility of biologically effective mutual display between the actual or potential mates. Yet such displays are frequent and often striking, and must have been seen by naturalists before Darwin wrote the *Descent of Man*.[30] I suspect that he was too deeply committed in his thinking to the ideas of female choice and male competition to envisage the possibility of mu-

[27] E.g. Ernst Mayr, *Systematics and the Origin of Species*, New York, 1942.
[28] *Origin*, p. 107.
[29] See P. J. Darlington, *Zoogeography*, New York and London, 1958.
[30] It is, however, a curious fact that no such displays seem to have been scientifically described until much later.

tual allaesthetic stimulation. Further, in his treatment of the subject he states that sexual selection "acts in a less rigorous manner than natural selection," because "the latter produces its effects by the life or death at all ages of the more or less successful competitor," while with the former, the less successful males merely "leave fewer, less vigorous or no offspring." [31]

This strange error springs, I would guess, from his failure—perhaps inevitable at the time—to think quantitatively on the subject, coupled with his adoption of the phrase *the struggle for existence,* with its implications of an all-or-nothing competition, life or death. If he had ever spelled out natural selection in modern terms, as being the result of the differential reproduction of variants, he would at once have seen that any form of selection can vary in rigour according to circumstances, and indeed that intra-sexual selection between males in a polygamous species is likely to attain maximum selective intensity.

Strangely enough, elsewhere Darwin drops his all-or-nothing view and assumes a differential action of natural selection. This is, so far as I know, the one major point which he failed to think out fully and on which he expressed divergent conclusions.

Though Darwin, like T. H. Huxley, thought very little of Lamarck's views on the mechanism of evolution—in a letter of 1844 to Hooker he writes "Heaven defend me from Lamarck nonsense of a 'tendency to progression,' 'adaptation from the slow willing of animals, etc.' " [32]—he did believe in the inheritance of certain "acquired characters"—the effects of the conditions of life and of use and disuse. Furthermore, he attached more importance to them in later editions of the *Origin.* It is this error, which for want of a better term we may loosely call Lamarckian, with which present-day biologists most often reproach Darwin.

It must be stressed, however, that he regarded these agencies as quite subsidiary to natural selection, which he consistently maintained was much the most important agency of evolutionary change.

These "Lamarckian" errors clearly sprang from the total ignorance of 19th century biology on the subject of heredity. Fleeming Jenkin pointed out in 1867 that, on the current theory of blending inheritance, even favourable new variations would tend to be swamped out of effective existence by crossing, if heritable variation in general was rare and infrequent. [33] It was to provide for sources of more abundant variation

---

[31] *Descent of Man,* 2d ed. p. 349; see also *Origin,* p. 89.

[32] *L. and L.,* II, 23; also 29, 39, 207, 215; III, 14, 15; and for Huxley's views, II, 189. Darwin came to adopt a similar attitude to the evolutionary views of his grandfather Erasmus Darwin, expressed in his *Zoonomia,* as being mainly mere speculation, insufficiently supported by facts.

[33] *L. and L.,* III, 167.

that Darwin came to ascribe increased importance to the evolutionary role of "acquired characters." Only when the actual genetic mechanism had been discovered and its particulate (non-blending) nature had been established, could it be shown—notably by R. A. Fisher—that Lamarckian (and orthogenetic) theories of evolution were not only unnecessary but inherently incorrect.

Disuse often does result in evolutionary degeneration: but, as H. J. Muller has shown, this is the result of mutation and selection, not of the direct inheritance of somatic effects.

Changed conditions again may have evolutionary results—but again not through their direct effects. They may result in increased variability, as Darwin stressed. But this is merely due to rare mutants and new combinations being able to survive in the altered conditions and also to their arising as a result of inbreeding.

In other cases a character which looks like a modification, a direct response to environmental conditions, turns out to be hereditary. We now know that such apparently Lamarckian results may be obtained in a non-Lamarckian way, by what Waddington calls *genetic assimilation*.[34] With characters which in normal stock are only produced by special environmental stimuli (for instance, reduced cross-veins in *Drosophila* wings by high temperatures), selection of those individuals showing the character in extreme form may, in a comparatively few generations, lead to the character appearing in a few individuals without exposure to the special stimulus; and further selection, in normal environmental conditions, will produce an overwhelming majority showing the character.

The developmental process leading to the phenotypic manifestation of such a character has both environmental and genetic determinants. During assimilation the genetic determinant has been strengthened, by selection for genes favouring manifestation, to a point at which the process has been genetically canalized and the environmental determinant is no longer required. But since selection acts not on genotypes but on phenotypes, the environmental determinant was originally necessary to produce something on which selection could operate. The result is a modernized version of Baldwin and Lloyd Morgan's organic selection. Thus assimilation, not the inheritance of acquired characters in the usual sense, could account for the origin of various adaptations, such as genetically determined callosities in the exact situations where they are specially required, and many adaptive features of plant ecotypes.

Other adaptations, however, such as those of the hard parts of

[34] See C. H. Waddington, *The Strategy of the Genes* (London: Allen and Unwin, 1957).

holometabolous insects, or those involving mimetic resemblance, demand explanation (as Darwin fully realized) in terms of natural selection acting on adaptively random genetic variation. But when virtually nothing was known about the mechanism of reproduction, heredity, and development, many phenomena were more readily interpreted on a non-selectionist basis.

It has been suggested that Darwin would have avoided falling into these pitfalls if only he had paid attention to Mendel's work, which was published in 1865, in plenty of time for Darwin to amend his views in later editions of the *Origin*. I do not think this is so. It needed nearly twenty years of intensive research on suitable material such as *Drosophila* before the findings of genetics could be fruitfully integrated with evolutionary theory. Before that, most geneticists, obsessed by the obvious mutations with large effects which they naturally first studied were led to anti-selectionist views and to the idea that evolution would normally take place by discontinuous steps, or even merely as the result of mutation-pressure. Only when they had arrived at a true picture of the genetic constitution as a flexible gene-complex in which many genes of small effect collaborate to produce phenotypic characters, only then could they see that discontinuity in the genetic basis of variation need not imply discontinuity in its phenotypic manifestation. Consequently evolutionary change, though due to selection of genetically discontinuous variants, can normally be continuous.

Darwin had already arrived at this correct conclusion without any knowledge of the underlying mechanisms involved. With his usual common sense he concentrated on phenotypes; accordingly, continuous variation and gradual change became essential in his thought. I suspect that if he had known of Mendel's results he would have regarded them as interesting but exceptional and relatively unimportant for evolution, as he had already done for other cases of large mutations and sharp segregation. A premature attempt at generalizing Mendelian principles would merely have weakened the central Darwinian principle of gradual slow change.

There is, finally, Darwin's failure to recognize explicitly the radical differences between man and other animals, especially between the process of evolution in man and in other animals. It is true that he speaks of high intellectual power and conscious morality as distinctive attributes of our species and implies that human speech is something *sui generis* as a means of communication; [35] it is true that he regards man as the highest product of evolution.[36] But nowhere does he point

[35] *Descent of Man*, 2d ed., p. 932.
[36] *Ibid.*, pp. 946–47.

out man's truly unique and most important characteristic—cumulative tradition, the capacity for transmitting experience and the fruits of experience from one generation to the next; nor does he discuss the implications of this new human mechanism of change, as he did so exhaustively for the biological mechanism of natural selection. Thus, while overwhelmed by the thought that modern Europeans must be descended from ignorant savages, like the naked Fuegians who burst on his astonished sight, he makes no attempt to discuss or even to point out the fact that evolution from the savage to the civilized state involves essentially not a biological but a cultural change.

Why was this? I suggest that it was because Darwin's primary and main aim was to provide convincing evidence that organisms were not immutable creations but had evolved by natural means from something different; and this implied a focussing of attention on their past history. This preoccupation of his with origins is revealed in the titles he chose for his two greatest works—the *Origin of Species* and *The Descent of Man*—though *The Evolution of Organisms* and *The Ascent of Man* would in fact have been more appropriate.

His tactics were probably sound: at the time, the main need was to establish on a firm basis the *fact* of evolution and its scientific comprehensibility. In recent years, however, we have turned our attention to the *course* of evolution; and as a result, have been enabled to reach a number of important conclusions about the evolutionary process in general, and our own place and role within it in particular. This has been largely thanks to the soundness of the foundations, both of fact and of idea, provided by Darwin.

That evolution is a natural process, involving man as well as all other organisms in its unbroken continuity: that natural selection inevitably generates novelty, adaptive improvement, and advance in general organization: that successful types tend to differentiate into dominant groups: that improvement of the mental capacities of life, or as I would prefer to put it, advance in the organization of awareness, has been one of the most striking trends in the evolution of higher animals, and has led naturally to the appearance of the distinctive mental and moral qualities of man—these ideas of Darwin, I would say, have been especially important for the later development of evolutionary theory.

The study of evolution's course, following up Darwin's ideas on divergence and the formation of dominant groups, has revealed that evolutionary advance occurs in a series of steps, through a succession of dominant types. This is the result of very long-term selection, selection between types or groups instead of between individuals. The more efficient type will automatically tend to spread and differentiate at the expense of the less efficient: it is as simple as that. As a result, the more efficient type evolves into a large and successful group, while earlier groups with which it competes are reduced. Taxonomic groups are thus organizational grades as well as phylogenetic units. And the grade is the unit of evolutionary advance. On the large and long-term scale this process results in the familiar but essential fact of the succession and replacement of large dominant groups, each embodying some important new improvement and constituting a new organizational grade.

Sooner or later, each group realizes all its inherent possibilities and becomes stabilized, incapable of major advance except through the rare event of some line evolving an organization with new advantages, and so permitting a break-through to a new grade of advance. This, it seems, can never happen twice, for competition with the established successful type will automatically prevent a second invasion of the same evolutionary territory.

This was an important clarification of the biological scene. Meanwhile, the window that Darwin opened into the world of life permitted a new and evolutionary view of other subjects. Men began studying the evolution of nebulae and stars, of languages and tools, of chemical elements, of social organizations. Eventually they were driven to view the universe at large *sub specie evolutionis,* and so to generalize the evolutionary concept in fullest measure. This extension of Darwin's central idea—of evolution by natural means—is giving us a new vision of the cosmos and of our human destiny.

Evolution in the most general terms is a natural process of irreversible change, which generates novelty, variety, and increase of organization: and all reality can be regarded in one aspect as evolution. Biological evolution is only one sector or phase of this total process. There is also the inorganic sector and the psycho-social or human sector. The phases succeed each other in time, the later being based on and evolving out of the earlier. The inorganic phase is pre-biological, the human is post-biological. Each sector or phase has its own characteristic method of operation, proceeds at its own tempo, possesses its own possibilities and limitations, and produces its own characteristic results, though the later phases incorporate some of the methods and results of the earlier ones.

The inorganic phase operates by physico-chemical interaction, proceeds with extreme slowness, and produces only low degrees of organization. On our earth and probably on a number of other planets, conditions favoured the production of more complex chemical compounds, culminating in substances, capable of self-reproduction and self-variation, and therefore subject to a new mechanism of change—

natural selection. The passing of this critical point initiated the organic phase of evolution, which proceeded at a much quicker tempo, produced far more variety, and reached far higher levels of organization. The great novelty of the biological phase was the emergence of awareness—psychological or mental capacities—to a position of increasing biological importance.

Eventually, in the line leading to man, the organization of awareness reached a level at which experience could be not only stored in the individual but transmitted cumulatively to later generations. This second critical point initiated the human or psycho-social phase of evolution. In this phase, though natural selection and physico-chemical interaction continued to operate, they were subsidiary to the new mechanism of change based on cumulative cultural tradition. As a result its tempo was again much accelerated, it reached still higher levels of organization, and it produced quite novel results, such as laws, philosophies, machines, and works of art.

In broadest terms, the biological phase of evolution stems from the new invention of self-reproducing matter; the human phase, from that of self-reproducing mind.

Man's acquisition of a second mechanism, over and above that of the chromosomes and genes, for securing both evolutionary continuity and evolutionary change, a mechanism based on his capacity for conceptual thought and symbolic language, enabled him to cross the barrier set by biological limitations and enter the virgin fields of psycho-social existence. By the same token he became the latest dominant type of life, shutting the door on the possibility of any other animal making the same advance and disputing his own unique position.

In the light of these facts and ideas, man's true destiny emerges in a startling new form. It is to be the chief agent for the future of evolution on this planet. Only in and through man can any further major advance be achieved—though equally he may inflict damage or distortion on the process, including his own evolving self.

It is in large measure due to Darwin's work on biological evolution that we now possess this new vision of human destiny, and only by using Darwin's naturalistic approach in tackling the problems of psycho-social evolution can we hope to understand that destiny better and to fulfil it more adequately.

Evolution in the psycho-social phase is primarily cultural: it is predominantly manifested by changes in human cultures, not in human bodies or human gene-complexes. (I am, of course, using *culture* in its broad anthropological and sociological sense, to include art and language, religion and social organization, as well as material culture.)

But, though it thus differs radically from evolution in the biological phase, the process is still a natural phenomenon, to be studied by the methods of science like other natural phenomena. Machines, works of art, social organizations, educational systems, agricultural methods, religions, yes, and even men's values and ideals, are natural phenomena, at once products of and efficient agencies in the process of cultural evolution. The rise and fall of empires and cultures is a natural phenomenon, just as much as the succession of dominant groups in biological evolution.

Cultural evolution is based on the cumulative transmission of experience and its fruits, which provides a second system of heredity and variation, in addition to the biological system embodied in the gene-complex: for brevity's sake we can call it tradition. Thus the selective mechanism which determines what elements shall be incorporated and what rejected in the system of tradition, and so decides between alternative courses of cultural evolution, must be primarily psychological or mental, involving human awareness instead of human genes, and directed towards the satisfaction of felt needs, instead of merely tending towards the survival of the more biologically fit: further, it operates only within the framework of human societies. We may call it *psycho-social selection.*

Though natural selection is an ordering principle, it operates blindly; it pushes life onwards from behind, and brings about improvement automatically, without conscious purpose or any awareness of an aim. Psycho-social selection too acts as an ordering principle. But it pulls man onwards from in front. For it always involves some awareness of an aim, some element of true purpose. Throughout biological evolution the selective mechanism remained essentially unchanged. But in psycho-social evolution the selective mechanism itself evolves as well as its products. It is a goal-selecting mechanism, and the goals that it selects will change with the picture of the world and of human nature provided by man's increasing knowledge. Thus as human comprehension, knowledge and understanding increase, the aims of evolving man can become more clearly defined, his purpose more conscious and more embracing.

In the light of our present knowledge man's most comprehensive aim is seen not as mere survival, not as numerical increase, not as increased complexity of organization or increased control over his environment, but as greater fulfilment—the fuller realization of more possibilities by the human species collectively and more of its component members individually.

Darwin ended *The Descent of Man* with this characteristic passage: "Man may be excused for feeling some pride at having risen, though not through his own exertions, to the very summit of the organic scale; and the fact of his having thus risen, instead of having been aboriginally placed there, may give him hope for a still higher destiny in the distant future. But we are not here concerned with hopes or fears, only with the truth as far as our reason permits us to discover it."

Today, building on the foundations provided by Darwinism, we can utilize evolutionary concepts in thinking about the history and future of our species. Human destiny need no longer be merely an affair of hopes and fears. In principle, it can be rationally defined on the basis of scientific knowledge, and rationally pursued by the aid of scientific methods. Once greater fulfilment is recognized as man's ultimate or dominant aim, we shall need a science of human possibilities to help guide the long course of psycho-social evolution that lies ahead.

On this centenary occasion we commemorate not only the birth and emergence of Darwinism, but also its achievement. In the past hundred years it has given us a comprehension of the biological past, and that comprehension is now beginning to illuminate the human future.

HARLOW SHAPLEY

ON THE EVIDENCES
OF INORGANIC EVOLUTION

Both to scholars and to laymen the term "evolution" generally elicits only biological pictures—apes that resemble humans, dogs that deviate far from the ancestral wolves, hybrid corn that shames the primitive grain from which it evolved. Indeed evolution and biology are so intimately associated that some may be surprised to find a paper by a cold-blooded astronomer in the midst of many by dedicated biologists and humanologists.

Perhaps I was invited because I sometimes lurk around marine biological stations and at times indulge in observations of the allegedly silly antics of ants and wasps. Now that I am admitted to this company I am inclined, ungraciously, to suggest that terrestrial biological evolution is but a rather small affair, a complicated side show, in the large evolutionary operation that the astronomer glimpses.

This down-grading of the human exhibit may not be a popular enterprise, and actually not too justifiable; it may be a bit premature. The cosmogonist, peering under the flap of the main tent, has as yet but a meager prospect of the cosmic circus. He can, however, already report loosely on some of the big acts as viewed from his awkward position and equipped, as he is, with only primitive optics. He may do much better. The evolution of his techniques and his ambitions may eventually justify ranking him considerably above the primal ooze from which his forebears emerged, some ten or fifteen galactic rotations ago (two or three billion of terrestrial years).

COSMIC EVOLUTION

The sun shines. The obviousness of that fact is exceeded only by the statement's profundity. For therein lies the answer to those who deny,

HARLOW SHAPLEY, Professor Emeritus of Astronomy at Harvard University, has earned international fame for his work as astronomer and lecturer at a great many universities, both in America and abroad. He is well known for his research in photometry and cosmogony, but he is no less acclaimed for his ability to write readable scientific books, such as *The Inner Metagalaxy* (1957) and *Of Stars and Men* (1958).

or at least question, on the grounds of mistaken theological orthodoxy, the occurrence of any kind of evolution.

There is nothing miraculous in sunshine. It represents the transfer across space of energy that is produced by atomic activities at the surface of a star. A lighted match is analogous. The match and the sun both send out to surrounding cooler environments their visible and invisible radiations. The energy stored in the molecules of the match and in the atoms of the sun flows outward from the hot sources, and by its leaving, the masses are reduced. Or, put otherwise, our sun grows less in mass second by second, hour by hour, year by year, simply because it shines. Inevitably and concurrently the volume and density must also change; therefore, through radiating, the sun evolves, and does so irreversibly. Sunlight requires solar evolution, and the rate of change in mass is measured by the basic principle tied up in Einstein's formula $M = E/c^2$.

By extension of the argument, starshine indicates that the billions of radiating stars also evolve. For when a star shines away some of its stored-up energy (E), and thereby loses mass (M), there occur of necessity changes in other related properties. Eventually the alterations in mass, temperature, size and density will be sufficient to affect noticeably the amount of radiation; and in a long, long time the changes will affect the biological situations on whatever life-bearing planets there may be in the star's family of dependents.

The foregoing preliminary argument has two aims: providing evidence that evolution is a cosmic operation, and setting the stage for inquiries about various facets of inorganic evolution. For example, do nebulae evolve? And star clusters? And even the mighty galaxies? And how about comets? Or, to get more human, how about the evolution of and *on* planets, on one in particular? Have the seas and mountains of this planet's crust changed with time? And the chemistry of the oceans and the soils?

Deepest of all inquiries for the non-biological evolutionist are questions concerning the mutation of the atoms, of which all matter is composed, and, at the other extreme of size, the origin, growth, and destiny of the total universe.

MAN'S INHERENT INCOMPETENCE

Many of these questions are beyond our present knowing, perhaps beyond the knowable. Before we undertake to present some partial answers, it might be well to intimate why we cannot hope to present the full and final response.

Briefly stated, it is because we are dumb. Congenitally dumb, innately, born in us, and there is not much that we can do about it except play spiritedly in the noble game of "Approach." We sometimes conceal our impotence, and our failure to attain omniscience, behind the neat phrase that it is, after all, better to search than to find. And sometimes we seek to justify our continuous nervous efforts by the argument that it is better to go as far as we can than to sit on our hands; better to grope hopefully, to approach truth bravely, even with our poor equipment for knowing, than to remain ignorantly idle and offer false panaceas, such as the claim that all and every question can be answered through reliance on a supernatural deity.

OUR DIMINISHING SIGNIFICANCE

My simple, perhaps too simple, diagnosis of our pandemic ailment is that we have been and still are bedeviled by a natural and persisting anthropocentrism. Temporary correctives are provided by science, but we suffer relapses and return to believing that we are somehow important and supremely powerful and comprehending in the universe. Of course we are not.[1] We have learned that fact slowly and accepted it but partially.

Anthro-to geo-to heliocentrism.—Two or three millennia ago, when early man began to explore and grope for answers to astronomical puzzles, the primeval human vanity and anthropocentric philosophy had to give way to geocentrism. That earth-center theory was a bit complicated, and eventually the simpler heliocentrism took over. It was simpler for the sincere scholar, though perhaps not so for the thoughtless, wrapped up in his self-esteem. There was also a bit of resistance on the part of the thoughtful; change incites resistance naturally. For example, in its early days Harvard College stood by the Ptolemaic interpretation—more than a century after the death-bed appearance of *De Revolutionibus Orbium Coelestium*.

The Copernican heliocentric cosmogony prevailed for more than three centuries and widened its range in that the sun eventually was considered to be not only central in its own planetary family, and in full command through gravitation, but it also appeared to be the central object for the whole stellar world. Central, but scarcely a ruling body, for the early telescopes had revealed millions of stars, and there was no good evidence that they were relatively small or weak and easily manageable. Admittedly the sun might not control the stellar universe; but the presumed central position of the sun and its planets supported emerging man's claim to some vague cosmic importance.

---

[1] Salvador Dali dissents: "The universe is a slight thing compared with the amplitude of a brow painted by Raphael."

Man is still emerging, we hopefully note; but he is still vain: a major portion of the discussion at this conference deals directly or indirectly with *Homo,* deals with a single genus among the thousands of genera on the crust of Solar Planet No. 3, which is at the edge of a billion-starred galaxy. Man's self-esteem is still visible to the unaided eye.

Heliocentrism to galactocentrism.—The heliocentric hypothesis stands firm so far as the local planets are concerned, but in 1917 the place of the sun, with respect to the trillians of stars, in our Milky Way and outside, came under closer scrutiny. The powerful photographic telescopes were rapidly piling up revelations about this overall system of stars and nebulae. In preceding decades researches had suggested to a few that the sun was not dead-center exactly, but essentially so; the Milky Way millions formed a continuous circular band of light, thus implying our central position; and the stars were found to fall off in frequency with distance in nearly all directions, again implying a central position, or so we argued.

Then came suspicions. When we learned how to estimate their distances, we found that the globular star clusters are concentrated in and around the southern Milky Way star clouds; the novae (exploding stars) are likewise more frequent in southern Sagittarius, where there are also more bright nebulosities and more super-luminous variable stars and star clouds than elsewhere along the star-filled band of the Milky Way.

These researches resulted—after a few brief struggles with a few cautious conservatives—in the establishment of the galactocentric hypothesis. The sun is no longer thought to be in a central position. Rather, the center of the Milky Way galaxy is now known to be some thirty thousand light years distant. (The direction to the central point we know accurately, but we are still working on the distance; cosmic dust clouds interfere with accurate distance-measuring.)

The displacement of sun and earth from positional importance, the sudden relegating of man and his biological investigators to the edge of one ordinary galaxy in an explorable universe of billions of galaxies —that humiliating (or inspiring) development is or should be the death knell of anthropocentrism. It should incite orienting thoughts by modern philosophers and theologians, and perhaps it has and will.

Many an ancient philosopher and divine, on the basis of relatively little knowledge of the universe, has urged humility as appropriate for man. A century ago Charles Darwin and his co-operators, especially Thomas H. Huxley, presented the case for biological humility. The further orienting of man goes on steadily in these days of feverish scientific inquiry. Physically we are minimized. But that should not seriously disturb us nor deflate our spirit, if we look at the situation objectively. All new revelations should promote our respect for the universe and our pride in the human mind. Would that the mind were more powerful, more penetrating, more free of delusions, free of silly hopes and prejudices. On the further orientation I shall presently comment. But first a sort of apologetic explanation of the above-mentioned "dumbness."

OUR SURVIVAL EQUIPMENT

The term "dumb" is used relatively. We do pretty well with what we have got. So do the other organisms. Our sense organs and our astonishing forebrains have developed and survived thus far through serving the immediate interests of the three s's—survival, sex, and shelter —the third, in a way, being a part of the first. Our kit of survival tools was not naturally equipped in the interest of abstract thought, nor for the unrolling of cosmic theory, nor for the building of this scientific conference at the University of Chicago. Survival struggles, not philosophical hypotheses, led us out of the jungles. In the interests of the survival of the individual, of the family, and especially of the species, we got clever, a few millennia ago, with our hands, with our game-catching tricks, with our sound-making apparatus.

These natural abilities fully sufficed for our survival as primates. Therefore, from an animal point of view, our subsequent human cultures and art-filled civilizations are useless extras; they must look like excrescences on the evolving stream of life, but I should like to point out, to the turtles, crinoids, conifers, and similar biological successes, that the gadgets devised by human civilizations (e.g., farming, medicine, housing) have up to now assisted very well in proliferating the human species; and that is one of the evolutionary goals. Up to now, yes; beyond now, question mark!

Many fringe benefits accrued to the civilized human species when the bonus of idleness came as a by-product of our easy and wide success in acquiring food and shelter. We had time to fiddle around with religion first of all, then with arithmetic, with astrological brainwashing, rhetoric, and the like.

If survival of the individual and of the species had demanded deep reasoning and close attention to logical methodology, we should have either failed—and attained long since to the oblivion stored in mammalian fossils—or we should have succeeded through developing our rational intellects a million years or so sooner than we have. If such development of reason had been required and achieved so long ago, the human brain might not still be in the rather confused and deplorable condition we find it. But fortunately, deep reasoning was not a survival requirement of the Early Pleistocene. Eat, procreate, live it up!—that was the original program for the primates, as it was for our colleagues throughout the animal and vegetable kingdoms. Our human ancestors carried it through, and after many a narrow squeak here we are. After a couple of billion years of competitive terrestrial biology, here we are assembled to assess the foibles and potentials of a few animal species, especially of man. In our anthropocentric eagerness, the cosmos is almost forgotten.

As I was saying, the physical orienting of *Homo* goes on but slowly. That assertion is developed a bit further to show that in power to comprehend we may rightly merit the intimation of inherent incompetence.

Does Life Exist Elsewhere?

Centuries ago, when the other known planets had been put in their correct places by terrestrial astronomers and recognized as comparable to the earth, speculators began to imagine other planetary biology than our own. The men on Mars, for instance, were exploited. This was all juicy meat for the fiction writers. The non-fictionists, to be sure, granted the possibility of low life on Mars—but life only of a vegetable sort, and not succulent vegetables at that. Martian algae and fungi were admitted as a possibility by those who measure and calculate about conditions on that cold, dry, thin-aired body.

In the past few decades, however, the picture has changed, not relative to the low-life prospects on Mars, but with regard to planets and life elsewhere. Several new scientific developments have joined in this further pin-pointing of the place of man in a universe of space-time and matter-energy. Four of them are (1) the discovery of the center of our galaxy, mentioned above; (2) the new biochemical researches on macromolecules; (3) the measurement of the expanding universe, and (4) the census of galaxies. All of these can usefully be more fully stated.

(1) The globular star clusters first contributed to the locating of the sun and planets on the perimeter of our galaxy, and showed our galaxy to be an immense system of some hundred thousand million stars more or less like the sun. Stellar counts, nebular distributions, stellar dynamics, and more recently radio astronomy have confirmed beyond undoing the peripheral position of the solar family. When spectrum analysis showed that the sun was a typical star, with no outstanding qualities except that it is our parent, our humbling thoughts about the mighty Milky Way increased in depth and compass. We began to ask seriously and scientifically if we of the earth

are the only living things in the universe, or are we merely the local sample of what creation and evolution can do.

(2) Other participants in this conference on evolution will fully treat of the great advances recently made in the fields of photosynthesis, virology, microbiology, and chemical biogenesis. I ask only to insert my conviction that the origin of life is an inevitable step in the gas and liquid evolution on a star-fed planet's surface when the chemical, physical, and climatic conditions are right; and the range of rightness can be wide, with much tolerance in the matters of temperature, atmospheric pressure, and the chemical constitution of air and water.

(3) That the red-shift of the lines in the spectra of external galaxies must be taken as an indication of the scattering in space of these huge stellar systems is all but universally accepted by the students of the subject. Nearly a thousand of these difficult objects have been measured for speed in the line of sight ("radial velocity"). In all directions the same result appears—the more distant the galaxy, the greater its speed of recession from the earthbound observer; and for hypothetical observers in other galaxies the same phenomenon appears. Unquestionably the universe is expanding, the galaxies are scattering. Where are they going? That question is in advance of the times. Where did they come from? To that question we have at least a tentative answer, namely, they came out of some more concentrated state of affairs. For if the galaxies are now scattering, the system of them (which we may call the metagalaxy or the universe) was smaller yesterday—more so last year, and a million years ago.

IMPLICATIONS OF THE EXPANDING UNIVERSE

We cannot deny, in the light of present knowedge, the evidence that a few thousand million years ago the stars and galaxies were densely crowded together. (We need not go so far as accepting literally Canon Lemaître's single Primeval Atom that contained the whole mass of the universe.) In the early crowding, things happened that cannot happen now—namely, the frequent colliding and disrupting of stars, whether they were in the same form and size as now or in a protostar state. These collisions were planet-makers and planet disrupters.

Doubtless it was a lively time in the cosmos when our present multillions of stars were a-borning in a medium that was rich in comets, disrupted stars, and planets, in interstellar clouds of gas and dust. Such confusion cannot easily occur now. Our times are relatively quiet; our spatial environment is thinly populated; our sun and its planets move around the galactic center in a calm 200,000,000-year cycle. During its past ten or fifteen revolutions our sun has fed without interruption the plants and animals on its No. 3 planet, quite undisturbed by turbulence such as prevailed in the early days.

The point of my excursion into cosmic genealogy is to emphasize the very high probability that millions of planetary births have occurred in our galaxy and trillions in the other galaxies. If we seek some origin for planetary systems other than the inevitable catastrophes of the crowded early days (for instance, the presently favored neo-Kantian shrinking-nebula hypothesis), the birth of planets is even more common than supposed above. A planetary family would probably be the fate of all stars except those in dense associations, such as double stars and clusters, where perturbations would oust planet-making material.

(4) The large telescopes have in recent years confirmed the earlier suspicion that the number of stars must be reckoned in what are commonly called "astronomical figures." From sampling star counts and measures of gravitational attraction throughout our galaxy, we estimate that the stars in our own system total more than 10^{11} equivalent suns. (Many of the stars are bigger and brighter than our sun, but a majority are of lesser stature.)

IMPLICATIONS OF THE STAR CENSUS

Other galaxies are like ours in composition—stars, gas, and dust. With the naked eye we can see three or four. Small telescopes dimly show a thousand; the larger instruments, used photographically, reveal millions, and no bottom! About a million are on the Harvard photographs; we have measured nearly half for position, brightness, and type. Some of the Californian and South African telescopes go deeper —still no end. Sampling indicates that more than a billion are within our present telescopic reach, which extends out a couple of billion light-years.

Why present these dizzy numbers? To emphasize the abundance of stars and its meaning to a conference on evolution. I would place the number as more than 10^{20}. These hundred thousand million billion stars are available for the maintenance of life on whatever planets there may be around them. All are radiating the kind of energy needed for photosynthesis and for animal and plant metabolism. Twenty per cent of them are essentially identical to our sun in size, luminosity, and chemistry.

THE UBIQUITY OF LIFE

The preceding four items have been advanced to support my easy belief that life is a common phenomenon in the universe. As I have put it in earlier discussions of the astronomical and biochemical situation,[2] we do not need the supernatural or the miraculous to account for the origin of life on this or other planets, and we have no justification whatever for assuming that long-enduring biological experiments are confined *only* to the surface of this planet, which circles an ordinary star out toward the edge of a typical galaxy among the billions. No justification exists for such a retreat toward anthropocentrism, and no reason for not suspecting that the biological heights (complexities) achieved here on Planet No. 3 have been numerously exceeded elsewhere.

There may be life (defined as "self-replication of macromolecules") of a quite different sort from that in which we on earth are evolved; but it seems not to be very likely. Our kind of chemistry is cosmoswide, according to spectroscopic evidence; our major physical laws are not earth-confined. I believe that in view of our experience with a million kinds of organisms on the earth's surface, we would recognize livingness on other planets if we could examine and analyze specimens.

In this local sample of what creation can do, man has assumed to himself a top position, and with some justification. To be sure, in his information-receivers—the sense organs—he is by other animals frequently outdone in sensitivity or range or both; better vision is found elsewhere, keener hearing, richer smell and taste, more sensitive touch. If he had always excelled every species in all these paths to reality, he might long ago have acquired a better mind for intellectual problems.

Other sense organs are conceivable. Man is wholly without effective organs for the recording of some physical phenomena, knowledge of which might open the door to better perception and fuller understanding. Magnetic phenomena, radio waves, even infrared and ultraviolet radiation, are not naturally available to him through sense organs. His brain apparently has not developed, with respect to excitation from such sources, as it has developed with respect to light, sound, touch, and smell. Among the billions of life-operating planets that probably exist in the universe there must be many where the highly sentient organisms are more fully and more effectively equipped than

[2] Shapley, *Of Stars and Men* (Beacon Press, 1958).

are the Terrestrials for informative reactions to external and internal environments. It is for this reason that I point out our deficiencies and our probably inborn incompetence.

INORGANIC EVOLUTION: THE EVIDENCE

To carry out the undertaking assumed in the title of my contribution, which has been only indirectly faced up to so far—that is, to present the case for *inorganic* evolution in the light of current thought—I plead inability to give a durable account because of today's rapid developments in observation and interpretation and because of the fragility of a number of the prevailing hypotheses. A few pages will suffice to show the trends of speculation on evolution for each of the most important areas: the material universe, the chemical elements, the galaxies, and the stars and planets. Those who report to this conference on paleontology and related subjects will presumably have concerned themselves to some extent with the evolution of the earth's crust, its oceans, and atmosphere.

ORIGIN OF THE UNIVERSE

Currently two incomplete and not very satisfactory hypotheses on the origin of the material universe have been seriously proposed and explored. In their present development one theory can be identified through associating it with the names of Lemaître and Gamow, and the other, with Bondi and Gold, and Hoyle.

In dealing with such ancient, complicated, and mysterious matters as the origin of the universe, we are hardly concerning ourselves with science *in sensu strictu*. The subject is stained with metaphysics, religion, and mental aberrations.

The primeval-atom theory.—To put it briefly, Canon Lemaître and his followers (there are not many of them) postulate an all-inclusive Primeval Atom, the radioactive bursting of which, some 10^{10} years ago, was The Creation. It is suggested that time and space also first appeared when the burst of the Primeval Atom inaugurated the expanding material universe. Immediately *after* the burst (an odd way to put it!) the well-known natural laws took complete charge, and what is now observed in the macrocosmos and the microcosmos has been the "natural" development of the universe. The natural operations include the scattering of the galaxies as a consequence of cosmic repulsion over-riding gravitation, and include the creation of the heavy chemical atoms out of quanta of energy and the proton-electron-neutron-positron-meson basic corpuscles. But this hypothesis, without considerable refinement and protection by sub-hypotheses, gets into trouble with certain observations and with some theory. For example, many stars are much too young to have been born in the original out-burst; but we can of course hypothecate subsequent secondary bursts.

The steady-state hypothesis.—As to the alternate hypothesis, the proposers and their followers (and again we note that they are not numerous) solve the problem of the original creation by saying that there never was one. The universe we know, according to this hy-pothesis, had no beginning and presumably will have no end; it is in a "steady state," and although there are numerous small-scale and localized progressions (evolution), the universe as a whole does not continuously change.

This second interpretation is also not wholly satisfactory, and it, too, may perish under the onslaught of observational data. So far it has survived, but in a few years it may be of historical interest only. Currently one of its difficulties is with the preliminary evidence that the universe is now expanding less rapidly than a billion years ago. This evidence from Palomar's Hale telescope suggests a pulsating uni-verse, and if it stands up under the pressure of further observation and calculation, the steady-state hypothesis will probably be withdrawn.

We appear, therefore, to be rather helpless with regard to explain-ing the origin of the universe. But once it is set going, we can do a little better at interpretation. Accepting the strong evidence of an expansion from a denser conglomeration of matter, we can say that the speed of metagalactic scattering is a linear or nearly linear func-tion of the distance, and the size is a function of time. The rate is still under investigation. The temporarily accepted expansion speed at a million light-years distance is only some 30 miles a second; but it is 3,000 miles a second at a hundred million, and 30,000 at a billion light-years distance.

Is space infinite? Can the speeds at great distances exceed 186,000 miles per second—the velocity of light? Those questions involve ex-trapolations too large to make our guesses dependable. But advances in theory and observation should in a few years make the guessing less wild. Even now, however, the various theoretical cosmogonists often give confident answers to cosmogonical questions, but the answers are rarely the same. 53113

With bold advances in cosmogony we may in the future hear less of a Creator and more of such things as "anti-matter," "mirror worlds," and "closed space-time." Finality, however, may always elude us. That the whole universe evolves can be our reasonable deduction, but just why it evolves, or from where, or where to—the answers to these ques-tions may be among the unknowable.

THE HIGHER ALCHEMY OF STARS

The many kinds of atoms that constitute living and inanimate matter on the earth show no evidence of currently growing in mass or of mutating, no evidence of changing now from one atomic species to another, with the exception, of course, of the natural radioactivity of a few relatively rare heavy atoms, such as uranium, thorium, and radium. But the radioactive change of radium into lead and helium, for example, is in itself a suggestion that under proper physical conditions other kinds of atoms might be transmuted. The alchemists tried to turn mercury into gold, for instance, but failed. They did not have enough heat or high enough atomic speeds. Our later cyclotrons have done it and established the higher alchemy.

The evidence that the masses of atoms of the heavy elements are integral multiples of the masses of lighter elements (when allowance is made for the isotope mixtures) naturally hints at atomic mutation, from simple to complex, from light to heavy. Somewhere and at some time matter has evolved. If the evolution did not occur on the earth or in it, where did it occur? And if not now, when?

There are those who believe, or at least suggest, that the birth of all the elements from simple hydrogen beginnings occurred at the time of the hypothetical burst of the hypothetical Primeval Atom. There would be at that time and place energy enough and elementary matter enough. Such a theory of the evolution of matter would indicate that the atoms are all essentially of the same age.

Others suggest that the transmutation of hydrogen into helium or deuterium, which is going on in practically all stars all the time, is supplemented by the natural high-temperature "cooking" of helium into some of the heavier atomic nuclei; and they would appeal to the rather frequent supernova explosions for the high temperature needed to synthesize the still heavier elements out of the lighter. As there have been, since the beginning of the expansion of the universe, possibly as many as a billion supernovae, and the explosion temperatures are unquestionably high, this cooking method of inciting atomic mutation and causing the evolution of matter is widely accepted.

Calculations show that at some tens of millions of degrees (absolute), the hydrogen fuel in average stars is transformed into helium ash. At pressures above 10^3 g/cc and temperatures of one or two hundred million degrees in the nuclei of giant stars, the helium in turn is transformed into the main isotopes of carbon, oxygen, and neon. At temperatures of a billion degrees, the elements magnesium, silicon, sulfur, argon, and calcium are synthesized from the carbon, oxygen, and neon. And at temperatures from two to five billion degrees, the nuclei of atoms like iron and nickel are made. In quiet, quasi-stable giant stars such temperatures as the foregoing are not normally reached, even at the tremendously compressed centers; but when a star blows up there is temperature to spare.

Current theory prescribes, however, that higher temperatures will not produce elements heavier than the iron group by thermal cooking; the trans-iron elements must come in large part from a slow building up through neutron capture or otherwise, and a small contribution can come as a product of the natural decay of the radioactive elements and from the fission of uranium 235.

The exploding supernova serves not only as a billion-degree oven for forming heavy atoms, but also as an agent for returning material to interstellar space for subsequent star-building. Also much material is returned to space through the leaking of matter at the turbulent surfaces of supergiant reddish stars, whose surface gravity is so weak because of their size that rapidly moving atoms cannot be retained.

In summary, the evolution of matter appears to be a synthesis inside the stars of the heavy atoms out of hydrogen, which is accepted as the primordial, abundant, and simple No. 1 element.[3] The synthesizing agency is high temperature and intense radiation. The atoms that mutate into heavier species as a result of rising temperature reach iron as a goal of stability. In 10^x years hydrogen will approach exhaustion and iron rise to top abundance. (The exponent x is not small!)

Although the evolution of matter is essentially a one-way process, except for natural radioactivity, an interesting cyclic phenomenon is involved. It is the continual gravitational forming of stars out of gas and dust and the explosive transformation of unstable stars by supernovation back into dust and gas again.

The earliest stars must have been made almost wholly of hydrogen, with helium and perhaps a little of the oxygen group of elements appearing as the central temperatures were increased above 10^7 degrees through the agency of gravitational compression. After the occasional supernovation spreads some of the evolved star stuff into space again, the "second-generation" stars can form from the interstellar dust, which then would contain some of the heavier elements as well as hydrogen. In time, some of these second-generation stars, it is surmised, would go through the supernova operation, and still heavier elements would be synthesized by the higher temperatures and dispersed in space; another generation of stars would then arise, and so on. Perhaps our sun is a third-generation star. And perhaps the details of this mixture of brave speculation, intricate calculation, and sound

[3] A full account of theories of the stellar synthesis of atoms, by Margaret and Geoffrey Burbidge, has appeared in *Science* (August 22, 1958).

interpretation are prematurely proposed. Nevertheless, the evolution of matter in stellar interiors appears to be a sound deduction from current theory and observation.

GALACTIC EVOLUTION

The evidence for inorganic evolution at the galaxy level is clear. It should suffice to point out that there are many kinds of galaxies. A gross classification would mention only the ellipsoidal systems, the spirals, and irregular galaxies like the Clouds of Magellan. A finer classification divides the spheroidals into eight subclasses, the spirals also into eight subclasses, and the irregulars into several ill-defined categories. All galaxies have one thing in common; they are star-composed. There is much local clustering of stars in the open-armed spirals and in the irregular galaxies, and also in them is much interstellar gas and dust. In them, consequently, stars are now being "born."

Finer classifications of galaxies, involving spectra, amount of included smog, characteristics of the spiral arms, etc., can be set up. Actually one might propose a class for every object, because exact duplicates seem to be very rare. It is always possible, however, to arrange the galaxies in a series, according either to form or to spectrum, and the existence of such a series immediately suggests evolution. Three other indicators of the progressive evolution of galaxies can be cited.

The first is that since galaxies are star-composed, and, as noted above, starshine is necessarily an indication of stellar evolution; so must galaxy-shine mean galactic evolution.

The second is that so far as we have been able to measure them, the galaxies are found to be rotating around central axes or nuclei, and the rotational speeds vary with distance from the axis. The consequential shearing action and turbulence smoothes out the clustering and tends to dissolve the spiral arms (in our galaxy as well as others). Therefore, the direction of progress, I believe, is from the irregular galaxies and open-armed spirals toward the closed-arm spirals and spheroidals. This, of course, means an evolution of form on the galactic level, and we cannot see it as reversible.

The third indicator of galactic evolution is that supergiant stars are numerous in the open-armed spirals and practically absent from the spheroidals. Such supergiants radiate away their mass so rapidly that in a few million years they will disappear. That again means evolution in the apparent structures, as well as in the light and the mass of galaxies. There is, however, a possibility that the supergiants are continually replaced by stars newly born from the generally present gas and dust.

No one questions but that galaxies, the great cosmic units of the universe, evolve; there is room, however, for fuller knowledge of the nature of the changes of form, light, and internal motion as a function of time.

The metagalaxy as a whole, as noted above, is expanding, but we know of thousands of clusters of galaxies where cosmic repulsion has not yet dissolved the gravitational organizations. Our own galaxy is in such a group, along with the Magellanic Clouds, the Andromeda triplet, and a few others, all of which are not more than two or three million light years distant. These groups of galaxies undoubtedly evolve, but at what rate we cannot say.

STELLAR EVOLUTION

Finally a few words on the evidence of stellar evolution. Here also we are able to put practically all stars into various continuous series. The *surface-temperature* series runs from about 3,000° to more than 30,000° centigrade—ranging from cool reddish stars through yellow and greenish to hot bluish stars like the bright stars in Orion. In *size* the series runs from stars less than a tenth the size of the sun to stars with a million times the sun's volume or more. In the *mean-density* series the variation is from the collapsed and degenerate white dwarfs, more than a thousand times the density of water, to the supergiant red stars, which are essentially vacua with densities a millionth that of water. There is no question that evolution, sometimes in strange ways, prevails along these series.

It is our current belief, subject, of course, to modifications as evidence increases, that the white dwarfs, such as the companion of the bright star Sirius, are at the end of their careers, or rather, that they represent a major approach toward the extinction they may never reach.

The beginnings of stars, that is, their birth out of the dust and gases of space, appear to be well represented by the lightless "globules" of matter in interstellar space, which can be detected only when they have bright diffuse nebulosity as a background. A few score of these protostars have been noted. In diameters they are very large compared with the greatest supergiant stars; but gravitational contraction is inevitable and eventually their interiors will heat up, energy of radiation will flow to the surface, and a faint reddish glow will herald the arrival of a new light in the firmament.

The stars, especially those in crowded regions and those deep in nebulosity, are subject to various vicissitudes. Some blow off their outer atmosphere and become novae; some blow up completely (super-novae). Some lose matter disastrously through centrifugal spilling out; and the giant red stars leak. Rapidly rotating stars may undergo fission into doubles or triples. Some apparently are born into loose gravitation-controlled groups like the Pleiades, and others, into the spectacular globular clusters. Everywhere the stars and their systems are evolving, some growing heavier by meteorite capture, all losing mass through their radiation.

One of the vicissitudes of star life, which we have mentioned above as inevitable and very common, is the birth of planets, some of which in turn bring forth self-replicating macromolecules and organisms.

HANS GAFFRON

THE ORIGIN OF LIFE

On the Propriety of Asking the Question

Every one of us entertains some kind of belief as to the origin of life. This belief is very likely made up in varying degrees from three major attitudes which can be easily discerned among our colleagues. The natural philosopher, being aware of the awe-inspiring cosmological discoveries and the triumph of the Darwin-Wallace theory of evolution, simply cannot help being sure that life evolved naturally from the non-living, but since he has still a difficult time understanding the nature of matter, he does not expect a perfectly logical and demonstrable solution to the problem of life in many a year, if ever. The humanist, filled with much traditional and little modern scientific knowledge, is indignant that a problem so transcendently profound should be regarded as belonging to the realm of the natural sciences and subject to judgments arrived at by laboratory manipulations. The experimenter, finally, with happy insouciance, expects his current results to produce the key which will unlock the door to the eternal mystery—if not tomorrow, certainly the day after.

Two years ago a conference was held in Moscow on the "origin of life." With its long list of distinguished participants, the published proceedings should amount to a catalog of the major ideas, the most relevant experiments, and practically all references to the subject in the literature.* The scientist familiar with the modern aspects of the question will, therefore, know where to obtain the detailed information he is seeking.

Only a few selected examples will be discussed in the following pages, for this paper is intended as a report to those who are not so well acquainted with the latest scientific approach to the problem but more aware of its historical and philosophical implications. In other

HANS GAFFRON is Professor of Biochemistry at the University of Chicago. German-born and educated, Professor Gaffron has achieved international acclaim for his research and writings on photosynthesis and the microbiology of plants.

* Recently published as *The Origin of Life on the Earth, Reports on the International Symposium of August, 1957, in Moscow*, edited by A. Oparin (Moscow: Publishing House of the Academy of Sciences, U.S.S.R., 1959).—Editor's Note.

words, I shall try to explain why scientists believe that the problem of *biopoesis* (a word coined by Pirie, meaning the "natural evolution of life out of the inorganic world") belongs in the realm of science and might be solvable.

How death is possible is a question that frightened mankind into profound thought thousands of years earlier than the corresponding question, How is life possible? Religion provided dogmatic answers, and during the Middle Ages one could be burned for not being quite satisfied with them. Only when modern natural science grew into a solid system did it become apparent that the second question poses the true problem. Once answered, the first problem is also solved. To destroy is so much easier than to build up. To maintain order requires continued effort; disorder comes naturally. Or, as we scientists say so learnedly: An increase in entropy is the expected course of events.

Life is the most peculiar case on earth of a continuous creation of elaborate order out of a random distribution of dissimilar constituents. That life is tied up directly or indirectly with the conversion of sunlight into heat explains only where the bulk of the energy to build up and maintain living matter comes from. But any black object efficiently converts daylight into heat—increases entropy—without in the least creating thereby any order to speak of. There must be a guiding principle which helps to produce living order at the expense of more disorder in the inorganic world. And this principle is effective within living matter only and nowhere else. The guiding power vanishes with death. It is a prime experience of modern man that only life produces life.

Together with the mind-body problem (how consciousness arises in living matter) and the problem of reason (how the incomprehensible can be comprehended), the question "What is life?" is considered one of the primary problems of existence.

It is a common experience that serious people feel uneasy when a biologist casually mentions that living matter must, of course, have originated from inorganic matter and that one day this may be proved experimentally. Such an attitude betrays the unphilosophical, uneducated, in short, materialistic approach typical of modern biochemists. It is an old story: Each time a new field of investigation is to be opened by a bold attack on what seemed insoluble or improbable before, there is resentment on the part of quite a large fraction of the thinking population.

One dilemma of our times—considered "the scientific age"—is that people outside science understand neither scientists, nor their motives, nor their choice of problems. As C. P. Snow (1959) remarks, "It isn't easy to pick up even the tone of the scientific experience at second hand. The most intelligent and receptive of non-scientists, with all the good will in the world, find it pretty difficult."

The date of the Moscow International Symposium "on the origin of life on earth"—August, 1957—will probably be remembered in later years as the time when it finally became respectable in scientific circles to admit a more than ideological interest in the problem of how to make life in the laboratory. The second paragraph of an English summary of the proceedings reads:

Real perspectives for the solution of the problem of the origins of life have been opened up for natural science by the method of dialectic materialism, which views life as a special form of matter in motion arising at a definite stage of the historic development of matter.

The fact that a conference with this theme was attended by many famous scientists from all over the world cannot, obviously, be construed to mean that the participants have discarded all critical sense, have been converted to dialectical materialism as a "Weltanschaung," and are ready to believe that the fundamental question is going to be solved in the course of a few years.

Kant, Goethe, Humboldt, and quite a few others before Darwin; Tyndall, Thomas Huxley, and all the better ones after Darwin, were not necessarily dialectical materialists. Long before our time they "helped to open real perspectives for the solution of the problem of the origin of life."

Why is it so difficult to agree that "materialism" is just a short name for a method—a set of rules—for making discoveries in the realm of verifiable reality, and that this method can be handled successfully by anyone, regardless of his private intuitions, beliefs, and hopes? The so-called "materialistic" approach is a necessity in the natural sciences.

What the citizen of the "scientific age" has still to learn is that the scientist, like the chess player, has to conform to the rules of his game. We cannot step above and beyond the rules which govern the universe, despite the undeniable fact that we can think of miracles. Not all of the rules are known, but one extrapolation from the totality of scientific experience seems justified: Reason, and only reason, is our means to reach an increasing understanding of the rules of the universe.

With this clearly in mind, the biologist foresees two possible solutions. He will either prove that life (and later, mind) arose in an orderly, understandable way, or prove that it is not possible to understand it at all. How many years must pass until this goal has been achieved is anybody's guess. But scientists have to proceed as if either the one or the other outcome is the certain reward of future intelligent work.

It should please the philosopher that the alleged triumph of materialism comes at a time when we have become pretty well convinced that matter is unrecognizable and mysterious. Kant said as much in 1770, and Tyndall in 1871. There is sufficient mysticism to please any vitalist in the fact that we observe macroscopically, by means of amplifier systems, very real and reproducible effects of elementary particles whose properties we cannot visualize. Matter transcends or escapes our comprehension. What is left are numbers and mathematical formulae that—quite magically—give us the power to make verifiable predictions.

What may irritate the humanists, understandably, about the natural sciences is, first, that spiritual progress can be had only at the price of hard practical work and not by thought alone,[1] and second, that good experiments may be done to some extent by rather mediocre and insensitive minds.

Though recent results in geochemistry, biochemistry, and biology have immeasurably encouraged the belief that our problem ought to be approached experimentally, the belief itself is not new at all. Ever since an orderly evolution of the cosmos could be dimly perceived as an all pervading principle revealed by the newly discovered laws of physics and astronomy, scientists have found it easier to dream of evolution than of a *de novo* creation of life.

This year is not only the centenary of the *Origin of Species* but that of the death of Alexander von Humboldt. Therefore, I have chosen from his writings an example (written about 1844) showing the thoughts prevailing among the great naturalists in the time before Darwin.

The discovery of each separate law of nature leads to the establishment of some other more general law, or at least indicates to the intelligent observer its existence. Nature, as a celebrated physiologist has defined it, and as the word was interpreted by the Greeks and Romans, is "that which is ever growing and ever unfolding itself in new forms." . . . In the midst of this immense variety, and this periodic transformation of

[1] Alexander von Humboldt in *Cosmos: Description of the Universe* (New York, 1850) says, "My intercourse with highly-gifted men early led me to discover that, without an earnest striving to attain to a knowledge of special branches of study, all attempts to give a grand and general view of the universe would be nothing more than a vain illusion."

John Tyndall in *Fragments of Science for Unscientific People* (London, 1871) says, "Failure, as I consider it to be, must, I think, await all attempts, however able, to deal with the material universe by logic and imagination, unaided by experiment and observation. . . . Let me remark here, that this power of pondering facts is one with which the ancients could be but imperfectly acquainted. They found the uncontrolled exercise of the imagination too pleasant to expend much time in gathering and brooding over facts."

animal and vegetable productions, we see incessantly revealed the primordial mystery of all organic development, that same problem of *metamorphosis* which Goethe has treated with more than common sagacity, and to the solution of which man is urged by his desire of reducing vital forms to the smallest number of fundamental types . . . the fruitful doctrine of evolution shows us how, in organic development, all that is formed is sketched out beforehand, and how the tissues of vegetable and animal matter uniformly arise from the multiplication and transformation of cells. . . . But if we would correctly comprehend nature, we must not entirely or absolutely separate the consideration of the present state of things from that of the successive phases through which they have passed. We can not form a just conception of their nature without looking back on the mode of their formation. It is not organic matter alone that is continually undergoing change, and being dissolved to form new combinations. The globe itself reveals at every phase of its existence the mystery of its former conditions (From Humboldt, 1850).

The fundamental intuition is there—but no precise theory. Only after Darwin was it possible to formulate the problem of the origin of life more precisely. And the physicist Tyndall, in his *Fragments of Science for Unscientific People,* did it so well in 1871 that nothing has had to be added since that time.

[Darwin] placed at the root of life a primordial germ, from which he conceived the amazing richness and variety of the life that now is upon the earth's surface might be deduced. If this hypothesis were true, it would not be final. The human imagination would infallibly look behind the germ, and, however hopeless the attempt, would enquire into the history of its genesis. . . . A desire immediately arises to connect the present life of our planet with the past. We wish to know something of our remotest ancestry. On its first detachment from the central mass, life, as we understand it, could hardly have been present on the earth. How then did it come there? . . . This leads us to the gist of our present enquiry, which is this:—Does life belong to what we call matter, or is it an independent principle inserted into matter at some suitable epoch—say when the physical conditions became such as to permit of the development of life? . . . Our difficulty is not with the *quality* of the problem, but with its *complexity;* and this difficulty might be met by the simple expansion of the faculties which we now possess.

Then came Pasteur and Mendel. The discussion broadened and even the philosophers found nourishment for their own kind of thinking which we may demonstrate with two more quotations, the first from a book called *The Origin and Nature of Life* by B. Moore, published early in this century.

Those who are inclined to think that the search after the mystery of life is illusory and leads no whither, or to no practical goal, have not studied the history of scientific advance with clear vision. The problem is not purely a philosophical one; on the other hand, it is an eminently practical and experimental one in itself, and the richest harvest that ever biological study yielded to mankind arose incidentally to an enquiry into the origin of life. . . . Life probably arose as a result of the operation of causes which may still be at work to-day causing life to arise afresh. Although Pasteur has conclusively proven that life did not originate in certain ways, that does not exclude the view that it arose in other ways. The problem is one that demands thought and experimental work, and is not an exploded chimera (Moore, 1911).

Only more recent geochemical and biological studies have made it plain (as we shall see below) that the time for biopoesis is not still in the present, as Moore thought, but is in the past. Favorable conditions no longer exist on earth; we can only hope to reproduce them in the laboratory.

The second quotation is from Bergson (1911). It was originally intended to describe Darwinian evolution, but it still serves to describe the stages of a pre-Darwinian evolutionary process about which we know next to nothing (although this "next to" is already filling an additional shelf in our libraries).

The evolution movement would be a simple one, and we should soon have been able to determine its direction, if life had described a single course, like that of a solid ball shot from a cannon. But it proceeds rather like a shell, which suddenly bursts into fragments, which fragments, being themselves shells, burst in their turn into fragments destined to burst again, and so on for a time incommensurably long. We perceive only what is nearest to us, namely, the scattered movements of the pulverized explosions. From them we have to go back, stage by stage, to the original movement.

This short glance on the recent history of our problem shows that many a great man was aware of its enormous difficulties, yet felt it quite proper not only to formulate the question but to conceive it as one which a scientist should be concerned about. How sure are we today that this is not a mistake? Perhaps a discerning mind can convince us that philosophy, or even metaphysics, is the only discipline which can truthfully promise us a reasonable answer.

DOES THE PROBLEM OF BIOPOESIS TRANSCEND THE LIMITS OF SCIENCE?

We have seen that after the announcement of the theory of natural selection, the problem of biopoesis was given a hypothetical expression shaped in terms now obvious to most of us, conveying the idea of a gradual evolution.

But there the similarity to the problem of Darwinian evolution ends. The greatness of Darwin and Wallace was their ability to discover the hidden design inside a richly decorated picture puzzle. The evidence was there all the time, a thousandfold, before the eyes of man. The new theory, anticipated in a more vague form by earlier naturalists, suddenly made sense of all this. Furthermore, the usefulness of the theory has been proved independently three times: first, by descriptive zoology; second, by genetics; and third, by biochemistry.

The situation in respect to biopoesis is exactly the reverse. There is a nice theory, but no shred of evidence, no single fact whatever, forces us to believe in it. What exists is only the scientists' wish not to admit a discontinuity in nature and not to assume a creative act forever beyond comprehension.

An extremely plausible proposition is no guarantee against committing a fundamental error. It is quite possible that life and its origin are truly insolvable problems, but the only way to find out whether this is so, and if so, to which class of insolvable problems they might belong, is to use the scientific method.

Limits to scientific knowledge are now generally characterized by three classes of problems:

First, problems which might be solved in principle by the repeated application of straightforward, proven methods where, however, the number of steps required in solving them is extremely great—a merely practical, but very real, impossibility.

Second, problems which cannot be solved in principle because the laws of nature, as far as we know (or have invented) them, clearly prove that no formula or device is conceivable which promises a solution.

Third, problems—often called metaphysical—which have been formulated disregarding the limits and the rules of the scientific method. Here the scientific interest lies in finding out where we may have made an error in classification. How many of these problems will one day be reformulated partially or totally to make them amenable to scientific analysis?

While preparing this manuscript, I came across a book published in 1958 by Professor H. Mehlberg entitled *The Reach of Science.* He writes:

Advances in dealing with problems of philosophy have often resulted in their being shifted from philosophy proper to science. . . . When traditionally philosophical problems concerning the nature of space and time; of causality; . . . of life; of thought . . . came to be included respectively in scientific cosmology, in atomic physics; . . . in theoretical biology [and] psychology . . . everybody felt that these special sciences had been endowed thereby with "philosophical implications." . . . Philosophical problems do not cease to be philosophical when they are transferred from one official department of organized knowledge to another or located on a higher level of inquiry, in order to make them amenable to scientific treatment.

In discussing the scientifically unsolvable problems, "those in science, those about science and those ordinarily classified as philosophical," he concludes that

there is nothing in the nature of the method of science which could prevent it from being applicable in principle to any problem that could be settled by any method whatsoever. . . . The universality of science consists in the fact that problems unsolvable by the scientific method are either indeterminate or answerable by false statements only. In other words, scientifically unsolvable problems have no solution and are therefore unsolvable by any other non-scientific method as well.

Mehlberg derives the strength for making these statements from his logical analysis of what should be considered as scientifically verifiable. "The extension of the concept of verifiability . . . exceeds by far the range of presently known scientific methods."

It is very unlikely that the participants in the great Moscow discussions on the origin of life first reassured themselves by thinking hard along the lines quoted above before deciding to consider the origin of life as a subject fit for experimental inquiry. Rather, it is the general climate of thought which has created an unshakable belief among biochemists that evolution of life from the inanimate is a matter of course. The incredible successes in the new sciences—particularly that of the newest, biology—has reinforced some inborn inclination of the human mind. The age-old wish to see intelligible order in the whole of nature has, in the course of the last two centuries, been fulfilled to such a degree that showing respect to some "eternal philosophical" questions has gone out of fashion. In addition, scientists—it is frequently said—"are so busy making discoveries that they have no time to think about what they are doing." When reminded of the above-mentioned gaps in the thinkable continuity of possible knowledge, scientists usually answer, "Let's first try to pave the road to the edge of the abyss with solid facts and then see whether we can bridge it or not."

Why the attitude toward this question has changed so markedly, why the vitalists have come upon bad times is understandable if we review the present status of all the sciences in relation to one another. Over a hundred years ago Humboldt (1850) wrote:

It remains to be considered whether, by the operation of thought, we may hope to reduce the immense diversity of phenomena comprised by the Cosmos to the unity of a principle, and the evidence afforded by rational truths. In the present state of empirical knowledge, we can scarcely flatter ourselves with such a hope. Experimental sciences, based on the observation of the external world, can not aspire to completeness; the nature of things, and the imperfection of our organs, are alike opposed to it. We shall never succeed in exhausting the immeasurable riches of nature; and no generation of men will ever have cause to boast of having comprehended the total aggregation of phenomena. It is only by distributing them into groups that we have been able, in the case of a few, to discover the empire of certain natural laws, grand and simple as nature itself. The extent of this empire will no doubt increase in proportion as physical sciences are more perfectly developed.

What was barely discernible in the times of Humboldt is now an overwhelming fact. For the first time in human history, the sciences which arose as separate disciplines are seen fused together, and the view stretches from the beginning to the end of thought. As Einstein wrote in 1934, "All of these endeavors are based on the belief that existence should have a completely harmonious structure. Today we have less ground than ever before for allowing ourselves to be forced away from this wonderful belief."

The scheme of Figure 1 may help to shorten the argument. The

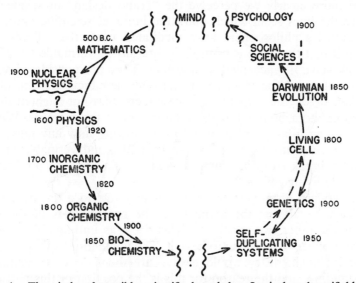

FIG. 1.—The circle of possible scientific knowledge. Logical and verifiable continuity is interrupted at three points. Two breaks isolate the mind: one from its biological basis and one from its own perception of reality. The third break occurs between living and non-living things. Science claims that this third break is not like the other two because it has been possible to circumscribe the main experimental difficulty standing in the way of closing it. Such insight is the first step for a reasonable attack upon any scientific problem. Lying within the realm of verifiable observation, this gap may be bridged in the foreseeable future—at least, long before any understanding of the other two seems possible on scientific terms.

outer numbers around the circle are the approximate dates when the separate fields of research were established as limited sciences obeying their own particular rules or laws. The inner numbers are the dates when it was shown that there was a logical transition from one field to the other. There is continuity of possible knowledge from applied mathematics (pure mathematics is another game of the mind) to the macromolecules, proteins, and enzymes of biochemistry. There is also continuity of possible knowledge from the observable behavior of a cell to the observable behavior of man. There is complete unity, if not uniformity, in the mechanisms that support all living things. The forces driving this living mechanism are exactly the same ones that drive inanimate events, and the parts are moving according to the same laws. I doubt whether the great scientists of the last century expected as much.

The structure of science, begun independently at different times, has grown together so harmoniously that it now presents a view of the whole far transcending in solidity and clarity the hopes of those who first dreamed about it. Needless to say, our scheme embraces human endeavours only insofar as they are directed by the objective methods of science.

The more clearly we perceive the "grand design" of science, the sharper the lines seem which mark the limits of scientific endeavors. For centuries philosophers have meditated upon these limits, with the result that the three gaps in the continuity of verifiable knowledge are now generally accepted as absolute. They are considered so not for lack of a method to discover fact after new fact; the task of discovering, or of "manufacturing," new facts does not frighten the inventors of atom bombs nor the interpreters of brain waves. What is missing is an unassailable, logical plan showing how any number of facts can be so arranged as to lead in a sure and verifiable manner without a break from inanimate matter to mind and its products by way of the living cell.

The modern discussion on biopoesis amounts to a flat denial that the chasm separating the living from the non-living is of the same class as the other two, or that it is as deep, as unthinkably wide, as the philosophers would like to have it. The contention is that a lecture course in biochemistry would easily cure them of a superstition of long standing, and the reason for this is the position of this particular gap in "the grand design" of science. Its place sustains the belief that it will be bridged by means which we can already foresee.[2]

---

[2] The other two gaps isolate the mind—on the one hand, from its own thought products and, on the other, from its biological basis. The nature of the problem concerning these discontinuities, which are not within the scope of this article, I shall characterize with the following quotations:

The scientist does not indulge in uninhibited speculation either. He believes that the problem will be solved for two reasons. First, he does not intend to bridge the gap in his own lifetime. Second, he has a pretty good conception of what is needed to get across the gap while using methods acceptable to science. That the eminent metaphysicist asserts the problem transcends human intelligence does not disturb him. The success of the sciences is due not to one man alone, but to the cooperation of hundreds of similarly trained minds—we have before us "the collective capacity of the race to discover universal principles."

For the scientist it is at least thinkable that the "living" quality arises from a complexity due to the completion of a pattern. It may differ only in the degree of complexity from a watch which can keep time only after it has been assembled and the last screw has been put into the proper place. For the emergence of a new quality and power unsuspected in the components of a machine, Schrödinger (1945) uses the telling analogy of the electric motor. The knowledge of the chemical and physical properties of its components is insufficient to

---

"The human mind must reflect the structure of the world in its own thought process. Of the eternal problems this is considered the most important one" (Shrader, in a review on E. Harris, 1954).

"The material universe is the complement of the intellect, and without the study of its laws reason would never have awoke to its higher forms of self-consciousness at all. It is the non-ego, through and by which the ego is endowed with self-discernment. . . . [Newton] had a great power of pondering. He could look into the darkest subject until it became entirely luminous. How this light arises we cannot explain; but, as a matter of fact, it does arise" (Tyndall, 1871).

"Our admiration for [Kepler] is accompanied by another feeling of admiration and reverence, the object of which is no man but the mysterious harmony of nature into which we are born. . . . It seems that the human mind has first to construct forms independently before we can find them in things. Kepler's marvelous achievement is a particularly fine example of the truth that knowledge cannot spring from experience alone but only from the comparison of the inventions of the intellect with observed facts" (Einstein, 1934).

As to the origin of consciousness, Humboldt (1850) wrote: "A physical delineation of nature terminates at the point where the sphere of intellect begins, and a new world of mind is opened to our view. It marks the limit, but does not pass it."

The position of the pragmatic materialist (in contrast to the true "believer") is illustrated again by Tyndall's remarks: "In affirming that the growth of the body is mechanical, and that thought, as exercised by us, has its correlative in the physics of the brain, I think that position of the 'Materialist' is stated, as far as that position is a tenable one. I think the materialist will be able finally to maintain this position against all attacks; but I do not think, in the present condition of the human mind, that he can pass beyond this position. . . . I do not think [the materialist] is entitled to say that his molecular groupings and his molecular motions explain everything. In reality they explain nothing. The utmost he can affirm is the association of two classes of phenomena, of whose real bond of union he is in absolute ignorance. The problem of the connection of body and soul is as insoluble in its modern form as it was in the prescientific ages."

When the scientist and the philosopher reach the shores of the unknowable, the scientist steps back, the metaphysician goes sailing.

convey the idea that if properly shaped and set in motion a structure of iron, copper, and rubber will produce electric current. Fortunately, we know the living cell. There is no need to deduce the living properties of a cell from its parts. We know what we are after. We see the motor running.

Biochemists and biologists today face each other across the gap. To them it seems to become less formidable day by day. This may be an illusion because the mere accumulation of bits of knowledge on both sides does not guarantee that a unifying theory will be discovered. On the other hand, it is imperative to collect as many facts as possible, since without them a verifiable theory is not likely to be found. The illusion of the scientist, therefore, is of quite another kind than that which moves a philosopher. The latter, a Hegel or a Bergson, seems to believe, strangely enough, that the knowledge which has become available just up to the date of writing is sufficient information to construct upon it a natural philosophy more satisfying and enduring than the ever-growing, ever-incomplete design of science.

The scientist, on the other hand, seems to be congenitally incapable of taking up metaphysics in relation to the problem of biopoesis unless he finds himself at the end of his practical wits; and this, as yet, has not happened.[3] There is so very much to be invented in terms of hypotheses and experiments that his power of intuition is thereby fully occupied.

"THE MOST IMPROBABLE AND THE MOST SIGNIFICANT EVENT IN THE HISTORY OF THE UNIVERSE"

These words of Sir Frederic G. Hopkins, used to end a book on enzymes (Dixon and Webb, 1958), refer, of course, to life on this earth. There is hardly a thinking person who is not inclined to subscribe whole-heartedly to the same feeling. Now the astronomers want to teach us otherwise. Shapley stresses the point that there must be untold millions of planets like ours in the heavens and that life is no more wonderful or unique than the rest of existence—in other words, an obvious part of the whole.

To most of us the evidence seems overwhelming that life is the result of not only one, but several "most improbable" events. There was only one primordial cell from which all life on earth evolved. There is only one chlorophyll, whose reactions feed the living world, and this it can do only with the aid of enzymes which are built up exclusively from only one class of optical isomers.

[3] The cases of Schrödinger and Weizäcker seem to show that theoretical physicists are more inclined than the rest of us to mix science with the art of metaphysics.

This builds up to the familiar picture of a "unique event." Unfortunately, a unique, that is "historical," event can be made an object of natural science only if we succeed in thinking of it as a realized example belonging to an *entire class* of possible events of the same kind. As I have said elsewhere (1957):

Of course, an extremely improbable event can happen any moment. Part of the fascination which the problem of the origin of life holds for us stems from the apparent necessity to believe in events which happened only once—tantamount to acts of special creation and therefore never to be observed in the laboratory. It would certainly be a triumph of science if it could be demonstrated convincingly that life must have arisen by a process which could occur hardly at all in the lifetime of any one of the planets which accompany billions of stars in millions of galaxies. This would convey upon the fact of our existence a significance reaching far beyond our earthly limits. Such a future finding seems however unlikely; for history has shown that with increasing knowledge our position in the universe is shifting farther and farther away from any imagined center of importance.

In our daily lives we often succumb to superstitions about strange events and their improbability, as if "once in a lifetime" or "once in the evolution of the earth" were something unusual and hard or impossible to understand. It is merely our personal interest and our deliberate attention combined with an inexact use of the word "understanding," which elevates any happening to this exalted position. And we can very often understand how something *has* happened, while recognizing that we could never have *predicted* that it would occur.

Our emotional attitude towards improbable events often depends on some additional knowledge or hope which we erroneously believe to be relevant to what happened before or afterwards.

In pondering the wonder of life, we may be led astray by some special knowledge we already have; for instance, that all life originated from one single "individual" cell. Is it really necessary for the solution of our problem to find out how this particular cell reached its place of eminence in the history of life? I don't believe so. The problem is to explain not the appearance of one particular primordial cell but rather the conditions favoring the emergence of an *entire class of primordial cells*. The question is how any kind of complexity can arise which has the characteristics that we attribute to, or recognize in, living cells. Uniqueness and uniformity of life, as we actually have it here on earth, we should accept as an historical circumstance but not consider it as scientifically relevant. For this way of looking at the problem, I would like to give credit to the astronomers. They have told us that there might be billions of planets in the universe where conditions must be rather similar to those which helped some of the elements on this earth "to get together and become alive."

Why, then, don't we have many forms of life; why this biochemical uniformity leading us backward to only one type of living thing? This can be easily explained on the principle of chance and selection. The first cell and its progeny either had the opportunity to spoil the chances for any following competitor—time enough to eat up all the food, for instance—or it was the survivor of an originally rather fair competition among several similar systems. We need this kind of "secondary" hypothesis very badly, as we shall see below, but it should be kept apart from those intended to explain the principle of biopoesis.

If we accept natural selection also in the evolution of the first living cells, and particularly as an explanation for uniform optical activity in biological substances, the appearance of complex self-reproducing units need not have been something which happened only once. The victory of only one line can be placed wherever one pleases; i.e., where, according to later information, it is most likely to have happened.

The notion that there may have been not *one* beginning of life but *many* makes the problem of biopoesis somewhat simpler.

The probability that life evolved on earth is the product of all the probabilities of the numerous single steps which have led to the final result. This puts a limit to the number of highly improbable or "unique" events we may assume to have happened. The fact that we are here has a definite numerical value.

Some steps must have taken a lot of time to establish themselves in the sequence. The guesses are that it took three billion years for the first cell(s) of the type we know to appear.[4] The entire Darwinian evolution, by comparison, took place in the one or two billion years that followed.

That it took so long for the first cell to establish itself might not be due at all to the inherent improbability of a certain intermediate chemical step. Where many chance occurrences have the potential power to direct all future development, the realization of that power depends on the historic *moment,* the right time. This right time might be a period of a million years or only a day. The geochemical conditions are part of the system, and life may have evolved numerous times only to be crushed by completely "uninteresting" accidents.

Considering all this, it seems more reasonable to give each intermediate step or event a probabality of one for the allotted time. Within that time it was certain to happen *and* to survive long enough

---

[4] In order not to get lost in semantic confusion, we must insist that our problem here, *biopoesis,* is the question of chemical-organic, or pre-cellular, or pre-Darwinian evolution, although the theory to be applied is the Darwinian one of chance variation followed by selection.

to support the next step—which means that the products of nearly all steps must have accumulated in quantity. To quote Pringle:

The ideal is so to specify the immanent and contingent elements that the degree of improbability at each transition of the system is reduced to a level which makes the whole process so probable in its course of development that it becomes possible to see that it is not only *possible* that it occurred in the way it did, but indeed *improbable* that it would have occurred in any other way (In Johnson, *et al.,* 1954).

Such probability considerations encourage us to keep probing for simpler, more reasonable solutions to those partial problems which appear nearly insoluble at the moment.

THE UNITY OF METABOLISM IN THE LIVING WORLD

To make a start on any problem in science, the time-tested recipe is to divide it into simpler ones. In our case these partial problems are (1) the biology (physiochemistry) of the intact living cell; (2) the analysis of cell constituents; (3) chemical *de novo* synthesis of such constituents; (4) the true reconstruction of metabolic reactions from "surviving" parts of living cells in vitro; and (5) model reactions which prove that metabolic reactions might, in principle, proceed along identical lines in simpler, non-living systems.

In studying the composition of cells obtained from different species or from different organs in one living organism, the biochemist has discovered two different sets of cell constituents. First, there is a most remarkable uniformity in those natural chemicals which have to do with the utilization of food, the source and transformation of chemical energy, the uptake of oxygen from the air, and the release of carbon dioxide. The number of vital substances involved in this is surprisingly small. Any variety is achieved by simple addition or substitution of parts to the same basic structure. This uniformity has reached a point where one single substance, one molecule, has become responsible for the existence of virtually all life on earth. This one molecule is chlorophyll, which functions as the key for the process of photosynthesis. It has a unique role and is the same in the phylogenetically oldest unicellular alga as in the youngest species of flowering plant. Thus, with a surprisingly small bag of tricks, nature accomplishes this awe-inspiring variety.

On the other hand, there are a large number of special substances which can be extracted from this or that particular plant or animal. The best known among these are the useful ones—the drugs or hormones, for instance. Their scattered and isolated occurrences in the living world quite obviously mark them as products of Darwinian evolution, characteristic properties of one species or even one single clone. It is a matter of temperament which one chooses to admire more—the plainness of the original invention or the greatness of the structure which evolved as a consequence of this.

To understand biopoesis, we obviously have to concentrate on those biochemical reactions which appear to be indispensable and which are alike in any living cell we choose to investigate. This is particularly true for those parts of the cell which guarantee the proper utilization of food and the propagation of the species. They are alike and function alike in the humblest unicellular plant or bacterium or the higher animals; and the most ancient organisms we know of would apparently be up-to-date today. This seems to be true also of those substances which in our era are the most characteristic constituents of living things as compared with non-living entities. These substances are the proteins and nucleic acids. The entire macroscopic evolution is determined by subtle changes in the molecules of these two kinds of substances.

Most proteins function as "enzymes," that is, catalytic agents facilitating reactions which without them would neither proceed so fast nor so specifically along one single pathway. Molecules of proteins and nucleic acids are "very big," with molecular weights ranging from the tens of thousands to a million. In order to function as enzymes, they often combine with simpler structures—molecules which rarely surpass a molecular weight of a thousand, such as chlorophyll or blood hemin (Fig. 2). Whatever chemical reactivity these simpler molecules

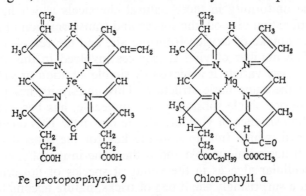

Fe protoporphyrin 9   Chlorophyll a

Fig. 2.—Structural formulas of an iron-porphyrin and of chlorophyll *a*

possess is strongly enhanced or even altered in combination with a fitting protein. These smaller reactive groups mostly have to do with the transfer of an electron or a hydrogen atom from one molecule to another—from "substrate" to "product." Their generic name is "prosthetic group," or "coenzyme," or "co-factor." If an organism is unable to synthesize them within its own cellular structure but must take them up as part of the food, they are known as "vitamins" in respect to that organism. It is interesting that the more primitive a cell is, the less likely it is to suffer from "vitamin deficiencies." These prosthetic groups or vitamins are the substances referred to above which are so few in number and shared by most living organisms. The simplest are single atoms of several metallic elements. They belong in the upper half of Mendeleyev's periodic table, beginning with magnesium as the lightest and ending with molybdenum as the heaviest. The truly heavy metals, such as mercury, silver, osmium, etc., are poisonous. Some organic chemicals which are found in all living cells are the pyridine nucleotides, flavins, pyridoxals, and porphyrins. Their structures are known, and most of them have been synthesized by the chemist.

Figure 2 compares the essential structure of two porphyrin derivatives. Chlorophylls containing magnesium are a specialty of the plant world. Porphyrins containing iron are best known from red-blooded animals, but they are present in all kinds of living cells. Hemoglobin, our own red blood pigment, has recently been discovered in the root nodules of leguminous plants. The parsimony of nature cannot be better illustrated than by the variety of specialized reactions served by the same chemicals. Catalase, peroxidase, and cytochromes exist in a number of sub-varieties, yet all employ the same iron-porphyrin. There are some thirty flavin enzymes, at least fifteen phosphopyridoxal catalysts, and over sixty enzymes in which magnesium is necessary for action.

How decisive the "right" combination can be is forcefully shown by the fact that without an atom of manganese in the photosynthetic apparatus the plant is unable to release oxygen from water. All the oxygen in the air, which made Darwinian evolution possible, has been developed by the specific combination of chlorophyll-protein with manganese-protein. A cell lives by breaking down (burning) food-stuffs. This provides the energy and in most cases also the material for further growth. The prime example among foods is sugar. The mechanism for sugar metabolism has been found to be so uniform that it surprises the biochemist when he finds a cell which insists on doing it in its own special way. The cell not only preserves parts of the original sugar molecules for its own purposes, but also some of the energy which went into the making of the sugar in the first place. Instead of coming out as heat as in an ordinary fire, the energy is preserved in the form of a very reactive chemical. And this chemical is again simplicity itself—a polymerized phosphoric acid. Three phosphoric acid groups in a row are attached to an organic residue, which increases stability and specificity. Its name is adenosine triphosphate

(ATP). Each time a phosphoric acid group is taken off and transferred somewhere else—or re-added—some 7,000 calories of "free energy" are paid out or received in connection with synthetic or breakdown reactions. There are other compounds which serve in a similar capacity as energy transfer agents—co-enzyme A, for instance —but ATP appears at the moment to be the main energy "currency." It is the same substance wherever we look in the living world.

The interesting thing from our point of view here is that these ubiquitous, simple compounds can be made to react as they do not only in cell extracts when still attached to the "surviving" protein, but essentially in the same way when pried loose from it. They take up or release hydrogen atoms from or to other plain chemicals, they combine with oxygen and oxidize something else partly to water, and so on. The reaction time is often much, much longer than it is in the cell, and the particular usefulness of the chemical step is lost because it happens out of context. But if it can be shown that such chemicals (prosthetic groups) might easily have been formed without the aid of living cells, by so-called "spontaneous chemical synthesis," a further point of circumstantial evidence will have been won to support the hypothesis of biopoesis.

REPRODUCTION

If we had a definition of life that was both empirically and logically flawless, it would be tantamount to having a useful scientific theory of life. Quite obviously, we do not. There are no unique laws applying to a living essence or living force, or to that degree of complexity which constitutes a new living quality. At this time—mid-twentieth century—it seems to be an unprofitable attitude to look for the emergence of any such special laws. We are just beginning to learn how to remodel the genetic plan in a microorganism—that is, to direct and steer the life process in a cell instead of only dismembering it. Thus, we may be as far removed from true insight into the essence of life as the man who first learned how to make fire was from the knowledge of Lavoisier. For the moment, therefore, an arbitrary agreement on what to call living or dead or potentially living is sufficient, just as a child can agree with another about what is a live dog, a dead dog, or a stuffed dog.[5] One has to ignore those people who love to waste time with arguments that lead nowhere.

The nineteenth century established that no other kind of matter could be found inside living things than was already known outside

---

[5] By "potentially living" I mean such phenomena as viruses and phages. See the article by E. A. Evans, following immediately in the present volume.

and that the laws of chemistry or physics were in no way distorted within cells by the presence of the "life force." This now seems trivial to us because this knowledge is insufficient to isolate and circumscribe even one partial problem characteristic of living matter only.

Before the industrial technique of building sensitive relay mechanisms having self-regulatory controls reached its present refinement, a purposeful behavior or a chemical response to stimuli was considered one of the most astounding aspects of the living cell. But today we have, for instance, electronic toys that are stimulated to run toward, or hide from, light and that are able to avoid or circumvent obstacles intended to stop them from reaching their goal.

Since the concept of heredity by means of "genes" acting on a molecular level became established much has been thought and written about the problem that not only the physics of larger structures, involving enormous numbers of atoms, but also that of single atoms or molecules, may determine the fate of living things; or, to say this in one phrase: the occurrence of mutations (provided that they can, indeed, be released by the chance reaction of a single atom).

But does this fact really lead us any further than the now familiar question concerning the reliability of an apparatus guided by a sensitive amplifier system that is constantly harassed by "molecular noise?" That a dust particle falling into a fine clockwork can stop it is not the problem; rather it is what happens after the accident, i.e., the question of self-repair. And this is part of the truly fundamental problem of the exact reproduction or duplication of a living unit.

It is not the basic principle or physical mechanism of self-regulating systems (which we call homeostasis or "feedback"), nor its sensitivity, nor its "purposeful" action that escapes our power of understanding; rather it is its complexity. It is the mechanism that provides for self-preservation, repair, and the transfer from a cell to its daughter cells of a blueprint of its own structure that has not as yet yielded to our analytical methods. Moreover, the "mistakes" in the transferred blueprint—the above-mentioned mutations in the genes and the slight imperfections in reproduction—have made Darwinian evolution possible. A less plastic mechanism than the biological one we know could only reproduce itself exactly or die. The more familiar one is with this problem, the more he is inclined to view it with the greatest respect.

And we are told that all this complexity has come into existence by a gradual process of spontaneous evolution!

The evolutionary side of the problem of self-duplication seems particularly difficult because even a complete analysis and full understanding of how it works in living cells (and how far we are from that!) might not help at all in speculating about how it came to be. Several intermediate evolutionary steps may have fallen into disuse. No cells exist any more which function according to a less efficient but more primitive and simpler pattern. A dividing cell reproduces everything it contains. The study of this process has revealed that the riddle of reproduction resides entirely in the duplication of the macromolecules—the proteins and nucleic acids—sometimes called the "self-duplicating molecules." When we think of their evolution, we should keep in mind that the self-duplication of macromolecules may be the last simplifying short-cut derived from a very involved and cumbersome way of roundabout duplication.

A recent paper by G. Allen (1957) contains a detailed speculation on what he calls "reflexive catalysis." "Any molecule that catalyzed the synthesis of one of its precursors in a system where these precursors eventually formed more of the same molecule would be reproducing itself in the sense required by natural selection." Further discussions of this may be found in the latest edition of Oparin's book (1957) and in the transactions of the Moscow Conference [see n., p. 39]. Actually, everybody knows what is needed. I doubt whether, in this case, anyone can re-invent the tricks of nature without continued experimentation with living proteins and with artificial amino-acid polymers.

The prosthetic groups—vitamins, co-enzymes, etc.—are the ever-recurring working parts of many enzymes. How these are made by the living cell belongs to the class of biochemical questions that are solvable in principle and, at the present time, constitute the bread and butter of biologists all over the world.

Some of these substances are synthesized in industrial laboratories by the ton and by methods which are quite remote from the natural reactions. Others are so difficult to make by orthodox chemical means that they have been synthesized only bit by bit in the course of fifty years; for example, the first synthesis of hemin. In such cases one can be sure that these complex molecules are put together by the living cell in a manner that the chemist did not anticipate. The most famous examples are the synthesis of porphyrins and sterols from acetate (Shemin, 1956). The natural way is short, direct, and efficient, and it employs enzymes. But, relying on the principle that the role of enzymes is mainly to speed up reactions which proceed by themselves, it is permissible to assume that such reactions did indeed happen in the pre-biotic era. Thus the evolution of these co-enzymes was independent of and may have preceded that of the proteins. Some biosynthetic processes clearly invite experimentation that will transfer them from the "living" enzymatic level to that of ordinary chemistry.

Complex reactions of this sort may have been going on in pre-cellular time and been taken over and incorporated at a later stage (see our later section on "chemical evolution").

Macromolecules

It is said that in order to investigate living cells one has to kill them. The more knowledge we get out of them, the deader they become. Finally, we shall have records of practically every single biochemical reaction going on in the cell and yet remain ignorant of the secret of the intact whole, the "gestalt" which is more than the sum of its parts.

The answer to this is simple. It is not true that a living cell must be killed to be studied, except in certain special biochemical analyses. But it is carefully kept alive in most other investigations, for we have means of seeing what goes on inside without damaging the cellular apparatus. Moreover, it is possible to extract from the living cells parts which continue to function as they did in the untouched unit (the mitochondria). They can survive for days or can even be stored at very low temperature for months. The cell boundary is, therefore, not essential for such fundamental reactions as respiration and energy storage. The next experimental problem is whether these catalytic cellular constituents need a cell wall to reproduce themselves—and this brings us to the problem of protein synthesis.

Half a century ago Emil Fischer succeeded in combining a few amino acids to give small chain-like molecules, so-called "peptides." Yet, despite the greatest efforts, the synthesis of true proteins and nucleic acids has so far remained the prerogative of the living cell. All the patents are held by nature.

Of all the partial problems contained in the question of biopoesis, protein synthesis is such a central one that, for the time being, it can serve as an adequate substitute for the whole. Conditions suitable for the evolution of life are (or were) those which favored the appearance of proteins. The baffling nature of this particular problem is most easily exemplified by the accompanying figures. The smallest parts of the whole the chemist can synthesize are the amino acids whose chemical formulas are shown in Figure 3. To make a protein they must be aligned and spliced together along a central chain made of carbon and nitrogen atoms in a simple and uniform composition: $C-N-C-C-N-$. The length of the chain may include several hundred such peptide bonds. But there are only two dozen amino acids in nature—and only twenty of them are ever recurring parts of active protein everywhere. Thus, the endless variety of protein-directed re-

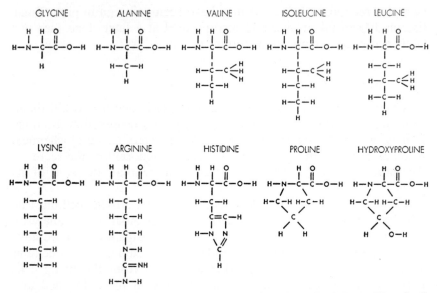

FIG. 3.—Structural formulas of some amino acids (from Paul Doty, "Proteins," *Scientific American,* September, 1957).

actions in one cell; the variations among the reactions which characterize different classes of cells; and the reactions which distinguish one animal from the other—all depend on the arrangement of the twenty amino acids, i.e., the particular permutation along the chain (Fig. 4). But that is not all; a free chain, unless stretched tight, can assume a very great number of shapes in space, and if constantly shaken—as the protein molecule is by the impact of the surrounding molecules—one shape would never exist longer than a split second.

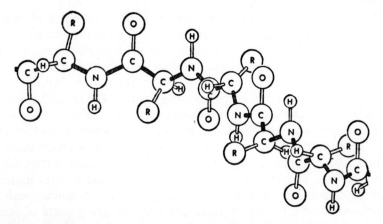

FIG. 4.—Random chain of amino acids (from P. Doty, *Scientific American*)

In order to keep its identity as to shape, the protein chain is carefully folded, mostly in spiral form, represented in Figures 5 and 6.

The arrangement along the chain plus the special folding provide the information which says what this particular protein molecule is able to do. Biochemical knowledge on this detailed level is still very scanty.

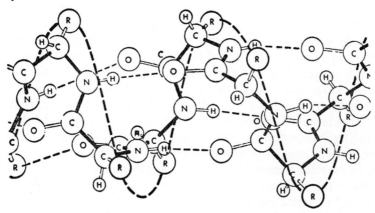

FIG. 5.—Coiled shape of an amino-acid chain (from P. Doty, *Scientific American*)

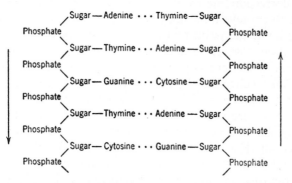

FIG. 6.—Schematic diagram of DNA. The two chains are antiparallel, shown by the arrows. Dotted lines between bases represent hydrogen bonding. The chains, which appear flat in the diagram, are actually wound around each other in the molecule.

But it is very important that once a protein molecule has come into existence it can do outside the cell whatever it does normally inside. The enormous field of enzyme biochemistry abounds with examples of protein catalysis in vitro. The entire sequence of reactions necessary to "digest" foodstuffs or to build up such cell constituents as sugars and fats can be reproduced in "dead" systems—cell extracts which have lost most other attributes of the intact cell, in particular the capacity to reproduce itself.

To a biochemist it seems only a matter of a few years of further imaginative work along this line until he may succeed in carving out of the cell the necessary combination of proteins and nucleic acids neatly aligned in one microstructure which, when fed the proper amino acids, will knit and fold together an entire protein in vitro— possibly one of the very proteins engaged in the process. How much of life, shall we say, has then been extracted into the test tube?

In biopoesis the big question is how protein molecules of unbelievable complexity, yet strict specificity and identity, can arise spontaneously without the aid of the living cell. To admit that we have no good answer does not mean we should accept bad ones or take recourse in miracles. It is always surprising to see how long it takes until what has become known, intellectually analyzed, and understood, is really believed. The evidence for Darwinian evolution should be a convincing demonstration that chance combinations and selection by contingent circumstances can lead progressively by small steps to an order of amazing complexity. But as soon as this notion is applied by analogy to the problem of macromolecules, ancient arguments against evolution by chance are dusted off and given a new polish.

A much cherished simile is the comparison of nature with a book, the letters corresponding to atoms, the words to molecules, the pages of the text to protein molecules, etc. This comparison is very useful in bringing home the point that chance cannot possibly be the builder of order and purpose as we find it everywhere in nature. By shaking a printer's box of letters—even if the letters have several kinds of selective hooks (chemical bonds) attached to them—we cannot expect a text to emerge which makes sense to us or, at least, to the theologians who are extremely fond of this argument. The error lies in assuming that the scientist already has an idea what the book of nature is about. For the scientist, the world is what it just happens to be and not what it ought to be. No wonder Bergson (1911) complains of "the disappointment of a mind that finds before it an order different from what it wants."

This old story of random letters producing an understandable text I repeat here because it is now usually presented in the disguise of probability calculations. Proteins are such complex structures that only once in many billion years under the most favorable conditions might the right number and the right kind of amino acids aggregate spontaneously to form an enzyme—and there are many, many enzyme molecules in a cell. Three conclusions follow:

1. There is a design, a driving force which eliminates chance, or most of it. (This mode of thought has slowly gone out of fashion in the course of the past thirty years.)

2. Improbable as it is, such an event is not thereby excluded; it can happen at any moment according to modern teaching in the field of statistics and probability. It must have happened once—and it is likely that it did, because it explains so nicely certain unique and uniform features in the living world. (This argument is still very much alive. If shown to be wrong for the problem of protein synthesis, it will be moved back one line and used for that of the nucleic acids. It will die in steps until improbable reactions have been eliminated altogether.)

3. If a postulated synthetic reaction is shown to be extremely improbable, this ought to be taken as proof that it never happened. There must be a simpler way—as roundabout as one wishes—but altogether having a much greater chance of success. (This point of view is in itself no help in finding the solution to the riddle.)

The most fruitful intuition of recent vintage may be that the idea of a self-duplicating molecule on the protein level has to be abandoned. No simple template idea could do justice to such degree of complexity, goes the argument. All proteins are synthesized, not with the aid of already existing identical amino-acid arrangements, but with the help of another, slightly simpler kind of macromolecule that only symbolizes this arrangement. It is said that the code for this arrangement is held by the nucleic acids—a structure made from only four basic compounds instead of twenty—but that sufficient variation can be achieved to arrange up to twenty dissimilar components into an unequivocal order (Fig. 7).

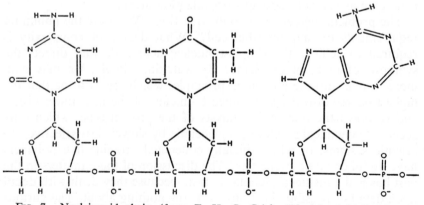

Fig. 7.—Nucleic-acid chain (from F. H. C. Crick, "Nucleic Acids," *Scientific American,* September, 1957).

One gets the impression that for the first time theoretical biochemistry is far ahead of the experimental art and exerts a very powerful influence on the course of the latter.

Thus, the problem of a spontaneous generation of catalytic proteins, as they are found in the living cell, and their replication forever after has been solved by declaring that it does not exist. How much have we gained by this conclusion? The burden of maintaining continuity and identity of living things has been relegated to the nucleic acids. They are now held responsible for their own duplication in addition to that of the proteins. The evidence is seen, for instance, in the behavior of chromosomes and in the multiplication of phages and viruses, which contain nucleic acids as the essentially immutable core. (That mutations *do* occur need not concern us here.) As is explained in the article that follows by Evans, phages and viruses can shed their "protein coat" and yet retain their "personality." A phage does this regularly while entering the bacterial cell. A specific new coat of protein is made for it and its offspring by the activity of the living cell. The latter may or may not die as a consequence of this unexpected service it is forced to perform.

In vitro duplication of nucleic acids at the expense of a homogeneous food solution has not been seen. This makes it likely that a number of enzymes have to assist in the "self-duplicating process"; in other words, the proteins are in this way repaying the favor of having been called into existence by the action of the nucleic acids. There is a mutual give and take; the one class of compounds cannot continue to exist without the other. And even if we are certain that the nucleic acids are superior in power as the masters of the cellular organization while the catalytic proteins are expendable servants, there is no clue as yet as to how this organization arose.

The problem then changes to the question, "What are the minimum requirements for a primordial cell?" What degree of complexity is required to achieve the simplest nucleic acid code that directs the synthesis of more of the same? By watching closely, we may gain more insight into the governing principle, which seems to be that the highest degree of order is obtained by means of the next lower order, and so down the line. Are catalysts of the protein type, which only accelerate chemical reactions, replaceable by slower, less selective, inorganic systems; or will artificially-concocted proteins like polymers have useful catalytic properties? The discussion of these matters in the past has had a medieval, scholastic taste because they dealt with detail upon detail of possible reactions we know nothing about. The curious will find plenty to read in the proceedings of the Moscow Conference. It is the relevant experiment which from now on deserves our attention.

OPTICAL ASYMMETRY

A phenomenon which is so difficult to explain that only a wonder, a unique event, seems to do it justice is the existence of only one of two possible asymmetrical configurations among cellular constituents.

The atoms in molecules are never arranged so flatly as their formulas appear on paper. The vast majority are structures in space. If such shapes are not symmetrical, they look alike but yet are different; they have the property that their image in a mirror has left and right sides interchanged. A familiar example is the relationship between left- and right-hand gloves. It is possible to stack left-hand gloves or right-hand gloves tightly, like paper cups or hats, and thus produce a smooth and even-looking structure, all of one kind. But one wrong glove—a right-hand one in a stack of lefts—would cause a visible break in the continuity of the structure. However, gloves are made not to be stacked but to be put on a pair of dissimilar but also asymmetrical shapes—one or the other hand. This is the way two different asymmetric molecules either reject or accept each other to form a "close fit."

The most common and most thoroughly studied case of an asymmetrical arrangement is found around a carbon atom which is attached to four different atoms or groups of atoms. Organic compounds containing such "asymmetric" carbon atoms rotate the plane of plane-polarized light (light that has gone through one polaroid sunglass, for instance). They are said to be "optically active." In this way it is possible to distinguish one shape of a molecule from its mirror image. The one turns the polarized light ray clockwise, the other counterclockwise. When the chemist synthesizes an optically active substance, he obtains equal amounts of the levo (l) and the dextro (d) rotating form. In such a "racemic" mixture the optical effects cancel each other out. Nothing can be seen until the two forms are separated. Procedures to do this efficiently are not easy to find because the ordinary chemical properties of l and d forms are so nearly identical. One agent which distinguishes them neatly and with the greatest of ease, to the last molecule, is the living cell.

Once a mechanism depends on asymmetric parts which must fit closely in order to function, it is easy to see that the best idea is to use parts of one type only, either left or right. A mirror image clock keeps time just as well as its counterpart—but parts made according to either the original blueprint or its mirror image are not interchangeable. The baffling discovery is that the entire living world now prefers only one series of amino acids. And there are enzymes that specifically destroy the molecules of the mirror-image series. It seems that during the time of the Darwinian evolution, the blueprint, or the code, for making proteins has not been reversed—not even accidentally flipped over, as it were. Even more than the identity of basic metabolic reactions, this fact ties us very strongly to one primordial cell which already had this configuration imprinted on it.

Biopoesis requires that this living cell should arise out of a pool of ordinary organic chemicals, and this presents a problem. When the chemist synthesizes asymmetrical molecules, he invariably produces equal amounts of both kinds. How did nature in the beginning succeed in doing otherwise? The standard answer is to assume that somewhere along the way an accidental synthesis of a complex, asymmetrical molecule occurred which, from this moment on, acted as a selecting catalyst for all further synthetic steps and thus determined the course of biopoesis for all time to come.

This must have happened only once during the duration of the entire epoch which favored such an event. For many people, the idea of a unique, creative moment has much emotional appeal. But from our actual experience with how things come about in the world around us, this looks like a very poor hypothesis.

It is simpler to allow the mirror image structures to make their spontaneous appearance with equal probability yet with sufficient time lag to give the progeny of the first molecule an advantage which dooms the heirs of the latecomer to eventual extinction. In other words, instead of assuming an incredible, unique event, we borrow from Darwinism the concept of selection by chance and say that the primordial cell, the ancestor of all life we know, is the sole survivor of perhaps three types of quasi-living things—left, right, and mixed ones. As far as I can see, it is George Wald who gave in detail the reasons why the problem of optical activity merges with that of the origin of proteins and their specific structures. The famous a helix structure shown in Figure 5 can, in principle, be the right-handed one or the left-handed one or even a mixed structure containing both l and d amino acids. Basing his discussion of this particular problem on the experiments of Doty, Lundberg, Young, and Blank, Wald argues that formation of mixed $d–l$ polymers proceeds more slowly, that the product is less stable than either the pure l or d configuration, and that for purely chemical reasons in a mixture of either d or l or $d–l$ polymers only the pure d or pure l compounds survive. Despite the fact that the probability of initial formation of pure l or d polypeptides is much smaller than that for the mixed compounds, it is a question of stability which, in the end, decides in favor of the pure systems.

The same argument can be used in the simpler case of the nucleic acids (Fig. 7). Whether the selection for one configuration occurred after a cell was formed or before the cell was completed is unimportant, and the idea of a unique and particularly improbable event need not be further entertained.

Chemical Evolution

In the preceding section we traced the front line of the analysis of living things as we perceive it today. Now we move across the gap from the living to the non-living to see how far science has come to recognize, or even to prove experimentally, that organic molecules of utmost complexity could have arisen from the original elementary conditions on this planet.

Inquiry into what we call "chemical evolution" ought to furnish evidence, first, that the right kind of organic raw material accumulated soon after the earth became sufficiently cool to permit this, and second, that there was a permanent flux of free energy of such low level as to let a spontaneous synthesis of more complex and correspondingly more fragile organic molecules stay ahead of their continuous decomposition.

On this side of the gap, far removed from the disquieting presence of truly living things, the problem appears deceptively simple. Recent contributions to our understanding of a possible chemical evolution have been remarkable—as we shall see. The enthusiasm of doers, as well as of onlookers, about this progress is quite justified within its frame of reference. It must not be forgotten that no matter what quantities of these organic chemicals may have been present on earth and how complex the individual molecules may have become in the course of a billion years, they were still completely lifeless.

During the last century the chemists have synthesized over a million different organic molecules. But only a small fraction of them are substances which have been found in living cells or which can be given to living cells to be used as food. The rest consist of chemicals which the cells have, as it were, never heard of. In fact, most man-made compounds are poisonous to life. Certain complex substances, known to us because we made them, have an astounding stability. The silicones, for instance—counterparts of the natural organic molecules in that silicone atoms take the place of the corresponding carbon atoms—resist practically all physical or chemical forces which have been destroying organic compounds on earth since the beginning of life. But nothing similar has been discovered outside the laboratory.

The ways of the chemist and of natural evolution have obviously been different. The last generation of biochemists has learned that to analyze and copy nature they need an ice box, not a Bunsen burner. Cellular chemistry proceeds at temperatures near the freezing point of water, and the separation of metabolic products is achieved by selective adsorption on surfaces, not by distillation at temperatures high above the boiling point of water. This difference in method determines which kind of substances are found in nature and which on the chemist's shelf.

The chemist knows how to make nearly all those small molecules from which the living cell builds the big ones: the sugars, amino acids, fatty acids, purines—in short, the basic constituents of our food. Furthermore, as said above, we know how to manufacture certain molecules of medium complexity (the vitamins) which the cell needs for respiration and fermentation.

If the natural organic compounds now on earth, serving as a guide, can tell us anything at all about the conditions prevailing during the first successful accumulation of organic matter billions of years ago, it is that the conditions were much milder than those usually prevailing in the chemist's kitchen.

Perhaps we must invoke the help of mild volcanic action to account for some special cooking, should the most reasonable future hypothesis of chemical evolution turn out to be incomplete without such steps. Good and, indeed, very interesting examples are the high molecular amino-acid polymers which Fox and colleagues have obtained by heating and melting the undiluted simple components (Fox and Harada, 1958).

In our time, organic substances derived from living matter do not stay around. They disappear for two reasons: they are either eaten by living organisms or burned by the oxygen of the air. The latter reaction may be as fast as an open fire or take hundreds of years of slow "autoxidation." Measured in geological periods, there is hardly a difference in the rates between these two ways of breakdown into water and carbon dioxide. When protected from the attack by living organisms or oxygen or excessively high temperatures, even very complex organic molecules are stable. Witness the natural oil and the various compounds which are found in it. It follows that a good reservoir of organic matter for biopoesis to work with could have accumulated only under (relatively) anaerobic conditions and only until the first organisms began to spread about the earth.

Oparin and Haldane were probably the first to point out that it is easier to imagine life to have evolved from a rich pool of organic matter than directly on a barren surface by photochemical reactions between carbon dioxide and water. Since then, discussions about the composition of the early atmosphere, the variety of surface minerals, their catalytic properties, and the thermodynamics of various model reactions copied from the textbooks of biochemistry have steadily widened.

The degree and frequency with which random action (Brownian

movement) is able to create or to increase order is fundamental. Once some basic pattern exists, further spontaneous chemical reactions may come under its directing influence. We are permitted to believe that this leads to a more elaborate order of a different kind. The latter may produce catalytic effects which cannot be deduced from the properties of the individual constituents of the system. Vague as it sounds, such must be the essence of any hypothesis purporting to explain a purely chemical evolution preceding the appearance of living organisms.

From among the various suggestions made by the geochemists and astronomers, who are the only ones in a position to know, the biologist is at liberty to choose what pleases him most. My predilection, and now probably that of most biochemists, is the hypothesis of Urey, since it was tested experimentally and found not wanting. This new development has considerably shortened the way towards the towering problem of biopoesis over the foothills of chemical evolution.

THE RAW MATERIAL FOR EVOLUTION

It is the task of the geochemists to give us a picture of the composition of the earth's surface at the time when organic substances first had a chance to survive long periods of time. Considering astronomical and geochemical evidence, Urey (1952) concludes that "the primitive atmospheres contained water, hydrogen, ammonia, and methane in unknown amounts and proportions. The equilibrium constants indicate that the hydrogen abundance must have been comparable to that of water."

We quote further:

Many researches directed toward the origin of life have assumed highly oxidizing conditions and hence start with the very difficult problem of producing compounds of reduced carbon from carbon dioxide without the aid of chlorophyl. It seems to me that these researches have missed the main point, namely, that life originated under reducing conditions or as reducing conditions changed to oxidizing conditions. . . . It would be interesting to estimate the time required for the appearance of the present oxidizing condition of the earth. . . . Did the reducing condition outlined above persist up to some 8×10^8 years ago? If so, the production of oxidized sulfur compounds would not have occurred to any very great extent. . . . Hydrogen must have been lost very slowly during the preceding two billion years, for the oxygen which must appear as the hydrogen is lost must eventually become carbon dioxide or iron oxide.

The two main points are: first, methane and not carbon dioxide furnished the bulk of the carbon for the first organic compounds; and second, free hydrogen was available as a reducing agent for quite a long time.

The test of this hypothesis came when Dr. Urey persuaded Dr. Miller to subject such an atmosphere to the impact of electrical discharges, or the action of ultraviolet light. Studies on the effect of ultraviolet upon organic substances in the gas or liquid phase are, as such, not new. They began about a century ago, yet this particular kind of experiment had not been done and the results proved to be truly exciting. A mixture of the abovementioned gases at a temperature between 80° and 90°C. yielded no less than twenty-five (racemic) amino acids, as well as acetic, formic, propionic, lactic, and glycolic acids, together with some unidentified polyhydroxy compounds and colored polymerized material. Acetic acid, CH_3COOH, and glycine, NH_2CH_2COOH, were obtained in large amounts. These compounds could not have been synthesized in the presence of oxygen, but small amounts of carbon monoxide and carbon dioxide were found, showing that some water must have been decomposed in the course of the experiments. Thus, under natural conditions, we need not insist that the early atmosphere was totally devoid of carbon dioxide.

In these laboratory experiments it is preferable to use electrical discharge instead of ultraviolet light to promote synthetic reactions in such a gas mixture. The reason is that with ultraviolet light the reaction becomes self-limiting. The products deposit on the inner surface of the vessel and prevent the short-wave light from reaching the gas mixture. This drawback did not exist on the earth's surface. We have no reason to doubt that sufficient raw material for a prolonged organic chemical evolution was available as soon as the temperatures on the earth's surface permitted the accumulation of some liquid water.

Since there was no oxygen in the early atmosphere, the compounds formed may have continued to accumulate for thousands of years. Only the ultraviolet radiation itself could have interfered with this accumulation and with the formation of even more complex molecules by eventually breaking them up again. The establishment of an equilibrium between photochemical synthesis and breakdown was probably postponed very effectively by the protective action of the oceans in which these different acids easily dissolved. To quote Urey again:

If half the present surface carbon existed as soluble organic compounds and only 10 per cent of the water of the present oceans existed on the surface of the primitive earth, the primitive oceans would have been approximately a 10 per cent solution of organic compounds. This would provide a very favorable situation for the origin of life.

It is an interesting fact that Miller's synthetic brew is a good growth medium for many microorganisms and food for nearly any cell. The living cell manufactures and uses these very same compounds quite differently, of course, and nearly always with the aid of enzymes. But the latter are mainly timesavers. Death overcomes living things so rapidly that a premium is set on speed of reproduction and replacement. Enzymatic specificity is also a timesaver and a means to prevent mishaps. But on a primitive level it might not be so essential. Enzyme specificity is comparable to the effect of unequal spacing of radio tube contacts. The completed radio apparatus would work perfectly well with tubes having no such conveniences. Only the time needed to assemble it in the proper way would be much prolonged.

The point has often been made that given certain reactants the products of enzymatic reactions should eventually be formed also in absence of the enzymes, provided that there is enough time for the reaction to go to completion.

This means that in 2×10^9 years those synthetic reactions which the cell is able to perform with the components present in Miller's aboriginal organic soup may indeed have happened in absence of the living cell. This is not a contradiction of the above statement that a specific, well-defined protein containing a hundred amino acids could never have been formed by spontaneous and random association. We are quite certain that the cell itself does not operate in such an unreasonable manner. More and more we have become aware that the living cell makes use of synthetic pathways which, except for the presence of proteins as catalysts, are surprisingly simple. The fascinating aspect of these experiments is that the next steps, the condensation of amino acids and of simple aliphatic acids into polymers or molecules with important catalytic properties, are also possible without the aid of a living cell. We shall have a look at two major examples—the formation of a-amino acid polymers and of porphyrins.

POLYMER a-AMINO ACIDS WITH PROTEIN-LIKE PROPERTIES

In the cell as it exists today, proteins are synthesized by the specific action of nucleic acid chains which in turn reproduce with the aid of protein enzymes. For such a circular process to get started, at least one major component with similar catalytic properties must have appeared spontaneously at some time.

Whether a replication process depends absolutely on the presence of true macromolecules, we do not know. According to our colleague at Chicago, Dr. Herbert S. Anker, it is quite possible that the enormous size of the molecules involved is the result of selection *after* the first properly reproducing system came into existence. We do know that amino acid polymers, somewhat similar to high-molecular natural proteins, can be formed spontaneously. Such polymers may even possess the distinctive structure of cellular proteins. This shows the extent of progress in recent years toward the synthesis of polypeptides and proteins. The methods employed are, as yet, extremely crude and so are the products. There is no way, for instance, to direct the assembly of various amino acids in any preselected sequence and slight chance of reproducing exactly the same polymer obtained in one experiment in the next test. Nevertheless, the importance of these observations should not be underrated. The conditions under which the artificial amino-acid polymers arise can be easily imagined to have occurred during the early period of organic evolution.

Could there be anything simpler than merely heating a mixture of amino acids? But this is just the way Fox and his co-workers obtained large, stable macromolecules composed of various peptide-linked amino acids. The method is purely empirical and the results are correspondingly unpredictable. Melting of dry amino acids is not a new type of experiment. What is new is the insight that a systematic investigation of reactions of this type may suddenly yield a clue how poly-amino acids with special catalytic properties could be formed.

The discovery of the specific spiral arrangements in the chains of natural proteins raised the problem how such a peculiar structure could be built up and maintained without the aid of the living cell. In a set of polymerization experiments by Doty and his colleagues, it was discovered that artificial peptides have a natural tendency to coil and to form a typical α-helix as soon as the length of the amino-acid chain goes beyond eight or ten members. Actually, once the coiling has started, the polymerization proceeds faster than before. Evidently a well-defined, rigid structure facilitates the addition of new members to the chain. Not only that: such a well-defined structure seems to promote also the separation and selection of macromolecules containing one of the two optical isomers. Racemic (d–l) polymers are possible, but they are less stable than either a pure d or l polymer coil. In contrast to the heating experiments of Fox, these polymerizations take place at normal, low temperatures. They still deviate from the biological pattern in two ways: the starting material—the monomers —are not amino acids per se but their carboxyanhydrides; and the less water contained in the solvent, the better the results.

These carboxyanhydrides are substances with a higher free energy content. In contact with water they have a tendency to release carbon dioxide spontaneously while being converted back to the respective amino acids. If this is prevented, they react with one another, evolve carbon dioxide, and form polymers of various lengths.

The range of artificial α-amino acid polymers, so far as molecular weight is concerned, equals that of the majority of natural proteins.

The products of these cold polymerizations in organic solvents can be controlled better, it seems, than those resulting from the Fox method at high temperatures, but a prerequisite is the proper supply of the reactive amino-acid derivative. Hence, the Doty-polymerization can serve as a model for a natural evolutionary step only if it can be shown that there is a plausible way for the N-carboxyanhydrides of the amino acid to have been formed under the conditions then prevailing. Past experience makes it more probable that the living cell uses energy-rich intermediates of another type—amino acids in combination with energy-rich phosphates. The spontaneous formation of such compounds should be studied.

PORPHYRINS

When we look at the picture of a chlorophyll molecule (Fig. 2) and remember that half a century of the most painstaking chemical studies by a succession of illustrious scientists was necessary to establish its formula and to synthesize some of its derivatives, the evolutionary way from the substances found in Miller's flask to chlorophyll seems indeed a long one. But this conclusion, which sounds reasonable, need not be correct. One of the most impressive and successful uses of carbon-14 as tracer in biochemical work has been in the elucidation of the way in which living cells synthesize the porphyrin ring. Shemin (1956) working with Carrothers demonstrated that it could all start with acetic acid and glycine. Simple condensations between these compounds yield, probably via succinic acid, δ-amino levulinic acid.

Two molecules of the latter condense to give a precursor pyrrole. The monopyrrole, porphobilinogen, then condenses again with itself (in a way we shall not discuss) yielding a porphyrin, a compound having the ring system which is the basis of many iron and magnesium-containing catalysts found in living cells.

In the living cell all these condensations are catalyzed by enzymes; where conditions are right, they take place in a matter of seconds. Will such reactions take place without the aid of living cells? Of course, the answer is Yes.

Shemin's condensations are of such a simple type that, speaking in terms of evolutionary time, they must have occurred almost immediately after acetic acid and glycine accumulated in the primary ocean or water puddles. Indeed, it has been shown that porphobilinogen will condense easily into a tetrapyrrole under laboratory conditions. Compared with the staggering problem of building up nucleic acids and protein chains, the origin of porphyrins (Fig. 8)

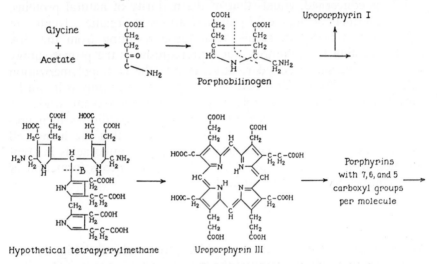

FIG. 8.—Natural synthesis of porphyrins from simple molecules

is a problem which is virtually solved—even though it may take a few years to find the right conditions for extending Miller's experiments to the point where porphyrins are spontaneously synthesized.

In evolutionary terms the gain due to an early appearance of porphyrins is very considerable. To judge from their distribution in the living world, it must have been decisive. Not only are porphyrins extremely stable under high temperatures, and other effects of radiation as well, but they avidly form complexes with all kinds of metals. Astonishing are the variety of uses to which porphyrins have been put in the living world, as well as the very small number of these catalysts which promote fundamental fermentative, respiratory, and photosynthetic reactions. These facts support the idea that porphyrins were already active in the very earliest quasi-living organic structures.

Once a certain metal-porphyrin attached itself to an amino-acid polymer and reacted faster than before, it had an enormous advantage over the catalysis by the unattached prosthetic group alone (cf. M. Calvin, 1956). The same holds for specificity. In order to envisage a gradual transition from the non-living to the living, we have to assume that after two billion years the conditions outside the first self-reproducing units must have approached those we find today inside what we call living protoplasm.

From the evolutionary point of view, the most important quality of porphyrins may be the fact that they are colored substances which catch the energy of visible light and make it available for chemical transformations.

SOURCES OF ENERGY AND PHOTOSYNTHESIS

The question of spontaneous synthetic reactions becomes somewhat more of a problem if they require a supply of free energy in order to proceed in the desired direction. Products which would rather turn back into the starting material while releasing heat can be made only by feeding in an excess of free energy and then preventing the back reaction by some special trick. This sequence must be repeated over and over again. Therefore, the question of the energy source for biopoesis and the means of applying the correct amounts are just as important as that of the source of raw materials. Furthermore, this source of energy must vary and become gentler and more specific lest the precious larger units fall apart again. A sequence from simple to more complex units in the chemical evolution requires appropriate changes in the mode of energy supply.

As sources of energy we must consider mainly the following: heat, chemical interactions, electrical discharges, and solar radiation. While volcanic action can produce some local heat, as well as chemical effects, it is the steady stream of radiation from the sun which provides the main driving force for all dis-equilibria on the surface of the earth.

What we may call the "Urey atmosphere" is colorless to our eyes. But its components strongly absorb the short-wave ultraviolet radiation, which amounts to about five per cent of the energy in the emission spectrum of the sun. The light quanta of this radiation are large enough to decompose molecular hydrogen, methane, ammonia, and water vapor. The resulting methyl, methylene, hydrogen, and hydroxyl radicals are the reactive chemicals which started and continued to drive the chemical evolution. By the time most of the hydrogen which was not present in the form of water or organic compounds had escaped from the atmosphere, traces of oxygen began to accumulate. The more oxygen appeared by the direct decomposition of water or later by the action of green plants, the more ozone was formed from it by ultraviolet light. (Ozone is now found in the upper layer of our atmosphere, where it intercepts nearly all the ultraviolet radiation —the very source of energy which originally promoted all major synthetic reactions.) This had two consequences. On the one hand, no more of the original organic material, the aliphatic and amino acids, could accumulate but, on the other hand, the stage was now set for the appearance of more and more complex organic structures to which irradiation with ultraviolet would have been fatal.

It has been assumed that this marked the end of the direct photochemical pressure on evolution until the time when the chlorophyll-containing organisms again found a way to make use of solar radiation for synthetic purposes. In the meantime evolution is supposed to have rolled along entirely at the expense of the free energy stored in a great variety of organic compounds. These continued to react spontaneously with each other or with the molecules of water wherever local conditions favored specific condensations, hydrations, dismutations, and oxido-reductions. This sounds implausible. If this had been so, the rate of evolution must have slowed down considerably until the evolution of oxygen by the first green cells provided for a better source of energy. But it is not very likely that during this long time light had no effect at all.

It is well known that iron or copper salts can produce photochemical effects with the energy of the light they absorb. In addition to the effects of ultraviolet radiation on organic molecules, we have to reckon with the photochemistry at longer wave lengths mediated by colored metal ions in solution. It is true that no photosynthesis of any sort based on light absorption by metal complexes is known in our living world. If it played a major role earlier in evolution, it did not survive. It was not suitable for incorporation into living organisms of the kind we know. But if, during the early period of the chemical evolution, well-known, natural pigments were formed which could make use of ordinary daylight, the situation must have been quite different.

A spontaneous synthesis of porphyrins from components found in Miller's experiment is perhaps the best example. If this happened, it must have had important consequences. Immediately at least one-third of the energy in the solar spectrum became available for photochemical reactions.

Furthermore, despite the large amount of energy present in daylight, this spectral region assures that the photochemistry is much milder than in the ultraviolet. Many of the bonds in an organic molecule that short-wave radiation can break in one absorption act now remain untouched. What a light-excited, dyestuff molecule can do instead is to transfer hydrogen atoms from one organic molecule to another—or to accelerate oxidation reactions which otherwise would occur only very slowly.

Thus, the first important role of porphyrins was not at all similar to the role of chlorophyll in green plants. There was not so much of an overall gain in the free energy content of the organic chemicals but rather a rapid photocatalytic conversion of one substance into another.

Photosynthesis, as we have it at the present time, is itself a product of a long evolution (Gaffron, 1957). It achieves its results with the aid of very specific enzyme systems and needs a complex structural organization. We are pretty certain that chlorophyll photosynthesis has evolved by making use of more primitive systems containing porphyrin compounds. We are also certain that it has provided for nearly all the energy and the raw materials for and in the living world since the start of the Darwinian evolution—but to what extent it really preceded the appearance of the typical living cell, we do not know. The problem of how an H–OH bond in a molecule of water is broken with the aid of light quanta that are not rich enough in energy to do this in one step has not been solved. It must be a very special achievement and bound to the structure of chlorophyll, because this is the only organic molecule on earth that is involved in this fundamental photochemical step.

Only recently it was discovered that the evolution of oxygen is a reaction rather separate from the photochemical decomposition of water. It depends on the catalytic action of manganese in its divalent ionic form. If manganese is withheld from growing plants, their photosynthetic process becomes incomplete and similar to that known to occur in certain primitive, light-dependent bacteria. These "purple bacteria," so-called because of their color, are anaerobic organisms. They reduce carbon dioxide in the light while oxidizing a great variety of inorganic and organic substances, such as molecular hydrogen or acetate, but they never release a trace of free oxygen. Purple bacteria may serve as a model of an evolutionary step just below that of the green plant. The lucky combination of the right porphyrin derivative with a special manganese-protein complex has led to the result which created those aerobic conditions that, in turn, made Darwinian evolution possible.

The Major Irreversible Geochemical Steps

It is hardly possible to avoid the conclusion that biopoesis on earth succeeded to the extent it did because of the particular sequence of geochemical steps and the duration of each of them. How closely such a sequence must be adhered to in order that chemical evolution in the end is crowned by the appearance of living organisms is a problem relevant to the question of life on other planets.

The importance of the Moscow Conference lies not in the great variety of things discussed, not in a new "triumph of materialism" (all science contributes to that), nor in the revelation of new discoveries (most of them had been said or had been known before), but, as I see it, in an impressive agreement on certain basic questions such as the major stages of terrestrial evolution which may be summarized as follows:

First: The anaerobic era of excess hydrogen. The energy source is ultraviolet, ionizing radiation, potential chemical energy, and local heating. This leads to an accumulation of organic substances of the "right kind." The "right kind" means compounds which are abundant in the living world and are universally utilized by living cells for the synthesis of vital cell constituents.

Second: The mainly anaerobic but hydrogen-poor period when traces of oxygen stop the action of ultraviolet by ozone formation. The energy source is local heat, organic chemicals, and visible light. The organic substances became more diversified, more complex. There is no dearth of hypotheses to account for inorganic or organic catalysis, with or without the aid of simple or complex interfaces. Between this and the next step, the first living things appeared in a way we are unable, as yet, to imagine.

Third: The era when early anaerobic organisms deplete the reservoir of organic substances. The source of energy from there on is photoreduction in living cells. At this time, it happens that one clone of cells outgrows all others and becomes the primordial seed for further rapid evolution in the established Darwinian sense.

Fourth: The era of photosynthesis. The evolution of free oxygen by the green plants radically changes the living conditions on earth by either killing obligate anaerobes or driving them "underground." The main source of energy from then on is the photosynthetic production of carbohydrates and of free oxygen. Oxygen itself becomes a secondary evolutionary force through the development of respiratory systems in chlorophyll-free "mutants." How accidental circumstances may determine whether an organism will survive such drastic changes as the step from anaerobic to aerobic conditions can be shown in an actual laboratory model.

Jensen and Thofern (1954) found a micrococcus strain which can grow very well heterotrophically under anaerobic conditions. On contact with oxygen the cells die because they have neither an efficient mechanism for destroying the hydrogen peroxide which might be formed nor a respiratory system. But, when the nutrient medium contains a simple iron porphyrin, ordinary protohemin, these bacteria survive in air. The hemin is taken up into the cells and there combines with the right kind of protein to provide the bacteria with catalase and respiratory enzymes. The presence or absence of hemin in the surroundings at the time oxygen reaches the cells determines their fate.

At the present time, we find ourselves at the end of the Darwinian evolution because we ourselves are responsible for its coming to an end. Man is now initiating the next or sixth step of terrestrial organic evolution.

We witness now an exponentially expanding phase of human activities based on purposeful endeavors. The general trend is towards the extinction of species after species of higher plants and animals, with the exception of those that are tolerated, deliberately cultivated, or conserved. In the near future man-made radiation may put life to an endurance test comparable only to the geological changes during its pre-Darwinian evolution. Should the last traces of life be extinguished by this novel means, the chances for a second biopoesis some billion years later will be definitely smaller than for the first event. Most organic matter will have been oxidized and decomposed, and there will be hardly any concentrated reservoirs of chemical free energy like the original hydrogen atmosphere. Whether spontaneous oxidation reaction will remove all oxygen from the atmosphere is doubtful and, consequently, also the likelihood that ultraviolet radiation may again serve as a prime source of energy for synthetic reactions.

It is more likely, however, that some lower form of life, a green alga for instance, may become radiation-resistant. Then, even if we should have been stupid enough to extinguish ourselves, there will be an opportunity for a repetition of an evolution of the kind we are familiar with.

OTHER PLANETS

Given the same favorable location and movement relative to the primary energy source—the central star—the opportunity for life to appear on any planet of "standard composition" depends very much on its size. The latter determines the rate at which the atmosphere covering the surface changes its composition. If the planet is small, it may have aged too fast. The biological development never moved beyond a certain level, and what was achieved may even have been wiped out later on. If the planet is somewhat larger than the earth, the appearance of life on it should be even more probable than it has been here since each geochemical phase could saturate itself with its particular possibilities. With a much larger size, one early or intermediate step could be held for eons.

Conditions on the surface of a planet may be such that enormous masses of organic material—and very complex ones at that—may have accumulated, yet all of the wrong type for further successful evolution. Or, we can imagine a sterile planet covered with organic "food" waiting for the right organism to be implanted from outside upon its fertile surface. One bacterial spore coming from outside into this culture medium would kindle the flame of life that otherwise might have appeared much later, or not at all.

Life on other planets must deviate in an unimaginable number of ways from what we know here on earth, so long as the potential choices in the evolutionary path have about equal probabilities to succeed. But the truly difficult stretches, those we have as yet not charted here on earth for our own evolution, might be rather similar. Just as many flat roads converge towards one mountain pass and on the other side diverge again, there might be one dominant principle which determines whether any kind of life has a chance to develop on a planet. Should we be able to examine Mars or Venus and find anything at all exciting, we shall have to distinguish between what is due to local conditions and what to laws that are universally valid.

Life on other planets might be such that it appears immediately familiar to the biochemist while not at all to the descriptive biologist. Outward shapes need not resemble what we are accustomed to see around us. These remarks sound trivial, but they point out some progress in the way we look at our problem. There is a fundamental difference between hunting for the unique event in the past which gave birth to everything else and searching for conditions which will bring forth an entire class of new complex systems. A unique event of the past cannot be reproduced nor understood if all causal connections have been erased. But a new class of possible reactions not only lends itself to scientific analysis but increases the likelihood of discovering the first primitive example by means of laboratory experiments.

What the astronomers tell us about Mars and Venus, the only ones we may hope to see more closely, is not very inviting. The one serious excuse to make strenuous efforts to get there is to satisfy our curiosity about biopoesis and a few other scientific questions. Whether such sport should be done at the expense of not settling pressing human problems first is very debatable. One interesting evolutionary aspect is that Venus, Earth, and Mars are supposed to have started under quite similar conditions. Yet, now the truly green pastures seem to exist only on our home planet. Urey (1952) says:

It is difficult to imagine that conditions on Venus and Mars could have been qualitatively different from those outlined for the earth. Venus may have retained somewhat less and Mars much less water, ammonia, and methane than the earth, though the variations in physical conditions could readily have been such that this was not true.

Venus has no water but very substantial quantities of carbon dioxide in its atmosphere, and this indicates that some water collected during the formation of the planet, since it seems to be the only cosmically available oxidizing agent for converting reduced carbon to carbon dioxide. Thus the protoplanet may have been at a slightly higher temperature so that water was retained less effectively than in the case of the earth.

On Mars biopoesis may have run relatively quickly through its first phase up to the time when lack of water and of hydrogen prevented any further development.

On Venus, obviously, no photosynthesis of the type displayed by the green plants has had a chance to convert the excess carbon dioxide into organic matter of presently living or fossil organisms.

Shapley's argument (earlier in this volume) for accepting life as a universal, unescapable phenomenon anywhere in the cosmos is based on the notion of a hundred-million-billion planets being quite similar to our earth, that is, upon the force of an awfully big number whose magic is neatly concealed behind the symbol 10^{17}. The only way to deal with facts which cannot be visualized is to get accustomed to them and to go ahead and work with them. After all, there are a thousand times more molecules of water in a droplet than earthlike planets in the universe.

For a scientist, the persuasiveness of big numbers is inescapable—indeed, crushing. Yet, in this case the conclusion derived from Shapley's argument should not be called knowledge, but faith; for the same type of argument—the big numbers applied in turn to cosmic distances, guarantees that we shall not be in a position to test the theory.

The implications of such a new faith, should it spread, are only beginning to dawn upon us. Considering the vastness of the universe, anything man can imagine within reason—that is, within the framework of the general rules of science and what we call laws of nature—is bound to be reality and truth somewhere. If a particular scientific daydream is not realized on earth, it is only so by reason of an irrelevant accident, which those possessed by scientific truth may feel entitled to set right—even using force against those who do not share their faith. Faith in the universality of life will be greatly weakened, however, should we fail after all to prove the point of this article, namely, the spontaneous evolution of life on earth.

On earth nature reflects upon itself in the mind of man. The great play of trial and error, chance and selection, when so mirrored—that is, seen from the point of view of a goal achieved—appears amazingly foreshortened. This projection we call purpose. It is a time-saving device from the evolutionary point of view. With a purpose, with a pre-conceived goal in mind, the vast majority of random trials necessary to get somewhere may be by-passed.

Compared with natural biopoesis, man has a great advantage. There is no reason to doubt that we shall re-discover, one by one, the physical and chemical conditions which once determined and directed the course of evolution. We may even reproduce the intermediate steps in the laboratory. But if, in addition, a long time—several million years—is of the essence because we must wait for some unique event to happen, it is obvious that our problem will not be solved; worse than that, we may even not be able to say why it can't be solved. But looking back upon the biochemical understanding gained during the span of one human generation, we have the right to be quite optimistic. In contrast to mindless nature which had to spend a billion years for the creation of life, mindful nature has a purpose and knows the outcome. Thus, the time needed to solve our problem may be less than a thousand years. After all, what we want is only to re-create the most primitive living entity.

The author wishes to express his gratitude to the Fels Fund for their generous financial support of his work.

LITERATURE

ALEXANDER, G. 1946. *Life, Its Nature and Origin.* New York: Reinhardt.

ALLEN, G. 1957. "Reflexive Catalysis, A Possible Mechanism of Molecular Duplication in Prebiological Evolution," *Am. Naturalist,* XCI, 65–78.

BERGSON, H. 1911. *Creative Evolution.* Trans. ARTHUR MITCHELL. New York: Henry Holt and Co.

BLUM, H. F. 1951. *Time's Arrow and Evolution.* Princeton: Princeton University Press.

BOYDEN, A. H. 1953. "Comparative Evolution with Specific Reference to Primitive Mechanisms," *Evolution,* VII, 21–30.

BREDER, C. M. 1942. "Evolutionary Hypotheses," *Zoologica,* XXVII, 131–43.

BRIDGMAN, P. W. 1950. *Reflections of a Physicist.* New York: Philosophical Library.

CALVIN, M. 1956. "Chemical Evolution," *Am. Sci.,* XLIV, 248.

CARPENTER, E. F., ed. 1955. *Transactions of the Conference on the Use of Solar Energy. IV. Photochemical Processes.* Tucson: University of Arizona Press.

DELBRÜCK, M., and REICHARDT, W. 1956. "I. System Analysis for the Light Growth Reactions of Phycomyces" in *Cellular Mechanisms in Differentiation and Growth,* D. RUDNICK, ed. Princeton: Princeton University Press.

DIXON, M. 1949. *Multi-enzyme Systems.* London: Cambridge University Press.

DIXON, M. and E. C. WEBB. 1958. *Enzymes.* New York: Academic Press.

DOTY, P., IMAHORI, K., and KLEMPERER, E. 1958. "The Solution,

Properties, and Configurations of a Polyampholytic Polypeptide, Copoly-L Lysine-L-Glutamic Acid," *Proc. Nat. Acad. Sci.,* XLIV, 428–31.

EINSTEIN, A. 1934. *Essays in Science.* New York: Philosophical Library.

FOX, S. W., and HARADA, K. 1958. "Thermal Copolymerization of Amino Acids to a Product Resembling Protein," *Science,* CXXVIII, 1214.

FRANCK, J. 1955. "Physical Problems of Photosynthesis," *Daedalus,* LVI, 17.

GAFFRON, H. 1957. "Photosynthesis and the Origin of Life," pp. 127–54 in *Rhythmic and Synthetic Processes in Growth,* D. RUDNICK, ed. Princeton: Princeton University Press.

GILLISPIE, C. C. 1958. "Lamarck and Darwin in the History of Science," *Am. Sci.* CLVI, 388–409.

GLASS, B. 1958. *A Summary of the Symposium on the Chemical Basis of Development,* pp. 855–922. (McCollum-Pratt Institute) Baltimore: Johns Hopkins University Press.

GRANICK, S. 1954. "Metabolism of Heme and Chlorophyll" in *Chemical Pathways of Metabolism, 2.* New York: Academic Press.

HARRIS, E. E. 1954. *Nature, Mind and Modern Science.* London: George Allen and Unwin.

HOROWITZ, N. H. 1945. "On the Evolution of Biochemical Syntheses," *Proc. Nat. Acad. Sci.,* XXXI, 153–57.

HOYLE, F. 1956. *Man and Materialism* ("World Perspective," Vol. 8.) New York: Harper and Bros.

HUMBOLDT, A. 1850. *Cosmos: Description of the Universe, Vol. I,* trans. E. C. OTTE. New York: Harper and Bros.

HUXLEY, J. 1939. *Essays of a Biologist.* London: Penguin Books, Ltd.

HUXLEY, J. S. 1942. *Evolution, The Modern Synthesis.* New York: Harper and Bros.

HUXLEY, J. S., HARDY, A. C. and FORD, E. B., eds. 1954. *Evolution as a Process.* London: George Allen and Unwin.

JEANS, J. 1935. *The Mysterious Universe.* London: Cambridge University Press.

JENSEN, J., and THOFERN, E. 1953–1954. *Zeit. f. Naturforsch.* V, 8b, pp. 599, 604, 697; V, 9b, p. 596.

JOHNSON, M. L., ABERCROMBIE, M., and FOGG, G. E., eds. 1954. *The Origin of Life.* ("New Biology No. 16") London: Penguin Books.

JONES, H. SPENCER. 1940. *Life on Other Worlds.* New York: The Macmillan Co.

JORDAN, P. 1955. *Science and the Course of History.* New Haven: Yale University Press.

KATCHALSKI, E., and SELA, M. 1957. "Synthesis and Chemical Properties of Poly Amino Acids," *Adv. in Protein Chem.,* XIII, 244–475.

KESSLER, E. 1955. "On the Role of Manganese in the Oxygen Evolving System of Photosynthesis," *Arch. Biochem. Biophys.* LIX, 527–29.

LANGMUIR, I. 1943. "Science, Common Sense, and Decency," *Science,* XCVII, 1.

LIPMANN, F., (chairman). 1958. "Symposium on Amino Acid Activation," *Proc. Nat. Acad. Sci.,* XLIV, 67–105.

LOVEJOY, A. O. 1936. *The Great Chain of Being.* Cambridge: Harvard University Press.

MACH, E. 1898. *Popular Scientific Lectures* (trans. T. J. MCCORMACK). Chicago: Open Court Publishing Co.

Macro-molecules, The Biological Replication of. 1958. 12th Symposium of the Society for Experimental Biology. New York: Academic Press.

"Macromolecules and Liquid Crystals, General Discussion on the Configuration and Interaction of," 1958. *Farad. Soc.,* XXV, 7–200.

MADISON, K. M. 1953. "The Organism and Its Origin," *Evolution,* VII, 211–27.

MEHLBERG, H. 1958. *The Reach of Science.* Toronto: University of Toronto Press.

MOORE, B. 1911. *The Origin and Nature of Life.* London: Williams and Norgate.

NEEDHAM, A. E. 1959. "The Origination of Life," *Quart. Rev. Biol.,* XXXIV, 189–209.

OPARIN, A. 1957. *Origin of Life on the Earth.* 3d. ed. New York: Academic Press.

PEARSON, K. 1937. *The Grammar of Science.* London: J. N. Dent and Sons, Ltd.

PIRIE, N. W. 1953. "Ideas and Assumptions About the Origin of Life," *Discovery,* XIV, 238–42.

――――. 1957. "The Origins of Life," *Nature,* CLXXX, 886.

SCHRÖDINGER, E. 1945. *What is Life?* London: Cambridge University Press.

――――. 1952. *Science and Humanism.* London: Cambridge University Press.

SHEMIN, D. 1956. "The Biosynthesis of Porphyrins; The Succinate-Glycine Cycle" in *Currents in Biochemical Research.* New York: Interscience Publishers.

SMITH, E. L., HILL, R. L., and KIMMEL, J. R. 1958. "Some Studies on the Structure and Activity of Papain" from *Symposium on Protein Structure,* A. NEUBERGER, ed. London: Methuen and Co., Ltd.

SNOW, C. P. 1959. "Review," p. 38 in *The Reporter,* Feb. 19.

TYNDALL, J. 1871. *Fragments of Science for Unscientific People.* London: Longmans, Green, and Co.

UREY, H. C. 1952. *The Planets.* New Haven: Yale University Press.

VAN NIEL, C. V. 1940. "The Biochemistry of Micro-organisms: An Approach to General and Comparative Biochemistry" in *The Cell and Protoplasm.* Washington, D.C.: The Science Press.

WALD, G. 1957. "The Origin of Optical Activity," *Annals of N.Y. Acad. Sci.,* LXIX, 352–68.

WEIZSÄCKER, C. V. 1949. *The History of Nature.* Chicago: University of Chicago Press.

E. A. EVANS, JR.

VIRUSES AND EVOLUTION

As recently as 1942, Julian Huxley could write: "Bacteria (and *a fortiori* viruses if they can be considered to be true organisms) . . . appear to be not only wholly asexual but premitotic. Their hereditary constitution is not differentiated into specialized parts with different functions. They have no genes in the sense of accurately quantized portions of hereditary substance and therefore they have no need for the accurate division of the genetic system which is accomplished by mitosis" (Huxley, 1942).

It is an index of the progress of our knowledge that we now know that not only bacteria but viruses do indeed have genes and that, further, the discovery of a variety of reproductive mechanisms in bacteria in addition to simple binary fission has disclosed striking similarities to the genetic processes in other organisms. A corresponding increase in our information concerning molecular structure, the mechanism of host-cell invasion and the process of reproduction, has occurred also for a number of viral agents (Adams, 1959; Burnet and Stanley, 1959). All of this, however, is not yet sufficient to offer a definitive answer to the problem of the specific evolutionary status of viruses in the hierarchy of living organisms. Even so, it becomes clear that viral particles have biological properties other than their occasional role as infectious and destructive agents.

Documentation of this statement requires a summary of the contemporary information regarding viruses.

1. All viruses contain, minimally, nucleic acid and protein, although other organic and inorganic components may be present (polyamines, lipids, coenzymes). The nucleic acid may be either deoxyribonucleic or ribonucleic acid. This is in marked contrast to all other known forms of living cells where both DNA and RNA are present, although the DNA is concentrated mainly in the nuclear structures while the RNA exist predominantly in the cytoplasm. In the ab-

E. A. EVANS, Jr. is Professor and Chairman of the Department of Biochemistry at the University of Chicago. An authority on virus reproduction, Dr. Evans was awarded the Eli Lilly prize in biological chemistry by the American Chemical Society in 1942. Since then, in addition to his research and teaching duties, he has served in various advisory capacities for the State Department.

85

sence of their hosts, viral particles, such as the bacteriophages, tobacco mosaic virus, influenza and poliomyelitis viruses do not show
demonstrable metabolic activity, do not contain energy "reservoirs"
nor require any source of energy to maintain their structure. It appears
therefore that we are dealing with structures which, although enormous in terms of molecular size, are bound by the usual covalent bonds
of organic substances, together with such other types of intramolecular
binding forces as operate, for example, in determining the particular
configuration of a protein molecule.

2. The viral protein is apparently physiologically heterogeneous
and, in the case of the bacterial viruses, continuing examination has
disclosed an increasing number of different roles for viral protein in
addition to its being responsible for viral antigenicity. In general, the
viral protein appears responsible for the following functions.

a) The viral protein serves as protection for the nucleic acid component, since the intact virus particles are not attacked by enzymes
that split nucleic acids.

b) The viral protein is involved in the specific introduction of viral
nucleic acid into the host cell or, conversely, in excluding viral nucleic acid from non-susceptible cells. The first case is illustrated by
coliphage T_2 where viral invasion involves (1) preliminary combination with the bacterial cell and eventual alteration of the structure of
the protein of the viral tail piece; (2) subsequent erosion of the host
cell wall adjacent to the attached virus by a lytic enzyme (protein)
present in the viral tail; and (3) contraction of still another protein
in the viral tail, presumably to facilitate the entrance of the viral
nucleic acid into the host cell (Kozloff, 1959). The second property
of the viral protein has been demonstrated in both bacterial and animal
virus infections. Removal of the distal portion of the virus tail from
coliphage T_2 permits the attack of host cell membranes impervious to
the intact virus. With human cells, the ribonucleic acid from poliomyelitis virus is capable of inducing and causing viral replication in
tissues not attacked by the original virus particle with intact protein
component (Holland, McLaren, and Syverton, 1959). The organ and
tissue specificity of animal viruses may be, then, a reflection of the nature of the protein component of the infectious particle.

c) In some but not all cases, the viral protein causes the death of
the host cell in the absence of viral replication. This can be demonstrated with nucleic acid-free "ghosts" of the T-even coliphages (Herriott, 1951). The lethal effect of such preparations may be due to
their demonstrated ability to attack and lyse cell walls from sensitive
host cells. Such a phenomenon has not been demonstrated with animal
viruses, and the protein component of temperate viruses causing lyso-

genic infections cannot possess such lethal properties (see below) although some mechanism for viral invasion must permit penetration of the cell wall.

3. The nucleic acid component of viral particles appears to be solely responsible for the intracellular synthesis of the complete virus particle. This has been clearly shown with tobacco mosaic virus, in which the ribonucleic acid component can be separated from the protein in a simple (and reversible) fashion (Fraenkel-Conrat and Williams, 1955; Gierer and Schramm, 1956). While the free ribonucleic acid is much less infective than the intact virus, it is unquestionably capable of causing the synthesis of infectious virus identical to that from which the ribonucleic acid was derived, and it undoubtedly carries the whole of the genetic information of the virus particle.[1] A similar role for the viral DNA of the bacterial viruses rests on experiments showing that viral protein (at least the major portion) remains outside the infected cell and is unnecessary for viral replication, once introduction of the viral nucleic acid has occurred (Hershey and Chase, 1952). Finally, very recent experiments with an animal virus (poliomyelitis) demonstrate a similar role for viral RNA here as well (Holland, McLaren, and Syverton, 1959). In all cases, then, the nucleic acid is the unique progenitor of viral replication.

Two types of viral infection, namely virulent and temperate, are known to occur in bacterial host cells, and these are suspected of having analogies in plant and animal tissues.

The first type of infection—the so-called virulent process (Adams, 1959)—involves the introduction of the phage DNA into the bacterial host by the sequence of events described above. The further events leading to the replication of the virus are obscure in detail (as is our information regarding the mechanism of biosynthesis of protein and nucleic acid in general) but are characterized by the following.

1. Presumable use of the metabolic machinery of the host (i.e., enzymes, etc.) for the synthesis of viral protein and viral DNA. These are manufactured separately, and indeed the respective synthetic processes can be experimentally differentiated. Mature infectious virus particles can be detected only in the later phase of viral replication.

2. Possible transfer of parent nucleic acid to viral progeny, at least in part, but the physiological significance of this is still uncertain.

3. Partial or complete (depending on viral strain) utilization of host DNA for viral replication, with a preliminary breakdown of this

---

[1] Present information is that the genetic material in all known organized cellular forms (and in those bacterial viruses thus far studied, and presumably in the herpes virus and the rabbit pappilloma virus) is DNA. With such viruses as the tobacco mosaic virus, polio, and influenza, the genetic role is apparently assumed by RNA.

into smaller fragments—probably to the oligonucleotide level (Evans, 1953).

The second type of infection—the lysogenic response to the temperate virus (Lwoff, 1953; Bertani, 1958)—is characterized by the introduction of viral DNA into the host cell (mechanism unknown) without immediate viral replication and host-cell destruction. Rather, the viral nucleic acid (or a portion of it) becomes attached to or incorporated into the genetic material of the host as so-called "prophage." As the host cell divides to reproduce, this viral portion is also reproduced and transmitted, along with the normal genetic units, to the host progeny. Under the proper circumstances and in the case of some bacterial strains, the prophage can be "induced" by physical agents such as X-rays or ultraviolet light or by a variety of chemical agents (usually mutagenic substances) into a vegetative form which gives rise to replicas of the original temperate virus, causing lysis of the host cell in a manner analogous to that seen in virulent infections. This association of the prophage with the host genetic unit may cause a change in the heritable characteristics of the infected host cell, with the virus carrying a portion of the genetic material (usually evident in terms of specific biochemical properties) from one bacterial cell to another. This last type of lysogenization is called "transduction" (Lederberg, 1958).

Two related phenomena, observed in bacterial cells, are pertinent to the ensuing discussion.

The first is the process of bacterial transformation in which genetic alteration can be caused in a wide variety of bacterial cells by the nucleic acid (DNA) derived from related bacterial strains of differing biochemical or physiological characteristics (Hotchkiss, 1955). The phenomenon is limited by specific requirements with respect to both the donor of the DNA and the physiological condition of the recipient. The process apparently involves a genuine alteration of the genetic material of the recipient (addition of the transforming principle to the host genome?) since the alteration is perpetuated in succeeding generations. The second phenomenon involves genetic recombination in such bacterial cells as *Escherichia coli* by a process involving, first, fusion of the mating cells followed by the unilateral, linear transfer of genetic material (nucleic acid?) from one mating type to another through a narrow intercellular bridge (Lederberg, 1958).

To return to virus infections: It is clear that the transduction of host genetic characters to a lysogenized cell is associated with incorporation or attachment of the nucleic acid of the temperate virus to the host genes; i.e., it involves essentially the genetic apparatus of the host. The transfer of host genetic characteristics in transduction need not be a matter of surprise when one considers (1) that isotopic tracer experiments demonstrate the utilization of host DNA for the manufacture of viral DNA to involve a preliminary breakdown to the oligonucleotide level; and (2) that the molecular size of the genetic unit may be of the order of only several nucleotides (see below). There is evidence that the process is limited, i.e., that only a certain number of prophages can be attached to or incorporated by a specific host cell. This last observation suggests the possibility that (in addition to being a means for effecting genetic recombination) lysogeny and the temperate viruses may offer a mechanism for the actual piecewise construction of genetic apparatus by a process of accretion, so that the present composition of a bacterial chromosome may represent the end result of an assembly of genetic units, added by successive lysogenizations. However, there is no experimental support for such a suggestion.

Our information regarding the process of replication of virulent virus indicates that the viral nucleic acid is converting the metabolic machinery of the host to its own replicative end. This could be considered as merely a redirection of pre-existing cytoplasmic mechanisms for nucleic acid and protein biosynthesis. However, it appears that the genetic apparatus of the host (using the term in the sense of the gene plus its associated metabolic machinery) is also involved inasmuch as one can show, for example, that infection by coliphage T_2 of an *E. coli* mutant requiring extracellular thymine results in the ready synthesis of thymine for the nucleic acid component of the viral progeny (5). The action of the transforming principles and the process of cellular fusion clearly involves a specific and intimate interaction of genetic units. What now appears equally true is that viral replication and behavior (at least in the cases cited) involves a similar process.

As of the moment, the most important contribution that viral research has made to evolutionary doctrine is in terms of approximate estimates of the molecular dimensions of the genetic unit. These have been calculated by Benzer (1957) and rest, in large part, on his own experiments with bacterial viruses. As with other species, it is possible to demonstrate with bacterial viruses that the hereditary factors are ordered in a one-dimensional array divisible by genetic recombination. The detection of vanishingly small proportions of recombinant types with certain mutants of the viral strains makes it possible to attain adequate resolution in genetic recombination experiments. Benzer's estimates of the molecular dimensions of the gene are in terms of its three distinct operations—namely, mutation, recombination, and function. The alteration that can give rise to a mutant form of organism appears to be not larger than five nucleotide pairs. The upper limit for the element that can be shown to be interchanged but is itself not divisible in genetic recombination experiments comprises two nucleotide pairs while a functional unit involving, say, the synthesis of a protein molecule may be a few thousand nucleotide pairs. Such knowledge brings within our horizon the possibility of equating genetic properties with molecular features of composition and structure of the deoxyribonucleic acid,[2] and we have suggestions (as yet unverified experimentally) as to how the sequence of bases in DNA could act as a code for determining, for example, the sequence of amino acids in proteins.

The new information that has made possible this valuable and fundamental achievement does not as yet answer the question as to the evolutionary origin of virus particles. Partially responsible for this (but only in part) is the fact that the submicrosopic biological agents called "filterable viruses" are grouped together, not in terms of apparent taxonomic unity, but by their common necessity to invade specific living cells and to replicate in them. The evolutionary origin of viruses can be discussed only in terms of a number of limited particular cases, and indeed one must heed André Lwoff's (1957) admonitory paraphrase of another Parisian that "viruses should be considered as viruses because viruses are viruses."

A variety of suggestions has been made with respect to the origin of the viruses, including the possibility that no single explanation is valid for the whole group; the existence of viruses containing either DNA or RNA (never both) indicates that such may indeed be the case. It has been suggested: (1) that viruses are descendants of a primitive form of life predating the appearance of organized cells; or (2) that they have evolved from more complicated cells (such as those now constituting their specific hosts) by the step-wise loss of all characteristics except the ultimate genetic code represented by DNA (the so-called retrograde evolutionary hypothesis). Still other suggestions propose that the specificity of virus-host cell relationships can be explained by (3) their descent from a common ancestor or that (4) in the case of the bacterial viruses, they may represent evolution from a primitive mechanism of sexuality—i.e., they are derived from normal cellular components. None of these can be entirely excluded or selected.

Certainly recognition of the fact that the functional portion of the known viruses is a replicating nucleic acid suggests that the problem of the evolution of the viruses can be associated with the question of the origin of the nucleic acids themselves. If our current information concerning the biosynthesis of these compounds in living cells is per-

[2] See Footnote 1.

tinent, these large nucleotide polymers are manufactured from smaller molecules. The heterocyclic ring of the purines is manufactured from carbon dioxide, formic acid, and the amino acids—glycine, aspartic and glutamic acids (in the form of their appropriate derivatives)—while the pyrimidine ring comes together from CO_2, urea, and succinic acid. The characteristic sugars and phosphoric acid molecules are apparently attached before the final closing of the purine and pyrimidine rings, and the resulting nucleosides in the form of di- or tri-phosphates polymerize to form the nucleic acid itself. What is important is that all the organic precursors would be abundantly available in the primitive solution of organic substances that is believed to precede the appearance of living organisms on the earth (see the paper by Gaffron elsewhere in this volume). At the moment these large acidic polymers were neutralized by a protective coat of basic protein (formed in the same organic solution), one could imagine them as the ancestor of both the viral nucleic acid and the nucleic acid of the gene and cytoplasm of the organized cell. In this view, then, the viruses are not degraded and parasitic offspring of more highly organized forms of life but a reflection of the most primitive and primordial type of macromolecular organization.

While the facts do not lead to a conclusive answer, it is possible to impose some faint aura of phylogenesis on the limited data pertinent to bacteria and the bacterial viruses. Since viral replication uses the metabolic machinery of the host cell, it seems plausible that this apparatus (either as such or in the organization of the cell) must have preceded the emergence of viral forms. One can begin with the simple asexual fission of the bacterial cell in which occasional mutation is the unique propulsion for genetic change. Succeeding this would be occasional mutation to cells capable of sexual fusion and direct genetic recombination. Here the material transferred is presumably the gene itself, i.e., DNA. This is the case with the transforming principles also. However, transformation could be of biological importance only in those circumstances in which accidental death of the donor cell liberated its DNA into the environment of the recipient since there is no evidence for DNA release during normal growth and metabolism.

It seems likely that the normal process of DNA replication in dividing cells would involve the reversible formation of DNA protein complexes. Mutation conferring on some portion of the genetic DNA the properties of prophage, (i.e., vegetative replication on induction) coupled with loss of ability to reverse an intermediate protein-nucleic acid stage, could account for the appearance of the nucleic acid-protein complex of the temperate virus. Alternatively, one can visualize a process of mutation, leading to increasing parasitism, which would reduce the donor partner in the cell fusion type of reproduction to its ultimate nucleic acid limit. If one assumed further that this portion of the DNA conferred on the fused gene the capacity for induction by ultraviolet light and other agents, the appearance of temperate virus particles could occur. Since such forms would be capable of effecting genetic recombination at a distance (i.e., acting essentially as bacterial sexual organs), they might possess survival advantages over those organisms requiring cellular fusion. Finally, mutation of the temperate to the virulent type of virus would seem not improbable, and, indeed, numerous examples are known of the mutual reversibility of lytic and lysogenic behavior.

It is clear from all this that the evolutionary role of virus particles cannot be specified. And indeed, since the conditions under which they appeared are unknown and quite possibly incapable of reconstruction, the question may remain permanently unanswered. Irrespective of whether the viruses preceded or followed the appearance of organized cellular forms, it seems certain that the virus particle is carried in the main line of organic evolution.

BIBLIOGRAPHY

Exhaustive documentation of the condensed statements of the text has not been attempted. The papers listed summarize, in general, various areas of research.

ADAMS, M. H. 1959. *Bacteriophages.* New York: Interscience Publishers.

BENZER, S. 1957. "The Elementary Units of Heredity." p. 70 in W. D. MCELROY and B. GLASS (eds.), *The Chemical Basis of Heredity.* Baltimore: Johns Hopkins Press.

BERTANI, G. 1958. "Lysogeny," p. 151 in *Advances in Virus Research,* Vol. 5. New York: Academic Press.

BURNET, F. M., and STANLEY, W. M. (eds.). 1959 *The Viruses.* 3 volumes. New York: Academic Press.

COHEN, S. S., and BARNER, H. D. 1954. "Studies on Unbalanced Growth in *E. coli,*" *Proc. Nat. Acad. Sci.,* XL, 885.

EVANS, E. A., JR. 1953. "The Origin of the Components of the Bacteriophage Particle," *Annales de l'Institut Pasteur,* LXXXIV, 129.

FRAENKEL-CONRAT, H., and WILLIAMS, R. C. 1955. "Reconstitution of Active Tobacco Mosaic Virus from its Inactive Protein and Nucleic Acid Components," *Proc. Nat. Acad. Sci.,* XLI, 690.

GIERER, A., and SCHRAMM, G. 1956. "Infectivity of Ribonucleic Acid from Tobacco Mosaic Virus," *Nature,* CLXXVII, 702.

HERRIOTT, R. M. 1951. "Nucleic Acid-free T_2 Virus "Ghosts" with Specific Biological Action," *J. Bact.,* LXI, 752.

HERSHEY, A. D., and CHASE, M. 1952. "Independent Functions of Viral

Protein and Nucleic Acid in Growth of Bacteriophage," *J. Gen. Physiol.,* XXXVI, 39.

HOLLAND, J. J., McLAREN, L. C., and SYVERTON, J. T. 1959. "Mammalian Cell-Virus Relationship. III. Poliovirus Production by Non-Primate Cells Exposed to Poliovirus Ribonucleic Acid.," *Proc. Soc. Exptl. Med. & Biol.,* C, 843.

HOTCHKISS, R. D. 1955. "The Biological Role of the Deoxypentose Nucleic Acids," p. 435 in E. CHARGAFF and J. N. DAVIDSON (eds.). *The Nucleic Acids,* Vol. 2. New York: Academic Press.

HUXLEY, J. 1942. *Evolution, The Modern Synthesis,* p. 131. New York: Harper and Bros.

KOZLOFF, L. M. 1959. *Structure and Function of Bacteriophage* T₂ *in Sulfur in Proteins,* p. 347. New York: Academic Press.

LEDERBERG, J. 1958. "Bacterial Reproduction," p. 69. *Harvey Lectures,* Vol. 53. New York: Academic Press.

LWOFF, A. 1953. "Lysogeny," *Bact. Rev.,* XVII, 269.

———. 1957. "The Concept of Virus," *J. Gen. Microbiol.,* XVII, 239.

BERNHARD RENSCH

THE LAWS OF EVOLUTION

Evolutionary research, pursued with growing intensity since the appearance of Charles Darwin's epoch-making book on the *Origin of Species,* yielded results which confirmed the theories of this universal biologist in all essential items. But the investigations also led to many new aspects of the phenomenon of evolution. Now these new results allow two kinds of conclusions, which seem to be very contradictory. On the one hand, evolution may be looked at as an undirected unique historical process; on the other hand, it seems to be determined by a great number of laws and rules. A decision between these two different conclusions will be very important for the philosophy of life. Therefore, this problem may be treated in some detail in this lecture.

It has been proved by chemical and serological investigations that apparently all species of animals and perhaps even most individuals have their own specific types of proteins. With regard to this fact, each species and—especially among mammals—each individual is unique.

Besides, the genetical and cytological inquiries have shown that in all well-analyzed animals and plants the number of genes is so large that the number of possible gene combinations is of an astronomic order. In this respect, too, each individual is something unique.

Mutation is undirected, primarily restricted only by the possibilities of chemical alterations of genes, perhaps by alteration of the bases of nucleotides. The conditions of selection also seem to occur at random. They are determined by factors changing frequently in the course of time. Hence, also, the special phylogeny of a species, a family, an order, or a class of animals and plants, i.e., the development of each special type of construction, is a unique event like all historic events (compare Dobzhansky, 1957).

However, we get quite another picture, if we consider all the laws

BERNHARD RENSCH is Professor of Zoology and Director of the Zoological Institute, University of Münster in West Germany. He is also Director of the Münster Museum of Natural History. Among the honors Prof. Rensch has received for his studies, embracing a wide variety of topics in comparative zoology, are the Leibnitz Medal of the Prussian Academy of Sciences (1938) and the Darwin-Wallace Medal of the Linnean Society (1958).

and rules restricting the primary undirectedness of evolution. Here we see that the phylogenetic processes are not always so unique as we could expect but that they follow certain lines which are more or less parallel in different lines of descent. Now, with regard to our question, it will be decisive to evaluate the extent of the effects of such laws. Hence it will be necessary to discuss briefly the main laws and rules of evolution and to ask how far the primary undirectedness of evolution is restricted and how far we are able to predict phylogenetic processes.

Charles Darwin (1859) already knew a number of such rules. Perhaps the most important of these rules states that the progeny of all species of animals and plants is so great that the increase in number of individuals would occur in geometrical progression. Furthermore, in many lines of descent Darwin recognized the general tendency of "gradual advancement of the organisation." He called it a "general principle . . . that natural selection is continually to economise every part of the organisation." He spoke of the "law" of the "unity of type," i.e., of the "agreement in structure of species of the same class," and he explained this "law" by the "unity of descent." He also discussed the biogenetic rule, already established by other authors, a rule which indicates that the phylogeny of a species is reflected to some extent in its ontogeny. And in his book on *The Variation of Animals and Plants* he treated different rules of correlation between organs and structures of the body.

Meanwhile, many other laws and rules of evolution have been discovered, and just this fact may be looked at as a most important progress during the last century (besides the discovery of numerous facts in paleontology and genetics, furnishing new evidence for the theory of evolution). At present the number of laws and rules governing evolution directly or indirectly is so large that we can only outline briefly the more important ones in the following chapters.

Later we have to ask whether and how far we can give a causal explanation for these rules and whether other types of laws besides causality were also involved. Hence a short epistomological discussion will be necessary. And, finally, we will have to ask, to what extent the laws of evolution themselves have been subjected to an evolution during the evolution of our earth, i.e., how far we may assume that the special evolutionary rules were potentially pre-existent and only became manifest on successive levels of increasing integration of living matter.

BIOLOGICAL LAWS AND RULES

With regard to our question, it is important to discuss briefly the nature and characteristics of "laws" and "rules" and the special kind of evolutionary laws.

In the first place, the biologist has to do with *causal laws,* which have been and will be found only by induction. Primarily, such laws are statements of processes which always occur in the same manner if certain spatial constellations of matter exist. Such single "natural laws" gain a special character by the fact that they are connected with one another in such a manner that special laws follow from more general laws and that all of them are based on the general law of causality. Hence many biological laws can be reduced to chemical and physical laws.

In the realm of living beings most processes are extraordinarily complex, and many special laws act together or interfere with one another. Thus "exceptions" to the laws result, and therefore we often speak of "rules" only and not of "laws." However, we must not forget that, finally, most "rules" are effected by laws, the complicated interactions of which we often cannot analyze and the results of which we cannot predict in each case.

Recently, physicists have supposed that microphysical laws are of only a statistical nature, because it is impossible to predict single microphysical processes. Such an assumption may lead to the conclusion that causal laws are valid only in macrophysical processes. However, this would be a false conclusion. If laws are valid in the macrophysical realm, they must already exist implicit in the realm of microphysical processes, the interaction of which determines the macrophysical and, hence, also the biological processes. We are only incapable of *predicting* special microphysical processes. But predictability is only the practical result of causal laws; it is not a necessary component of their definition.

Besides the predominating laws of causality, however, in the evolutionary laws two other kinds of laws also participate, a fact which most biologists do not realize. Evolutionary research is not restricted to the somatic phylogeny but deals also with the psychic development, with psychogenesis. With absolute certainty we can suppose the existence of psychic phenomena, that is to say, sensations, ideas, feelings, etc., only in man (more exactly: only each Ego for its own self). However, it is an obvious consequence of uttermost probability that psychic processes also exist in animals, at least in higher ones. We are convinced that a dog or a parrot is not only a physiological machine but a being capable of seeing, hearing, remembering, feeling pleasure, etc. Hence psychic phenomena (awareness in its broader sense) surely did not arise suddenly in the course of phylogeny (for instance, in *Pithecanthropus*) as something which was absolutely new and peculiar.

These psychic phenomena do not belong to causal processes. When we see a red flower and when we pluck it, an uninterrupted causal process goes on, beginning with the entering of light rays of certain wave lengths into the eye and inducing an excitation in the sense cells of the retina running to the optic center in the forebrain and from there to motor regions and further, by the pyramidal tract, to the fingers (processes which we may prove electrophysiologically), but the sensation "red" runs parallel to only a part of this process. The fact that it is to excitations by wave lengths of about 670 mμ that the sensation "red" runs parallel and to excitations by wave lengths of 520 mμ for "green," and not vice-versa, cannot be explained by causal laws. In such cases we have to do with *laws of parallelism,* i.e., with laws governing this running parallel of certain phenomena (of something "psychic") to certain excitations of the brain or sense organs. In a corresponding manner also other phenomena like ideas and feelings run parallel to causal physiological processes in the brain. As most, if not all, animals show reactions to light, temperature, chemical substances, touch, etc., it is obvious to presume at least sensations running parallel to such "sense reactions." But we must not presume that in lower animals such sensations are imbedded in a continuous stream of consciousness as in man (compare Rensch, 1954).

A third type of basic laws participating in evolutionary laws are the *logical laws.* They refer to relations of things existing at the same time, not to processes in the succession of time, like causality. They are valid for causal as well as for psychic components (more exactly: components of parallelism). The sentence "if two things are equal to a third thing, they are also equal to each other," is not only valid for material things, e.g., for three molecules, but also for three identical sensations of red, as, for instance, three red points in my visual image (compare Ziehen, 1920, 1927).

How decisive for evolution the logical laws are may easily be shown by the assumption that these laws would *not* be valid. Let us take, for example, the reduplication of a gene, so that we have two identical genes. If the newly formed second gene reduplicated again, then this third gene would not be equal to the first one. Hence a continued identical reproduction of genes would not occur, and a genetical constancy would be as impossible as an adaptation to a habitat and as the existence of a species.

In a similar manner, more or less all evolutionary laws and rules are also governed by logical laws, independently of our human think-ing—for instance, when the equality of sexual releasers of the female guarantees reproduction, when allometrical growth proceeds accord-ing to a mathematical formula. (At last the whole algebra is a special field of logic.) Parallel to the increasing integration of different chem-ical compounds forming an organism in the course of evolution, the manifestation of more and more complicated mathematical relations and therefore of logical laws became possible.

As the logical laws are valid for causal as well as for psychic com-ponents (components of parallelism), they cannot only be looked at as laws of human thinking. On the contrary, human thinking de-veloped phylogenetically by adapting itself to the universal logical laws. Wrong thinking was corrected by selection when it was not enough in agreement with the causal facts of the environment or with the psychic laws. Hence logical laws as well as causal laws were also valid before man existed and before there were any organisms on the earth.

Now the laws of living beings have a specific character, as they are mostly *systemic laws* (compare Rensch, 1949). As is well known, life can be characterized only by certain performances (like growth, re-production, metabolism, reactions to stimuli, etc.), each of which may also appear in non-living matter (for instance, in fluid crystals), which, however, are typical of life, if they exist together in an individualized system of proteins and proteids. Are the factors determining the whole-ness and the constancy of such living individuals specific "factors of wholeness" underlying corresponding "systemic laws"? Or are these systemic laws also only complications of the laws of causality?

We may presume that living systems, that is to say, organisms, arose step by step by evolution and that, right from the beginning, a genetic constancy must have been guaranteed, so that the first pre-stages of living beings could adapt themselves to a certain environment, in which they found possibilities for feeding, hiding, and reproduction. When, later, more complicated multicellular organisms developed, the in-dividuals of each species formed a special system, the structures and functions of which worked together harmoniously and achieved the main functions of life by this acting together. An organ shows per-formances which are not simply the sum total of all single perform-ances. A nerve cell, for example, is capable only of conducting ex-citations and keeping perhaps engrams. A complex of many nerve cells—a brain—however, works not only by summing up all single excitations, but it is also capable of reacting in a specific manner to a certain part of the excitations, it is capable of comprehending a "gestalt."

If we now try to analyze the structures and functions of organs, like a brain, which are characterized by their performances as a whole system, we find many *correlations,* that is to say, we find a dependence of many single processes with one another. For example, we may state that in neighboring neurons the fluctuations of potentials do not go on in the same manner as they arrived from different sense cells but adjust themselves, that they "step in." Thus such groups of cells show a new systemic function, a uniform rhythm.

Similar findings can be made when we analyze other results of living systemic performances. If, for example, the body size of a vertebrate animal is altered during phylogeny, many correlative tracts will also be altered, because the single organs and structures have special growth ratios. In a larger animal those organs which grow more quickly than the whole body will become disproportionate and eventually excessively large, whereas organs growing with negative allometry will become relatively small and sometimes even vestigial. Parallel with such changes in proportions of organs and structures, their functions also may be altered. Generally, larger animals have a lower metabolism, their period of individual development is longer, they reach a higher age, etc.

However, by such analyses of systemic characters and laws we can always state that the correlations are altered by *causal* relations. Biological laws (*sensu strictiori*) are special laws only so far as they act on more complicated levels of integration. With regard to their nature, they are still causal laws.

Similar systemic laws also exist among psychic components. When an eye develops phylogenetically, beginning with a simple accumulation of sense cells reacting to light and ending with a vesicular eye with a lens, then the effect is not only a summing-up of more excitations of sense cells, but it becomes possible to comprehend certain shapes, certain "gestalten." The laws of "gestalt" comprehension are a novum on the phylogenetic level of vesicular eyes, but with regard to their nature they are still psychic laws (or, more correctly, laws of parallelism).

Summing up, we may state that in the somatic and psychic evolution of organisms three universal categories of laws are effective: laws of causality, laws of psychic parallelism, and laws of logic. It is very probable that here we have to do with "eternal" laws directing all processes of the universe. Such an assumption is compatible with all our scientific experience, and it facilitates a universal conception of the world. With regard to our evolutionary questions, we cannot discuss these general problems in more detail, but we shall have to mention them once again later.

After this unavoidable discussion of the nature of biological laws we may now consider the special laws of evolution, in order to answer our main question, to what degree phylogeny is determined.

SPECIFIC LAWS OF EVOLUTION

As already mentioned, the processes in living organisms are very complex, and they interfere to such a degree that the biological laws have many exceptions and that we had better speak of "rules." This is also true for evolutionary "laws." But such rules, too, show that evolution is not undirected and random but comprehensible and predictable to a large degree. Now *it will be necessary to evaluate this degree of determination.* For such an evaluation we first need a brief survey of the different types of evolutionary laws. Then we may try to evaluate in a rather well-known category in homoiothermic animals if undirected or forced evolution normally prevailed. In this context the special question will be important if and how far evolutionary progress was determined by rules and if even the evolution of man was necessitated.

It is not easy to classify the manifold rules of evolution, as there are different possibilities. For our purpose it may be sufficient to distinguish two main categories: (1) the laws and rules mainly determined by the internal structure and functions of the organisms and (2) the rules which are mainly determined by the interaction with the environment. It is not possible to define these two categories definitely, as most internal processes are connected with processes of metabolism and therefore also with the environment. But in practice it is possible to distinguish rather well between both categories, because the first category deals more or less with rules of genetics, physiology, and developmental physiology, whereas the second category deals mainly with laws of selection and with ecological laws.

The rather great number of physiological laws and rules is of importance, as they greatly restrict the possibilities of evolutionary alteration. Undirected mutation cannot effect any kind of alterations of species but only those which still guarantee the processes of life.

AUTONOMOUS LAWS AND RULES OF LIVING BEINGS

One of the most fundamental laws on the level of living organisms is the statement that the long-lasting constancy of the species is effected by the identical reduplication of genes. A second fundamental law states that these stable genes, however, show mutations in approximately constant intervals (mutation rates). As we do not know exceptions, we may really speak of two "laws." They are the basic laws of evolution as the mutations yield the raw material for most phylogenetic alterations especially for those which lead to new types of construction.

The causality of spontaneous mutation could not yet be elucidated. Hence it is impossible to predict when a certain mutation will occur. With regard to this fact a mutation is similar to a microphysical event, which, too, can only be stated statistically. But in my opinion it is not justifiable to consider such "statistical laws" as a special category of laws besides the causal laws. As already mentioned, we have to assume that also in the realm of microphysics the processes are "caused," as otherwise the causal relations in macrophysical processes could not result. In the microphysical realm there is no chance to analyze the processes to such a degree that they would become predictable (because of complementarity). For spontaneous mutation, however, we may have some hope that their causation may some day become comprehensible and in some cases even predictable. This hope seems to be justified by various modern findings: (1) The reproduction and the "hybridization" of some bacteriophages (which have many analogies to genes) have shown that, for constancy and mutation, only the nucleoproteids are important (compare Hershey and Chase, 1952). (2) The structure of these nucleoproteids becomes more and more elucidated. If the hypothesis of Watson and Crick (1953) is confirmed, that is to say, if the molecules of nucleoproteids really contain two spiral chains of nucleic acid, then it may be possible that mutation occurs by separation and recombinations of these spirals (complementary combination by change of purine bases in the interior of the sugar-phosphate-spirals). (3) Investigations on the chemical release of mutations have made it probable that spontaneous mutation is partly caused chemically as natural mutagenous compounds also exist (for example, hydrogen peroxide or phenol). Moreover, in some cases chemical mutation seems to be restricted to some special types. (4) There is some hope that electron-microscopical research on chromosomes will contribute to the elucidation of mutation.

However, the general rule that spontaneous mutation occurs in an undirected manner remains untouched by such hope of future causal explanation. This undirectedness is further strengthened by the fact that, besides gene mutation, there also exist chromosome, genome, plastid, and plasma mutation; that some mutants are dominant, most of them, however, recessive; that some mutants are harmful or lethal, some others advantageous; etc. The process of mutation itself is confined only by the possibilities of molecular rearrangements. This fact becomes evident by the statement that the same mutations always appear in certain ratios and that many back-mutations also exist. The possibilities of chromosome mutations, too, are restricted to some extent, as there are parts of chromosomes which are unsuited for translocations, inversions, and deletions.

The effect of mutations is also reduced by the fact that all somatic mutations are irrelevant for evolution. Moreover, all those mutations of gene cells are unimportant which disturb the normal development too much (lethal mutations). Of little importance also are most of the numerous mutations causing a strong decrease in viability or fertility.

Moreover, the primary undirectedness of mutations is limited by other *developmental* conditions. Most (if not all) mutations have a pleiotropic effect, that is to say, they are not confined to the control of one biochemical process only. Pleiotropy is caused mainly by the fact that all biochemical processes during development occur in the wholeness of an individual and that therefore many correlations exist between the developing organs and structures. The different systems do not function independently of one another; for instance, all organs of vertebrates need nerves and blood vessels. Hence such different systems cannot be altered independently during the course of evolution. In addition, some material competition may exist between parts of the body which grow at the same time (compare Rensch, 1954, chap. 6 B III). Hence only such mutants are able to survive as do not disturb too much the harmony of the whole organism.

As those mutations which alter early embryonic stages normally cause stronger disorders than those which control later stages, most phylogenetic alterations occur in the sense of late deviations or additions to the final stages (compare Rensch, 1954b). Here we have to do with a general rule which has been formulated in a different manner by such a rule. By such a rule it is possible to characterize the fact that earliest embryonic stages are normally more conservative than later stages, that is to say, that the characters of the species develop after the characters of the genus and these after the characters of the family (rule of Von Baer). Or we may speak of the biogenetic rule stating that ontogeny shows a certain recapitulation of phylogeny (although, of course, ontogenetic and phylogenetic stages may be compared only to a certain degree).

The possibilities of ontogenetic alterations of all structures and organs are also restricted by numerous other correlations. As many of them are the same in related animals because of the similarity of their anatomical construction, it is possible to formulate many *special rules of evolution*. Some of them are valid for some phyla, others for some classes or only some orders or families. In order to analyze these rules, in our Zoological Institute at Münster we specially analyzed the correlations between *body size* and size of organs. It may be sufficient to enumerate some of the more important rules which are valid among the warm-blooded animals.

In most cases the skull grows with positive allometry (in relation to the whole body) before birth and afterward (in some cases only some time after birth) with negative allometry. If cristae or tori develop on the vertex or on other parts of the skull, they grow with positive allometry in relation to the whole skull. The same holds good for horns, nose-horns, and antlers. Livers, kidneys, and hearts grow with negative allometry in later postnatal stages. In nearly all cases the facial bones of the skull grow with positive allometry in relation to the whole skull. Among mammals, the young ones, which are bound to their nest at first, have legs which grow with positive allometry after birth. Among hoofed animals, in which the young ones move about shortly after birth, the legs grow with negative allometry. Tails of long-tailed mammals normally grow with positive allometry after birth. Excessive teeth like the canines of carnivores, pigs, monkeys, etc., or the incisors of elephants grow with positive allometry in relation to the face bones. The brain grows with strong positive allometry in relation to the body before birth, with negative allometry sooner or later after birth. The forebrain normally grows with positive allometry in relation to the whole brain after birth, at least in later stages. Among mammals the isocortex of the forebrain (the most complicated and most progressive region of the cortex) grows with positive allometry in relation to the whole forebrain. The eyes grow with positive allometry in relation to the whole skull before birth and with negative allometry after birth (at least in later stages). The thickness of the retina grows with negative allometry in relation to the size of the bulb.

These rules can be proved by many examples (compare Rensch, 1954, 1958). Numerous special investigations about the alterations in the changing relative size of organs during ontogeny exist, but in some cases only one species has been treated. Hence a verification based on a larger number of species is still lacking in some cases. However, as far as we may judge at present, the number of exceptions is small. Random tests of single stages of birds or mammals, the ontogeny of which is not yet analyzed totally, show that we already may predict the above-mentioned correlations with a high degree of probability.

All these rules, the number of which may be multiplied in the future, have been developed during phylogeny because they have proved to be advantageous. For example, it was an advantage that brain and eyes grow with positive allometry before birth, because these organs have to function in a manifold manner immediately or soon after birth. Of all the publications containing special corresponding measurements of ontogenetic proportions, only the following may be mentioned: Jackson (1913), Krüger (1922), Donaldson (1924), Latimer (1925a, b; 1939), Arataki (1926), Saller (1927), Kaufmann (1927), Denzer (1938), Portmann (1938), Siwe (1938), Portmann and Sutter (1940), Sutter (1943), Rensch (1948, 1954, 1958), Harde (1949), Schlabritzky (1953), Krumschmidt (1956).

Other rules of individual development refer to the sequence of differentiation. Among warm-blooded animals there is a general rule of anteroposterior development stating that the differentiation of the skeleton proceeds from the front part of the body toward the back. Less conspicuous is the sequence in a proximodistal direction in the extremities. Now the developmental rules of correlation are effective in phylogeny not only by restricting the primary undirectedness of the alterations. Moreover, they cause a special type of evolutionary rules. If a growth gradiant, that is to say, the allometrical exponent a in the allometrical equation $y = bx^a$, remains constant in a line of descent while the body size increases successively (following Cope's rule), all proportions of organs and structures will be shifted corresponding to their allometric relations. Among mammals in most cases, the skull and the brain become relatively smaller; the cristae and tori more excessive; the extremities relatively longer (except in hoofed animals); the forebrain and especially the isocortex relatively larger; the eyes and the inner ear relatively smaller; the retina relatively thinner; liver, kidneys, and hearts relatively smaller. Of course, these *phylogenetic rules of allometry* do not always run entirely parallel with the corresponding ontogenetic rules because the relative size of single organs and hence also their growth ratios were altered by special adaptation. The general allometric tendency of the main stages of growth, however, very often remains the same. If such phylogenetic rules of allometry are valid for a larger group of related species, that is to say, for a whole family or for an order and hence for the species in all lines of descent, then we may expect that recent species of different body size will show the same differences in proportions. Hence, in such cases, we may investigate recent species of different body size as models of the lines of descent.

The primary undirectedness of the evolution is also restricted by *physiological laws* and the physiological necessities of correlative acting-together of different structures. A few examples showing this may be chosen again from the realm of warm-blooded animals, to which we shall confine the evaluation of forced and undirected phylogeny.

The "law of specific sense energies" caused the phylogenetic tendency to protect the sense cells against inadequate stimuli. It will therefore be impossible for visual sense organs capable of comprehending a whole picture to originate in which the sense cells lie in the periphery, i.e., in the outer cell layer of the epidermis, because then mechanical and chemical stimulations would effect misleading visual excitations. For the same reason, auditory cells could not be displaced to the surface. Furthermore, alterations of well-functioning eyes could not occur in such a manner that the regions of the cornea, the lens, or the vitreous body would become non-transparent tissues or that the retina would not be sufficiently provided with blood. In mammals the head could not become disproportionately large because this would cause mechanical difficulties. Hence a stronger increase in the cortex could occur only by folding. All evolutionary restrictions of this kind seem to be so self-explanatory that usually we do not formulate such "rules." However, we should not overlook the fact that an extraordinarily large number of such restrictions exists for all types of anatomical constructions of classes, orders, families, genera, etc., with regard to the wholeness of the body and to single organs and structures.

In addition, allometric shifts have the effect that large homoiothermous species lose less heat than smaller species because of their relatively smaller body surface. Hence they show a slower frequency of heart beat and breathing, the onset of maturity will be later, and their ontogeny needs a longer time. The animals will also become older. The increase in size of the brain neurons and the relative increase in the isocortex have the effect that large species are generally more capable of learning more tasks and more complicated tasks and of retaining for a longer period than smaller species (compare Rensch, 1956, 1958).

LAWS OF INTERACTION WITH THE ENVIRONMENT

Even more conspicuous than the cases mentioned so far are the restrictions of evolution by laws and rules of selection. As all living beings are subjected to selection by their inanimate environment and by other organisms (enemies, parasites, competitors) in all stages of their individual cycle, the number of corresponding evolutionary rules is nearly unlimited. Moreover, besides more general rules there are many special ones which are valid only for special types of constructions, that is to say, for orders, families, genera, and other smaller categories of animals or plants. In our context it may be sufficient to enumerate the more general rules which are important for mammals and birds.

As mentioned earlier Darwin recognized some basic rules of selection. Many other rules have been found only in more recent years. We shall characterize them only by short references. (1) All living beings show such a surplus of progeny that, by this fact, a strong and manifold selection must occur, prohibiting an increase in individuals in geometrical progression. (2) The offspring of species taking care of their eggs or young is less in number than in related species not taking care of their progeny. The European cuckoo, for example, lays many more eggs than its hosts. (The rule is much more conspicuous among fishes or insects.) (3) Natural selection by the inanimate and animate environment always eliminates more disadvantageous than advantageous varieties or species (especially with regard to the degree of fertility). (4) The effect of selection is quicker in smaller populations than in larger ones. Hence speciation is quicker in the former. (5) In smaller populations (for instance, on very small islands) the fluctuations of population size reduce the variability and effect homozygosity for single characters (for example, black races of lizards on the smallest islands of the Balearic Islands). (6) Polymorphy and changes in the environment increase, monotony reduces, the tempo of evolution. (7) Marine animals generally show a slower evolution than do land animals because of the stronger uniformity of their habitat and the larger size of their populations (more conspicuous among lower animals than among mammals and birds). (8) Animals capable of more intense propagation (i.e., of greater "vagility") show less speciation and race formation than do slowly spreading animals. Hence migratory birds show less race formation than do non-migratory species, large species less race formation than smaller related species (Rensch, 1933, 1939). (9) When new types of advantageous construction have originated, in most cases a quick radiation of species, genera, and higher categories begins. Such "explosive" radiation is especially conspicuous from the origin of many new orders and families of birds in the Jurassic period and of mammals in the Eocene. (10) In the course of evolution the speed of radiation and transformation slackens, corresponding to the increasing adaptation to suitable habitats. This may be exemplified by the odd-toed hoofed animals (Mesaxonia) which gave rise to 15 new subfamilies in the Eocene but to only 4 in the Oligocene, 2 in the Miocene, 1 in the Pliocene, and none in the Pleistocene (compare Hennig, 1932). Correspondingly, most orders of birds originated in the Jurassic and in the early Tertiary and probably none in the Pliocene and Pleistocene (compare also Rensch, 1954, Figs. 22 and 23). (11) In most lines of descent of non-flying animals the body size was successively enlarged (Cope's rule). There are only very few exceptions to this rule among mammals

(Rensch, 1954). Among flying mammals and birds the rule is valid only in limited realms of body size because the growth of the body volume occurs three-dimensionally, whereas the effect of the wing increases in only two dimensions. (12) Normally, phylogeny leads to growing adaptation, which may be shown in most lines of descent. (13) As more perfect structures and functions are advantageous, especially those which effect a greater plasticity and a greater independence of the environment, most lines of descent tend toward evolutionary progress. This may be exemplified by the increase and improvement in the brain of vertebrates or of mammals as a whole or of single lines of descent, as in horses, several families of carnivores, primates, etc. (14) Evolutionary progress normally begins with unspecialized types (Cope's "law of the unspecialized"). Thus hoofed animals originated from unspecialized small Protungulata; all families of carnivores, whales, and primates from small Insectivora. (15) Most groups of functions and organ systems tend toward increasing centralization during phylogeny (for example, by formation of brains, eyes, hearts, kidneys, etc.).

Very numerous are *more special rules* of adaptation of different groups of animals to certain habitats or certain environmental factors. (16) Animals, the enemies of which find their prey by the eyes, develop protecting colors or shapes (including threatening colorations and mimicry). (17) Birds which are active during dawn or night do not develop red, yellow, green, or blue colors of feathers (owls, nightjars, etc.). (18). Birds of temperate and colder regions are adapted to their rather colorless winter environment by more brownish or grayish colors, whereas tropical birds show more vivid colors. Calculating the birds with vivid colors (with red, blue, yellow, green, or violet marks), I found 13.3 per cent of such species among the breeding birds of Germany, but 23.7 per cent of the species breeding on the Lesser Sunda Islands Lomhok, Sumbawa, and Flores (Rensch, 1930). (19) Birds breeding in holes have white or very light eggs; species breeding in open nests have eggs with protective colors. The few species among the latter (like ducks, grebes) showing exceptions have a special instinct to hide the eggs when the birds leave their nest. (20) Birds breeding in open nests, at least the breeding sex (normally the female) show protective colors, whereas species breeding in holes may be colored vividly in both sexes (like kingfishers, rollers, parrots, woodpeckers, etc.). (21) In birds and mammals the number of species is much larger in tropical regions than in temperate or cold regions of the same size. In Sumatra, for example, 438 species of breeding birds exist; in Germany, only 242. This rule probably has no exceptions. It is caused by several facts: the greater number of habitats in the tropics, the smaller size of tropical populations, and the more intense selection in the tropics (because of the higher number of competing species, more enemies, and more generations). (22) In colder regions the geographical races of warm-blooded animals are larger than the races of the same species in warmer regions (Bergmann's rule). This rule depends on the stronger selection by minimum temperatures in colder countries. For palearctic and nearctic birds I calculated 20–30 per cent of exceptions, on the average (for 4 palearctic families of non-migratory birds only 8 per cent); for palearctic and nearctic mammals, 30–40 per cent (Rensch, 1933, 1936). (23) In colder regions the geographical races of mammals have relatively shorter ears, feet, and tails; the races of birds correspondingly shorter feet and bills than races of the same species in warmer regions (Allen's rule). For palearctic and nearctic birds I calculated 11–31 per cent of exceptions for bills, 20–25 per cent for feet; for nearctic mammals 16 per cent of exceptions for the ears, 36 per cent for the hind feet, and 31 per cent for the tails (Rensch, 1933, 1936). This rule depends partly (not totally) on a negative allometry of the more exposed parts of the body. (24) Geographical races of birds, especially of migrating species inhabiting colder regions, have more pointed, mechanically more effective, wings than races of the same species from warmer regions. The difference is brought about by a relative shortening of the first primary and of the third to fifth primaries and also by a shortening of the arm feathers. Sometimes only one of the three shortenings occurs. When I stated this rule (Rensch, 1934, 1936) I found 19 per cent exceptions (with none of the shortenings). (25) Races of birds and mammals inhabiting colder regions show less reddish-brown pheomelanin in their feathers or hairs than do races of the same species of more temperate regions. (26) In warmer and moister regions the geographical races of birds and mammals have more blackish melanin in feathers or hairs, compared with races of the same species from cooler or dryer regions. (27) In very dry countries races of birds and mammals show more yellowish, light-reddish-brown pheomelanins than do races of the same species from moister regions. I call the three last-mentioned rules Gloger's rule. In palearctic titmice and nuthatches I found 6 per cent of exceptions; in skylarks 12 per cent; in mammals of western Europe 12 per cent (Rensch, 1933). (28) Birds of tropical regions normally have less tight feathers than do species of colder regions. (29) Mammals of tropical regions show relatively shorter hairs and less wool hairs than do related races or species from colder regions. I do not know exceptions to this rule. (30) In tropical countries the birds lay less eggs per clutch than do races of the same species from cooler regions. Comparing Indian and European races of the same species, I found 9 per cent of exceptions (Rensch, 1934). (31) Tropical birds have relatively smaller hearts, livers, stomachs, and kidneys and a relatively shorter intestine than do closely related races or species *of the same size* from colder regions (figures in Rensch, 1956). (32) Migratory species of birds which are distributed over several climatic regions show less or no inherited migratory instincts in subtropical and tropical countries. I do not know any exception to this rule. (33) The basic metabolism and the heart-beat frequency of tropical birds are lower than in related species *of the same size* from colder regions (figures in Winkel, 1951; Salt, 1952; Saxena, 1957). These climatic rules, too, may easily be multiplied by analyzing other organs and functions.

RESTRICTION OF UNDIRECTED EVOLUTION

For mammals and birds we enumerated more than 60 different rules restricting the primary undirectedness of evolution (if we regard the rules for single organs like heart, liver, kidneys, etc., as special rules). It was necessary to enumerate these rules, in order to evaluate the degree by which the primary undirectedness is changed into a forced evolution. We may best elucidate the effect of these rules by estimating how far we may *predict* the structure and functions of a warm-blooded new species, which will be discovered in the future.

A. EXAMPLE: If a songbird is discovered in tropical Brazil which is closely related to a species of the same genus in North America, we may predict with about 70–100 per cent probability that this tropical species will show the following characters: (1) smaller size, (2) relatively longer bill, (3) relatively longer feet, (4) relatively longer tail, (5) more roundish shape of the wings, especially the first and third to fifth primaries relatively shorter, (6) less dense feathers or less duneparts, (7) feathers with more melanin, (8) less eggs per clutch, (9) without inherited migratory instinct, (10) differences in relative size of interior organs (depending also on the body size), (11) differences in metabolism (also depending on special body size), (12) shorter life-span.

B. EXAMPLE: If somewhere a new genus of carnivore is discovered which is much smaller than a related species living in the same region, then we may expect with high probability the following characters: (1) head relatively larger, (2) face bones relatively shorter, (3) skull with less pronounced cristae and tori, (4) canines relatively shorter, (5) brain relatively larger, (6) forebrain relatively smaller in relation to the brain as a whole, (7) isocortex relatively less developed, (8) neurons of the brain with fewer dendrites, (9) eyes relatively larger, (10) retina relatively thicker, (11) lens more roundish, (12) inner ear relatively larger, (13) heart and (14) liver and (15) kidneys relatively larger, (16) intestine relatively shorter, (17) hairs relatively longer, (18) tail and (19) feet and (20) ears relatively longer, (21) basic metabolism relatively higher, (22) period of gestation and whole ontogeny shorter, (23) body size of newborn young relatively larger, (24) duration of life shorter, (25) less capability of learning, and (26) less capability of retaining.

C. EXAMPLE: If in Pliocene deposits a new carnivorous mammal is discovered which is closely related to species only known from Eocene and Oligocene deposits, then we may expect with high probability the following characters: (1) body size larger (Cope's rule), (2) forebrain relatively larger in relation to the whole brain, (3) forebrain more folded, (4) face bones relatively longer, (5) cristae and tori more pronounced, (6) canines relatively longer, (7) all teeth more specialized, (8) orbitals (and eyes) relatively smaller, (9) ears and (10) tail and (11) feet relatively longer.

For all three examples we could, of course, enumerate more probable characters if we specified the genus and its special evolutionary rules (for instance, special tendencies for development of tubercles of teeth or for excessive development of certain regions of feathers). However, these three examples and the large number of general rules quoted above may be sufficient to show that, in spite of primary undirectedness, evolutionary alterations occur in forced directions to a large degree. After all, every generalization in the field of biology means a restriction of evolutionary possibilities.

Of course, such predictions are especially important with regard to fossil animals, because they enable us to state their probable functions and their mode of living. In the case of our third example, for instance, we could add further predictions. Such a larger and more progressive Pliocene carnivore would also learn more and would retain for a longer period; it would have a relatively lower basic metabolism, a lower frequency of heart beat and breathing, a longer gestation period, and a longer duration of life.

The growing knowledge of evolutionary laws and rules leads to theoretical conceptions of general importance. We get the impression that, to a large extent, the origin of the enormous multitude of former and recent species has been a forced process. As soon as the first living beings originated and their genes mutated, better- or worse-adapted varieties arose, and automatically natural selection began to work. This selection has also been strengthened by the normal reproduction which delivers too many offspring. Even by bipartition of Protozoa and Protophyta the number of individuals would increase in geometrical progression if no selection counteracted. By spreading and by selection of varieties, a radiation of species has been initiated which must automatically lead to a phylogenetic ramification. As an increasing complexity of living beings allowed the development of a more rational structure and function by division of labor and centralization, it was obvious that evolutionary progress resulted in many lines of descent. As a more rational, i.e., more plastic, reaction to the animated and the non-animated environment was advantageous, an increase of the number of nerve cells and a centralization took place. Hence in many lines of descent an enlargement and improvement of brains occurred in a parallel manner. Hence the most complicated brains were one of the necessary prerequisites for the origin of man. That *Homo sapiens* originated from monkeys and not from any other group of higher animals was also caused by the following facts: (1) only monkeys had grasping hands of universal versatility, which could be used well for the making of tools because they were innervated by the pyramidal tract of the forebrain. (2) After birth the ontogenetic development of monkeys was so slow that a relatively long juvenile phase resulted, during which an investigation of the environment by playing and an accumulation of experience was possible. (3) The social life of monkeys was an indispensable base for the development of human tradition and human language. Hence the evolution of man, too, was necessitated to a large degree. We need not regard our origin as only a product of undirected mutation and random effects of selection!

Finally, the multitude of evolutionary laws and rules, being complex manifestations of universal laws of causality, parallelism, and logic, lead to the deduction that living beings could have originated also on other cosmic bodies, assuming that the conditions of life were similar to those on our planet. And an evolution could have led in similar directions in spite of the uniqueness of each individual. As an enormous number of fixed stars (about 10 billion) and of extragalactic cosmic systems (more than 80 million) exist, such a similarity of conditions to those on our earth is not at all improbable.

EPIGENETIC MANIFESTATION OF LAWS

The special laws and rules of evolution are characteristic of the level of life, i.e., of a developmentally possible level of the universe. Finally, these laws are also causal laws and, as far as psychogenesis is involved, also laws of parallel co-ordination of ("psychic") phenomena. Now it is important to consider that the laws of evolution have also been subjected to an evolution or, more precisely, that they have been subjected to a successive epigenetic manifestation based on the general laws of causality and parallelism. Mendel's rules could become effective only after sexuality had developed. The biogenetic rule could become manifest only after species with an individual cycle had developed. Bergmann's rule could become effective only after homoiothermous animals had developed. Hence we have to do with evolutionary laws, which became manifest only after a certain level of complication had developed. But, finally, the potentiality for all these laws and rules already existed through the laws of causality. They are potential effects of universal laws already *implicit,* existing before life developed.

This aspect may perhaps seem rather strange at first glance. However, we must not forget that cosmic evolution shows similar conditions. As long as a cosmic body is in the stage of a gas ball, many physical laws cannot yet become effective. The lever laws, pendulum laws, the laws of falling speed or of capillarity or of light refraction in lenses, etc., can become manifest (in the sense of an epigenesis) only after solid matter, i.e., a system with new characters, is developed. Here, too, we have to do with systemic laws, *implicitly* existing before, in consequence of the universal law of causality.

We may also conceive psychogenesis as successive complications of sensations, imaginations, and processes of thinking, because this is more probable than the assumption of a sudden appearance of the facts of awareness and of the laws of co-ordination of psychic phenomena with causal processes. This would mean that an epigenetic manifestation of the laws of parallelism occurred, corresponding with the successive phylogeny of sense organs and brains. Then we would have to assume that, for instance, the special modality of auditory sensations was already potentially existing but became manifest only as soon as corresponding sense organs originated in some classes of animals like insects, fishes, Amphibia, etc.

Summing up, we may assume that the whole evolution of the cosmos, including the evolution of living beings, was pre-existing in consequence of the "eternal" cosmic laws of causality, parallelism, and logic. However, up to now, such an assumption can be only a philosophical working hypothesis. For a definite evaluation we need much more special investigations, in order to analyze the laws and rules stated so far and to discover new ones. Hence the evolution of our knowledge about evolutionary laws will proceed in the same way that Darwin opened with such great success. At present, we may say that we are already far beyond the place which the ingenious English scientist had reached a hundred years ago.

BIBLIOGRAPHY

ANTHONY, H. E. 1928. *Field Book of North American Mammals.* New York and London.

ARATAKI, M. 1926. "On the Postnatal Growth of the Kidney . . . (Albino Rat)," *Amer. Jour. Anat.,* XXXVI, 399–436.

DARWIN, CHARLES. 1859. *On the Origin of Species by Means of Natural Selection.* London. Reprint: London: Watts & Co., 1950.

————. 1868. *The Variation of Animals and Plants under Domestication.* London.

DENZER, H. 1938. "Masse und Gewichte zur vergleichenden Anatomie und Histologie der Vertebratenniere." In JUNK-OPPENHEIMER-WEIS-BACH, *Tab. biol. period.,* Vol. XV. Den Haag: W. Junk.

DOBZHANSKY, TH. 1957. *Evolution, Genetics, and Man.* New York: John Wiley & Sons, and London: Chapman & Hall.

DONALDSON, H. H. 1924. *The Rat.* ("Mem. Wistar Inst. Anat. and Biol.," No. 6.) Philadelphia.

HARDE, K. W. 1949. "Das postnatale Wachstum cytoarchitektonischer Einheiten im Grosshirn der weissen Maus," *Zool. Jahrb., Abt. Anat.,* LXX, 225–68.

HENNIG, E. 1932. *Wesen und Wege der Paläontologie.* Berlin: Bornträger.

HERSHEY, A. D., and CHASE, M. 1952. "Independent Functions of Viral Protein and Nucleic Acid in Growth of Bacteriophage," *Jour. Gen. Physiol.,* XXXVI, 39–56.

HUXLEY, J. S. 1932. *Problems of Relative Growth.* London.

JACKSON, C. M. 1913. "Postnatal Growth and Variability of the Body and the Various Organs in the Albino Rat," *Amer. Jour. Anat.,* XV, 1–68.

KAUFMANN, L. 1927. "Recherches sur la croissance du corps et des organes du pigeon," *Biol. gen.,* III, 105–18.

KRÜGER, W. 1922. "Ein Beitrag zur Anatomie des Pferdeherzens mit besonderer Berücksichtigung von Herzmassen und Gewichten." Diss. Tierärztl. Hochschule, Berlin.

KRUMSCHMIDT, E. 1956. "Postnatale Wachstumsgradienten von Hirnteilen bei Haushuhnrassen unterschiedlicher Körpergrösse," *Zeitschr. Morphol. u. Ökol. Tiere,* XLV, 113–45.

LATIMER, H. B. 1925*a*. "The Relative Postnatal Growth of the Systems and Organs of the Chicken," *Anat. Rec.,* XXXI, 233–53.

————. 1925*b*. "The Postnatal Growth of the Central Nervous System of the Chicken," *Jour. Comp. Neurol.,* XXXVIII, 251–97.

————. 1938. "The Prenatal Growth of the Cat." VIII, *Growth,* III, 89–108.

MILLER, G. S. 1912. *Catalogue of the Mammals of Western Europe.* London.

NEWELL, N. D. 1949. "Phyletic Size Increase, an Important Trend, Illustrated by Fossil Invertebrates," *Evolution,* III, 103–24.

PORTMANN, A. 1938. "Beiträge zur Kenntnis der postembryonalen Entwicklung der Vögel," *Rev. suisse zool.,* XLV, 273–348.

PORTMANN, A., and SUTTER, E. 1940. "Über die postembryonale Entwicklung des Gehirns bei Vögeln," *Rev. suisse zool.*, XLVII, 195.

RENSCH, B. 1924. "Das Dépérétsche Gesetz und die Regel von der Kleinheit der Inselformen als Spezialfall des Bergmannschen Gesetzes," *Zeitschr. indukt. Abstamm. u. Vererbungsl.*, XXXV, 139–55.

———. 1930. *Eine biologische Reise nach den Kleinen Sunda-Inseln.* Berlin: Bornträger.

———. 1933. "Zoologische Systematik und Artbildungsproblem," *Verhandl. Deutsch. Zool. Gesellsch.*, pp. 19–83.

———. 1936. "Studien über klimatische Parallelität der Merkmalsausprägung bei Vögeln und Säugern," *Arch. Naturgesch.*, N.F., V, 317–63.

———. 1938a. "Einwirkung des Klimas bei der Ausprägung von Vogelrassen, mit besonderer Berücksichtigung der Flügelform und der Eizahl," *Proc. 8. Internat. Ornith. Cong. Oxford (1934)*, pp. 285–311.

———. 1938b. "Bestehen die Regeln klimatischer Parallelität bei der Merkmalsausprägung von homöothermen Tieren zu Recht?" *Arch. f. Naturgesch.*, N.F., VII, 364–89.

———. 1938c. "Klimatische Auslese von Grössenvarianten," *ibid.*

———. 1940. "Die ganzheitliche Auswirkung der Grössenauslese am Vogelskelett," *Jour. Ornithol.*, LXXXVIII, 373–88.

———. 1948. "Organproportionen und Körpergrösse bei Vögeln und Säugetieren," *Zool. Jahrb., Abt. allg. Zool.*, LXI, 337–412.

———. 1949. "Biologische Gefügegesetzlichkeit." In JOACHIM JUNGIUS-GESELLSCHAFT, *Das Problem der Gesetzlichkeit*, pp. 117–37. Hamburg.

———. 1954a. *Neuere Probleme der Abstammungslehre: Die transspezifische Evolution.* Stuttgart: Enke, 1. Aufl. 1947; 2. Aufl. 1954.

———. 1954b. "Die phylogenetische Abwandlung der Ontogenese." In G. HEBERER, *Evolution der Organismen*, pp. 103–30. 2d ed. Stuttgart: G. Fischer.

———. 1956a. "Increase of Learning Capability with Increase of Brain-Size," *Amer. Naturalist*, XC, 81–95.

———. 1956b. "Relative Organmasse bei tropischen Warmblütern," *Zool. Anz.*, CLVI, 106–24.

———. 1958. "Die Abhängigkeit der Struktur und der Leistungen tierischer Gehirne von ihrer Grösse," *Naturwiss.*, XLV, 145–54.

RIDGWAY, R., et al. 1914. *Birds of North and Middle America*, Vols. II–VI. Washington.

SALLER, K. 1927. "Untersuchungen über das Wachstum bei Säugetieren (Nagern). I," *Arch. Entw. Mech.*, CXI, 453.

SALT, G. W. 1952. "The Relation of Metabolism to Climate and Distribution in Three Finches of the Genus *Carpodacas*," *Ecol. Mono.*, XXII, 121–52.

SAXENA, B. B. 1957. "Unterschiede physiologischer Konstanten bei Finkenvögeln aus verschiedenen Klimazonen," *Zeitschr., vergl. Physiol.*, XL, 376–96.

SCHLABRITZKY, E. 1953. "Die Bedeutung der Wachstumsgradienten für die Proportionierung der Organe verschieden grosser Haushuhnrassen," *Zeitschr. Morphol. u. Ökol. Tiere*, XLI, 278–310.

SIMPSON, G. G. 1953. *The Major Features of Evolution.* New York: Columbia University Press.

SIWE, J. A. 1938. "Das Nervensystem." In PETER, WETZEL, and HEIDE-RICH, *Handb. Anat. d. Kindes,* II, 590–728.

SUTTER, E. 1943. *Über das embryonale und postembryonale Hirnwachstum bei Hühnern und Sperlingsvögeln.* ("Denkschr. schweiz. naturforsch. Gesellsch." Vol. LXXV, Abh. 1.)

WADDINGTON, C. H. 1958. *The Strategy of the Genes.* London: Unwin & Allen.

WATSON, J. D., and CRICK, F. H. C. 1953. Genetical Implications of the Structure of Desoxyribonucleic Acid," *Nature,* CLXXI, 964–67.

WESTERGAARD, M. 1957. "Chemical Mutagenesis in Relation to the Concept of the Gene," *Experientia,* XIII, 224–34.

WINKEL, K. 1951. "Vergleichende Untersuchungen einiger physiologischer Konstanten bei Vögeln aus verschiedenen Klimazonen," *Zool. Jahrb., Abt. Syst.,* LXXX, 256–76.

ZIEHEN, TH. 1927. *Das Problem der Gesetze.* ("Hallische Universitätsreden," No. 33.) Halle.

———. 1939, 1939. *Erkenntnistheorie,* Parts 1 and 2. Jena: G. Fischer.

GEORGE GAYLORD SIMPSON

THE HISTORY OF LIFE

HISTORY IN BIOLOGY

THE NATURE OF HISTORY

The cosmos has two broad aspects. It has, in the first place, immanent characteristics, qualities that are inherent in the very nature of matter-energy. As far as our knowledge extends, they are the same everywhere and at all times. The physical sciences are primarily and mainly concerned with that aspect of the universe: the nature and activities or energies of gravity, of radiation, of subatomic particles, of atoms, of molecules, of larger mechanical systems, and the like. Much of biology also relates to the immanent characteristics of organisms and their functional parts. That is in the broadest sense the physiological side of biology, embracing not only physiology in the narrower or classical sense but also such subjects as biochemistry and biophysics, physiological genetics, experimental embryology, functional psychology, and more. Some biologists (vitalists and dualists) have reservations, but most now agree that the immanent qualities of organisms are exactly the same as those of inorganic systems. The difference is not in those qualities but in the special structures of the organic systems and their incomparably greater complexity. Given a particular system, it follows the same unchanging laws regardless of whether it is organic or inorganic.

The key words "given a particular system" introduce the other major aspect of the cosmos: configuration or structure and organization. With certain minor or extremely speculative exceptions, most people before the eighteenth century thought of this aspect as likewise essentially unchanging. The hills are "everlasting." If a rainstorm passes or a sparrow falls, it is only as other storms have passed

GEORGE GAYLORD SIMPSON was long associated with The American Museum of Natural History, New York City, where the present paper was written. He has recently become Alexander Agassiz Professor of Vertebrate Paleontology in The Museum of Comparative Zoology at Harvard College, Cambridge, Mass. Research studies and expeditions in search of fossil animals have won him countless honors, and he is the author of several well-known books on evolution. Most recently he has edited (with his wife, Anne Roe) the monumental *Behavior and Evolution* (Yale University Press, 1958).

117

and sparrows fallen and as still others of just the same kind will follow just the same course in the future. The explanation, if there was an explanation, was no different from that of the non-structural elements of nature. Both the immanent and the configurational were simply given, probably by the creative acts of gods. Knowledge that there is an essential difference, an explanatory distinction, between the two came at first from two main sources—geologists and social historians.

Geologists observed that the hills are by no means everlasting but bear within themselves the evident traumata of birth and stigmata of death. If the geologists thought at first in terms of catastrophes and of acts of God, they were only using time-hallowed concepts and words from which no one could quickly free himself. After all, the expression "act of God" is still part of our legal paraphernalia and is used by learned men who know quite well that the act in question had natural causes. No matter what they thought of causes, the pioneer geologists learned that the configuration of the earth is continually changing, that it has a history. Hence it follows that the structure of the earth—and, by an extension quickly made, that of the whole physical universe—is not immanent but is at any moment a transient state within a historical sequence. Catastrophic and transcendental concepts of the forces involved were abandoned as the uniformitarians (especially Hutton, Playfair, Lyell) demonstrated the ability of the immanent and currently observable "laws of nature" to bring about the historical changes in physical configuration.

In the field of human history, changes in social structure and the human condition were generally evident, so that a thoroughgoing belief in static configuration was hardly possible to even the earliest historians. It was nevertheless characteristic of this same period, late eighteenth and early nineteenth centuries, that belief in progressive historical change became widespread. Mankind had not merely fallen from innocence or degenerated from a golden age. Its history was not merely repetitive, with dynasties falling like sparrows, only to be replaced by their like. Human history came to be seen as a sequence of progressively different—perhaps progressively higher—states. The social scientists were, and still are, far less successful than the physical scientists in identifying the changeless immanent forces that produce the transient configurations. Nevertheless, the parallel contrast of structure and process was clearly seen and the fact that structure can be explained not solely by function but also, or mainly, by history.

Still, before Darwin the historical aspect and explanation of configuration was not generally believed applicable to biology. It is, of course, well known that some biologists had ideas about organic evolution before Darwin, but the admittedly great interest of that fact is largely antiquarian. Darwin's predecessors were seldom clear and never convincing in applying historical concepts to the configurations of living systems, other, at least, than that of human society. Even Lamarck, much the most thorough and lucid of pre-Darwinian evolutionists, did not achieve clear separation of the immanent and the historical in biology. His evolutionary biology, like the non-evolutionary biology of the transcendental "nature philosophers" (such as Goethe and Owen), involved a given, pre-existing, or eternal configuration of the organic realm. But Lamarck believed that the working-out of this pattern, which is the course of evolution, was gradual and also that the details were somewhat flexible.[1] The pattern was not, for those reasons, any less inherent in nature. The system actually proposed by Lamarck (very different from that of the so-called neo-Lamarckians) involves a belief in the essential immanence of at least the major features of organic configuration. That belief is still sometimes supported, usually by non-scientists who hope thus to reconcile evolution with a personalist conception of deity: the supposedly immanent pattern of evolution is the plan or idea of an anthropomorphic god. Most biologists have rejected that view, and, with all due credit to his precursors, the rejection stems from Darwin.

Darwin used a different approach and a different terminology, but it is quite clear throughout the *Origin of Species* that he had at last brought into biology the enlightening distinction previously achieved by geology and cosmogony and also by sociology, although that science was still in a confused and poorly validated form. He saw that the configuration of organic systems results from and is explained by sequences of historical events, which follow no inherent pattern but are produced by processes that are inherent in the nature of the cosmos. The distinction appears in various forms in recent discussions of biology. Thus Mayr (1958) discusses two "approaches within any branch of biology, the functional [concerned with immanent characteristics] and the evolutionary [concerned with the history of configurations]." Pittendrigh similarly (1958) divides the explanation of biological phenomena into evolutionary (i.e., historical) and physiological (i.e., immanent).[2]

---

[1] For Lamarck the inheritance of acquired characters, also accepted by Darwin and most nineteenth-century biologists, accounted for *deviations* from the main and supposedly immanent pattern of evolution and had nothing to do with that pattern. The results of such inheritance, if it really existed, would be non-immanent and truly historical. Neo-Lamarckism was a historical theory on that basis, stemming, only in small part from Lamarck.

[2] Pittendrigh also follows some other biologists in recognizing a third mode of explanation, which he calls "functional," by which is meant the utility of given characteristics to the organism or to a genetic group of organisms. In our present terms this is not a third alternative to the historical-immanent dichotomy. It is a historical resultant which, as adaptation, contains the major clue to the way in which immanent forces have acted in the course of history.

THE USES OF HISTORY

In its simplest form, biological history would consist of the sequence of organisms that have occupied the earth since the origin of life. Such, to the extent that they are observable or can be inferred, are the basic historical facts. Like all observational data, they achieve scientific interest and explanatory value only when relationships among them are established. In evolutionary biology, one relationship is paramount: the genetical relations that are reconstructed as phylogeny. Along with this go the changes in structure and concomitantly in function that have occurred within the various phyletic lineages. Then there are geographic factors: places of first appearance and subsequent changes in distribution of the lineages. There are, further, the compositions of whole biotas, their ecological structures, and the changes that have occurred in these. And all such changes, whether of lineages or of biotas, of course occur within the historical framework of time. That brings in not only the data of succession but also those of rate: rates of change of different characteristics of a lineage, of a lineage as a whole, of some lineages as compared with others, of broader groups and whole biotas.

Those are the things that have happened in history, its events and certain of the relationships among them, the configurations and changes in them that have occurred at various levels. It is possible to make or to seek some further generalizations about the history of configurations. Is there some great, over-all tendency, such as perhaps an increase in diversity? Are there some common trends affecting individuals in lineages, perhaps becoming larger, more complex, or in some way more differentiated? If such trends exist, do they tend to continue indefinitely? At uniform rates? Some questions of that sort will be considered later (beginning on page 455). If we could answer all of them, the strictly configurational side of history would be in our hands. Nevertheless, we still would not have achieved a full understanding of history or have exhausted the usefulness of historical data.

In the broad sweep of history we are almost completely debarred from direct observation of the immanent forces involved. We see results, not causes. It is to some, indeed to a considerable, extent possible to infer causes from their results. Nevertheless, the inferences are often equivocal unless they can be controlled by more direct study of the immanent processes involved. Such study necessarily depends on observation of living organisms, both in free nature and under the more controlled, but more artificial, conditions of experimentation. But here a difficulty of time scale arises. The processes of organic history usually act exceedingly slowly. It is more the rule than the exception for a really appreciable change in a given lineage to take a million years or more. Such spans of time have not as yet been available for scientific observation of living animals. It is true that artificial intensification of change can produce evident effects within a few generations of some experimental subjects, but then the enormous difference from natural rates must in itself raise some doubts as to whether the processes are the same.

A most fundamental use of the historical record is, then, to check conclusions based on living animals by confronting them with the results of evolution through the tremendous sweep of geological time. The primary question is whether simple extrapolation from observed immanent processes can account for the events of history or whether one must postulate either a change in those processes—which would then, by definition, cease to be really immanent—or the existence of immanent characteristics that have not been identified in systems now living. In either case, since the causation of history is plainly neither single nor simple, only the long record of events can validate inference as to which processes have been involved, or have been more effective, in given instances and under varying circumstances. The whole matter of extrapolation requires such control. It is at least possible a priori that the kinds of change strikingly exemplified in ten years of experimentation are insignificant in a million years of evolution and that other kinds, minimized or ignored in the laboratory, dominate the actual history.

THE EVIDENCE FOR HISTORY

Complete knowledge of the individual events in the history of life is absolutely unobtainable, even in principle. Fortunately, this does not mean, at least in principle, that we cannot hope to attain an essentially complete set of generalizations about such events or an essentially complete formulation of the immanent "laws of nature" involved. We do not need the record of all species to learn how species originate, nor must we see every bird fly to know how birds fly. Correct and full conclusions as to generalizations and theories can be drawn from a millionth or a billionth part of the possible evidence for them. If that is not true, then the universe is not orderly, and the whole pursuit of human knowledge is forever vain. It is, however, only too well known to all of us that incorrect and incomplete conclusions can be drawn from a large body of evidence, perhaps in principle even from the whole body of evidence pertinent to a given point. It therefore behooves us to consider carefully the nature of available evidence and its adequacy.

Historical evidence is, broadly, of two kinds, which are, however, less distinct than may appear at first sight. In one case we observe the outcome of history at a given time and infer the events and processes that have produced that result. In the other case we observe successive states and follow the course of change through time. The comparative method, based on evidence from (essentially) a single point in time, applies equally well to the present or the past.[3] The present has, however, a special status in this respect. Only for the present can our knowledge of the configurations of organic systems be made as complete as needs dictate and time and instrumentation permit. That is, the *complete* configurations do exist and hence are accessible now, but they are not preserved from any past time. Moreover, only in the present, with organisms actually alive and functioning, can we directly observe the immanent functions as distinct from any of their past results. But here the method is no longer strictly comparative of contemporaneous phenomena, and that distinction partly breaks down, for processes can be observed only through changes in time. The distinction becomes not between contemporaneous and successive items of evidence but between successive items through a short or a long time.

The great drawback of the comparative method and of contemporaneous evidence is that they are not in themselves historical in nature. The drawing of historical conclusions from them is therefore full of pitfalls unless it can be adequately controlled by *directly* historical evidence. Darwin (1859, 1872) was well aware of this problem and gave an unusually interesting example:

> If we look to forms very distinct, for instance to the horse and tapir, we have no reason to suppose that links ever existed directly intermediate between them, but between each and an unknown common parent. The common parent . . . may have differed considerably from both, even perhaps more than they differ from each other. Hence in all such cases we should be unable to recognize the parent form of any two or more species . . . unless . . . we had a nearly perfect chain of the intermediate links.

It happens that an animal very near the common parent of horse and tapir was actually known when Darwin wrote. It was by no means structurally intermediate between horse and tapir, it did differ considerably from both, and its relationships went unrecognized until nearly perfect chains of intermediate links leading, respectively, to

---

[3] The comparative method is, of course, used in interpretation of contemporaneous fossils. Moreover, the method is still comparative, and the evidence has the same status as if it were contemporaneous, when the observations apply to quite different times but the differences ascribable to time are negligible, cannot be evaluated, or for any other reason are left out of consideration. That is true in a surprisingly large number of paleontological studies.

horse and tapir were discovered, which was well after Darwin.[4] Darwin's cautionary remarks retain their full force for the incomparably greater number of species for which such chains of intermediate links (i.e., adequate and directly historical items of evidence) have not yet been found.

Directly historical evidence either involves lengths of time that are, to the historian of life, infinitesimally short or is drawn from the preserved parts of organisms long dead. The advantage of direct relationship to history is in both cases partly offset by severe limitation of the kinds of observations that can be made. Moreover, in the latter case the chances of preservation and discovery are such that the available items of evidence, even of the possible kinds of evidence, are most stringently limited. It therefore becomes necessary to consider with particular care the adequacy of such evidence and the possible significance of its deficiencies. That is the next main topic to which I shall turn.

THE FOSSIL RECORD

THE PRESERVATION OF ANCIENT LIFE

On a moment's thought it is obvious that all the fossils now available for study in all the learned institutions of the world compared with all the organisms that ever lived cannot represent as much as one in a million, or a billion, or some astronomically higher figure. Moreover, among those available fossils, not a single one, not even the most exceptional, represents a really complete individual with all its tissues and organs just as they were at the moment of death. The fossil record is only a sample of the history of life, an exceedingly small sample and an intensely biased one. Interpretation of the sample will be excessively uncertain and, indeed, inevitably wrong unless the conditions of sampling and the nature of bias are well understood. Fortunately, we

---

[4] The ancestral form known before Darwin wrote the *Origin of Species* was *Hyracotherium*, described and named in 1840 (*Eohippus* is a late synonym). It is supposed to be *slightly* closer to horses than to tapirs and so is classified as a member of the horse suborder and family. The contemporaneous *Homogalax* (not described until 1881 and later) may be *slightly* closer to tapirs and for that reason is now classified in a different suborder and family from *Hyracotherium*. Nevertheless, *Hyracotherium* and *Homogalax* are almost identical in structure, to such an extent that the most skilled paleontologists long failed to distinguish them correctly and even now are likely to mistake specimens of one for the other. We thus have here, as near as does not matter, not only the common parent of horse and tapir but also the common ancestry of two major divisions (suborders) of mammals. It is not much like any of its present descendants and would be completely unpredictable from the latter.

are beginning to have a good, although still incomplete, understanding of those factors.

The record is biased, to begin with, because as a rule only the parts of organisms most resistant to distortion and decay become abundant and identifiable fossils. The exceptions are quite numerous in the aggregate, but they form a minor proportion of the fossil record and are so sporadic that they rarely leave a continuous, readily followed record of any one group. We do know some visceral parts of the woolly mammoth, and fossil jellyfishes are known from the Cambrian onward; but the soft anatomy of extinct proboscideans is known in only that one, nearly recent species, and the scattered finds of ancient jellyfishes reveal practically nothing of real interest. Several groups of soft-bodied organisms of outstanding abundance and biological importance today, such as the nematodes or the bacteria, are either completely unknown as fossils or so poorly known that their record has no historical value whatever at present.

The fact that so many organisms are soft-bodied and can fossilize only under exceptional circumstances is widely familiar. It may be of greater interest to note how many groups do nevertheless have specifically identifiable resistant parts and have left good records. Table 1

TABLE 1

REPRESENTATION OF PHYLA AND CLASSES OF ALL ORGANISMS IN FOSSIL RECORD
AS TO SPECIFICALLY IDENTIFIABLE RESISTANT PARTS *

	PHYLA			CLASSES		
	*With	*Without	Total	*With	*Without	Total
Number known	15	19	34	51	40	91
Percentage known by specifically identified fossils	100	12	56	100	8	64
Percentage with extensive fossil records, for some subgroups at least	87	0	38	82	0	46
Percentage with very abundant, widespread fossil records ...	67	0	29	39	0	22

gives an idea of the proportions of major groups that could leave a fossil record and of those that have done so.[5] More than two-fifths of the phyla and more than half the classes have either no fossil record at all or one too sporadic to be of much value in evolutionary studies.

[5] The classification is essentially that of Simpson, Pittendrigh, and Tiffany (1957). Some authorities recognize a few more phyla and many more classes. There is also a subjective element in classing fossils as "identifiable," "extensive," and "very abundant." Nevertheless, the figures in Table 1 probably give a fair idea of relative representation of major taxa as fossils.

But of those with parts apt for fossilization and recognition, all do have some fossil record, and for a large majority of them the record is extensive and highly useful. Among these groups apt for sampling as fossils, about two-thirds of the phyla and two-fifths of the classes are extremely abundant in the fossil record and provide the best samples for historical study. The exceptionally favorable classes are widely scattered in the system, including protistans, algae, higher plants, coelenterates, bryozoans, brachiopods, mollusks, arthropods, echinoderms, and vertebrates. Obviously, it is correct that lack of resistant parts has led to loss of all record of many historical *events*. There is, nevertheless, every reason to believe that it has not prevented sampling of major groups so diverse and so extensive that all the historical *principles* should be exemplified.[6]

The possession of readily preservable hard parts is clearly not enough, in itself, to assure that a given organism will indeed be preserved as a fossil. The overwhelming majority of organisms are quickly destroyed or made unrecognizable, hard parts and all, by predation, by scavenging, by decay, by chemical action, or by attrition in transport. The few that escape that fate must (with a few exceptions) be buried quickly (within days or at most a few years) in sediments free of organisms of decay or chemicals competent to destroy the hard parts. It is further necessary (with, again, exceptions of little importance) that they should not subsequently have been exposed by erosion or obliterated by metamorphism of the inclosing sediments until the present time. These factors inevitably reduce the volume of the record and make the assembling of adequate samples more difficult. They would, however, have little importance for interpretation of the history if they acted without bias: if, that is, all taxa of organisms with hard parts had about the same chance, no matter how small the chance, of preservation. Unfortunately, this is not true. The chances are enormously unequal for different taxa, and these conditions of preservation involve great taxonomic bias.

In the first place, the chances of burial are affected to some extent by the habits of organisms, even when all have suitable hard parts and live in the same general environment. In the sea, benthonic sessile or burrowing forms are much more likely to be preserved than pelagic or planktonic ones. Remains of the latter are evidently more liable to dispersal or destruction before burial. On land there is also an evident bias against preservation of volant animals. In most deposits birds and bats are much rarer than terrestrial mammals even when there is

---

[6] The only serious reservation concerns history before the organization of the nucleus and the origin of mitosis. That may have involved principles different from any sufficiently exemplified in the fossil record. That is the opinion of Boyden (1953).

reason to believe that they were no less numerous. Doubtless there are many such habitus factors that bias representation, but no adequate study of them has been made, as far as I know. It has even been suggested that intelligence or alertness (e.g., in fossil apes and men) has decreased chances of inclusion in the fossil record. Individuals may, for instance, be too smart to be caught in a bog or quicksand, an accident that differentially promotes fossil preservation.

There is, next, a bias of association frequently inherent in the conditions of burial: organisms buried together, constituting a thanatocenosis, did not necessarily live together in a biocenosis. For instance, in the sea the plankton and nekton are not, as a rule, in true living association with the benthos, but they will be buried, if at all, with the latter. Wind may bring together in one thanatocenosis leaves and, especially, pollen from great distances and from quite different biocenoses. Other agents of transport, notably streams and currents, also commonly carry the remains of organisms from their living habitat and deposit them under quite different conditions. These agents and others, such as waves, also frequently sort remains so that the smaller, for instance, are deposited in one place and the larger in another or so that some size groups, more fragile species, etc., are not deposited at all in recognizable form. The result is, again, a thanatocenosis markedly unlike any biocenosis. The mass occurrence of fossils, such as fishes, is also likely to be misleading as to the living environment even if it does occur geographically in the place where the organisms ordinarily lived. The mass occurrence in itself usually indicates that conditions at the time of death were not those of the life-environment but, quite the contrary, were such that the organisms could not stay alive.

Beyond the likelihood of any one animal's being buried and of preservation of associations, burial competent for preservation in the fossil record is likely only in areas where sedimentation predominates over erosion for appropriate, usually long, periods of time. Regions of predominant deposition are ecologically different from those of predominant erosion and are likely to be occupied by different species or higher taxa. The record is therefore greatly biased, the taxa characteristic of regions of erosion being, as a rule, totally absent or much less often sporadically represented by individuals that happen to have been transported into an environment of deposition. (And the transportation, itself, tends to destroy otherwise fossilizable remains or to reduce their identifiability.) For example, on land the terrestrial and fresh-water taxa of well-drained uplands have extremely little chance of preservation as fossils. The chances are better in inland basins and valleys with bottoms below at least a local base level, but even in such situations eventual erosion is likely. There are a fair number of fossiliferous upland basin and valley deposits of ages back to about the beginning of the Cenozoic (their extent generally diminishing with increasing age), but there are very few from the Mesozoic and perhaps none from the Paleozoic. The continental (non-marine) record consists predominantly of valleys and plains near sea level (at or below continental base level) and of deltas. In the United States of today, for instance, really extensive deposits likely to preserve many non-marine fossils for a few million years are now being formed only in our two great deltas (Mississippi and Colorado) and in the undrained Great Basin. Some millions of years from now the much more numerous taxa of other regions will be represented rarely, if at all, except by scraps that happen to have washed into one of these areas or into the sea.

Deposition is much more widespread in marine environments, and bias due solely to this factor is correspondingly less. Nevertheless, sedimentation is usually extremely slow in the vast reaches of the open sea, and the chances of destruction of hard parts before adequate burial are even greater than on land. The shore region, broadly speaking,[7] is of special interest from an evolutionary point of view: the diversity of organisms (mostly animals) is here maximal, the environments vary much more widely than elsewhere in or near the sea, and the chances of isolation (hence of speciation) are markedly greater. Here the balance of deposition and erosion, as Darwin observed and discussed in a remarkably modern way, depends largely on whether the shore line is emergent or submergent or on whether the local base level is falling or rising relative to a given plane of previous deposition. Deposits of an emergent shore are likely soon to be eroded and have little chance of becoming part of the geological record. On a submergent shore the chances are comparatively excellent.

That brings up another biasing aspect of deposition and erosion that was stressed and well discussed by Darwin: the temporal discontinuity of all known rock sequences. Darwin's concern was with the frequent sudden appearance of species (and other taxa) in the record, which might seem to contradict his thesis of gradual evolution. He demonstrated that there is no contradiction when, as is generally the case, the new forms appear after a stratigraphic hiatus. That point will also concern us in a subsequent section of this essay. Here we are concerned with the fact that the universal occurrence of hiatuses also introduces sampling bias in the available record. Interruption of sedimentation may be so short that there is no appreciable change in en-

---

[7] The expression is purposely vague, as I mean to include not only the littoral zone as technically defined but also the shallower parts, at least, of the neritic zone to seaward, and beaches and dunes, lagoons, estuaries, brackish parts of deltas, etc., to landward.

vironment or biota (in stratigraphy such breaks are called "diastems"). Even minimal interruption may produce bias if, for instance, it is seasonal and hence eliminates from record some life-stages or some mobile species of seasonal occurrence in the given area. Long interruptions (represented by unconformities in stratigraphy), commonly involving omission of whole epochs or periods, are much less numerous, but they do occur in every known rock sequence. They frequently involve environmental change and the corresponding bias, the earlier biotic facies having no later record in the region and vice versa. Even without change of facies, bias is introduced because there will be regional taxa confined to unrepresented times, and they have no chance of preservation.

Table 2 gives a complex illustration of bias due in part to combined effects of habitus and depositional factors, and in part to inaccessibility to collectors, the next topic for discussion. It cannot be assumed that the habitat distribution of fossil higher bony fishes (teleosts) was exactly like that of the living genera, but it is highly probable that the

TABLE 2

PERCENTAGE OF GENERA OF RECENT AND KNOWN FOSSIL TELEOSTS
FOUND IN VARIOUS ENVIRONMENTS

(Unpublished Data, Rearranged, from Bobb Schaeffer)

Environment	Per Cent Recent Genera	Per Cent Known Fossil Genera
Fresh water:		
Still	2 ⎫	22 *
Both still and running	14 ⎬ 16	
Running only	14 ⎭	0.2 †
Total	30	22
Marine:		
Shallow	57	70
Deep	13	8
Total	70	78

* Found in lake deposits, but this presumably includes a representative proportion of genera that occurred in both lakes and streams.
† Genera found in stream but not in lake deposits.

resemblance was much closer than the actually described fossils indicate. The record for fishes of streams is greatly deficient, largely because fish remains are most likely to be broken up into unidentifiable fragments or totally destroyed in such an environment. The record for deep marine waters is also, although less, deficient, partly because of slow deposition and extensive decay or consumption before effective burial and partly because deep-sea deposits are rarely exposed on land

and accessible to collectors. No exposed deposits of the very deepest (hadal) waters have been surely identified.

THE SAMPLING OF THE RECORD

The remains actually preserved as fossils are only an extremely small sample of those that once lived and, as we have seen, a strongly biased sample. The process of obtaining specimens for study is another sampling, obtaining a minute subsample of the already much reduced sample. Here further biases of new kinds are introduced. Some bias involves the natural availability of fossils under present conditions, and some has to do with the human activity of collecting. There is, finally, bias in the study of fossils that have been found.

No matter how many or what kinds of organisms have been preserved in ancient sediments, they are usually unavailable for study unless they are now at or near the dry-land surface of the earth. This requirement is not much modified by the fact that some fossils have been found in the ocean bed by dredging and in cores especially taken for that purpose and that many more have been recovered from oil wells or from other deep drilling on land. Submarine specimens taken by present techniques are still very few and mostly from the last moments of geological time. With some exceptions, well cuttings and cores yield faunas hardly differing, if at all, from those obtainable from surface localities in the same general areas. Both the submarine and the subsurface samples are strongly biased in favor of microfossils. It is, then, generally true that a useful fossil record is available only from such sediments as have never been far below present land surfaces or have been uplifted and that have, in either case, been exposed by erosion.

If the chances of such exposure were roughly equal for ancient sediments of all environments, regions, and ages, the requirement of exposure would, again, attenuate but would not bias the available samples. But, again, those chances are not equal in any of the three mentioned respects. As regards environment, the bias for this cause alone is probably slight for continental deposits but is certainly very strong for marine deposits. The vast majority of marine fossiliferous rocks now exposed on land were formed at comparatively small depths, under a hundred fathoms (littoral and neritic zones) in spite of the fact that only a very small proportion of the seas is so shallow. The proportion was larger in some past epochs but was never as great as that of deeper waters. Exposures of sediments from intermediate depths, between 100 and 2,000 fathoms (the bathyal zone) occur but are rare. It is questionable whether there are any exposures of sediments from really great depths, below about 2,000 fathoms (abyssal and hadal). Thus the available samples are extremely biased as to depth of water at the time and place of deposition (see Table 2). This bias is, however, partly offset by the facts that the biotas of shallow waters are much the richest and that there are comparatively few (but absolutely a significant number of) taxa confined to waters (and bottoms) more than 100 fathoms deep.

There is also bias in the fact that one can seldom follow exposures of rocks of one given environment very far both in extent and in time. Thus a shore deposit of one limited age may be exposed at a particular locality, but extensions of the deposit laterally at the same time or vertically through earlier and later ages are generally quite restricted. (And eventually such extension ceases because the deposits simply do not exist, having been eroded or never having been laid down.)

In any case, regardless of facies or environment, the geographical extension of the record is always extremely spotty and yields a record highly biased in this respect. Essentially the entire surface of the globe has been inhabited for a very long time, and the greater part since the earliest history of life. For unbiased geographical sampling we would need collections for *each* successive age rather evenly scattered at intervals of, say, a hundred miles or preferably even less. No such a set of sampling stations, or anything even remotely like it, is available for *any* past age, nor could it possibly be in the nature of things. To begin with, there are no exposures at all over the more than two-thirds of the surface of the globe now covered by seas. On land there is no place where rocks of more than a few ages, let alone of *all* ages, occur within a distance of a hundred miles. The mere fact that exposures in a given place are of a certain age (or quite a restricted sequence of ages) practically excludes the possibility of learning what organisms lived there at any other times. From another point of view, there are vast areas where fossiliferous exposures of certain ages are lacking; there are, for instance, no Jurassic exposures anywhere in central or eastern North America. And there are other vast areas, such as the Canadian shield, with few or no fossils of any age.

The requirement of exposure has also introduced a bias more directly related to age and involving both environmental and geographical coverage. Because exposures occur on land and because later beds cover earlier, marine environments are progressively less, and land environments progressively more, represented in later stages of geological history. Because of erosion and superposed deposition, the areal extent of exposures tends to be larger, the younger the rocks. There is considerable fluctuation in both respects, but the general tendencies are quite clear and have certainly biased the availability of the record.

The requirement of exposure involves, finally, a strong regional bias dependent on present climates. Even though rocks may be nominally exposed in the sense that they reach the surface or near it and appear on geological surface maps, they may be so deeply weathered or so covered with vegetation that it is virtually impossible to find fossils in them. The most essential factors are humidity, rainfall, and drainage, all of which are regional and therefore bias the geographical distribution of the available record. In regions of high humidity and rainfall or poor drainage, the collecting possibilities may merely be reduced over-all, as in much of eastern coastal North America, where collecting may be virtually confined to stream banks, sea cliffs, and man-made excavations. Or, as in vast stretches of tropical rain forest, collecting may be almost impossible. On a world-wide scale, geographical representation of the tropics in the available record is quite deficient for this reason. On the other hand, our High Plains and Southwest have become famous for fossils not because their rocks are exceptionally fossiliferous but because the climate has promoted erosion and development of badlands in which large collections can readily be made.

Biases involved in the exploration for fossils and in their identification are the only ones over which the paleontologist can exert any considerable direct control. In spite of the possibility of control, these biases are still quite significant in the present state of knowledge. Darwin pointed out that in his day there had been little geological exploration outside Europe and the United States and that the past life of other regions was comparatively, or in many instances absolutely, unknown. There is now no large region completely unknown geologically or paleontologically, but there are still extensive areas quite inadequately known in those respects: central and western Australia, parts of central Asia, much of central South America and central Africa, and others. New, although now comparatively small, fossil fields are still being found in western North America, probably the most extensively explored area on earth in this respect. In general, however, it is the most inaccessible regions and those farthest from paleontological institutions that represent major gaps in available knowledge.

Even in well-known fossil fields the intensity or effectiveness of effort has varied enormously, with a corresponding bias in the record as it appears in technical publication. There have never been enough paleontologists to work all fields to the same extent and with every useful technique. Individual tastes and even vogues in research have resulted in much larger collections from some fields and some ages than from others. Taxonomic, as well as geographical, bias is involved. Collectors interested in certain and not all taxa, as most are, concentrate their efforts on beds and localities richest in those taxa. They may even discard or ignore other taxa that happen to be found. Methods of collecting also have taxonomic bias. Foraminifera and plesiosaurs, for instance, frequently occur in the same beds, but the methods of finding and collecting them are so entirely different that the collector of one group is not likely even to notice that the other exists. As another example, there are three principal methods of finding and collecting fossil mammals: (1) surface prospecting for scattered individual specimens; (2) quarrying an evident concentration of bones, which may consist of a single species or of many; and (3) breaking down and screening large quantities of matrix to recover the specimens, especially of small animals, rather sparsely dispersed in it. Experience has shown that each method commonly produces species, even from the same bed, not found by the other methods. Moreover, the different methods may produce ecologically different assemblages. If two or all three methods would be productive but have not been used, there is a decided collecting bias.

Table 3 exemplifies radical differences in collections made in the same beds by different methods. As usual, the differences have several different causes. In this case the main effect is probably ecological, the scattered surface specimens representing mainly the fauna of open floodplains and the quarry concentrations the fauna of forested

TABLE 3

Comparison of Percentages of Specimens of Orders of Fossil Mammals Found in Surface and Quarry Collections of Same Age and Region (Middle Paleocene of Crazy Mountain Field, Montana)

(Data from Simpson, 1937)

Orders	Several Surface Localities	One Quarry
Multituberculata	9	24
Insectivora	1	18
Primates	0	20
Carnivora	53	13
Condylarthra	37	24
Pantodonta	0	1

swampy areas. There are, however, doubtless also effects from method of collecting, smaller animals being more likely to be found by quarrying even though also present on the surface, and from intensity of collecting, the larger quarry collections being more likely to include rare species.

There is also a collecting bias of recognizability. Some fossils, because of size, color, or form, are much easier to distinguish and hence to find than are others. Some very small fossils are practically invisible in the field and are never found unless special methods are applied, such as collecting matrix on the chance and examining it microscopically, after various suitable preparation techniques. Also some individuals are much better at finding some fossils than others, and an element of personality enters in. There is, further, a bias of identifiability that enters both into collecting and into subsequent study. For instance, the dispersed skeleton of a fossil armadillo includes hundreds of bony scutes, each one of which can usually be identified to species. Each would normally be collected, and each would be a separate record of occurrence of that species. The skeleton of another, scuteless mammal, if equally fragmented and dispersed, might include few or no specifically identifiable bits. The pieces probably would not be collected or, if collected, identified. Identifiable records, if any, for such a species would be so few as to give a very false impression of comparative abundance.

There is, last of all, bias in research and publication. Apart from such things as individual differences in taxa recognized, opinions as to affinities, and other idiosyncrasies, effects of this bias are most evident when comparisons are made of the numbers of taxa, at various levels, present at successive times. The hope would, of course, be that the numbers counted from publications would have a fairly constant ratio to the numbers actually present in the rocks and these, in turn, to the numbers that lived at a given time. But the former ratio may be strongly affected by the amount of taxonomic effort devoted to the various groups and times. Extensive study and publication of a given group or time will produce a sudden apparent increase in numbers of taxa corresponding to no real increase in nature. Cooper and Williams (1952) have called these "monographic bursts" and have given examples. A similar spurious increase in numbers of published taxa results from taxonomic splitting, from the work of an author who uses very narrow subjective criteria for species and tends to put most species in separate genera, many genera in separate families, etc. For instance, the increase in numbers of species and genera of reptiles in the Permian has evidently been exaggerated by the work of the late Robert Broom, who listed as distinct many specific and generic names that most of his colleagues consider synonyms.

In summary, the main (still not *all*) causes of bias in the published record as we have it may be tabulated as follows:

I. Biases of preservation
   A. From characteristics of the organisms
      1. Differences in physical fossilizability, especially presence or absence of hard parts

2. Impossibility of complete preservation of any individual, and difference in parts preserved in different groups
3. Differences in habits and habitus affecting likelihood of fossilization

B. From conditions of burial and subsequent preservation
  1. Differences between biocenosis and thanatocenosis
  2. Correlation of predominant sedimentation or erosion with different habitats and environments
  3. Differential destruction after burial (e.g., by metasomatism, metamorphism, or erosion)
  4. Differential effects of breaks in sedimentation

II. Biases of collection
  A. From requirement of recent exposure or near-exposure
    1. Different chances of exposure of sediments of different environments
    2. Limited and varying geographic distribution of exposed sediments of a given age or origin
    3. Correlation of available facies and of extent of exposure with age
    4. Correlation of effective exposure with present regional climates
  B. From the processes of discovery
    1. Differences in accessibility of actual or potential fossil fields
    2. Differences in total collecting effort
    3. Differences in collecting methods
    4. Differences in recognizability of fossils in the field
  C. From identification and other study
    1. Differences in identifiability of preserved parts
    2. Differences in recency and intensity of monographing
    3. Individual idiosyncrasies of students, especially splitting or lumping

ADEQUACY OF THE RECORD

The factors just discussed under the name of "bias" are, for the most part, those usually considered (as those known to him were by Darwin) as causes for the "imperfection" or "incompleteness" of the record. This less usual approach has been made in order to stress the modern attitude and methodology of inference from samples and also the fact that bias and incompleteness are not the same. Incompleteness, as usually understood, has to do with the fraction of species (or other taxa) known among all that actually lived. Bias has to do with the fidelity with which a known sample represents a population in some defined respect. A sample with one specimen each of all the species of an ancient fauna or flora would be taxonomically complete, but it would be hopelessly biased with respect, for instance, to the relative abundance of those species. Similarly, it is evident that a highly incomplete sample could be unbiased for purposes of some particular inference.

Few concrete estimates of completeness have been made, and those few are subject to large uncertainties. They are, nevertheless, of interest and real value even if they indicate only a broad order of magnitude. Most general, but also least certain, is estimation of over-all completeness for all organisms through all of the history of life. I (Simpson, 1952) have estimated the total number of species through all time as probably between 50 and 4,000 million, with 500 million as a reasonable single figure for magnitude. Cailleux (1954) estimated 17–860 million, with a medial figure of 150 million, but his assumption of a constant geometric rate of increase seems to me almost certainly wrong and likely to give figures that are too low. By my figures (or guesses) perhaps 300 million species were animals. Muller and Campbell (1954) have estimated that about 1,000,000 living and few over 91,000 species of fossil animals have been described. If so, the proportion of extinct species now actually known may be about 0.03 per cent. In any event, it is probably on the order of hundredths and possibly even thousandths of 1 per cent: a discouraging conclusion!

This extreme incompleteness is, however, unduly influenced by a few classes (especially Insecta) and phyla (especially the "worms") for which the record is exceptionally poor. Teichert (1956) has attempted an estimate of how many species are actually preserved as fossils, omitting the Precambrian because, whatever the reason, it does have few fossils and omitting the insects and soft-bodied invertebrates because of their comparatively poor chances of preservation. His total estimate is about 10 million, of which 7 or 8 million are presumed to be animals (including animal-like protists). He considers 10 million "at least 20, perhaps 50 times as many as the number of fossil species known to science." For animals Teichert's figures are more than 70 times the number of described species as carefully estimated by Muller and Campbell. Teichert apparently assumes that all species of animals with skeletons, except insects, have been preserved from the Cambrian onward and are available to collectors. That evidently exaggerated assumption must tend to make his figure decidedly too high. On the other hand, the soft-bodied invertebrates and insects, omitted by Teichert, are only comparatively rare as fossils. Their absolute numbers in the fossil record are large and may be expected to increase with more intensive collecting and the use of new methods. This tends to make Teichert's figure too low. Perhaps the two opposite errors tend to cancel out.

It is a guess, but a reasonably educated one, that on the order of

1 to 10 per cent of all species that ever lived are recoverable as fossils and that, of those, on the order of 1 to 10 per cent have so far been found and described. The task of describing recoverable species is no more than well begun, and when (if ever) it is finished, the record will still be very incomplete.

These estimates of the great incompleteness of the currently known record may give much too gloomy an impression of the usefulness of that record and of its adequacy for solving problems of evolution. The incompleteness must, to be sure, be kept in mind, but the present record is certainly highly useful and also quite adequate for many purposes. Knowledge of all species would not necessarily be much more useful than knowledge of a small sample of them. Indeed, for purposes of generalization and theory it would be impossible to deal with all species, and sampling would be essential. It does no harm that nature did the sampling, if we can estimate the kinds and extents of nature's biases.

In the first place, although the species is a basic unit and some evolutionary problems can be studied only at that level, there are many still more important problems of phylogeny, structural change, faunal development, and the like that can be studied just as well or even better in terms of genera or higher taxa. A small sample of species represents a much higher percentage of genera, still higher of families, and so on. Table 4 exemplifies this relationship. Continued intensive sampling from 1900 to 1941 more than doubled the number of known

TABLE 4

Taxa of Fossil Mammals Known from White River Group
(Oligocene) in 1899 and 1941 *

(Data Mainly from Scott and Jepson, 1936–41, Modified)

	Families	Genera	Species
Known in 1941	39	95	228
Known in 1899			
Number	31	60	120
Per cent of 1941 total .	79	63	47

* Taxa considered invalid in 1941, or in a few instances later, are not counted. Families and genera of which a species was known in 1899 are counted as known even if named later. Taxa known in 1899 but not from the White River group are counted as then unknown.

species but increased the number of known genera by little more than half and that of known families by only one-eighth. The numbers of taxa originally present in these faunas is not known, but it is clear that a sampling very incomplete for species was decidedly more complete for genera and still more for families. This is not an extreme example;

the discrepancy in recovery of species and higher taxa is frequently greater.

Another approach is by sampling experiments on faunas in which all or nearly all the taxa are known, hence necessarily recent faunas. Table 5 exemplifies such experiments for a relatively very small

TABLE 5

SAMPLING EXPERIMENT ON LAND MAMMALS OF NEW GUINEA, CELEBES, AND ADJACENT ISLANDS

(Based on List and Classification of Laurie and Hill, 1954)

	Orders	Families	Genera	Species
Total taxa in fauna	8	20	121	352
Taxa included in random sampling of 35 species:				
Number	5	11	23	35
Per cent	63	55	19	10

sample. It was postulated that probability of discovery was the same for all species, a false postulate but a legitimate simplification that is unlikely to affect the pertinent results seriously. Only 10 per cent of the species were selected at random, by numbering all the species and using a table of random numbers. That small sample, surely less complete than the samples of most well-worked fossil faunas, still included about a fifth of the genera, more than half the families, and almost two-thirds of the orders.

There is a related but distinct question as to the extent to which a local fauna may represent that of a larger region or a distant area. This is especially pertinent to paleontological sampling, in which the area available for collecting from beds of any one age is always far less than the area actually occupied by faunas of a given sort at that time. In this respect, too, there is evidence that local samples may be much more adequate than might appear at first sight, especially above the level of species. Table 6 is a somewhat extreme example from fossil faunas of the same age. The faunas compared are in the same broad category (land mammals) but are quite different in representation of included facies, as indicated by the small number of species (only seven) in common and by more detailed ecological analysis. Yet knowledge of the larger fauna, alone, would include 70 per cent of the total genera, 89 per cent of the families, and all the orders. Both samples are surely incomplete, but renewed planned intensive sampling should increase the percentage of representation from either fauna alone: it happens that the facies best represented in collections

TABLE 6

<small>COMPARISON OF MIDDLE PALEOCENE MAMMALS OF NEW MEXICO AND MONTANA</small>
(Data Mainly from Matthew, 1937, and Simpson, 1937, with Later Modifications)

	Orders	Families	Genera	Species
New Mexico:				
Number	7	15	32	61
Per cent	100	79	56	52
Montana:				
Number	7	17	40	63
Per cent	100	89	70	54
Total	7	19	57	117

from Montana is at present least represented in those from New Mexico and vice versa.

Another approach to this aspect of sampling can, again, be based on completely known recent faunas. An example is given in Table 7. This example is also rather extreme, for the two areas compared, although in the same broad faunal region, are extremely different in

TABLE 7

<small>COMPARISON OF RECENT LAND (NON-VOLANT) MAMMALS OF
FLORIDA AND NEW MEXICO</small>

((Data from Simpson, 1936)

	Orders	Families	Genera	Species
Florida:				
Number	5	13	27	33
Per cent	83	65	43	21
New Mexico:				
Number	6	19	54	133
Per cent	100	95	86	83
Total	6	20	63	160

climate, topography, and general ecological conditions. Yet the larger fauna includes the great majority of the total genera and almost all the families, and even the much smaller fauna has 43 per cent of the genera and 65 per cent of the families.

Given the fact that the over-all sampling of past life is and must always be highly incomplete, the fact that samples of various groups, times, and places vary so tremendously is actually an advantage, making the record more adequate for our purposes. At the two extremes, some desirable samples simply do not exist, but others are nearly complete. A rough estimate, at least, can often be made of the adequacy of a particular sample, and historical problems can be studied by examples based on the most adequate available evidence. The probable reliability of conclusions can also be judged within increasingly close limits.

One approach to judgment of the taxonomic adequacy of samples is the rate of discovery and the intensity of exploration. This matter has been well discussed by Newell (1959) [8] and needs only brief mention here. Recent mammals and birds, for instance, have been collected practically everywhere that they occur. At present the discovery of a clean-cut new species is a rare event, and discovery of truly new genera has virtually ceased. We may be sure that we now know nearly, if not quite, all the specific and higher taxa of those classes. Collecting of recent insects, on the contrary, still produces many new species and a proportion of higher taxa, so that knowledge of those animals is evidently still highly incomplete. Discovery of new taxa among fossils has not ceased in any group and is still accelerating in most. It has, nevertheless, definitely slowed down for some groups, such as the ammonites, and it appears that our knowledge of those groups (as far as they are actually accessible in the rocks) is nearing completion.

It is, further, possible to estimate within broad limits how large an ancient biota is likely to have been and therefore what percentage of its taxa are represented in known collections. One approach is exemplified by the unusual but enlightening example of the Pleistocene mammals of Florida.

There is reason to believe that all or nearly all the native species of mammals living in peninsular Florida in historic times were already present there in the Late Pleistocene. The time elapsed is not long enough for the normal evolution of distinctly new species. Florida's geographic and climatic situation is such that the immigration of species in Late Pleistocene and Recent is improbable. (In many areas it is not only probable but has in fact occurred to a significant extent.) On this reasonable postulate, the percentage of Recent species recovered from Late Pleistocene deposits should reflect, in some degree, the percentage of recovery of the whole Pleistocene fauna. The conditions are favorable, because Late Pleistocene deposits rich in fossil mammals are widespread in peninsular Florida and have been intensively studied,

---

[8] Newell's cited work covers almost the same ground as the present essay but does so in quite a different way. That two students can treat the same topics with so little repetition is evidence of the complexity of the subject. I had the privilege of reading Newell's paper before this manuscript was in final form, and I have profited from it, but, on the whole, our papers are independent.

even though not, as yet, by methods likely to recover all extremely small or exceptionally rare forms.

The results are given in Table 8. As would be expected a priori and from experience elsewhere, recovery of very small and of arboreal mammals is poor—one-third to one-half of species presumed present —and recovery of volant mammals (bats) is altogether inadequate— less than one-tenth. On the other hand, recovery of other species (terrestrial, fossorial, or amphibious and of moderate to large size) is

TABLE 8

RECOVERY OF RECENT SPECIES OF MAMMALS FROM PLEISTOCENE OF
PENINSULAR FLORIDA AND ESTIMATION OF TOTAL PLEISTOCENE
SPECIES AND RECOVERY
(New Compilation of Data from Many Sources)

a) Recent Species and Their Recovery from the Pleistocene

	TOTAL RECENT SPECIES		RECENT SPECIES KNOWN FROM PLEISTOCENE		RECOVERY OF RECENT SPECIES
	No.	Per Cent	No.	Per Cent	(Per Cent)
1. *Low-recovery groups:*					
a) Head-body length < 4″ ..	6	14	3	11	50
b) Arboreal	3	7	1	4	33
c) Volant	11	26	1	4	9
Total	20	47	5	19	25
2. *High-recovery groups:* Head-body length > 4″, terrestrial, fossorial, or amphibious	23	53	22	81	96
Grand total	43	100	27	100	63

b) Pleistocene Fauna

	Also Recent in Florida	Also Recent Not in Florida	Extinct	Total	Per Cent
1. *Low-recovery groups:*					
a) Head-body length < 4″	3	0	1	4	7
b) Arboreal	1	0	0	1	2
c) Volant	1	0	1	2	3
Total	5	0	2	7	11
2. *High-recovery groups*	22	5	27	54	89
Grand totals	27	5	29	61	100
Per Cent of Pleistocene Total	44	8	48	100	...

TABLE 8—*Continued*

c) Estimation of Total Pleistocene Fauna from Numbers of Known Species

	KNOWN No.	POSTULATED RECOVERY (*Per Cent*)	ESTIMATED		POSTULATED RECOVERY (*Per Cent*)	ESTIMATED	
			No.	*Per Cent*		No.	*Per Cent*
1. *Low-recovery groups:*							
a) Head-body length < 4″	4	50	8	9	—	—	—
b) Arboreal ..	1	33	3	3	—	—	—
c) Volant ...	2	9	22	25	—	—	—
Total	7	21 *	33	37	25 †	28	33
2. *High-recovery groups*	54	96	56	63	96	56	67
Grand totals	61	69 *	89	100	73 *	84	100

* Weighted mean recovery; figure not in previous tables.
† Unweighted mean recovery for total low-recovery groups.

almost complete, only one recent species lacking out of twenty-three. (The missing species is the mink, *Mustela vison,* which was probably rare; the Pleistocene record of the cougar, *Felis concolor,* is not quite certain but is probable.) Recovery is 25 per cent for very small, arboreal, and volant mammals combined, 96 per cent for others, and 63 per cent over-all.

These figures do not at once yield a good estimate of recovery of all Pleistocene species, because extinction was differential with respect to chances of recovery. More than half (56 per cent) of the known Pleistocene species are either totally extinct (48 per cent) or no longer live in Florida (8 per cent) (see Table 8b). Of these, only a minute proportion (6 per cent of species now extinct or otherwise absent in Florida) belong in the low-recovery categories of very small, arboreal, or volant species. That figure is of course biased by the very fact of low recovery. If we use the estimates of recovery derived from living species (Table 8c) the low-recovery groups probably constituted from 33 to 37 per cent of the whole Late Pleistocene fauna. In the Recent fauna, 47 per cent of species belong to low-recovery groups. Thus high-recovery groups (mostly large terrestrial species) were more numerous in the Pleistocene, and a larger percentage of them became extinct, either locally or completely. On this basis, over-all recovery from the Pleistocene is estimated as about 70 per cent or more (69 to 73 per cent on different postulates), whereas total Pleistocene recoveries of Recent species are only 63 per cent. Both figures will, of course, be increased by more intensive collecting, especially if this is more directed toward recovery of the smallest and rarest forms.

That method is inapplicable to those fossil faunas—the great majority—in which the presence of Recent taxa is not an acceptable postulate. It still is possible to judge broadly whether the faunal composition and diversity indicated by the samples is representative of a fauna that is reasonable on various, especially ecological, grounds. In most faunas there will, for instance, be a reasonably expectable ratio between herbivores and carnivores, small and large animals, etc. One example among the many possible is given in Table 9. The com-

TABLE 9 *

COMPARISON OF GENERA IN AN ANCIENT AND TWO RECENT FAUNAS OF NON-VOLANT LAND MAMMALS

| | WESTERN SOUTH DAKOTA | | | | RECENT PORTUGUESE EAST AFRICA | |
| | MIDDLE OLIGOCENE | | RECENT | | | |
	No.	Per Cent	No.	Per Cent	No.	Per Cent
Insectivores and small to moderate omnivores	3	7	3	7	12	15
Small herbivores (mostly rodents)	13	30	22	54	25	32
Large herbivores and a few omnivores (mostly ungulates)	19	44	5	12	24	30
Carnivores	8	19	11	27	18	23
Total	43	...	41	...	79	...

* Data for the fossil fauna somewhat modified from Scott and Jepsen (1936–41); data for Portuguese East Africa mainly from Ellerman, Morrison-Scott, and Hayman (1955); data for Recent South Dakota somewhat modified from Over and Churchill (1941).

parison of the samples of Middle Oligocene non-volant mammals of western South Dakota with the Recent fauna of the same region indicates that the ancient fauna must have been richer. The sampling cannot be complete but already includes more genera than the Recent fauna. The composition also is evidently different, the ancient fauna much richer in ungulates and poorer in rodents, a difference doubtless exaggerated by, but not wholly due to, sampling error. On a balance of evidence, the environments differed in that this area in the Middle Oligocene was lower, wetter, with more equable temperatures, and more extensively forested. The environment of Portuguese East Africa is surely not the same but is probably more like Middle Oligocene South Dakota than is Recent South Dakota. The general ecological makeup of the mid-Oligocene and East African faunas is, indeed, more similar, despite the fact that the actual taxa are completely different below the family level. These comparisons and some other considerations suggest that surely half and probably two-thirds or more of the Middle Oligocene genera are known and that those not yet known are mainly carnivores (individually much less abundant than herbivores) and very small mammals (with less recoverability than large mammals by previous collecting methods).

A final point about the adequacy of the record to be made here (among many others that might be made) has to do mainly with the relationships between bias and the current aims of historical studies. The list of sources of bias given on a previous page is downright appalling if viewed in isolation. It might seem to vitiate any paleontological generalizations. Yet the mere fact that these biases are known and listed makes reliable generalizations possible. It makes it increasingly possible to seek out samples least biased with respect to any particular generalization. It is also becoming increasingly possible to make suitable allowance for biases that are present in otherwise usable samples.

In Darwin's day and down practically to our own, concern with the adequacy of the fossil record was almost entirely with its degree of completeness, taxonomically and anatomically. We are, of course, still interested—even primarily interested—in that point, but we are also increasingly interested in others. Many of the questions of bias would hardly arise, were it not for the fact that we are now demanding much more and different kinds of information from the record. We are, for instance, investigating the relative abundance of individuals of various species within a fauna or its ecological makeup (summary examples in Tables 3 and 8; see also, e.g., Shotwell, 1955). It is even becoming possible to construct mortality curves and age pyramids or to measure selection intensity in fossil populations (e.g., Kurtén, 1953, 1958). Such studies as these greatly increase the usefulness and significance of the record, but they bring up questions of sampling bias that were of no importance when the only concern was with taxonomy and anatomy. For some problems—for instance, those of geographic subspeciation—bias in available samples is so great that paleontologists have not yet successfully coped with them. For an increasing range of problems, however, conscious attention to bias in selecting samples and devising methods permits exemplary generalizations.

THE PRECAMBRIAN–CAMBRIAN PROBLEM

Fossils are abundant only from the Cambrian onward, which is probably not more than one-fourth the whole history of life. Algae and plantlike protistans are known without doubt from various Precambrian rocks, the oldest of them well over 1,500 million years old (Tyler and Barghoorn, 1954; Barghoorn, 1957). Precambrian fossils are, however, widely scattered in place and time and do not constitute a continuous or, as yet, even a particularly enlightening record. Equally scattered but rather numerous animals have been reported from the Precambrian, but all are in serious doubt. There is in every reported instance question as to whether the claimed fossils really are organic, or are animals, or are of truly Precambrian age (Schindewolf, 1956). The best evidence—and it is not impressive—is of trails that may have been made by wormlike animals.

Then, with the beginning of the Cambrian, unquestionable, abundant, and quite varied fossil animals appear. The suddenness can be exaggerated, for the various major groups straggle in through the Cambrian, a period of some 75 million years, and the following Ordovician. There is also some question whether the beds defined as the base of the Cambrian, just because they do contain varied animal remains, are everywhere synchronous. Nevertheless, the change is great and abrupt. This is not only the most puzzling feature of the whole fossil record but also its greatest apparent inadequacy.

Darwin was aware of this problem, even more striking in his day than in ours,[9] when it is still striking enough. He said of it: "The case at present must remain inexplicable; and may be truly urged as a valid argument against the views here entertained" (Darwin, 1872, chap. x). His fear was that the abrupt appearance of many fairly advanced animals in the Cambrian might negate the whole idea of evolution. Only a few near the lunatic fringe of science would now draw such a conclusion, but a problem still remains. Darwin's "case" is still not clearly explained with sufficient positive evidence. Is it explicable on principles illustrated by the Cambrian and later record, or must we consider our usable record as a mere tag-end from which we cannot infer principles operative during much the greater part of the whole history?

Most of the hypotheses that have been proposed to account for these peculiarities of the known record are represented in the following tabulation: [10]

I. Few organisms existed in fact before the Cambrian, and many then came into existence suddenly. (The known record is to be taken as a reasonable sample.)

[9] The only supposed Precambrian fossil definitely known to Darwin was the so-called *Eozoon,* which is now considered inorganic. Many Cambrian fossils were already known.

[10] Most of these hypotheses are mentioned in different form by Axelrod (1958), and his references suffice for access to previous literature.

A. Special creation occurred intensively (although not for the first time) at the beginning of the Paleozoic.

B. Basic "typostrophism" then occurred.

II. There was extensive Precambrian evolution, but the known samples are grossly inadequate until the Cambrian.

A. Most Precambrian fossils have been destroyed by metamorphism, less effective on Cambrian and later rocks.

B. Few Precambrian but many Cambrian and later exposures represent times, facies, and places where organisms lived.

1. Precambrian rocks are mainly marine, and organisms were then mainly fresh-water; or, alternatively, the rocks were mainly fresh-water and the organisms marine.

   a) Cambrian and later rocks include fresh-water or alternatively marine deposits unlike those of the Precambrian.

   b) Organisms spread to the sea or alternatively to fresh-water at the beginning of the Cambrian.

2. Major evolution occurred in a Proterozoic-Paleozoic hiatus (Walcott's "Lipalian") not represented by known rocks.

3. Precambrian organisms were mostly in environments (e.g., abysses and overlying waters, narrow littoral zones) the rocks of which are not now widely exposed. In the Cambrian, organisms spread more extensively to other environments.

4. Precambrian organisms were of very local geographic distribution, in areas where Precambrian rocks happen not now to be exposed. Distribution became much wider in the Cambrian.

C. Precambrian organisms were mostly soft-bodied and unlikely to be preserved. At and after the beginning of the Cambrian there was exceptionally rapid evolution (whatever its mechanism) of diverse groups with hard parts.

1. The chemistry of Precambrian waters prevented extensive formation of skeletons, e.g., because of acidity or of lack of calcium. The chemistry changed abruptly at the beginning of the Cambrian.

2. Skeletons were comparatively non-adaptive in the Precambrian. In the Cambrian they became adaptive, through new environmental stress, heightened competition or predation, changes in habitus, etc., and were then developed by "explosive evolution" powered by strong natural selection.

3. Genetical factors for skeleton formation were lacking in the Precambrian and suddenly began to appear at the beginning of the Cambrian, perhaps by "magnimutation" or "typostrophism."

D. A reasonably good Precambrian record exists but has been much less adequately sampled than the later record.

1. Exploration of the Precambrian has simply been less intensive.

2. Precambrian exposures of fairly unaltered sedimentary rocks are much less extensive than for the Cambrian and later periods.

3. Most Precambrian fossils are too small to be found by ordinary

collecting methods or, for some other structural reason, are not readily recognizable. Organisms suddenly become larger or their hard parts more recognizable in the Cambrian.

Certain of these hypotheses can be ruled out almost completely as strongly opposed by present evidence: I A (evolution is a fact); II B 1 (Precambrian organisms must have been predominantly marine and there are surely marine sediments among known Precambrian rocks); II B 2 (in some sedimentary sections there is no significant hiatus here); II C 1 (there is no known mechanism for such a sudden change in water chemistry and there is good evidence that no such change occurred at this time). Some others, although they can hardly be discarded out of hand, are extremely unlikely on theoretical or other grounds: I B, II C 3 (such abrupt evolutionary processes, ruled by mutation alone, are incompatible with the most widely held evolutionary theories); II B 4 (in the very great span of the Precambrian it is hardly conceivable that distribution would remain limited by geographic factors alone, without strong ecological or facial factors).

All the other hypotheses probably are true to the extent, at least, that they have attenuated the Precambrian relative to the later fossil record.

II A.—It is true that Precambrian rocks are more extensively metamorphosed and that this must have reduced the proportionate representation of Precambrian organisms as fossils. Nevertheless, there are many little-altered Precambrian sedimentary rocks, and the change in amount of metamorphism is not so abrupt as the change in fossil content.

II B 3.—Preserved Precambrian sediments differ widely in facies and doubtless represent a number of quite distinct environments. The range is nevertheless restricted. For instance, it is reasonably certain that no known Precambrian rocks were deposited on uplands and probable that none are abyssal marine. It is, further, probable on theoretical grounds that life began in shallow marine waters, along shores and in tidal pools, or in brackish lagoons. Even long after life arose and after many small planktonic forms had spread to the open seas, those variable and partly isolated marginal environments are the most likely sites for progressive evolution and for extensive speciation. Deposits of such environments probably occur among preserved Precambrian sedimentary rocks, but, if so, their exposures are few and extremely limited in extent. It is, nevertheless, hard to believe that for well over a billion years progressive groups, even though evolved in the littoral zone, never spread to the neritic zone in abundance. On this score, however, we can point to later and documented examples of comparatively rapid occupation of environments hitherto sparsely

occupied, if at all. The invasion of fresh-water and terrestrial environments in the Paleozoic is the outstanding example. If, around the beginning of the Cambrian, there was, for unknown reasons, a biological
breakthrough from littoral into neritic environments, it would follow
that evolution would be extremely rapid ("explosive," in a usual but
somewhat inept expression), both phyletically (by progression) and
in proliferation of taxa. That speeding-up of evolution at a more basic
level would be even more drastic than in later, recorded episodes and
would in itself help to explain the relatively abrupt Cambrian change.
This explanation of the Precambrian–Cambrian contrast is cogently
supported by the most recent author to discuss the subject, Axelrod
(1958).

II C 2.—If there was accelerated evolution and ecological expansion around the beginning of the Cambrian, this certainly would involve great intensification of natural selection for many different kinds
of organisms. In many, although not all, ways of life possibly involved
in the radiation, skeletons would be advantageous for various reasons:
resistance to water movement in sessile forms (especially important in
the littoral region), passive defense against predators or other consumers, mechanical aid in more effective locomotion, and others. If
skeletons did in fact develop in a few groups, there would be tremendous pressure for similar or competing groups also to develop skeletons or to become extinct. That would go far toward explaining why
many different groups of organisms might have developed skeletons
at more or less the same time. (The view that so many distinct taxa
just happened quite independently to mutate into skeleton-bearing
forms, C 3 above, is really incredible.) If, as seems probable, the time
involved was short only compared to the whole span of evolution but
was absolutely rather long—some tens of millions of years or perhaps
even a hundred million or so—that would support, rather than disprove, this hypothesis. If, as is also at least possible, skeletons had
appeared quite early in some limited taxa and special environments
(such as the littoral zone) and only much later became really common
and widespread, this hypothesis would still be applicable to the latter
episode. It is nevertheless necessary to remember that this argument is
at present completely theoretical or negative and that there is really
no positive evidence on it, either pro or con.

II D 1.—Certainly much less time has been spent hunting for fossils
in Precambrian rocks than in comparable exposures of any later dates,
if only because the efforts that have been made were so unrewarded.
The recent discovery (Tyler and Barghoorn, 1954) that special techniques do reveal hitherto quite unsuspected Precambrian fossils leaves
no doubt that the deficiency of record is partly due to lack of appro-

priate effort. Yet this cannot be the whole explanation or perhaps even a major factor. Many skilled collectors have searched the Precambrian, and fossils at all similar to those of the Cambrian would certainly have been found if other factors were even approximately equal.

II D 2.—It is true that known exposures of potentially fossil-bearing rocks of Precambrian age are far less extensive than for later eras. Doubtless this has attenuated the Precambrian record, but it cannot in itself explain the comparative abruptness of the change.

II D 3.—In view of the very widespread tendency for organisms (or animals, at least) to become larger in the course of evolution, it is reasonable to postulate that Precambrian forms averaged considerably smaller than those of later ages. This factor probably has somewhat impeded recovery of the Precambrian record, especially its earlier parts. It is, however, probably of no real help in explaining the Precambrian–Cambrian change. Some microscopic fossils have been recovered from the Precambrian, and their number is increasing. They are, as would be expected, as recognizable as their later counterparts. It is extremely improbable that the many early Cambrian megafossils had only or predominantly microscopic ancestors in the late Precambrian.

The very earliest organisms during the first millions or hundreds of millions of years of the history of life were undoubtedly all very small, soft-bodied, and more or less restricted to special environments from which few or no sediments have been preserved without, at least, considerable metamorphism. It is not strange that no record has been found for the very beginning of the history. There is little hope that such a record ever will be found. The paucity of record in later Precambrian time and especially the contrast between Precambrian and Cambrian do require further explanation. The factors discussed above might, in conjunction, explain these peculiarities of the record. Whether they do or not and what relative importance can be assigned to the various factors are at present almost entirely hypothetical questions. It is, however, much too early to abandon hope that more positive evidence will be found. In the meantime, these considerations show that the peculiarities of the known Precambrian–Cambrian record are, if not positively *explained,* theoretically *explicable* on the basis of principles operative and, in some degree, illustrated in the later parts of the history. It would, then, be contrary to the canon of parsimony to postulate the existence of some additional principle peculiar to the earlier part of the history, even though we do not now have sufficient evidence to exclude the possibility beyond all doubt.

THE SUDDEN APPEARANCE OF HIGHER CATEGORIES

It is a feature of the known fossil record that most taxa appear abruptly. They are not, as a rule, led up to by a sequence of almost imperceptibly changing forerunners such as Darwin believed should be usual in evolution. A great many sequences of two or a few temporally intergrading species are known, but even at this level most species appear without known *immediate* ancestors, and really long, perfectly complete sequences of numerous species are exceedingly rare. Sequences of genera, immediately successive or nearly so at that level (not necessarily represented by the exact populations involved in the transition from one genus to the next), are more common and may be longer than known sequences of species. But the appearance of a new genus in the record is usually more abrupt than the appearance of a new species: the gaps involved are generally larger, that is, when a new genus appears in the record it is usually well separated morphologically from the most nearly similar other known genera. This phenomenon becomes more universal and more intense as the hierarchy of categories is ascended. Gaps among known species are sporadic and often small. Gaps among known orders, classes, and phyla are systematic and almost always large.

These peculiarities of the record pose one of the most important theoretical problems in the whole history of life: Is the sudden appearance of higher categories a phenomenon of evolution or of the record only, due to sampling bias and other inadequacies? I have discussed this question at such great length elsewhere (especially Simpson, 1953) that I need do no more here than summarize with irreducible brevity and add comments on a few points that I may not have sufficiently stressed before.

In the first place, the "either . . . or" question is not necessarily answered exclusively by either one of the alternatives. There is little doubt that the rise of a higher category has frequently involved exceptionally fast evolution, change at rates considerably higher than those normally involved in the better-recorded sequences. To that extent the sudden appearance of higher categories is almost certainly influenced by a real evolutionary phenomenon. But this does not exclude the possibility that the origins of those categories were by graded transition, even though some phases occurred at unusually rapid rates. The gaps, then, would not, as such, truly represent an evolutionary phenomenon ("saltation," "typostrophism," "magnimutation," etc.) but only a sampling effect.

Second, there are well-grounded theoretical reasons why organisms in the major transition sequences may be less recoverable as fossils, so that the record would be biased against representation of them in our collections. The rapidity of their evolution would, in itself, produce such a bias. In such transitions the populations involved were probably in most cases, if not in all, notably smaller in size and much more restricted in distribution than their most successful, abundant, and widespread descendants that appear with apparent suddenness in the record as we know it. Those are potentially very strong biasing factors. Moreover, many higher categories appear in the record at times (e.g., Triassic, Paleocene) following geographic conditions such that there were few deposits of facies appropriate for preservation of the ancestors of the groups that do appear suddenly. There are other, but probably less important, biasing factors (Simpson, 1953). In sum, these considerations strongly suggest that the probability of collecting a representative of a species in a transition to a new higher category is decidedly less than for species within the category after it is fully established.

There is a further point that has been noticed before but that seems to me now to have been insufficiently emphasized or appreciated. Even if sampling were quite unbiased, with any one species just as likely to be preserved and found as any other, incomplete sampling and taxonomic conventions would produce, purely as artifacts, gaps between taxa that would be more systematically present and larger as the hierarchy was ascended. This can be demonstrated not only as a logical statistical consequence but also by simple paper experiments, one of which is summarized in Table 10. Draw a phylogenetic tree, either

TABLE 10 *

RESULTS OF EXPERIMENT IN SAMPLING A PHYLOGENY

(Experiment Described in Text)

Category	No. "Known" Taxa	Gaps (Number of "Unknown" Species) between Taxa within Single Units of Next Higher Category		
		No.	Range	Mean
Species	35	26	0–8	2.8
Genera	16	12	2–13	8.2
Families	4	3	8–13	10.3

* Number of original species presumed to have existed: 350; number selected by random sampling: 35.

hypothetical or deduced for a real group of organisms. Divide all its lineages into numbered species, postulated as of the same "size" (taking up equal lengths on the lines). Draw a sample of say 10 to 15 per cent of the species at random and mark these as "known," i.e., discovered as fossils, the others being "unknown." The resemblance and affinity between any two species is postulated as approximately proportional to the least number of intervening species along lineages in either direction. Classify the "known" species into genera, families, etc., as you would actual specimens.

Most of the "known" species will be isolated, but a few sequences of two, three, or possibly more will probably occur. In the experiment of Table 10 there were three sequences of two contiguous species and one of three. There will also be longer sequences with a few short gaps. Tabulate the gaps by length (number of intervening "unknown" species) for species within genera, genera within families, families within superfamilies, etc. It will be found that the mean length of gaps is small for species, larger for genera, still larger for families, and so on. That is just the situation in the record as actually known. The lower limit of the range for any category will be not more and generally distinctly less than for the next higher category. For species it will probably be zero. For genera it may be zero, but this is unlikely. For still higher categories it will almost certainly be above zero: there are systematic gaps between those categories, as in the actual record. The upper limit does not decrease and tends to increase, the higher the category. (In Table 10, based on a comparatively simple phylogeny that tends to minimize the contrasts, the upper limit is the same for genera and families.) Similarly, in the known record the largest gaps are between the highest categories.

Thus the observed gaps in the record are fairly analogous to what would be expected from random sampling of originally continuous sequences without gaps. The correspondence becomes exact if allowance is made for biases almost certainly present. The presence, relative extent, and distribution of the gaps can be *predicted* from the postulate that no gaps were really present in the original structural and phylogenetic sequences. Other predictions can be made, and their fulfilment seems further to establish the postulate as true beyond serious question. Here are some examples.

1. On this postulate, intensive sampling should rarely, but occasionally, produce forms scattered more or less randomly within what are otherwise major gaps. This happens: *Archaeopteryx* in the reptile-bird gap is the most famous example.

2. Direct generic sequences should be more common than direct specific sequences. That is true of the record, and it may appear anomalous in view of the fact that gaps between genera are likely to be more frequent and large than between species. The prediction follows from these considerations: Sampling strongly favors the largest, most widespread specific populations. But, on an average, smaller and

more local populations are more numerous. A large population is no more likely and may well be less likely to give rise to a new genus than a small population. Therefore, the chance of finding successive genera represented by species that are not necessarily successive is greater, on an average, than the chances of finding successive species.[11]

3. Some taxa should reappear after absence from the record for spans comparable to the gaps in the record characteristic of the hierarchic categories involved. That is notoriously true of the living coelacanths and monoplacophoran mollusks, the youngest known fossils of which are Cretaceous and Silurian, respectively. Other, less sensational examples are fairly common and often tend, as would also be predicted, to be inversely proportional to the knowledge (or intensity of sampling) of the group involved. For instance, for scyphozoans, a poorly sampled group, there is an enormous gap from Cambrian to Jurassic and for condylarths, a well-sampled group, a much shorter gap from Eocene to Miocene.

Some Generalizations and Interpretations

over-all descriptive processes

If we had no direct record of the history of life, three alternatives might seem most logical. Most obvious would be the supposition that seems to be exemplified in the world we see, the only one of which we have any human record: a dynamic equilibrium with individuals being born and dying, populations waxing and waning, but no apparent over-all trend. That is, of course, essentially the creationist dogma, but it could also be an outcome of evolution. With realization of the fact of evolution, two other possibilities (both of which were more dimly involved in much earlier speculations) become clearer. There might be a steady progression step-by-step from, as the saying goes, amoeba to man, with each earlier and lower stage remaining static or, at least, in stabilized equilibrium after the next higher stage arose from it. Or there might be a steady expansion and fragmentation of the world of life as organisms occupied all environments and different forms became increasingly specialized for particular niches within those environments.

The last two alternatives are not mutually exclusive, and both ideas

---

[11] The prediction would indeed still follow if any one species of a genus were as likely as any other to give origin to a new genus. The basically sufficient conditions for the prediction are that genera have, on an average, more than one species, which is obviously true, and that two successive species in one genus do not usually both have much higher probability of discovery than the average for all the species of known genera, which must hold more often than not.

have always been and indeed still are simultaneously involved in most thinking about evolution. They do not, moreover, exclude the first alternative, for it would seem that neither progression nor expansion can go on forever and that an equilibrium must at last be reached. Opinions differ as to whether it has already been reached. The record now acquired plainly shows that all three processes are indeed intricately interwoven in the fabric of history but that the pattern is even more complicated than any intermixture of those three motifs. Another equally important element occurs: extinction.[12]

It seems curious now that savants ever argued as to whether species can become extinct. Thomas Jefferson on religious grounds and Lamarck for more scientific reasons agreed that extinction had not occurred, even while Cuvier was demonstrating that it had. A priori there is no strictly logical necessity for it. Why should progression and expansion not simply fill the world with living things that would then preserve their status? Only the fossil record could establish the really startling fact that extinction is the *usual* fate of species and that it has made history quite different from what once seemed logical to Lamarck and many other logical men.[13]

The fossil record suffices to confirm that the history of life has involved, in the main, these four grand processes: expansion, progression, equilibrium (or stabilization), and extinction.[14] No one of these has been constant or dominant over-all. No one characterizes all or-

[12] By "extinction" I mean the death of a line of descent without any further descendents whatever, not the transformation of the line into a group to which we give a different name. Nothing like, for instance, the prosimians directly ancestral to man now exists, but they are not extinct. They have simply lived on as, eventually, men.

[13] Jefferson's argument was that God created "nature's chain" from which no link could be lost lest the whole system "should evanish by piecemeal" (Jefferson, 1799). Lamarck was concerned with arguing that supposedly extinct species had evolved into different living species (as, in fact, many of them had) and in denying the reality of Cuvier's catastrophes (which, in fact, were not real). Lamarck (1809) did admit "une simple possibilité" that some large animals might have been wiped out, but only by man.

[14] In terms of Huxley's analysis (e.g., 1958): diversification or cladogenesis (= expansion), persistence or stasigenesis (= equilibrium), and improvement or anagenesis (= progression). The terminological equations are not quite exact, because Huxley's analysis does not follow precisely the same lines, but the distinctions are not very important. Huxley defines extinction as "negative persistence," but here there may be a significant difference in the two approaches. (Of course, that does not mean that either is exclusively correct; they are just different and may be equally valid.) Extinction may and indeed usually does involve groups that never were persistent (had not reached "stasigenesis"). Persistence and progression could both be as logically called "negative extinction." From our present point of view, extinction is a positive factor, especially in its over-all effect on *other* groups than those becoming extinct. A simple but not too forced analogy is that I would choose, for certain descriptive purposes, to think of emptying a bottle as a positive action and not simply as the negative of filling it (progression) or of leaving it full either just so (static equilibrium) or with equal flow in and out (dynamic equilibrium).

ganisms at any given time or at all times for any given organisms. Moreover, they are never independent, but each process depends on and in turn helps to determine all the others. The result is extremely complex, but it can be analyzed in its broader and some of its minor lines, at least in a descriptive way. Causal analysis is, as usual, more difficult and less secure, but it is possible, and herein are the deepest meanings and the highest rewards of the study of the history of life.

EXPANSION AND EQUILIBRIUM

It would seem to be a logical necessity of organic evolution that life began with only a few kinds (perhaps, but not necessarily, only one) of organisms, probably also only a few individuals, if individuality was then definable. Expansion must, then, have been especially prominent in those truly primeval days. The fossil record gives no really useful evidence on this point, which remains purely logical or hypothetical, even though it is perhaps the most common statement made about evolution in general.

The fossil record does pick up what seems to be the end—certainly not the beginning and probably not the acme—of an early (not the earliest) major expansion of life. We do not know what happened around and just before the beginning of the Cambrian, but it almost certainly involved an expansion of some sort. The record continues to expand through the Cambrian and well into the Ordovician, and this is almost certainly a reflection of a real phenomenon rather than a mere sampling effect.

Table 11 shows a clear increase in number of known major groups (phyla and classes) from Early Cambrian to Middle Ordovician. When comparison is made with Recent marine animals that would probably occur in the earlier record if present, the number of phyla is now the same as in the Middle Ordovician, and the number of classes is actually slightly smaller. Numerous relatively unfossilizable soft-bodied groups—those absent or extremely rare in any part of the fossil record—are omitted from the Recent count, but there is no reason to believe that their trend in diversity was notably different from that of the groups recorded as fossils. (Indeed, these less fossilizable groups may well have been relatively *more* common in the Cambrian.) Comparison of lower hierarchic categories, especially of genera and species, is too uncertain to be significant; we can be sure that at these levels the Cambrian and Ordovician record is highly incomplete but cannot usefully estimate just how incomplete.

It is concluded that basically, at the level of classes and above, the diversity of the marine fauna increased into the Middle Ordovician but has not increased since then. Doubtless it has fluctuated, and this must

TABLE 11

NUMBERS OF MARINE ANIMAL PHYLA AND
CLASSES IN CAMBRIAN, ORDOVICIAN,
AND RECENT

Time	Phyla	Classes
Cambrian:		
Early	8	12
Middle *	10	20
Late	11	22
Ordovician:		
Early	11	27
Middle †	12	33
Late	12	33
Recent ‡	12	31

* The graptolites (Graptolithina) of middle Cambrian through late Ordovician (and
later) are counted as a class, not also as a
phylum. The consensus is that they belong
to an otherwise known phylum, but opinions
differ as to which phylum.

† The phylum Chordata is tabulated as
first appearing in the middle Ordovician.

‡ Recent groups tabulated are marine only
and are those also known from Cambrian or
Ordovician or considered likely to have been
found if they had lived then. Those whose
absence from the known record of the Cambrian and Ordovician would be likely even if
they then existed have been omitted.

notably have been true of lower taxonomic levels, but the major expansion of marine animals was evidently complete in the Ordovician
and has been more or less in equilibrium since then. The living phyla
are the same as those of the Ordovician, and, at this most fundamental level of all, the subsequent equilibrium has been static. Within
the phyla, however, the equilibrium has been quite dynamic. Several
of the classes and an increasing proportion of the lesser groups have
become extinct and have been replaced by groups of separate origin.
The proportion of Ordovician species that have living descendants is
unknown but is certainly minute.

The maintenance of such dynamic equilibrium involves repeated
contractions and expansions within the pattern even while the over-all
diversity remains roughly constant within broad limits. There is a
relay effect, and this is perhaps the element we would least expect if
we did not have the fossil record to demonstrate it. A broad ecological
zone may remain approximately filled for long periods of time, but
the groups actually occupying it may change radically, one relaying
the other. Thus the diversity of hoofed herbivorous mammals changed

only within broad limits from about Late Paleocene into the Pleistocene, but the predominant groups were first various archaic orders, then perissodactyls, and finally artiodactyls. Data for the area that is now nearctic North America are given in Table 12. Here there has been a

TABLE 12

RELAY IN NEARCTIC UNGULATES: PERCENTAGE OF GENERA BELONGING TO VARIOUS ORDERS IN CENOZOIC EPOCHS

	Archaic Orders *	Proboscidea	Perissodactyla	Artiodactyla	Total No.
Recent	0	0	0	100	10
Pleistocene ...	0	11	11	78	27
Pliocene	0	20	20	61	46
Miocene	0	6	22	72	69
Oligocene	0	0	38	62	47
Eocene	14	0	52	33	84
Paleocene	100	0	0	0	36

* Condylarths, pantodonts, uintatheres, and one notoungulate.

marked decline in total diversity since the Miocene, a complex phenomenon probably due to a variety of factors: relay by non-ungulates, increasing dominance of a few exceptionally successful species, floral and climatic changes, and probably other influences. However that may be, the relay phenomenon within this broad ecological type is evident.

The example shows that relaying may occur during times of expansion, equilibrium, and decline of numbers of taxa and is not confined to equilibrium phases. On a still broader scale, relay during expansion is illustrated by the land vertebrates. With fluctuations and shorter times of stasis and moderate contraction, that expansion continued from the Devonian well into the Cenozoic, but the main expansive activity was at first among amphibians, then reptiles, and finally mammals.

The last example is part of the second major over-all expansion of animals shown in the record, following the marine expansion seen in the Cambrian and Ordovician. It reflects spread into another major environment or complex of environments—that of the land. That began, as far as the record shows, slowly in the Silurian, was in full swing in the Carboniferous, and continued with fluctuations and some setbacks well into the Cenozoic. No new phylum was involved and only a few of the older, previously aquatic phyla (hardly any forms outside the Mollusca, Arthropoda, and Chordata), and a modest number of classes, but the terrestrial fauna became extremely diverse at the levels from orders to species.

Those features of the record and some others are reflected in Table 13. The exact numbers there given have little significance, since no two tabulators would agree exactly as to which groups are "well-recorded" or would use just the same classification. Certain general features seem, however, to be reliable. All sufficiently known phyla and an absolute majority of known classes first appear in the Cambrian and Ordovician. No phylum is known to have arisen since then, and only a few classes are known to have arisen since the Carboniferous— only one (Mammalia) is tabulated; at least one more (Aves) is known to have originated after the Carboniferous, and a few more may have.

Basic stabilization of marine invertebrate faunas well before the end of the Paleozoic is evident at the level of phyla and classes. The orders, especially, also reflect approach to stabilization in the Ordovician, but there is another proliferation of orders in the Carboniferous and a sequence of them through the Mesozoic. Those for the most part represent relay phenomena, new groups replacing old in a fluctuating dynamic equilibrium. The marine vertebrates expanded and stabilized much later than did the invertebrates. This was in part a relay of invertebrates by vertebrates. The aquatic vertebrates reached a near-equilibrium in both classes and orders by the end of the Devonian. Renewed proliferation of orders in the Middle to Late Mesozoic and (not shown by the tabulation but probable on other data) Early Cenozoic involves relays and probably also a renewed expansion (both involving almost solely the teleosts).

Proliferation of land vertebrates approached an early and temporary equilibrium in the Carboniferous, mainly among the imperfectly terrestrial amphibians. A relay plus a definite new expansion into fully terrestrial habitats occurred among the reptiles, especially in the Jurassic, and is evident in the table at the ordinal level. Another relay and still further expansion involve the Cenozoic mammals. Although not tabulated, there was also a great expansion of birds mainly in the latest Mesozoic and Early Cenozoic. This was in small part a relay (replacing pterosaurs), but it was mainly an expansion into a new set of ecological situations, most of which were previously empty or non-existent. A concomitant great expansion of mainly volant non-aquatic invertebrates (especially insects) also occurred and probably was not stabilized until well into the Cenozoic. The record is still too poor for reliable tabulation, but the broad event is evident. (Both these expansions and some others correlate with Late Mesozoic expansion of angiospermous plants, which created innumerable previously non-existent niches for animals.)

The relays and post-Ordovician expansions of special groups reached up to the ordinal level and occurred at various times including

TABLE 13

Times of First Appearance in Fossil Record of Well-recorded Groups of Animals

| Time | Invertebrates,* Mostly Marine | | | Vertebrates † | | | | Totals | | |
| | Phyla | Classes | Orders | Fishes | | Tetrapods | | Phyla | Classes | Orders |
				Classes	Orders	Classes	Orders			
Cenozoic	0	0	4	0	—‡	0	25	0	0	29 ‡
Cretaceous	0	0	10	0	5	0	3	0	0	18
Jurassic	0	0	11	0	5	1	8	0	1	24
Triassic	0	0	9	0	3	0	10	0	0	22
Permian	0	0	1	0	1	0	3	0	0	5
Carboniferous	0	3	22	2	0	1	9	0	4	31
Devonian	0	6	9	1	11	1	1	0	9	21
Silurian	0	3	6	1	5	0	0	0	4	11
Ordovician	1	14	46	1	1	0	0	2 §	15	47
Cambrian	6	21	32	0	0	0	0	6	21	32

* Omitting insects and other groups with poor records.

† Omitting birds and lesser groups with poor records.

‡ Many orders of teleosts appear with fair records in the Cenozoic, but their systematics is so poorly established that they are omitted. This makes the total for Cenozoic orders relatively too small.

§ The second phylum, additional to that in the first column, is Chordata.

the Cenozoic. For those reasons there is no apparent over-all diminution in the rise of new orders of animals, from Cambrian to Cenozoic, in sharp contrast to the situation as regards classes and phyla. That contrast would be still more striking if reliable figures were at hand for three groups omitted from the present tabulation and particularly rich in orders of comparatively late origin: insects, teleost fishes, and birds. There are, of course, fluctuations, notably lows in the Silurian and Permian which are probably original phenomena and not sampling errors.

MORE ABOUT THE ORIGINS OF HIGHER CATEGORIES

It was noted earlier that taxa usually appear suddenly in the record and that there is a tendency for the sudden appearance to be more systematic and the gaps larger, the higher the taxonomic category. Those facts have been adduced in support of a theory that all taxa, and most strikingly the higher taxa, arise by saltation (magnimutation, systemic mutation, or typostrophism) (see especially Schindewolf, 1950). But it has already been indicated that the facts do not, indeed, either require or warrant such an interpretation. The sudden appearances and the gaps are in part artifacts of sampling and of the taxonomic system. So far as they demand any further explanation, the facts further suggest that groups involved in the origin of higher categories have often been evolving at exceptionally rapid (but not saltatory) rates and may have had other characteristics that reduced their chances of inclusion in the known record. Those points have been sufficiently made here and elsewhere (especially Simpson, 1944, 1953).

It has now been shown further that higher categories—classes and phyla at least—tend to appear early in the (post–Precambrian) record, that their rates of first appearances declined rapidly after the Cambrian, and that very few have appeared since the Paleozoic. While rejecting the theory of saltatory origins, Brough (1958) has emphasized the early appearances of higher categories and the evidence that they originated at exceptionally rapid rates of evolution, both as to phyletic change and as to diversification. He argues from these features of the record that the "surging phases of evolution" in which occurs "the institution of new groups of high systematic value" involved successive non-random mutations occurring at "fantastically high" rates and that "in these movements Natural Selection seems to have played little part." This is not the place for full consideration of Brough's views, but, because they are new, authoritative, and pertinent to our present theme, they do require some notice here.

Brough's argument is almost entirely negative. There is no positive evidence at all for "fantastically high" mutation rates in the Cambrian or at any other time. He maintains that the only alternative explanations are (1) evolution in small populations or (2) general acceleration of evolution in periods of environmental instability. He then discards explanation 1 because there are no reliable data on the subject and 2 because there is some good evidence against it in certain instances. That leaves, in his opinion, only one further alternative: (3) non-random mutation at high rates. Such an argument by elimination is convincing only if it weighs all reasonable alternatives. But here the first alternative has not really been weighed at all, and the three together do not, in my opinion, cover all possibilities or even the most pertinent ones.[15]

The most important alternatives seem to me to be main control by (*a*) natural selection or (*b*) successive non-random mutations. Control by natural selection does not require, and is indeed somewhat opposed by, the suggestion that populations were small. In many instances, at least, of the origin of higher categories control by selection does require a sort of accelerated breakthrough into an adaptive zone new for the groups in question. The possible conditions for such breakthroughs are quite complex and have been sufficiently discussed by Simpson (1953). The rapidity of evolution called for by the record is no greater than has actually been observed to occur in nature and produced in the laboratory definitely under the control of natural selection.[16]

As for the antiquity of higher categories, this is again in part an artifact, on two bases. First, since we assume (in retrospect) that a taxon of higher category arose with the appearance of the *earliest*

---

[15] Brough discards his first alternative out of hand because of the lack of reliable data, but he does not note that the third alternative, which he accepts, is still more strikingly unsupported by actual or possible data. He seems to ascribe his three alternatives to me (citing Simpson, 1944 and 1953), but I find this somewhat misleading. As to 1, I explicitly stated that populations involved in origins of higher categories need not have been small at any time and could not have been continuously small (Simpson, 1953, pp. 354, 356). As to 2, I concluded that major episodes of evolution are not principally due to cyclic or episodic environmental stress (1953, pp. 241–44). My previous studies did not accept *any* of Brough's three alternatives as the controlling causes of episodes of accelerated evolution or higher categories, but considered at least the first two as possible contributing causes in some, evidently not all, instances.

[16] The changes involved in observed and experimental cases are necessarily on a small scale, being limited to lengths of time infinitesimally short from a geological point of view. But the rates exemplified are certainly more than adequate to give rise to higher categories if projected over the spans of time probably involved. Whether a factor (such as population size or mutation rate) can be *directly* observed in fossils seems to me not to bear logically on its importance for evolution. After all, reproduction can rarely be observed in fossils, but we must assume that it occurred! It is at least of interest that intensity of selection can be measured, if not immediately observed, in fossils in favorable instances (e.g., Kurtén, 1958). Such instances do not, at present, include populations in course of a major breakthrough, but the possibility is not excluded.

included lower taxon, the higher categories must necessarily be of greater *average* age than the lower. Second, the descendants of any expanding or progressively diverging stock will tend formally to represent a larger (or more distinctive, or both) taxon, the longer the process continues, so that again the very nature of classification insures that larger or more distinctive (higher) taxa will, on an *average,* be older than smaller or less distinctive (lower) taxa. From about the level of orders (already a markedly high category to most taxonomists) downward, no further explanation of the antiquity of higher categories may be required. At those levels, if required, and at the levels of classes and phyla, where a further explanation is definitely required, there is an explanation that is at least plausible. This is that, once basic radiation and differentiation have occurred, their products are in possession of the ecological field. It is, on selectionist principles, extremely unlikely that basic differentiation will be repeated and extremely likely that new groups, including both relays and breakthroughs, will occur *within* the broad categories already established, *in esse et in posse.*

These and other less striking considerations seem to make successive, non-random mutation at high rates a hypothesis unnecessary to explain the record as it stands. It also seems to be much the less probable hypothesis, in further view of the following considerations. First, successive mutations, non-random with respect to adaptation, are not known to occur. Second, according to established principles of population genetics, their rates would have to be far beyond anything known to occur, in order for them to take over control of evolutionary direction from even moderate intensities of selection, at levels that *are* known to occur.

RADIATION AND EXTINCTION

Darwin tells us in his *Autobiography* (Edited by Nora Barlow, 1958):

> At that time [1844] I overlooked one problem of great importance. . . . This problem is the tendency in organic beings descended from the same stock to diverge in character as they become modified. . . . I can remember the very spot in the road . . . when to my joy the solution came to me. . . . The solution, as I believe, is that the modified offspring of all dominant and increasing forms tend to become adapted to many and highly diversified places in the economy of nature.

That is, of course, the principle of adaptive radiation, the "discovery" of which has enhanced several reputations since Darwin.

Darwin (1872, chap. xi) also perceived a relationship between the origin of new and the extinction of older groups. He concluded that, in later geological times at least, there was what has here been called a dynamic equilibrium and that "the production of new forms has caused the extinction of about the same number of old forms." He considered that the forms thus becoming extinct would, not invariably but as a rule, be those most closely related to the new forms.

Those processes envisaged by Darwin are fully confirmed by our greater knowledge of the paleontological record. Among the details of the history is a continual replacement of species by related species and genera by related genera. On a broader scale we now see, even more clearly than Darwin did, that every marked expansion of a group, whether it be a genus or a phylum or the whole animal kingdom, is an adaptive radiation. Each starts with a group of a certain adaptive status in a particular range of environments. (Such a group is "generalized" only in the sense that it is not irrevocably committed to a special, narrow range.) Each radiates by a combination of two processes: a parceling-out of a broader ecological range among more specifically adapted separate lines of descent and the invasion of new ecological niches by modifications of the ancestral adaptation.

From what has already been said, it is evident that there are primary expansions and relaying expansions, the patterns within both kinds of expansions normally being those of adaptive radiation. Primary expansion represents the occupation of hitherto empty ecological situations, as in the occupation of the seas from the Precambrian into the Ordovician and the later occupation of the lands. The scale need not be so grand or the events so ancient. The relatively recent occupation of the Galápagos Islands by finches was a primary radiation. In such events extinction may occur, especially on the small scale of species expanding at the expense of closely related species, as stressed by Darwin; but here extinction is almost irrelevant to the main phenomenon.

A relay expansion is a reoccupation, frequently or even typically, by a group that is *not* closely related to the one replaced. Extinction is an essential part of this phenomenon, for relay does not occur unless the older group is reduced in scope or entirely eliminated. In many, probably most, instances the contraction of one group and expansion of another are concomitant and are almost certainly causally related, that is, the spread of the relaying group is itself the cause or one of the causes of extinction. A well-documented example is the radiation of invading Pliocene-Pleistocene North American mammals in South America and the concomitant extinction of many old natives of South America (Simpson, 1950a). Another striking example has gone on before our eyes as the expanding introduced placentals have caused restriction of marsupials in Australia, but there the invasion is so recent that a true adaptive radiation of the invaders has not had time to occur. It will presently be noted that one group may be relayed by several. It is also true that several groups may be relayed by one, as has clearly happened in Australia and probably also among North American ungulates since the Miocene (see Table 12).

In other, more puzzling instances extinction seems definitely to have preceded the relaying expansion, and the causal relationship is apparently reversed: new radiation occurs because of prior extinction, instead of extinction resulting from the radiation. There are, as Darwin also noted but did not stress, causes of extinction other than competitive replacement. The most striking example is the relaying of most of the Mesozoic reptiles by Cenozoic mammals, with no evidence that their temporal distributions overlapped.[17]

Another point well exemplified by the Mesozoic reptiles versus the Cenozoic mammals is that a replacing group may be able to exploit an ecological situation more intensely and to subdivide it more finely than the older group. The Cenozoic mammals do cover roughly the same ecological range as older reptiles, but they are far more diverse, with many more different specific adaptations. Similar phenomena have occurred with some frequency in other groups, for instance in fishes with the expansion of the teleosts.

In saying that animals of a given sort of adaptation are, if they become extinct, replaced or relayed by others, there is no implication that the later forms will be structurally similar. It suffices that the food, the habitat, in general the *Lebensraum* of an earlier group be utilized by a later one. The replacers may be very different in size and other characters, and one group may be replaced by several others, each partly occupying the previous situation. There are no mammals really at all like any dinosaurs, but the dinosaurs' places are thoroughly taken by diverse mammals. This is another conclusion from the record that could hardly be grasped in Darwin's day. He followed Buckland (a non-evolutionist) in thinking that "extinct species can all be classed either in still existing groups, or between them." That is true only at levels so broad that the statement is almost meaningless or in a still quite broad ecological and not phylogenetic sense. Surely no one would now claim, for instance, that the dinosaurs (a few of which were known to Darwin) belong in any meaningful way either to or between still existing groups, even though there are living mem-

---

[17] Early Paleocene mammals are known only from the Rocky Mountain region of the United States, and it is quite possible that some dinosaurs did survive into that epoch elsewhere. But Cretaceous dinosaurs are known from every continent (except Antarctica, which may never have had any mammals), and nowhere are they known to be associated with mammals that could possibly have competed with them. Competition is still less likely between the marine reptiles, which disappear from the record before the end of the Cretaceous, and the replacing whales, which do not appear until well into the Eocene (after the Paleocene).

bers (the crocodiles) of the same subclass. A less familiar but even more extreme example is provided by the graptolites, a once abundant, long extinct group so unlike any Recent animals that it is doubtful what phylum they belong to, if, indeed, they should not be placed in a phylum of their own.[18]

Innumerable extinct groups have been relayed by organisms markedly different from those replaced. Almost all ancient radiations of considerable scope include some extinct groups strangely different from any later groups, even though some later groups do seem in most cases to have occupied their ecological positions. Examples include the hippurites among mollusks, dicynodonts among reptiles, diatrymids among birds, uintatheres among mammals, and many others. Only in some rather late radiations that still have not definitely passed their acme, do strikingly unique extinct groups seem to be absent—for instance, in Late Mesozoic and Cenozoic angiosperms, insects, or teleosts. And even in them the apparent absence of (to recent eyes) really queer extinct groups may be due to ignorance.

Here the question arises whether certain extinct groups have in fact been relayed or whether, as environments have evolved, the ecological opportunities exploited by those groups have not simply ceased to exist. An unequivocal answer is hardly possible. There is no real doubt that relaying has often occurred, and the impression is that it is usual. The fact that extinct groups are often so different from the survivors makes it impossible in some instances to be explicit as to the identities of possibly relaying groups. The ecology of graptolites, for instance, is not clear enough to identify relaying groups precisely, but there are plenty of possibilities: for the sessile forms perhaps various bryozoans and coelenterates; for the planktonic graptolites various protozoans and small arthropods.

Relaying, as between dinosaurs and mammals, apparently can be delayed and so might be delayed indefinitely. Environments do change, and so some must wholly disappear. Yet I can think of few extinct groups of which it can confidently be said that relay has not occurred. A fairly typical example of the *possibility* is provided by the chalicotheres, an extinct group of large, clawed ungulates. Their way of life has been the subject of some wild surmises, but it is really unknown. There is nothing at all like them today, so perhaps their ecological

---

[18] Following the work of Kozlowski (1948), many invertebrate paleontologists (e.g., Moore, Lalicker, and Fischer, 1952; Bulman, 1955) have considered the graptolites as chordates, but this view was strongly controverted in a neglected study by Bohlin (1950), and the most recent studies seem to confirm an old opinion that the graptolites were highly aberrant coelenterates (Decker and Hassinger, 1958). They were certainly radically different from any Recent animals in spite of a superficial resemblance to pterobranchs and to some living coelenterates.

niche is now empty or no longer exists, but how can one decide? It might be too close to a circular argument to reason that the niche no longer exists from the fact that the chalicotheres became extinct or from the "fact" (not really known to be a fact) that there is no ecological replacement for them.

There is a widespread impression that radiations have tended to become smaller in scope (cover smaller ecological ranges and involve lower taxonomic levels) in the course of geological time. That doubtless has a measure of truth, but it requires qualification. Primary radiations, although they can be of any extent, can be the largest of all, and a really large primary radiation can occur only once. Thereafter a new radiation in the same ecological field will necessarily be a relay. The last major primary radiations were in the occupation of land and air, essentially completed in the Mesozoic. The surprising thing is not that it was so early but that it was so late, at least 1,500 million years after the origin of life! Relaying radiations do not have such wide possible scope and characteristically occur, in taxonomic terms, at the level of orders and below. The data of Table 13 suggest that there has been no over-all tendency for them to decrease in either number or scope since the Cambrian. None of ordinal scope has occurred since the Early Cenozoic, but that may be merely because it takes a great deal of time to develop that scope. A radiation that started in the later Cenozoic would not yet have reached a degree of divergence designated as ordinal in current taxonomy.

Although relaying radiations have not tended to decrease regularly, they are not randomly distributed in time. There have been several definite times when major extinctions, up to about the ordinal level, have been especially prevalent, and, as would be expected, these are accompanied by the beginnings and followed by the peaks of major relaying radiations. The first such episode for animals (after the Cambrian) has extinctions distributed around the Silurian-Devonian boundary, with a complex of relaying radiations in the Devonian and into the Carboniferous, where that expansion reaches its acme. Those relays, as now known, are all in marine environments. Insects and amphibians appear in the Devonian, reptiles in the Carboniferous. Those are parts of a primary radiation, but the coincidence with intense relaying radiation may be significant. The next major episode of extinction-then-radiation is in the late Permian and the Triassic, again mainly marine but also affecting some terrestrial groups. The last on this major scale, mainly terrestrial but also in part marine, was the famous Late Cretaceous–Early Cenozoic changeover. Similar episodes of shorter duration and less intensity also occur, for instance, in Late Triassic–Early Jurassic (extinction of many archaic reptiles, origin of mammals, almost complete relay among ammonites, etc.).

The division of later geological time into Paleozoic, Mesozoic, and Cenozoic is based on the major extinctions-relays of the Permian-Triassic and Cretaceous-Tertiary. The Paleozoic could well have been divided into two eras at the Silurian-Devonian boundary, but that episode is not quite so striking and was not so well known to early geologists. It has often been noted that the history of land plants would support a different division of "Paleophytic," "Mesophytic," and "Cenophytic." The primary radiation was mostly Devonian, when there was much relaying and some primary radiation among animals, and the first great extinction-then-relay was Permian-Triassic, coinciding with a similar episode among animals. The last major episode of that sort among land plants was, however, Jurassic-Cretaceous, and there was no really important change between Mesozoic and Cenozoic.

The Triassic-Jurassic episode among animals, although unknown to Darwin, strikingly illustrates one of his points (1872, chap. xi): "To feel no surprise at the rarity of a species, and yet to marvel greatly when the species ceases to exist, is much the same as . . . to feel no surprise at sickness, but, when the sick man dies, to wonder and to suspect that he died by some deed of violence." Only one family (Phylloceratidae), perhaps even only one genus (*Phylloceras* or its immediate ancestor), of ammonites survived the Triassic, but from that (one might think almost chance) survival the group became tremendously diverse by relay. The total extinction of ammonites around the end of the Cretaceous differs only in that no genus happened to survive. The event is no more wonderful than the near-extinction at the end of the Triassic and need have no other cause—whatever that wholly unknown cause may be!

Another of Darwin's opinions about extinction is not completely substantiated by better knowledge of the record: "that the extinction of a whole group of species is generally a slower process than their production." That is frequently true, but the exact opposite is also frequently true. (Darwin noted that there are exceptions to his rule, citing the Cretaceous ammonites.) There is great diversity in patterns of expansion and contraction and a general rule can hardly be formulated. (On this and the whole subject of adaptive radiations see, e.g., Henbest, 1952; Simpson, 1953; and citations there.)

TRENDS

The history of life is decidedly non-random. This is evident in many features of the record, including such points already discussed as the phenomena of relays and of major replacements at defined times. It is, however, still more striking in two other phenomena copiously documented by fossils. Both have to do with evolutionary trends: first, that the direction of morphological (hence also functional and behavioral) change in a given lineage often continues without significant deviation for long periods of time and, second, that similar or parallel trends often appear either simultaneously or successively in numerous different, usually related, lineages. These phenomena are far from universal; they are not "laws" of evolution; but they are so common and so thoroughly established by concrete evidence that they demand a definite, effective directional force among the evolutionary processes. They rule out any theory of purely random evolution, such as the rather naïve mutationism that had considerable support earlier in the twentieth century. What directional forces the data do demand, or permit, is one of the most important questions to be asked of the fossil record.

This is another problem that I have discussed at such length elsewhere that I do not propose to dwell long on it here, despite its importance (especially Simpson, 1953; see also Simpson, 1950b, and other discussions in Piveteau et al., 1950, some of which reach conclusions quite opposed to mine).

The most important point to repeat about trends in particular lineages is that they must be isolated and studied carefully in true temporal sequences, not accepted as vague generalizations or arranged subjectively from scattered individual observations. Perhaps the most widely known example is the evolution of Equus from "little eohippus," frequently represented as a steady "orthogenetic" progression. Examined with care, it is nothing of the sort (Simpson, 1953, Fig. 34). Size, for instance, was approximately stable for the first 20 million years or so, then tended to increase on an average, although from time to time various branches stopped becoming larger or perhaps even became smaller (the latter possibility has been subject to greater doubt since 1953). Different lineages progressed at very unequal rates, so that at any one time in the later Tertiary there were horses of extremely different sizes, some larger than any living horse and some at least as small as their Oligocene forebears. Molarization of the premolars was rather steadily progressive for perhaps 25 million years and then ceased to evolve in all lines. Change in number of toes and foot structure was never a steady trend but was transformed quite rapidly three times, and each of the last two times saw various lineages that were *not* affected and remained on the evolutionary level reached earlier. (This example also illustrates another important phenomenon that cannot here be further discussed: adaptive stabilization.)

Another famous example, that of the supposed "orthogenetic" increase in size of canines in sabertooths (or "sabertoothed tigers," but they were not tigers), is apparently spurious. It can be supported only by a subjective arrangement of animals that were not in the same or closely related lineages and are not taken in their actual temporal sequence. As far as real analysis has yet gone, no tendency toward increase in size of those teeth is evident among truly related animals in their real sequence.

It is not the point that trends are really nonexistent; they certainly are real and frequent, but the doctrine of "orthogenesis" has grossly exaggerated their frequency, duration, and continuity. They may be absent in a given phylogeny (except as any change has *some* extent of duration and *some* direction). They start and stop, sometimes apparently erratically. They are occasionally reversed. They do not endure indefinitely, the usual order of magnitude being some 10^7 years and in real, established examples rarely, if ever, longer than about 5×10^7 years at anything like constant rate and direction. Even in one lineage, different structural changes commonly occur at different times and different rates. Progressive changes often occur in a series of fairly abrupt (not, however, instantaneous as far as can be established) steps and not in a continuous trend. Comparatively few paleontologists now accept the theory of orthogenesis, as an inherent tendency for evolution to proceed indefinitely on a certain route, once embarked on it. The record just does not support that generalization (Jepsen, 1949).

The phenomenon of parallel trends may be illustrated by a particularly striking, large-scale example. The living mammals, monotremes excepted, are clearly of monophyletic derivation from reptiles. Long ago I suggested that the known Mesozoic mammals are not (Simpson, 1928; surely the idea must have occurred to someone before that but I know no earlier clear and evidential statement of it). That idea has been strongly supported by later studies (especially Olson, 1944; Patterson, 1956; Kermack and Mussett, 1958) and now seems well established. At least six different lineages probably crossed the conventional line providing the usual structural distinction between reptiles and mammals at about the same time and each one independently: tritylodonts, multituberculates, triconodonts, symmetrodonts, docodonts, and pantotheres.[19] The marsupials and placentals are derived

[19] Late mammal-like reptiles and earliest mammals now known intergrade so perfectly that anatomical definition depends arbitrarily on a single point: the nature of the articulation of mandible and skull. Even that is not clear-cut, because opinion differs as to whether "reptiles" became "mammals" when they acquired a dentary-squamosal articulation (Kermack and Mussett, 1958) or when the articular-quadrate articulation (not known ever to have been lost) ceased to function as suspensorium (Crompton, 1958). That makes a difference as to when or whether certain groups became "mammals," but not as to the multiplicity of groups that did. The tritylodonts,

from the pantotheres (*sensu lato,* at least). The monotremes may be derived from one of the other Mesozoic orders such as the docodonts (Kermack and Mussett, 1958) or may represent still another separate crossing of the line.

On the reptilian side, numerous different lineages of the order Therapsida were independently acquiring various mammal-like characters. Some of the evidence is summarized in Table 14. The full situation was much more striking and complex, for other groups of therapsids were also evolving more or less in parallel with these, and within all groups there were many distinct lineages with considerable

TABLE 14

INDEPENDENT, PROGRESSIVE ACQUISITION OF MAMMAL-LIKE CHARACTERS
BY VARIOUS GROUPS OF THERAPSID REPTILES

(Data from Olson, 1944)

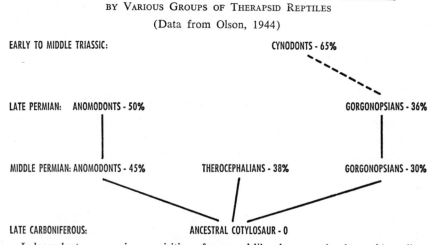

Independent, progressive acquisition of mammal-like characters by therapsid reptiles. Primitive reptilian morphology is represented by zero; fully mammalian morphology by 100 per cent. Continuing the table upward, by the Middle Jurassic the mammalian condition had been closely approached—perhaps between 85 and 95 per cent—independently by several different offshoots from the Therapsida. The 100 per cent level is known to have been reached by the Late Cretaceous, and good but incomplete evidence indicates that it may have been reached by the end of the Jurassic.

in which jaw suspension has been described in print (Young, 1947; Kühne, 1956), may not have been mammals by either definition, but some tritylodonts quite likely were by the first definition, and so, in all probability, were one or more groups not mentioned above (e.g., the so-called ictidosaurs and protodonts). The last (at this writing) publication on the subject (Kühne, 1958) would reduce the number of independent crossings of the "reptile-mammal" line but still indicates them as multiple. It should also be noted that it is not certain, but is probable, that the articular and quadrate always became ear bones when they ceased to be a suspensorium.

parallel advance toward mammalian structure in various ways. In the face of all this evidence it is no longer possible to accept the earlier argument that a change so intricate as incorporation of bones of the lower jaw into the ear could only have happened once. It happened several or many times.

That example is exceptional both in taxonomic level and in the magnitude of the changes involved. The phenomenon that it represents is, however, extremely common. The existence of parallel evolution has, of course, been known for a long time. It is one of the few major evolutionary phenomena that were not clearly recognized by Darwin, but it was familiar to paleontologists by the 1890's (see Haas and Simpson, 1946). Even so, we are only now beginning to realize quite how pervasive it is and how many of our taxa are, in the terminology of Huxley (1958), grades but not clades, that is, evolutionary levels often (not invariably) reached independently by different lineages rather than strictly monophyletic units. (Grades and clades may, however, coincide.)

As can also be seen in Table 14, parallel evolution generally occurs at different rates and to different degrees in the different groups affected by it. In the characters studied by Olson (1944), the early anomodonts (=dicynodonts) were far more mammal-like than contemporaneous gorgonopsians, but the anomodonts became extinct long before reaching the structural reptile-mammal line, while some probable descendants of the gorgonopsians crossed that line. Another essential point is that parallelism involves only certain characters, while other characters in the same animals may evolve in quite different directions in different lineages. While the anomodonts and gorgonopsians were both independently acquiring some of the same mammal-like features, they were also each acquiring their own peculiar characteristics, so that late anomodonts and gorgonopsians were very different indeed. Also the six groups previously mentioned as having separately crossed the arbitrary reptile-mammal line are radically dissimilar in most ways except those that place them all by definition in the grade (not clade) Mammalia. It is, then, necessary in such episodes to distinguish clearly between the features involved (at different rates and in different degrees) in parallel evolution and those simultaneously involved in adaptive radiation.

What are the possible theoretical or causal explanations of these phenomena? The principal alternatives that have adherents today are natural selection, directional mutation, and a vitalistic or perfectionistic inner urge or inherent tendency. The selectionist theory is that a trend is adaptive for the lineage involved, that it continues only as long as it is adaptive, that it stops when adaptation is as complete as selection can make it in given circumstances, and that it changes or the group becomes extinct if a different direction of evolution becomes adaptive. Often the adaptive nature of a trend seems apparent. Often it is not apparent, but the postulate still seems required to account for otherwise erratic features of trends. In instances of parallel evolution the selectionist theory is that changes actually occurring in parallel are adaptive over the whole ecological range occupied by the group, while those divergent (radiating) within the group are adaptations to special niches within that range. At the least, that is plausible in such cases as that of the therapsids and earliest mammals. The parallel changes are involved in development of homeothermy, of more homeostatic and efficient metabolism, of improved sensory and central nervous functions, and of more efficient reproduction—all characteristics that can hardly have failed to be adaptive in those environments for any animals that were structurally and genetically able to develop them. The divergent characters are almost obviously specializations for particular and diverse ways of life.

Brough (1958) makes a special point of parallel trends as evidence for his theory of control of major features of evolution by successive non-random mutations. In this connection he does not refute or, indeed, really discuss the selectionist explanation of parallelism, which offers an explanation more plausible than his own.[20] His hypothesis rests mainly on other grounds, and it is unnecessary to add to the brief discussion of it on a previous page.

The phenomena here discussed have been the principal evidence cited for vitalist, "endogenous," or perfectionist theories of evolution. Those theories are basically appeals to ignorance or examples of the naming fallacy, because "entelechy," "inherent tendency," "aristogenesis," and the like have never been defined in terms of objective, material causes and, in fact, are usually advocated as names for unknown causes postulated as indefinable in such terms. We may, indeed, be ignorant of the causes of trends, or the causes may, indeed, be transcendental, but naming our ignorance does not alleviate it, and postulating the transcendental always stultifies inquiry. There is some material basis for judgment. If such views are true, there should be

---

[20] The full explanation under the modern synthetic theory of evolution involves other factors than selection, which is the main non-random element but far from being the whole story. Obviously, selection is always acting on genetic systems *already* established, and the possible mutations and directions of change are markedly circumscribed. Mutation is an element in the process, but that is far from saying that the direction and incidence of mutations in themselves *determine* the occurrence and direction of trends.

observable trend phenomena inexplicable in any other way. It has been claimed that the frequency or universality of indefinitely continued, invariant, non-adaptive trends is such a phenomenon; but we have seen that trends really evident in the fossil record do not have such characteristics and are readily explicable by known material causes.

MORPHOGENY, IRREVOCABILITY, TRANSFORMATION

As a biological term the word "evolution" was originally applied to ontogeny. It meant embryological development, especially but not exclusively under the theory of preformation. Only relatively recently, especially since Darwin, has "evolution" been understood as strictly phylogenetic. The terms "morphogeny" and "morphogenetic" still suffer from that ambiguity, being currently applied indifferently to the embryological origin of anatomical structure in individuals and to the phylogenetic development of structure in the course of evolution. Following the latter usage, paleontologists have been much concerned with abstracting from the fossil record so-called morphogenetic laws. These, generally far from being laws in the physical sense, are usually generalized descriptions of trends that have occurred widely and among numerous organisms only distantly related. In no case are these universal. They are in most instances merely frequent and not demonstrably usual.

Only two such descriptive generalizations will be mentioned by way of example. It is unlikely that others would require different theoretical interpretations. The first is the tendency for the individuals in populations to become larger as evolution proceeds. This is probably the most widespread trend yet observed among animals, with known examples ranging from protozoans to man (e.g., Newell, 1949). Yet it is at least as common for organisms to persist without any consistent trend for change in size, and changes toward smaller size, although apparently unusual, have certainly occurred. There is, again, no real evidence in favor of mutational control or inherent tendency. In intraspecific competition under a great variety of circumstances, individuals slightly, but only slightly, above the population mean size are evidently favored by natural selection. Rensch (1954) has noted a variety of reasons for adaptive advantage in the trend toward larger size when it does occur.

The second example is of a kind of morphogeny less widespread but more complex and more interesting. This is the tendency for a series of similar anatomical parts, often segmental, to become reduced in number while the remaining parts become less similar (more differentiated in structure and function). Crustacean appendages are a striking instance, and there are many others.[21] Here, too, exactly the opposite has also happened, although apparently much less frequently. For example, the vertebrae of snakes have become more numerous and less differentiated than were those of their legged ancestors. The descriptive aspects of such phenomena have been well discussed by Gregory (1951 and early studies there cited) under the terms of "anisomerism" (differentiation of serial structures) and "polyisomerism" (serial repetition of similar structures).

Changes of those sorts illustrate particularly well a broad morphogenetic principle, as distinct from descriptive generalizations such as have now been exemplified. Historical change is always a modification of an existing configuration. In morphogeny it starts with a given adult structure, which is produced by a given developmental sequence, which, in turn, is controlled by a given genetic system. Mutations, the really new materials for evolution, affect the genetic end. Selection, the non-random element of evolution, acts anywhere or everywhere along the line. Both are circumscribed by what is already there, a configuration resulting from the whole past. The past is irrevocable, and therefore evolution is irrevocable, not only in the sense of irreversibility [22]—an earlier configuration can never be regained—but also in that of indelibility—past configurations cannot be wholly effaced (except in a certain sense by extinction, but even extinct groups have influenced later configurations).

Nothing in the recorded history of life arises de novo. All is transformed from what went before. That is richly exemplified by transformation in a more technical sense: the adaptation to new uses of

[21] The history of the "discovery" of this "law" has not been written but would be full of human interest and of enlightenment on the psychology of scientists and the history of science. The germs, at least, of the idea are distinctly present in Goethe's idealistic morphology and later in the work of Owen, the last (1804–92) great figure of that school. Darwin derived the morphological generalization from Owen and gave it an evolutionary meaning. Much of Darwin's genius was of just that sort, infusing evolutionary significance into observations and generalizations already established in a different context. Darwin, who was no historian, did not always know the sources of the ideas that he transformed in this way, but in this instance he did cite Owen. Much later essentially the same evolutionary "law" was still more clearly expressed by Stromer (1912) and by Williston (1914), each of whom thought he had discovered it. It has been most fully and explicitly discussed by Gregory, who at first credited it to Williston as "Williston's law" (Gregory *et al.,* 1935) and later to Stromer (Gregory, 1941), who had emphatically demanded recognition as its discoverer. There are many such instances of rediscovery, generally, of course, in somewhat altered and refined form, of principles known to Darwin and earlier students. In such instances it can hardly be claimed that one true discoverer is identifiable.

[22] Another principle that has been repeatedly "discovered." It used to be called "Dollo's law." I (Simpson, 1953) once pointed out that it "was plainly stated by Scott before Dollo, and for all I know by others before Scott." I now somewhat shamefacedly recall that a form of it was stated by Darwin before Scott—and for all I know by others before Darwin!

previous structures, physiological processes, and behaviors. Structural examples, the only ones *directly* visible in the fossil record, have innumerable examples: the famous transformations of gill arches to jaws and much later of certain bones of the lower jaw to auditory ossicles; the transformations of pectoral fins to forelegs and of forelegs divergently to flippers, wings, and arms—but why multiply examples when so many are now familiar and the list is almost endless (see almost any comparative anatomy, e.g., Romer, 1949). In physiology we need only mention the transformation of endostyle to thyroid gland or the changing targets of hormones (e.g., Beach, 1958). In behavior some of the ethological displacement activities are brilliant examples (e.g., Hinde and Tinbergen, 1958).

CONCLUSION, SOME PHILOSOPHICAL PROBLEMS

All science is philosophical, and the only philosophies capable of validation are those of scientists. Both scientists and philosophers frequently object to those statements, and some of their objections are valid, but the statements have a residual truth that cannot be wished away. A scientist cannot so much as make an observation without reliance on a philosophical premise, such as the by no means self-evident minimal premise that there really is something to observe! And, at the very least, his observations place restrictions on what can in any meaningful sense be true. What kind of universe is this we live in? It is, among other things, the kind in which life's history could and did occur. We can learn more about our kind of universe from that history than from pure reason and at least as much as (I think rather more than) from the stars or the atoms. Some of the evidence is now before you, and I propose to state a few personal conclusions, wasting no words and attempting little further argument.

THE PROBLEM OF ORDER

The problem of order is that of uniformitarianism or of immanence in a special guise. The universe *is* orderly. It has certain built-in characteristics that came we know not whence or why but that are determinable and that have not changed during the course of recoverable history. This does not mean, as some uniformitarians have supposed, that configurations have only varied about a mean. There have been times when erosion of the earth's crust predominated and times when deposition was pre-eminent. The effects of those processes have been progressive, not merely fluctuating. Organic evolution has been faster and more basic at times in the past than it is now or is ever likely to be again. But in both those and all other cases the immanent processes have been unchanging.

Of course, that cannot be *proved*. It fits the evidence, and it fits better than any opposing conclusion, but the evidence could itself be misleading. We cannot disprove the postulate that the universe was created one second ago, complete with all our apparent memories of our own earlier days, or that it was not created in 4004 B.C. with all the apparent record of earlier billions of years. But that would not make sense, and we must pretend, at least, that both we and the universe are sane.

THE PROBLEM OF UTILITY

The problem of utility is the problem of teleology, whether evolution has goals or ends and, if so, what and whose those ends may be. Again there seems to me to be only one answer, even though a somewhat complex one, that is thoroughly congruent with all the evidence and that is validated in that sense. The organization of organisms certainly has utility, and the evolution leading to them has that utility as a goal in a sense. That sense is, however, quite special and does not at all correspond with teleology in the classic meaning of correspondence with a preordained plan, with divine Providence, or with purposes especially relevant to the human species. The utility of any feature of organisms is with respect to the population (not invariably the individual) of those organisms at any given time. It is not related to usefulness to any other organisms; it follows no pre-existent plan; and it is not prospective toward any future goal. The over-all and universal goal is a posteriori at the given moment and is simply survival, which involves comparative success in reproduction.[23]

This is not to say that all features of all organisms are useful to them at every moment in time. Some features reflect a utility now past, hence vestigial organs and many characteristics involved in transformations. The vast body of evidence for the irrevocability of evolution shows that the structures of organisms were not created or evolved, shiny and new, *for* the organisms but were evolved *by* the organisms from what history made available to them. Then, too, some features perhaps without utility have evidently been carried along by subtle connection with features that are useful. It is also possible, but debatable, that some characteristics have no connection with utility. It still is true (i.e., is the most reasonable conclusion from a vast body

[23] Pittendrigh (1958) has proposed that this principle, so distinct from teleology in the usual sense, be called "teleonomy."

of evidence) that utility is the principle that makes evolution orderly to the extent that it is in fact orderly.

The history of life is obviously, indeed tautologically, *progressive* by one definition. It proceeds by successive stages or, better, gradations through an indefinitely prolonged series of conditions (configurations), each derived from and differing from those preceding it, and that is a usual understanding of the words "progressive change." The problem is whether the history is also progressive in the quite different sense of involving, on the whole, change *for the better*. But "better" is an evaluation, meaningless unless one can designate better for whom and in whose judgment or in what sense. In line with our conclusion on utility, the most obvious reply would be, "Better for each separate population of organisms in the sense of being useful to it." But, a conclusion on utility having been reached, that further statement is banal and adds nothing of interest. It does not begin to tell us what we really want to know.

If a useful function comes to be performed more effectively or if a new function adds to utility, then there has been improvement. It is meaningful to consider such improvement as progress, and, while involving the concept of usefulness, that statement does add something to the previous conclusion on utility. The limb of a mammal cannot be considered an improvement over the fin of a fish, because neither performs more effectively the functions of the other or adds (without equivalent loss) to the functions of the other. But some fins function better as fins than others, and some legs as legs. There is improvement among fins and among legs, but not between the two. What is better depends on where they are. Some improvements are far more general: the vertebrate eye is in an extremely broad sense an improvement over a protozoan's light-sensitive pigment spot. That is still not a completely general example. The vertebrate eye is an improvement only if accompanied by a nervous system able to organize the sensations received and a behavioral system able to make that information practically useful. Hence one improvement requires others, or it is not, in fact, an improvement and will not arise in the course of evolution. Plants have their own improvements, and it would be no improvement for them to have eyes even if a vertebrate-like nervous system accompanied them. The only universal improvements are in those features common to all organisms and involved in the origin of life.

With those definitions and restrictions, progress is certainly a usual feature of the history of life. Most of the events of evolution seem to be either improvements or transformations, using "transformations" here more in the sense of breakthroughs which involve changed functions and hence changed avenues of improvement. This is not contradicted by the fact that progress can be absent or reversed in certain instances, and it is only superficially paradoxical that the absence or reversal may even be useful.

Up to now, at least, man stands as the high point of evolutionary progress. He can do many more things than any plant and can do almost anything that any animal can do, and generally better. The ability to use tools and artifacts in this connection is, of course, one of man's *biological* improvements.

THE PROBLEM OF PURPOSE

There is no fact in the history of life that requires a postulate of purpose external to the organisms themselves. It could, of course, be maintained that the whole system, purposeless itself, was created for a purpose or that purposes not required by the evidence may nevertheless exist. Such speculation is without control, incapable of validation, and therefore altogether vain. We do know, however, that purposes peculiar to and arising within organisms exist as one of the great marvels of life. We know it because we form purposes ourselves. We do not know how general such purposes are among organisms. Must a purpose be conscious, and, if so, how far does consciousness extend? Perhaps it is only a matter of definition, and perhaps there is some sense in which purpose is one of the universal improvements of living over non-living.

BIBLIOGRAPHY

AXELROD, D. I. 1958. "Early Cambrian Marine Fauna," *Science* CCXXVIII, 7–9.

BARGHOORN, E. S. 1957. "Origin of Life," *Mem. Geol. Soc. America,* II, No. 67, 75–86.

BEACH, F. A. 1958. "Evolutionary Aspects of Psychoendocrinology." In *Behavior and Evolution,* ed. A. ROE and G. G. SIMPSON, pp. 81–102. New Haven: Yale University Press.

BOHLIN, B. 1950. "The Affinities of the Graptolites," *Bull. Geol. Inst. Uppsala,* XXXIV, 107–13.

BOYDEN, A. A. 1953. "Comparative Evolution with Special Reference to Primitive Mechanisms," *Evolution,* VII, 21–30.

BROUGH, J. 1958. "Time and Evolution." In *Studies on Fossil Vertebrates* . . . , ed. T. S. WESTOLL, pp. 16–38. London.

BULMAN, O. M. B. 1955. *Graptolithina: Treatise on Invertebrate Paleontology,* Part V. New York and Lawrence (Kan.)

CAILLEUX, A. 1954. "How Many Species?" *Evolution,* VIII, 82–83.

COOPER, G. A., and WILLIAMS, A. 1952. "Significance of the Stratigraphic Distribution of Brachiopods." In HENBEST, 1952, pp. 326–37.

CROMPTON, A. W. 1958. "The Cranial Morphology of a New Genus and Species of Ictidosaurian," *Proc. Zool. Soc. London,* CXXX, 183–216.

DARWIN, C. 1859. *On the Origin of Species by Means of Natural Selection.* London. [The first edition; consulted in the New York reprint of 1951.]

———. 1872. *Origin of Species by Means of Natural Selection.* 6th ed. London.

———. 1958. *The Autobiography of Charles Darwin, 1809–1882, with Original Omissions Restored.* Edited with appendix and notes by his granddaughter, NORA BARLOW. London.

DECKER, C. E., and HASSINGER, N. 1958. "What Higher Magnification Is Doing for the Study of Graptolites," *Jour. Paleontal.,* XXXII, 697–700.

ELLERMAN, J. R., MORRISON-SCOTT, T. C. S., and HAYMAN, R. W. 1953. *Southern African Mammals 1758 to 1951: A Reclassification.* London: British Museum.

GREGORY, W. K. 1951. *Evolution Emerging.* 2 vols. New York.

GREGORY, W. K., *et al.* 1935. " 'Williston's Law' Relating to the Evolution of Skull Bones in the Vertebrates," *Amer. Jour. Phys. Anthropol.,* XX, 123–52.

HAAS, O., and SIMPSON, G. G. 1946. "Analysis of Some Phylogenetic Terms with Attempts at Redefinition," *Proc. Amer. Phil. Soc.,* XC, 319–49.

HENBEST, L. G. (ed.). 1952. "Distribution of Evolutionary Explosions in Geologic Time," *Jour. Paleontol.,* XXVI, 298–394.

HINDE, R. A., and TINBERGEN, N. 1958. "The Comparative Study of Species-specific Behavior." In *Behavior and Evolution,* ed. A. ROE and G. G. SIMPSON, pp. 251–68. New Haven: Yale University Press.

HUXLEY, J. S. 1958. "Evolutionary Processes and Taxonomy with Special Reference to Grades," *Uppsala Univ. Arssks.,* pp. 21–38.

JEFFERSON, T. 1799. "A Memoir on the Discovery of Certain Bones of a Quadruped of the Clawed Kind in the Western Parts of Virginia," *Trans. Amer. Phil. Soc.,* IV (O.S.), 246–60.

JEPSEN, G. L. 1949. "Selection, 'Orthogenesis,' and the Fossil Record," *Proc. Amer. Phil. Soc.,* XCIII, 479–500.

KERMACK, K. A., and MUSSETT, F. 1958. "The Jaw Articulation in Mesozoic Mammals," *Proc. XVth Internat. Cong. Zool.,* Sec. V, Paper 8.

KOZLOWSKI, R. 1947. "Les Affinités des graptolithes," *Biol. Rev.,* XXII, 93–108.

KÜHNE, W. G. 1956. *The Liassic therapsid Oligokyphus.* London: British Museum.

———. 1958. "Rhaetische Triconodonten aus Glamorgan, ihre Stellung zwischen den Klassen Reptilia und Mammalia und ihre Bedeutung für die Reichart'sche Theorie," *Paläont. Zeitschr.,* XXXII, 197–235.

KURTÉN, B. 1953. "On the Variation and Population Dynamics of Fossil and Recent Mammal Populations," *Acta Zool. Fennica,* No. 76.

———. 1958. "Life and Death of the Pleistocene Cave Bear," *ibid.,* No. 95, pp. 1–59.

LAMARCH, J. 1809. *Philosophie zoologique.* Paris.

LAURIE, E. M. O., and HILL, J. E. 1954. *List of Land Mammals of New Guinea, Celebes, and Adjacent Islands.* London: British Museum.

MATTHEW, W. D. 1937. "Paleocene Faunas of the San Juan Basin, New Mexico," *Trans. Amer. Phil. Soc.,* N.S., XXX, i–viii, 1–510.

MAYR, E. 1958. "Behavior and Systematics." In *Behavior and Evolution,* ed. A. ROE and G. G. SIMPSON, pp. 341–362. New Haven: Yale University Press.

MOORE, R. C., LALICKER, C. G., and FISCHER, A. G. 1952. *Invertebrate Fossils.* New York.

MULLER, S. W., and CAMPBELL, A. 1954. "The Relative Number of Living and Fossil Species of Animals," *Systematic Zoöl.,* III, 168–70.

NEWELL, N. D. 1949. "Phyletic Size Increase—an Important Trend Illustrated by Fossil Invertebrates," *Evolution,* III, 103–24.

―――. 1959. [Unpublished manuscript; will appear in *Proc. Amer. Phil. Soc.*]

OLSON, E. C. 1944. *Origin of Mammals Based upon Cranial Morphology of the Therapsid Suborders.* (Geol. Soc. America, Special Papers, No. 55.)

OVER, W. H., and CHURCHILL, E. P. 1941. "Mammals of South Dakota." Vermillion (S.D.) [Mimeographed by the museum and zoölogy department of the University of South Dakota.)

PATTERSON, B. 1956. "Early Cretaceous Mammals and the Evolution of Mammalian Molar Teeth," *Fieldiana: Geol.,* III, 1–105.

PITTENDRIGH, C. S. 1958. "Adaptation, Natural Selection, and Behavior." In *Behavior and Evolution,* ed. A. ROE and G. G. Simpson, pp. 390–416. New Haven: Yale University Press.

PIVETEAU, J., STENSIO, E. A., WATSON, D. M. S., WESTOLL, T. S., ARAMBOURG, C., TEILHARD DE CHARDIN, P., HALDANE, J. B. S., PRENANT, M., SIMPSON, G. G., CUÉNOT, L., VIRET, J., GRASSÉ, P.-P., and CAULLERY, M. 1950. *Paléontologie (Paris, Avril 1947): Colloques Internat. du Centre Nat. de la Rech. Scientifique,* No. 21. [The list of "membres participants" at the beginning of this volume omits one of the participants and authors and includes four attendants at the conference who have no remarks published in the volume; the list here given is that of the actual authors in the sequence of first appearance in the printed work; no editor is named.]

RENSCH, B. 1954. *Neuere Probleme der Abstammungslehre.* 2d ed. Stuttgart.

ROE, A., and SIMPSON, G. G. (eds.). 1958. *Behavior and Evolution.* New Haven: Yale University Press.

ROMER, A. S. 1949. *The Vertebrate Body.* Philadelphia and London.

SCHINDEWOLF, O. H. 1950. *Grundfragen der Paläontologie.* Stuttgart.

―――. 1956. *Über präkambrische Fossilien: Geotek. Symp. zu Ehren v. Hans Stille.* Münster.

SCOTT, W. B., and JEPSEN, G. L. 1936–41. "The Mammalian Faunas of the White River Oligocene," *Trans. Amer. Phil. Soc.,* N.S., Vol. XXVIII, Parts I–V. [A. E. Wood is author of two parts.]

SHOTWELL, J. A. 1955. "An Approach to the Paleoecology of Mammals," *Ecology,* XXXVI, 327–37.

SIMPSON, G. G. 1928. *A Catalogue of the Mesozoic Mammalia in the Geological Department of the British Museum.* London: British Museum.

————. 1936. "Data on the Relationships of Local and Continental Mammalian Faunas," *Jour. Paleontol.,* X, 410–14.

————. 1937. *The Fort Union of the Crazy Mountain field, Montana, and Its Mammalian Faunas.* (U.S. Nat. Mus., Bull. 169.)

————. 1944. *Tempo and Mode in Evolution.* New York.

————. 1950a. "History of the Faunas of Latin America," *Amer. Scientist,* XXXVIII, 361–89.

————. 1950b. "L'Orthogénèse et la théorie synthétique de l'évolution," In PIVETEAU *et al., Paléontologie,* pp. 123–163.

————. 1952. "How Many Species?" *Evolution,* VI, 342.

————. 1953. *Major Features of Evolution.* New York.

SIMPSON, G. G., PITTENDRIGH, C. S., and TIFFANY, L. H. 1957. *Life: An Introduction to Biology.* New York.

STROMER, E. 1912. *Lehrbuch der Paläozoologie.* Vol. II: *Schlussbetrachtungen.* Leipzig.

TEICHERT, C. 1956. "How Many Fossil Species?" *Jour. Paleontol.,* XXX, 967–69.

TYLER, S. A., and BARGHOORN, E. S. 1954. "Occurrence of Structurally Preserved Plants in Precambrian Rocks on the Canadian Shield," *Science,* CXIX, 606–8.

WESTOLL, T. S. (ed.). 1958. *Studies on Fossil Vertebrates Presented to David Meredith Seares Watson.* London.

WILLISTON, S. W. 1914. *Water Reptiles of the Past and Present.* Chicago.

YOUNG, C. C. 1947. "Mammal-like Reptiles from Lufeng, Yunnan, China," *Proc. Zool. Soc. London,* CXVII, 537–97.

E. B. FORD

EVOLUTION IN PROGRESS

Owing to the generosity of the Nuffield Foundation, it became possible in 1951 to establish genetic laboratories in the University of Oxford. This provided an opportunity to develop the experimental study of evolution by a combination of ecology and genetics. I had begun work on these lines during the 1914–18 war. In order to extend it, new or modified techniques had to be devised during the succeeding years and situations identified in which evolution proceeds fast enough in wild populations to be detected and analysed within a reasonably short space of time. This may occur (1) when marked numerical fluctuations affect isolated colonies; (2) when multifactorial or polygenic characters can be studied either in populations subdivided into groups inhabiting ecologically distinct areas or whenever such characters are subjected to powerful selection pressures; (3) in all types of polymorphism. The definition of the latter condition and its recognition as a distinct entity with special evolutionary properties formed an essential step in these investigations. The methods employed in them involve the quantitative study of wild populations, having strict regard to their ecology, combined with laboratory genetics, as well as the foundation of experimental colonies, using appropriate controls.

In general, the amount of observation or experiment so far carried out upon evolution in wild populations or, indeed, upon ecological genetics as a whole is surprisingly small. One thinks especially of the splendid work done by Dobzhansky upon chromosome polymorphism in *Drosophila pseudoobscura* and *D. persimilis* and of the studies of L. R. Dice and his associates upon the genetics of wild mice of various genera and species; of the combined genetic and ecological investigations of E. M. Marsden-Jones and W. B. Turrill upon *Silene* and those of J. W. Gregor on *Plantago*. There is, of course, much more, but its bulk is small indeed when compared with genetic work as a whole,

EDMUND BRISCO FORD, F.R.S., is Director of the Genetic Laboratories at Oxford University. Among the many important posts he has filled are included presidency of the Genetical Society of Great Britain and Representative of the British Empire on the permanent International Committee on Genetics.

and much of it is sporadic rather than a part of a concerted advance upon evolutionary genetics. This is surprising, for evolution is the fundamental problem of biology while observation and experiment are the fundamental tools of science; yet one can to some extent detect the reasons for it. Few geneticists are also ecologists. Moreover, one wonders what proportion of genetic work, apart from that upon domestic animals and cultivated plants, has been conducted on *Drosophila,* especially *D. melanogaster,* and *Neurospora;* certainly it must be very large. It is a mere platitude to say that these two organisms are of fundamental importance in studying the physical basis of heredity and many other aspects of genetics, including the analysis of artificial populations in the laboratory. Yet one can scarcely speak of the ecology of *Neurospora* while *D. melanogaster,* in particular, provides notably poor ecological material; for little is known of its larval, and almost nothing of its imaginal, ecology.

It is high time to use genetics more fully in the study of naturally occurring evolution, and, to do so effectively, forms other than *D. melanogaster* and *Neurospora* will have to be employed. The choice of a suitable species for study is of crucial importance in any program of biological research. Yet it seems to be an art rather than a science, at least in the sense that it has frequently proved difficult to rationalize even the most appropriate decisions. Actually, they must often be reached by a thorough, though perhaps unconscious, grasp of the essentials of the problems to be solved, estimated in the light of much knowledge and experience.

ISOLATED COLONIES, FLUCTUATING IN NUMBERS

It will be worthwhile to consider a few of the instances in which evolution has been studied by observation and experiment, using the three situations already mentioned in which the changes involved take place rapidly. The occurrence of marked fluctuations in numbers affecting isolated communities was the first of these to be analysed in the program of research, extending over forty years, to which attention has just been drawn. The initial work, on a colony of the Nymphaline butterfly *Euphydryas (Melitaea) aurinia,* was started in 1917, using records extending back to 1881. It has so often been described (see, e.g., Ford, 1957*b*) that it need only be summarized briefly here.

The species has but one brood in the year. It had been abundant in an isolated swampy locality of about ten acres from 1881 to 1897. Subsequently, however, it gradually became less numerous until, when the direct observations began, the imagines were very rare, and they remained so for two more years. Throughout the whole of this period, both of former abundance and of later rarity, they were remarkably constant in appearance. In 1920 a great increase in numbers took place which continued until 1924, by which time the butterfly was immensely common during the few weeks it is on the wing, and it continued to be so until the observations ceased after 1935. During the period of rapid increase, from 1920 to 1924, a great outburst of variability occurred in size, colour, and pattern, and those individuals which departed most from the normal form of the species were frequently deformed and were clumsy on the wing or actually unable to fly. Once the numbers were restabilized at a high level, from 1925 onward, the insects became markedly constant once more; but the form which now characterized the colony was recognisably different from that which did so before the outburst of variation. An opportunity for evolution had occurred, and the opportunity had been taken.

Evidently the great variability was not due to the segregation of recessives in a population so small as to be closely inbreeding: it did not occur until the numbers were rising rapidly. On the contrary, the whole series of phenomena is explicable on the lines suggested when they were first reported (Ford and Ford, 1930). It was pointed out that the environment is never constant, and when it favours a population some aspects of selection will be relaxed. The numbers will therefore increase, and genes normally unable to establish themselves will spread. They can then be combined in new ways, some of which may interact advantageously. Such useful combinations will be at a premium when the numerical increase is arrested or reversed because of the onset of less favourable or of stable conditions. At that time stricter selection eliminates the less satisfactory genes and gene combinations which had been allowed to establish themselves in easier circumstances. Thus numerical increase prepares the way for numerical decline and the contrary, associated with alternating periods of high and low variability. The new gene combinations so easily produced during these cycles would require an immense time to achieve in a numerically constant population. An additional point not incorporated in the original conclusions is here to be noticed: that selection will favour the development of close linkage between those genes which interact in a satisfactory way, so tending to hold them together.

POLYGENIC CHARACTERS IN ISOLATION

No population of animals in the world has been so fully quantified as the isolated colony of the moth *Panaxia dominula* Hypsidae, at

Cothill near Oxford (see p. 190). It occupies a marsh of about fifteen acres. The species has one generation in the year, and by the technique of marking, release, and recapture (for details see Fisher and Ford, 1947), first applied to the Lepidoptera by Dowdeswell, Fisher, and Ford (1940), it has been possible to assess the number of individuals flying every season from 1941 to 1958. This has fluctuated greatly, varying from a minimum of about 1,000 in 1943 to a maximum of about 14,000–18,000 in 1957. The difference from one generation to the next may be considerable: a total of 10,000–12,000 in 1954, compared with 1,500–2,500 the year following. Though this does not bear a simple direct relationship to the gene frequency of the polymorphism which is being studied, it doubtless contributes to the changes observed in it, the magnitude of which provides such definite evidence against the theory of random genetic drift.

As clearly pointed out by Waddington (1957), we have long distinguished between two aspects of that concept (e.g. Dowdeswell and Ford, 1953): first, one in which a population permanently remains small enough for chance fluctuations to have an important effect upon the frequencies of its various genes; second, the occasional extreme reduction in numbers to such a low level that the genetic constitution of the survivors and the random changes in gene frequency occurring at this period may temporarily influence the genetic constitution of an isolated population, which would then be subject alternately to selection and to "drift." We have considered these two possibilities, only to reject them in view of the widespread evidence of powerful selection pressures in natural populations.

The second of them is, in fact, approximately equivalent to the "founder" principle of Mayr (1954). Waddington (1957), who names it "intermittent drift," regards it as capable of explaining one aspect of our work on the Satyrine butterfly *Maniola jurtina:* that conducted in the Isles of Scilly. This constitutes a study of ecological genetics and evolution in progress, using the second of the situations indicated on page 181, that of polygenic variation in isolated communities. The character employed as a criterion in this investigation is the number of spots on the underside of the hind wings, which can take values from 0 to 5. Breeding experiments have demonstrated that the genes controlling them are of importance for the survival of the insect. It has been found that the frequency distribution of female spotting is generally constant on each island, but, while it takes different values on five of small size (40 acres or less), it is similar on three much larger ones (682 acres or more), though migration from one to another of these is excluded. Waddington attributes the severally distinct natures of the small island populations to the effect of past reduction, or reductions, to a few specimens whose genetic outfit has influenced the future populations on the islands. He holds that the much greater size of those on each of the large islands would prevent their reduction, even at a minimum, to a few "founders," so preserving an original spotting type. Such a conclusion is wholly inconsistent with observed facts, only a few of which need be mentioned here.

The small island populations are much too large for the study of such an event. However, this is possible in a more restricted habitat: an isolated locality on Tresco, the "Farm Area," which we have already described (Dowdeswell, Ford, and McWhirter, 1957). Its female spot distribution, though of a most exceptional kind, was effectively similar throughout the years 1954 (when first studied), 1955, and 1956:

$$(\chi^2_{(6)} = 5.428, \text{ with } P \text{ approximately} = 0.5).$$

It has a large mode at 2 spots and differs significantly,

$$(\chi^2_{(3)} = 13.813, \text{ with } P < 0.01),$$

from that found on the main area of the island during these years. There the frequencies at 0, 1, and 2 spots were approximately equal, and they were also stabilized throughout the three years in question,

$$(\chi^2_{(6)} = 4.064, \text{ with } P > 0.5),$$

and, indeed, since first studied in 1950.

The population in the Farm Area must have been of the order of 100–150 flying insects per day while we were collecting there in 1954–56, an estimate based upon mark, release, and recapture work and upon detailed observations on the site. In 1957 the locality had become much denuded of its vegetation, which is of a most exceptional kind, differing greatly from that of the rest of the island (Dowdeswell, Ford, and McWhirter, 1957), and the butterfly was barely surviving: intensive collecting by two people for one day in excellent conditions yielded only 4 specimens, all females. The following year (1958) the numbers had, however, risen again: two collectors (K. G. McWhirter and E. R. Creed) obtained 36 specimens in two days. Direct observation, inaccurate though this can be, suggested a population of about 50–100 flying insects per day. The 20 females which the captures included made it clear that the colony had retained its exceptional qualities, with a large mode at 2 spots, differing markedly from the condition found in the adjoining main area of the island: for the comparison with the three years before the numerical collapse of the previous season,

$$\chi^2_{(1)} = 0.605, \text{ with } P > 0.3$$

(using Yates's correction). This return to a highly characteristic spot distribution is directly opposed to Waddington's contention; it will, moreover, be noticed that, as an alternative theory, migration is excluded, since no similar population exists on Tresco. The results indicate powerful selection operating to adjust the butterfly to its environment in the Farm Area. The full data of this work have so far been published for the early years only; those for the later years are now being prepared for the press. I am much obliged to my colleagues K. G. McWhirter and E. R. Creed for allowing me to quote results which they obtained in 1958.

It is important to notice that the concept of "intermittent drift" is entirely distinct from the effects of selection when operating upon extreme fluctuations in numbers as described on pages 182–83. This may force the population after its numerical decline and recrudescence to maintain the particular character which it had previously or, by utilizing new and advantageous gene combinations, to adapt itself in a distinct way or by distinct means. We have obtained no evidence for "intermittent drift" and much to show that selection pressures in nature are too great for it to be effective.

A view very similar to that favoured by Waddington had already been put forward by Dobzhansky and Pavlovsky (1957) to account for the spot frequencies of the *Maniola jurtina* populations in Scilly. They believed that these differed from one to another of the small islands, owing partly to selection and partly, and to a substantial extent, to the diverse genetic constitution of "founders" arriving by occasional migration, also that the numbers on the large islands never sink low enough to produce random deviations from a standard Scillonian form. They reached this conclusion on the basis of highly original work upon colonies of *D. pseudoobscura* in population cages, the variable character used being certain of the well-known chromosome types. Some of these populations were derived from a few specimens (10 males and 10 females) and others from many (4,000 flies about equally male and female). They were thus thought to represent the small and the large island situations, respectively. This, however, they do not do, because the ecology of the different islands in Scilly is markedly distinct (though Dobzhansky and Pavlovsky, who have never been there, surprisingly state that "their environments appear rather uniform"). Yet the population cages of *Drosophila* were designed to be environmentally similar, hence allowing no assessment of the relative importance of the genetic constitution of the founders and of subsequent selection.

It is clear that a small number of "founders" may lack certain major genes. But the number of polygenes with similar and cumulative effects controlling any quantitative character is likely to be large (Darlington and Mather, 1956), so that the possible genetic diversity will be immense. Thus the effects of strong selection, adjusting the population to diverse habitats, must be of such importance as to obliterate any "founder effect" at this evolutionary level. Of their power to do so we have clear evidence in Scilly from several sources, in addition to the work on the Farm Area just described.

On the island of Tean, two populations of *M. jurtina* isolated from each other by an unsuitable terrain have each extended their range. They have done so because of the marked ecological changes produced by the removal of a herd of cattle. In so expanding, one of them (spreading from "Area 1" into "Area 2") had remained unaltered, spotting being bimodal in the females, while the other (spreading from "Area 5" into "Area 4") had undergone a change from a bimodal to a unimodal female spotting distribution (Ford, 1957*b*, Fig. 9)—and that in a single season, from 1953 to 1954.

Two points are to be noticed here. First, we are faced with the question why an extension of territory had no effect on the female spot frequency of one population but a marked effect on that of the other. The answer seems to be supplied by the difference in their environments. In the first instance, the ecology of the old habitat ("Area 1") had been reproduced in the new ("Area 2"), where the growth of grass, from a lawnlike condition uninhabitable by the butterfly, had been accompanied by the spread of sheltering bracken. In the second, the ecology of the new habitat is unlike that of the old, or, indeed, of anywhere else on the small islands of Scilly; for, in place of another "lawn" unsuited to the insect, the grass here has become tall and haylike without bracken. The other point demanding attention is that a difference in spotting, comparable with that characterizing different small islands, can occur in a single generation in a population which had not been reduced to a few founders or, indeed, declined in numbers.

Furthermore, we now know that, also in a single generation, a marked change in a previously stabilized spotting can affect the butterflies, amounting to many thousands, which inhabit a large island (the main area of Tresco). This took place when the vegetation was greatly modified owing to the abnormal spring and early summer of 1957.

The examples mentioned here comprise a few only of those showing that the characteristic features of the *M. jurtina* populations in Scilly can be produced without reduction to a few individuals, while the special characteristics of a population can survive such an event. It is, of course, always open to those who advocate "intermittent drift" or a "founder" principle to maintain that these concepts are contributory only and play a part, together with selection, in the evolution of *M. jurtina* in Scilly (or in any other isolated population of whatever species). The selectionist interpretation has been fully established; these suggested additional or alternative theories are at present hypothetical. Until they too can be demonstrated, they belong to the range of unsupported scientific speculation to be shaved away with William of Occam's razor. It may be added that the evolutionary changes occurring in these populations are now being analysed by the technique of founding an artificial colony on an island from which the species was absent. This work has already been in hand for five seasons, and it should soon be possible to report upon it.

POLYGENIC CHARACTERS UNDER SELECTION PRESSURES

We have here been considering the study of evolution using multi-factorial or polygenic characters in isolated populations. It remains to give an instance of the other form of this technique, in which such variation is examined under what must be powerful selection pressures, though without isolation.

This is supplied by our studies on the same species, *M. jurtina*, on the British mainland, where it is one of the commonest and most widespread of butterflies. We have analysed its variation in terms of spot frequencies in many parts of the country (Creed, Dowdeswell, Ford, and McWhirter, 1959), but we shall here summarize only a few of the results, those obtained in West Devon and East Cornwall, the two southwestern counties of England, each of them having a north and a south coast.

The female spot frequencies have proved uniform and stabilized, descending from a single large mode at 0 spots, in a highly diversified series of localities in the western half of Devon both coastal and in-land. Yet in the eastern half of Cornwall they take a different form, being bimodal, with a greater mode at 0 spots and a lesser at 2. This also is stabilized and maintained over a wide area both close to and far from the sea. By sampling localities progressively westward in Devon, it was discovered in 1956 that these two spot frequencies, each maintained over an extensive range of country and within our experience for four years, changed from one to the other in a few yards—at a single low field-hedge across which the insects were constantly flying.

Until the succeeding year, it was possible to suppose that two formerly isolated races, which had for a time evolved independently, had extended their ranges and met. It is well known that, in such circumstances, they may retain their distinct genetic adjustments even when they spread until they interbreed at the boundary between them; the hybrid constitution will almost necessarily be less well adapted than either of the parental types and will therefore be eliminated. An instance of this kind is provided by the remarkably narrow intermediate zone, only three miles wide, between *Peromyscus polyonotus polyonotus* and *P. p. albifrons* in Florida (Sumner, 1930).

However, in 1957 we found that the distinction between the West Devon and the East Cornish forms of *M. jurtina* remained almost as sharp as before. There was, indeed, an intermediate population between them, but, in the transect we studied, it occupied an area only a hundred and fifty yards wide. Yet the interface between the two races had moved three miles eastward. In view of its life-history, no population of *M. jurtina* could spread and replace another from one generation to the next (it will be remembered that the species has but one brood in the year) over so great a distance. Thus the sharp boundary between the two stabilizations must be visualized as a change not from one to another genetically isolated population but from one to another set of selective forces. This is supported by an extraordinary "reverse-cline" effect, in which the characteristics of the two spotting types actually become exaggerated as they approach each other (Creed *et al.*, 1959). These results were confirmed by extensive work in 1958. They are consistent only with extremely powerful selection pressures operating on the genes which control spotting.

POLYMORPHISM

The third situation which promotes rapid evolution in wild populations is polymorphism. This is defined as "the occurrence together in the same habitat of two or more discontinuous forms of a species in such proportions that the rarest of them cannot be maintained merely by recurrent mutation" (Ford, 1940*a*). It thus excludes geographical, seasonal, and continuous variation, as well as the effects of purely disadvantageous mutant genes. That is to say, the condition is one in which major genes and supergenes, and their allelomorphs, possess selective advantages, balanced, save where stability has not yet been attained, by disadvantages. Thus having regard to the frequencies of the phases and the fact that the whole polymorphic situation is itself the result of selection of an accurate kind because it is balanced, it provides outstanding opportunities for rapid evolution. It is not necessary here to retrace the arguments which demonstrate that the genes concerned cannot be selectively neutral, as this has often been done in the past (e.g., Ford, 1957*a*).

The study of a multifactorial or polygenic character in *M. jurtina* has demonstrated the importance of selection in the evolution of isolated populations compared either with the founder concept or with random survival. So, too, has polymorphism, using that of the moth *Panaxia dominula* at Cothill near Oxford, already referred to in another connection (p. 183). It is controlled by a single pair of allelomorphs, all three genotypes of which can be recognized visibly. This enables their gene frequencies to be calculated, which has been done each generation, of which there is one per year, from 1939 to 1958 inclusive. The rarer allelomorph of the switch gene has varied in frequency from 11.1 per cent of available loci (in 1940) to 1.1 per cent (in 1955). The number of insects comprising the population has also been assessed by the marking, release, and recapture of specimens from 1941 onward. Now it is possible to calculate whether changes in gene frequency can be due to chance fluctuations, provided that the size of the population in which they occur is known. The necessary data are here all available and prove that the observed fluctuations in the occurrence of the gene are too great to be due to random genetic drift; they must be the result of selection, varying in direction and intensity year by year (Sheppard, 1956).

These results were criticized by Sewall Wright (1948) when they were published by Fisher and Ford (1947). Further studies in successive seasons made it possible for Sheppard (1951) to refute the objections point by point in a way that seems to have proved unanswerable.

The three phases of this polymorphism are distinguished by their wing markings. Sheppard (1952) has, however, shown that the genes controlling them also have a curious effect upon the mating habits; for the female prefers to pair with a male belonging to any other genotype than her own. This in itself tends to produce diversity but not to an extent that can fully account for its maintenance here. That is principally dependent upon another and fundamental aspect of polymorphism: one which leads to a superiority of the heterozygote, because the advantageous effects of the controlling gene will become dominant and the disadvantageous ones recessive (Fisher, 1930; Sheppard, 1953). Thus the heterozygotes will evoke advantages only, while both homozygotes will be associated with some advantageous and some disadvantageous qualities. Most of these will be of a physiological kind affecting viability and reproductive capacity.

The existence of such heterozygous advantages can be deduced from work on the polymorphism of colour and banding in the snail *Cepea nemoralis*. This has been carried out by Cain and Sheppard (1950). It demonstrates this and other aspects of the subject with especial clarity.

Yellow shells (greenish when the animal is within) are recessive to pink, while brown is due either to another allelomorph or to a linked gene acting upon one or both of the other colours. Also unbanded shells are dominant to banded, while there is linkage between the genes for colour and banding.

Cain and Sheppard found that if one selects from their localities five with the most green vegetation at ground level and five with the most brown, the lowest proportion of yellow shells in the green habitat is 41 per cent, and the highest in the brown is 17 per cent. Also the lowest proportion of unbanded shells on a uniform background, such as downland grass, is 59 per cent, and the highest on a varied one, such as a mixed hedgerow, is 22 per cent. Intermediate habitats tend to intermediate values, and this is true also of colour. They have demonstrated that these frequencies, in which colour pattern is related to background, are controlled by predators, among which the song thrush, *Turdus philomelos*, is particularly important. This bird has the habit of carrying the shells to favourite stones, where it breaks them open. There the fragments accumulate, so that it can be determined by comparison whether or not such elimination is at random. In fact, in each type of locality the birds remove a heavy excess of the inappropriate forms, in regard to both banding and colour. Yet, though this occurs season after season, the different colonies do not become uniform. That is to say, their diversity must automatically have evolved as a balanced polymorphism favouring the heterozygotes, within the ambit of which the frequencies of the phases are controlled by selection.

There will be a tendency for genes which interact in a favourable way to become linked. The cross-over values between them will then be reduced by further selection. It is not chance that those controlling such related aspects of polymorphism as colour and banding are in this instance, and indeed in many others, found to be carried on the same chromosome. Evidence, moreover, is accumulating to show that the cross-over values vary from one *Cepea* colony to another (Cain and Sheppard, 1954). Thus differing phases will tend to be held together according to the ecological requirements of each population.

The Batesian mimicry of butterflies throws much light upon the maintenance of polymorphism, which it automatically generates. This is controlled by switch genes and supergenes responsible for evoking one or another set of mimetic resemblances, each of which is gradually evolved and perfected by selection acting upon the gene complex. That view, originally suggested by Fisher (1927), has been considerably developed subsequently by Fisher (1930) and Ford (1937, 1945), who have accumulated so much evidence for it, including the study of forms intermediate between those determined by a single genetic difference, that its validity has not been in serious doubt. However, it is being completely substantiated at the present time by C. A. Clarke and P. M. Sheppard, who are conducting extensive breeding experiments upon the African mimic *Papilio dardanus*. They are providing, for the first time, a detailed genetic analysis of mimicry, a subject which provides outstanding opportunities for the experimental study of evolution. Their success in rearing large numbers of a tropical butterfly in England has required the solution of technical problems so considerable as to have discouraged others from undertaking the work.

It should be mentioned here that in 1945 Goldschmidt made an attempt to resuscitate in a new form the old view that the different phases of a Batesian mimic, with all their adaptive resemblances of colour, shape, and pattern, arose ready-made by mutation. I have, however, shown that his hypothesis is based upon such misinterpretations and errors of fact that it cannot be taken seriously (Ford, 1953). There was, however, one matter raised by Goldschmidt that had not at the time been subjected to proof. As an essential part of his theory he says (Goldschmidt, 1945, p. 213): "Thus I confidently expect that future research will reveal that the differences between geographic races of mimics (and models) will be of a multiple and allelic character involving the locus controlling the mimetic pattern." Clarke and Sheppard (preliminary report, 1958) have now obtained the information needed to test this view. They have made the necessary crosses between the forms of *P. dardanus* which mimic *Amauris niavius* on the west and east coasts of Africa, respectively. Their results show that, as expected on the concept of the gradual evolution of mimetic forms, the difference between them is multifactorial, resulting from selection acting upon the gene complex. Thus Goldschmidt's "confident" prediction proves to have been incorrect.

It is a matter of much interest that Batesian mimicry itself would seem to provide all the diversity needed to maintain polymorphism, since the different mimetic forms will be balanced at such frequencies that each receives equal protection. Even so, it has long been realized that the physiological superiority of the heterozygote, which will automatically arise in polymorphism, must affect mimetic forms, also, providing, as it were, an additional basis for diversity. A small amount of information derived from breeding work on *P. polytes* and *Hypolimnas misippus* has indeed actually demonstrated a deficiency of the homozygous dominants, producing a 2:1 ratio or an approach to it where a 3:1 ratio was to be expected (see Ford, 1953).

The industrial melanism of moths provides the most striking instance of evolution ever actually witnessed in any organism, animal or plant. Dark or black forms of about sixty species are now spreading in the industrial areas of Britain, or have been doing so during the last hundred years. So much so that in the peppered moth, *Biston betularia,* and some others they have in certain districts passed from the status of rare aberrations to occupy 95–98 per cent of the population. A similar change is occurring also in Continental Europe and in the United States, though it has not been studied in any detail there.

Only those species are affected which rest upon tree trunks and similarly exposed situations, deriving protection from their resemblance to bark or lichen. The pale, cryptically coloured specimens are consequently well concealed in unpolluted country but are conspicuous in areas blackened by smoke. These protective advantages and disadvantages are reversed for the melanics, which consequently had no opportunity of establishing themselves before the Industrial Revolution. This accounts for some aspects of their recent spectacular success, provided that we assume that the resting moths are selectively eliminated by insectivorous birds: a contention which, however, both ornithologists and entomologists until lately denied. The recent work of Kettlewell (1955, 1956a, b), who has subjected industrial melanism to careful analysis, has proved them both wrong. He has established that such predation is common and highly destructive but that the act is performed so rapidly that it requires accurately planned observations to detect it.

There are, however, two other features of industrial melanism which add further complexities to it. First, having established themselves initially in manufacturing districts, melanic moths have spread far into rural areas. This proves to be due to the unexpectedly great drift of smoke with the prevailing westerly winds of Britain: the typical pale insects have not been superseded in the country to the westward of industrial regions.

Second, the successful dark forms differ physiologically as well as in colour from the normal light ones, since they prove to be hardier. The advantage is doubtless restricted to, or greater in, the heterozygotes, a subject which requires further investigation. This difference in viability was originally discovered in *Boarmia repandata* Selidosemidae, by experiments which involved partial starvation of the broods (Ford, 1940b) but affects the other species also. Yet it is not a mere outcome of the physiology associated with increased melanin production, since there are numerous black varieties which have never established themselves and which are much less hardy than the normal. It is indeed suggested that all genes conferring a physiological advantage have spread unless they also evoke some counterbalancing disadvantage, such as obliterating the cryptic colour pattern upon which the safety of the insect ordinarily depends. Only when melanism is converted from a handicap to an asset by changing conditions, can such genes be utilized. Doubtless also the hardier larvae of the melanics are the better able to survive when feeding on polluted food. All the dark forms which have established themselves have been dominants, or occasionally semi-dominants—a curious feature of the situation upon which the work of Kettlewell is at present throwing light.

Industrial melanism allows polymorphism to be studied from its inception. Owing to the evolution of heterozygous advantage, it is unlikely that the pale individuals will in any of the species be reduced to the status of rare varieties maintained merely by recurrent mutation. They will probably not decline below 1 or 2 per cent of the population, a frequency to which some of them have already arrived in certain areas. This would maintain the rarer gene at from 10 to 14.1 per cent of available loci, even if all three genotypes were equally viable. That figure will, however, be somewhat increased by heterozygous advantage. Moreover, the handicap of the cryptic pale forms may be reduced by selection acting on appropriate multifactorial or polygenic variation. In a similar way, Kettlewell has actually demonstrated that the black variety of *Biston betularia* has not only spread but changed in appearance. It has become more extreme—and, no doubt, that is to say more dominant—since it began to establish itself about the middle of the last century.

The evolution of the heterozygous advantage in polymorphism makes it possible to predict certain important attributions of that condition which are not obvious to mere inspection. Of this, recent trends in human genetics bear witness. As soon as it was recognized that the blood groups are polymorphic, with all that this implies (Ford, 1942), it became evident that they must be balanced in the population by contending advantages and disadvantages. A logical deduction from that conclusion led to the prediction (Ford, 1945) that members of these different serological types would not be equally susceptible to specific diseases—a conclusion which has since been verified, with results of medical importance (see Sheppard, 1959). The value of the blood groups as criteria in anthropology is, moreover, placed in its true setting. It had long been held that they were important in this connection because selectively neutral. In reality, their importance is undoubted, but for precisely the opposite reason: because their frequencies are adaptive, they must be adjusted to the genetic constitution of each race, changes within which will be reflected in them. Thus it is the polymorphism concept which invests the blood groups with their significance for the study of human evolution.

BIBLIOGRAPHY

CAIN, A. J., and SHEPPARD, P. M. 1950. *Heredity,* IV, 275–94.
———. 1954. *Genetics,* XXXIX, 89–116.
CLARKE, C. A., and SHEPPARD, P. M. 1958. *Proc. Roy. Ent. Soc.,* C, XXIII, 1–3.
CREED, E. R., DOWDESWELL, W. H., FORD, E. B., and McWHIRTER, K. G. 1959. *Heredity,* XIII (in press).
DARLINGTON, C. D., and MATHER, K. 1949. *The Elements of Genetics.* London: Allen & Unwin.
DOBZHANSKY, T., and PAVLOVSKY, O. 1957. *Evolution,* XI, 311–19.
DOWDESWELL, W. H., FISHER, R. A., and FORD, E. B. 1940. *Ann. Eugenics,* X, 123–36.
DOWDESWELL, W. H., and FORD, E. B. 1953. *Symposia Soc. Exper. Biol.,* VII, 254–73.
DOWDESWELL, W. H., FORD, E. B., and McWHIRTER, K. G. 1957. *Heredity,* XI, 51–65.
FISHER, R. A. 1927. *Trans. Ent. Soc. London,* LXXV, 269–78.
———. 1930. *The Genetical Theory of Natural Selection.* Oxford: Oxford University Press.
FISHER, R. A., and FORD, E. B. 1947. *Heredity,* I, 143–74.
FORD, E. B. 1937. *Biol. Rev.,* XII, 461–503.
———. 1940a. In *The New Systematics,* pp. 493–513. Oxford: Oxford University Press.
———. 1940b. *Ann. Eugenics,* X, 227–52.
———. 1942. *Genetics for Medical Students.* 1st ed. London: Methuen & Co.
———. 1945. *Biol. Rev.,* XX, 73–88.
———. 1953. *Adv. Genet.,* V, 43–87.
———. 1957a. *Nature,* CLXXX, 1315–19.
———. 1957b. *Mendelism and Evolution.* 6th ed. London: Methuen & Co.
FORD, H. D., and FORD, E. B. 1930. *Trans. Ent. Soc. London,* LXXVIII, 345–51.
GOLDSCHMIDT, R. 1945. *Quart. Rev. Biol.,* XX, 147–64, 205–30.
KETTLEWELL, H. B. D. 1955. *Heredity,* IX, 323–42.
———. 1956a. *Ibid.,* X, 287–301.
———. 1956b. *Proc. Roy Soc. London,* B, CXLV, 297–303.
Mayr, E. 1954. In *Evolution as a Process,* pp. 157–80. London: Allen & Unwin.
SHEPPARD, P. M. 1951. *Heredity,* V, 349–78.

SHEPPARD, P. M. 1952. *Ibid.,* VI, 239–41.

————. 1953. *Symposia Soc. Exper. Biol.,* VII, 274–89.

————. 1956. *Proc. Roy. Soc. London, B,* CLXV, 308–15.

————. 1959. *Symposia Soc. Study Human Biol.* (in press).

SUMNER, F. B. 1930. *Jour. Genet.,* XXIII, 275–376.

WADDINGTON, C. H. 1957. *The Strategy of the Gene.* London: Allen & Unwin.

WRIGHT, SEWALL. 1948. *Evolution,* II, 279–94.

G. LEDYARD STEBBINS

THE COMPARATIVE EVOLUTION
OF GENETIC SYSTEMS

At the present time, a century after Darwin, we have almost reached another turning point in our study of evolution. The last third of the century has been occupied chiefly with evolutionary universals. Biologists have established firmly the fact that mutation, recombination, and selection are essential processes for the continued evolution of most, if not all, types of organisms and have defined the accessory roles of reproductive isolation and the effects of chance in many of them. One of our tasks for the immediate future, is, of course, to gain more precise knowledge of each of these individual processes, but of equal or even greater importance is the need for a better understanding of the interrelationships between them. To advance our knowledge in this direction, we must start with the premise, which has become apparent from many lines of evidence, that the relative importance to evolution of mutation, recombination, and selection differs widely from one group of organisms to another and that we can understand the interrelationships between them only by shifting our emphasis from a general study of evolutionary universals to a comparative survey of particular situations. Hence the evolution of the future is comparative evolution.

The importance of comparative evolution as a discipline for the future has already been stressed by Huxley (1942) and White (1954), and Darlington (1939, 1958) has explored to some extent one important phase of this problem, the evolution of systems for genetic recombination. This phase was discussed further by the author (Stebbins, 1950, chap. 5), and the present paper is a restatement of the hypotheses presented at that time in the light of new evidence which has been obtained during the past ten years.

The basic postulates for these hypotheses were stated by Mather

G. LEDYARD STEBBINS is Professor of Genetics at the University of California at Davis. A former president of the Society for the Study of Evolution, Professor Stebbins has specialized in that aspect of plant life which is reflected in the title of his well-known text, *Variation and Evolution in Plants* (New York: Columbia University Press, 1950).

(1943) as follows. In cross-fertilizing organisms, the best-adapted individuals are most likely to possess a large number of allelic pairs in the heterozygous condition. Consequently, they are likely to produce among their progeny many segregates which deviate from their own optimum mode toward genotypes less well adapted to the environment of the population. Production of these inferior segregates reduces the reproductive capacity and consequently the over-all fitness of the population, so long as it remains in a constant environment. Heterozygosity, however, increases the evolutionary flexibility of the population, since some of the segregates from heterozygotes are likely to be better adapted to many of the changes which the environment may undergo in the future, and, by natural selection of these better-adapted deviants, the modal values of the population will be shifted in response to the changing environment. In self-fertilizing or asexual organisms natural selection will establish true breeding lines consisting entirely of individuals with optimum fitness, but in the absence of crossing between genetically different lines the flexibility of the population will be low, since segregants adapted to new environments will not appear. Hence a population cannot possess at the same time optimum fitness and maximum flexibility. It must strike a compromise between these opposing requirements. Consequently, the frequency of genetic recombination, which determines the nature of the compromise, is itself an adaptive character and will be subject to natural selection. Since recombination frequency is in turn determined by a large series of characteristics both external and governing the amount of outcrossing as well as internal and consisting of the various characteristics of the chromosomal apparatus, natural selection will affect a large number of characteristics indirectly because of their influence on genetic recombination. These characteristics are collectively termed the "genetic system," which can be said to have an evolutionary course of its own. This will be expressed by regular variation in the nature of the compromise between fitness and flexibility which this system determines.

In his earlier discussion the present author suggested that the particular compromise found would vary greatly from one group of organisms to another and would depend largely upon population structure, as well as upon the structural and developmental complexity of the organism concerned. Furthermore, a survey of the different compromises found in the animal and plant kingdoms showed that the evolution of the genetic system does not progress only in the direction from little to maximal recombination. The evolving evolutionary line is often placed in a situation where survival depends upon increasing the immediate fitness of the population to particular circumstances.

Under such conditions, natural selection will favor a compromise level which increases genetic constancy, at least temporarily, and the system will revert to one with less emphasis on recombination. Many of the peculiar situations which we find in higher plants and animals, such as regular self-fertilization in highly complex flowers which appear to have evolved as devices for cross-pollination, chiasma localization, inversion heterozygosity, male haploidy in the Hymenoptera, lack of crossing-over in male *Drosophila,* various complex changes in the number and form of the chromosomes—all these have evolved in response to oscillations in the selective value of genetic recombination during evolution.

SEXUAL AND ASEXUAL REPRODUCTION IN MICROORGANISMS

Until recently, the diversity of sexual cycles existing in different organisms was believed to have one constant, common denominator, the chromosomes and their behavior. In any particular individual the genes were regarded as arranged along the chromosomes in a definite linear order, and the chromosomes were looked upon as integral units, which could not lose or gain genes without seriously unbalancing the organism. Furthermore, the number of chromosomes was regarded as constant for an individual, either diploid or haploid, at least in the germ line, and the elaborate complexity of mitosis and meiosis was believed to have evolved as a way of maintaining this constancy of the chromosomal cycle. These phenomena are so intimately connected with each other in all organisms from *Chlamydomonas* and *Paramecium* to man and the oak tree that many biologists have come to regard them as inseparable and inevitable accompaniments of sexuality. In fact, one cytologist went so far as to suggest that all the phenomena associated with meiosis in higher organisms must have arisen together in one great mutational step.

Recent studies of bacteria have, however, shown that in them the chromosomal cycle does not have the constancy which it has in other organisms. In the coli bacillus (*Escherichia coli*) strains have now been obtained (Hfr, F$^+$, and F$^-$) which undergo regular genetic recombination (Wollman, Jacob, and Hayes, 1956). This differs, however, from sexuality in higher organisms in that only a part of the single linkage group or "chromosome" of an F$^+$ or Hfr cell combines with the F$^-$ cell to form the zygote, and the size of this part is directly correlated with the length of time allowed for cellular fusion. In other bacteria genetic recombination has been induced artificially by adding the chemical substance DNA (desoxyribose nucleic acid) derived from one strain to a culture of a different strain, and it has been shown to occur regularly through transduction, which is the transfer of DNA particles from one strain of bacteria to another by means of certain types of bacteriophage (Lederberg, 1955). These three types of transfer differ genetically in the size of the linkage group being transferred. This is smallest in transformation, intermediate in transduction, and largest after cellular fusion. The existence of these three types of recombination, collectively termed "meromixis" (Wollman, Jacob, and Hayes, 1956) is itself indirect evidence that the genetic material is less highly integrated in bacteria than in such organisms as higher plants and animals, as well as *Neurospora* and *Chlamydomonas*. Bacteria violate a principle which was once believed to be essential to Mendelian genetics—the integrity of the gametic chromosomal complement, from which no genetic material could be lost unless it was already present in duplicate.

This lower genetic integration of bacteria is associated with the absence of morphologically well-defined chromosomes and of a nuclear membrane, spindle fibers, asters, and other structures commonly associated with the nuclear behavior of higher organisms. We can reasonably assume, therefore, that in other types of bacteria, as well as in the blue-green algae, which share with bacteria a low degree of structural organization of their nuclear material, genetic recombination, if it is discovered in them, will also prove to have some of the peculiarities found in *Escherichia*, *Salmonella*, and *Pneumococcus*. Hence genetic and morphological evidence combine to emphasize the basic importance of the distinction made by Lwoff (1943) between the Procaryota, which include bacteria, blue-green algae, and such viruses as may be considered living, and the Eucaryota, which comprise all other organisms.

One of the most remarkable discoveries of modern genetics is that the viruses associated with bacteria, or bacteriophage, possess distinct genes which recombine in much the same way as do those of higher organisms (Benzer, 1955; Lederberg, 1957). Since, however, the DNA of these viruses is closely similar to and in part identical with that of their bacterial hosts (Lederberg, 1957) and since each strain of phage can exist only in association with a particular type of bacteria, the genetic systems of bacteria and phage are interconnected in a more intimate fashion than are those of any two other types of organisms. These discoveries are still new, and additional information about the genetic system in phage is accumulating very rapidly. Furthermore, the genetic systems in other viruses are still largely unknown but must be presumed to be different, because of fundamental differences in the chemical organization of different viruses (Cohen,

1955). Hence, any speculations about the relationship between the genetic systems of viruses and of other organisms (if, in fact, viruses are to be regarded as organisms at all) would appear to be premature.

These new facts about genetic recombination in microorganisms present to the evolutionist two problems of basic importance. First, are these recombination systems newly developed in the organisms in which they have been found, or are they relics of systems which were more widespread in their ancestors? In other words, were the Procaryota basically and primitively without genetic recombination, the known examples being crude experiments with this process which never had widespread significance; or did some type of genetic recombination exist in the earliest forms of life, only to be lost or largely suppressed in the modern Procaryota? Second, why have the Procaryota been highly successful, having evolved a great variety of diverse types which have occupied a large number of different ecological niches, without developing the genetic mechanisms which appear to be so essential to continued evolution in the Eucaryota?

Regarding the origin of sexual recombination, Boyden (1953) and Darlington (1958) have maintained that it evolved relatively late, after the nuclear mechanism and mitotic division had already been perfected. On the other hand, Haldane (1954), Hutner (1955), and Dougherty (1955) believe that some form of genetic recombination evolved with the earliest organisms. Boyden and Darlington both base their arguments upon two assumptions, first, that sexuality is rare or lacking in all existing primitive organisms and occurs regularly only in types which are at least as complex as flagellates (*Chlamydomonas*). Second, in all Eucaryota, this process involves a regular and very precise alternation of haploid and diploid nuclear conditions, from which even the slightest deviations reduce the efficiency of cellular metabolism. Sexual fusion always involves entire nuclei. The argument is that such a sexual cycle could not have evolved until the elaborate structures which govern the equal division and separation of chromosomes in mitotic division had become perfected.

The other authors, Dougherty in particular, maintain that the asexual condition in all modern types is derived. Dougherty's argument is based upon the presence of the various mechanisms described above for genetic recombination in Procaryota, which show that in them the fusion and precise division of whole nuclei is not essential to metabolic efficiency.

The present author agrees essentially with Dougherty, except that he believes that the term "sexuality" should be confined to the precise nuclear behavior found in Eucaryota. Following Wollman, Jacob, and Hayes, he would apply the term "meromixis" to all types of genetic recombination known in the Procaryota. In general, the extension of the meaning of well-known and widely used terms to cover newly discovered phenomena of a fundamentally different nature tends to confuse, rather than clarify, scientific description. For the same reason, he doubts the wisdom of using the term "chromosome" for the gene string of the Procaryota, although the processes of linkage and crossing-over appear to be similar enough in the two groups that the same terms can be used.

Two more arguments can be added to those of Dougherty in favor of the primitiveness of genetic recombination. In the first place, genetic evidence suggests that recombination through cellular fusion in the K12 strain of *Escherichia coli,* the only species of bacteria in which this process has been carefully studied, was originally a general phenomenon and has disappeared in most modern strains of the species through inhibition. A condition which promotes frequent recombination (Hfr) has been found twice as an apparent mutation, once as a result of treatment with nitrogen mustard, and once spontaneously. Now the experience of geneticists with higher organisms indicates that mutations which occur repeatedly most often involve the loss of some acquired property. A typical example which also includes a change in genetic systems is the experience of Lewis (1951) with mutations at the self-incompatibility locus in *Oenothera organensis.* Mutations at this locus induced by X-radiation, as well as those occurring spontaneously, all produced self-compatibility through inactivation of this locus. No "constructive" mutations to new incompatibility loci were found in the hundreds of millions of gametes which were tested. By analogy, one might suggest that the mutations to Hfr in *E. coli* are removals of a genetic mechanism which had previously been built up in the organism inhibiting genetic recombination and that Hfr is therefore the original condition which existed in its ancestral stock.

The second argument is that reversions from sexuality to the asexual condition through inhibition of the sexual process have occurred repeatedly in most of the phyla of Eucaryota and have been particularly frequent in the fungi, which are the most similar to bacteria in their mode of life. The reasons why we might expect to find inhibition of genetic recombination most frequent in organisms of this type will be discussed below.

In discussing the reasons for the evolutionary success of the Procaryota in competition with the much more highly organized Eucaryota, we begin the main theme of this article: the adaptive relationship between the genetic system and the mode of life of the organisms possessing it. The most obvious difference between Procaryota and Eucaryota is the low degree of structural organization found in the cells of the Procaryota. The latter organisms possess the basic chemical substances DNA, RNA, and proteins in essentially the same form as those in the Eucaryota, and their enzyme systems are equally numerous and complex, or even more so. But their DNA is organized into a gene string which, even during division, has no recognizable structural features such as the centromere and the surrounding membrane which characterizes the metaphase and anaphase chromosomes of Eucaryota. Furthermore, the DNA of Procaryota appears to be at all times in contact with the cytoplasmic protein, while in Eucaryota these two cellular components are permanently separated from each other either by the nuclear membrane during the metabolic or "resting" stage or by the chromosomal membrane during mitosis. This separation is probably fundamental to the cellular metabolism of Eucaryota, since it permits a sharp division of labor between those enzymatic processes involving synthesis of DNA and those which are concerned with the synthesis of RNA and protein. Furthermore, the cytoplasm of the Procaryota apparently lacks, or possesses only the rudiments of, such organized structures as vacuoles, mitochondria, and chloroplasts, all of which must permit a greater division of labor in the cytoplasm of Eucaryota.

This lower degree of intracellular differentiation found in the Procaryota is associated with the equally low degree of intercellular differentiation which they possess. Most of them are able to form only two kinds of cells, those which are actively metabolic and growing, and resting cells or spores, containing dense concentrations of living material and surrounded by one or more thick, almost impermeable membranes. This condition exists in many of the lower Eucaryota but is by no means characteristic of the group as a whole.

As to their mode of life, the majority of Procaryota are free-living saprophytes, which digest and absorb organic food from the surrounding medium. They do this in a great variety of different ways, with or without the aid of oxygen, and through the action of a large number of different enzyme systems. One outstanding property is their physiological versatility, exemplified by Kluyver's (Kluyver and Van Niel, 1956) remarkable description of *Micrococcus denitrificans*. Although some of this versatility results from the ability of bacterial colonies to produce adaptive mutants, much of it is due to the fact that a single genotype can respond to different substrates by developing suitable enzyme systems, the so-called inducible enzymes. The particular enzyme system that functions depends upon the environmental substrate of the bacterial cell. Only two explanations can be given for this behavior. One would be to assume that bacteria contain genes or gene complexes which are themselves versatile, so that they can influence the production of various chemically related enzymes, depending upon their biochemical environment. The other would be to accept the one-gene–one-primary-function hypothesis for bacteria as for other organisms but to suppose that bacteria contain many genes which function only in certain environments, so that a bacterial cell which spends its entire life in a single environment makes use of only a part of its genes, the remainder of them being perpetuated solely because of the advantage which they confer on the genotype of greater phenotypic flexibility. In view of the similarity between bacteria and molds in the types of biochemical mutations which can be produced in them, the latter hypothesis is the more probable.

The latest hypotheses concerning the evolution of the earliest forms of life, those of Horowitz (1945) and particularly Van Niel (Kluyver and Van Niel, 1956), maintain that the saprophytic form of metabolism is more primitive than the autotrophic existence of the chemosynthetic and photosynthetic forms. The argument is that the synthesis of food from inorganic media requires a far more complex battery of enzyme systems than the primitive forms of saprophytism, and must therefore have resulted from a long process of biochemical evolution. If we agree with most scientists who have discussed the origin of life in believing that the first living things appeared as the culmination of a long sequence of evolution of organic compounds at the chemical level, then we are no longer faced with the difficulty of accounting for the nutrition of these primitive saprophytes; they lived on the surrounding organic compounds which had not yet evolved to the living condition. As these compounds became exhausted, natural selection favored mutations responsible for the synthesis of additional enzyme systems, until organisms appeared which could manufacture all their necessary food from inorganic compounds plus carbon dioxide, using radiant energy from sunlight.

This type of biochemical evolution took place in several separate lines, culminating in the chemosynthetic bacteria, particularly the sulfur bacteria, the photosynthetic bacteria, and the blue-green algae. Another line presumably led to the most primitive Eucaryota, the green flagellates. The most successful autotrophic Procaryota, the Myxophyceae or blue-green algae, owe their success to two properties, their ability to withstand great extremes of the environment and to persist in a living but dormant condition for long periods of time, which makes possible their passive dissemination over great distances. According to Crow (1924), a single genotype of a blue-green alga when placed in different environments, can take on a variety of forms, many of which have been ranked by taxonomists as separate species or even genera. Hence the approximately 1,400 species of blue-green algae currently recognized (Smith, 1955) may represent environmental modifications of a considerably smaller number of diverse genotypes. No other group of organisms has attained a world-wide distribution in such a diversity of habitats and such great abundance on the basis of the evolution of such a small number of different genetic types. Furthermore, the blue-green algae are the oldest known organisms. Fossil types which resemble modern genera have been found in Precambrian rocks more than 1,000 million years old (Tyler and Barghoorn, 1954). The blue-green algae, therefore, appear to be the most extreme examples known of evolutionary stabilization. Genetic recombination is unknown in them. In addition to autotrophic forms, the saprophytic bacteria have repeatedly produced parasitic or pathogenic derivatives, some of them with extreme biochemical specialization.

From the information given above, an admittedly speculative account will be reconstructed of the most likely course of evolution of genetic systems in the Procaryota. Genetic recombination is believed to have existed in the very first forms of life. During the later stages of the long course of evolution at the chemical level which preceded the appearance of self-reproducing living organisms (Oparin, 1957), fusion between chemically different droplets or coazervates of protein and related substances may have played an important role in the formation of new and more complex organic systems. For this reason, the ability of coazervate droplets to be attracted toward and fuse with other droplets may have been perpetuated along with the tendency toward self-reproduction. If the droplets were widely dispersed in the primeval water, this would have been particularly important. When the droplets had reached the stage of self-reproduction by developing a system based upon the existence of DNA, which forms the genetic material of all living organisms, they still retained the ability to fuse with each other and to produce a certain number of chemical recombinations as a result of such fusions. Furthermore, this ability was at first non-specific. Because of the simplicity of their enzyme systems, any of these earliest organisms could unite with any other without impairing the viability of the recombination products. But divergent evolution soon set in and, with it, a tendency for organisms to fuse only with others like them—the first reproductive isolation. By the time the first autotrophic organisms and saprophytic bacteria similar to modern forms had evolved, this tendency was already fully developed.

During the period when these organisms were acquiring new enzymatic functions (Horowitz, 1945; Kluyver and Van Niel, 1956), the selective advantage of recombination in promoting variability would have been high, and the process probably occurred frequently. But as mechanisms became perfected for the use of radiant energy and oxygen in autotrophic metabolism, as well as for rapid aerobic metabolism in saprophytes, devices for maintaining them at a constant level of efficiency began to have a higher selective value than those which promoted change. Moreover, since these organisms had already acquired their present ability for rapid self-duplication, rare mutations could play an important role in adaptation. In such organisms, regular fusion of genetically unlike cells followed by recombination would increase their variability beyond the optimum for their mode of life. Furthermore, their populations include such an enormous number of individuals in close contact with each other that, unless inhibitions to cellular fusion were present, this process would be extremely common. For this reason, most modern Procaryota have built up inhibitory mechanisms which prevent or greatly restrict genetic recombination.

Once this system was perfected, continued evolutionary success at the same level was achieved in two ways. One was the perfection of mechanisms for resisting extremes of the environment and for ease of passive dissemination, resulting in evolutionary stabilization unaccompanied by extinction, as in Myxophyceae. The other was continued evolution at the biochemical level, with increasing specialization of saprophytes to particular organic media and with the evolution of increasingly complex and specialized parasitic pathogens. This specialization has been accompanied by loss of biochemical functions, as emphasized by Lwoff (1943), and probably also of many of the genes themselves. It has reached its ultimate culmination in the disease bacteria and viruses of mammals, including man.

Among the autotrophic organisms which had reached this level of biochemical complexity, there apparently were some which went in for further differentiation of their cellular structures. The photosynthetic pigments became inclosed in elaborately constructed plastids, while the respiratory mechanisms became concentrated in specialized bodies or mitochondria. Further independence of the external environment was provided by the evolution of bodies for storage, or pyrenoids, while receptor-effector systems in the form of eye spots and flagella of a more complex structure than those of the bacteria permitted more precise adjustment to the external environment. The cell thus evolved from a relatively primitive system, which exhibited its versatility in differential responses to varying external environments, to a highly complex and precisely integrated chamber, in which a large number of different biochemical reactions can be carried on simultaneously in close proximity to each other.

The control and particularly the development of such a system requires the integrated co-operation of a large number of genes with different functions, and each function must be in precise equilibrium with the others. As it evolved, therefore, natural selection strongly favored the corresponding diversification of the genetic material, and each particular type of cellular structure came to require for its development a more and more precise relationship of the different types of genes to each other. Such organisms could not tolerate the existence either of genes with generalized functions or of genes which could function only under certain external environments. Consequently, a series of mutational steps brought about the evolution of mitosis and meiosis as they exist in Eucaryota, which insure the exact transmission of all the genetic material to the vegetative cells and an equally precise union and segregation during sexual reproduction.

Darlington (1939, 1958) and Crosby (1955) have maintained that mitosis and meiosis, with all their complex structural features, must have evolved at one step, through the establishment of a single "macromutation." In the colorful simile of Darlington, "anything intermediate upsets the apple cart." But this supposition is based upon the assumption that even the most primitive organisms, like the Eucaryota, can function efficiently only if they receive the exact complement of genetic material, both qualitatively and quantitatively, which was contained in the parental cell or cells, an assumption which, as we have seen, is not valid in reference to genetic recombination in bacteria. To continue the simile of Darlington, the apple cart is, in fact, frequently upset in primitive organisms. But the cart contains relatively few apples, and these are replaced with comparative ease, so that the upset is a minor incident which these organisms can take in their stride.

EVOLUTION OF DIPLOIDY AND ALTERNATION OF GENERATIONS

There seems to be little doubt that the most primitive Eucaryota were haploid organisms. If they were sexual, as is maintained in this article, the only diploid nucleus was the zygote, which always divided by means of two meiotic divisions. This condition persists in green flagellates (Phytomonadina), many groups of green algae, the primitive Bangiales and Nemalionales among the red algae, many groups of water molds among the fungi, in those non-green flagellates which have well-authenticated examples of sexual reproduction (Chrysomonadina, Dinoflagellata, some Polymastigina), and in some of the Sporozoa among the higher Protozoa. All these groups are relatively simple in morphological structure, and, except for the red algae, their relationship to flagellates is widely recognized. When we combine these facts with recent evidence showing that bacteria possess only one or at most a small number of linkage groups, the conclusion that the most primitive Eucaryota were haploid seems almost unavoidable. The hypothesis that they were primitively sexual seems not to have been widely held, since Wenrich (1954*b*) reports that more than 263 hypotheses have been advanced to account for the origin of sex in primitive Eucaryota. Wenrich himself feels that the evidence is equivocal and that no decision can yet be made as to whether sex is primitive or whether it arose repeatedly in the different relatively specialized groups which are known to possess sexual cycles. This is a healthy skepticism, but, as has been outlined above, the evidence from genetic recombination in bacteria and viruses is rendering increasingly plausible the hypothesis maintained by Dougherty and the present author, that typical sexuality as found in the green flagellates has evolved gradually from the more primitive, less precise mechanisms for recombination existing in bacteria. The largely asexual condition found in many groups of flagellates and in the ameboid Protozoa can be explained on the same basis as in bacteria. These organisms are well adapted to a relatively stable environment or, if inhabiting a variable, unstable environment, can reproduce so rapidly and can change their adaptive properties so easily by single mutations that genetic recombination has a relatively low selective advantage in them and so has very frequently disappeared in favor of rapid asexual multiplication.

Organisms with a haploid life-cycle have given rise to life-cycles with partial or complete diploidy in a large number of unrelated groups. The most common types of life-cycle are illustrated in Figure 1. The fungi have been purposely omitted from this diagram because of their vast array of complex, highly specialized situations. They will be considered separately in the next section of this article.

Two different types of life-cycle have been derived directly from the original haploid type—those which are completely diploid except for the gametes and those with equal alternation of morphologically similar diploid and haploid generations. Diploid cycles occur in all the ciliate Protozoa (subphylum Ciliophora), in some groups of Sporozoa and a few genera of the Polymastigina, and probably, but as yet on the basis of too little evidence, in the Foraminifera and Radiolaria (Wenrich, 1954*a*). The Metazoa or higher animals are exclusively diploid and may well have arisen from Protozoa which had already acquired a diploid life-cycle. In plants, diploid cycles are known in some green algae (Siphonales, Siphonocladales, Dasycladales), in the diatoms, in the Cyclosporeae or Fucales among the brown algae (Papenfuss, 1957), and in yeasts among the fungi.

In the algae the haploid life-cycle has given rise most often to isomorphic alternation of generations, i.e., a cycle with morpholog-

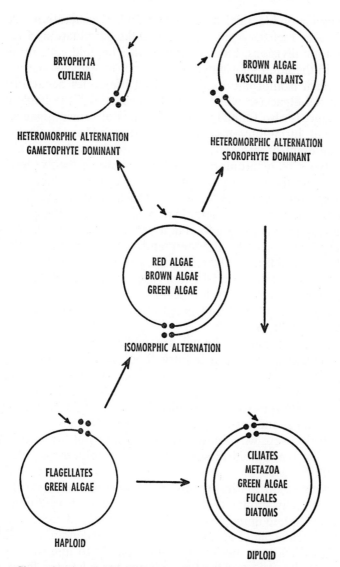

FIG. 1.—Chart showing the phylogenetic relationships between the principal types of chromosomal cycles and the groups, not including fungi, in which they are found. The haploid generation is indicated by a single line, the diploid generation by two parallel lines. The position of meiosis is indicated by four spheres, representing its four products; that of fertilization by an arrow indicating the entrance of a gamete from a different individual.

ically similar or identical haploid and diploid generations. As in the diploid cycle, meiosis is suppressed, and the germination of the zygote is by mitotic divisions, but, in contrast, the haploid cells produced by meiosis in the adult sporophyte behave not as gametes but as asexual spores. Such isomorphic haploid-diploid life-cycles occur in the majority of red algae (in which a third "generation," the haploid carposporic stage, is also found), in many orders of brown algae with relatively small, little-differentiated plant bodies, and in species belonging to two different orders (Ulvales, Cladophorales) of green algae.

Two types of heteromorphic life-cycles are probably derived secondarily from the isomorphic type. In one of these a large, long-lived diploid sporophyte alternates with a much smaller, evanescent, and often parasitic haploid gametophyte, while in the other type the haploid gametophyte is the predominant generation and the sporophyte is relatively inconspicuous. Predominantly diploid cycles are found in several orders of brown algae, particularly those with relatively large, complex plant bodies, and in the vascular plants or Tracheophyta. Predominantly haploid cycles occur in one genus of brown algae (*Cutleria*), in a few red and green algae, and the mosses and liverworts, or Bryophyta.

The greatly expanded knowledge which botanists have acquired during the past quarter of a century about the life-cycles of algae and fungi has required a drastic revision of our thinking about the reasons for the origin of new types of life-cycles, including the dominance of the diploid sporophyte in vascular land plants. When bryophytes, vascular plants, and certain green algae were the only plants of which the life-cycles were well known, the hypothesis put forward by Bower (1908) that the diploid life-cycle evolved in response to life on land could still be accepted. Now, however, we recognize that the most conspicuous of all marine plants, the larger brown algae, have life-cycles essentially similar to those of ferns or even resembling those of completely diploid animals, while the same is true of some of the more complex green algae (Papenfuss, 1957). Hence conquest of the sea by large plants has been bound up with diploidy to almost as great an extent as has conquest of the land. On the other hand, a large proportion of the fungi, the terrestrial Phycomycetes and the Ascomycetes, have completely freed themselves of an aquatic medium without acquiring a diploid life-cycle similar to that of vascular plants. Hence we must seek something more than a simple change in the external environment to explain the elaborate alterations of life-cycle which plants have evolved.

The phylogenetic relationships between these types of life-cycle have been a favorite subject for botanical theories and arguments ever since the discovery of the alternation of generations by Hofmeister more than a hundred years ago. The reasons for this are obvious; the differentiation of the major divisions of the higher plants is intimately connected with changes in the alternation of generations. During the latter part of the nineteenth and early twentieth centuries the weight of botanical opinion, led by such outstanding figures as Celakovsky, Sachs, R. von Wettstein, F. O. Bower, and D. H. Campbell, leaned toward the antithetic or intercalation theory, according to which the diploid or sporophytic generation was intercalated into its position between two haploid gametophytes through the progressive "steriliza-tion" of spore-bearing tissue which existed originally in a sporangium produced directly by the zygote. Supporters of this theory, therefore, maintain that the bryophytes form an intermediate stage between haploid algae and predominantly diploid vascular plants.

Recent evidence has, however, weighted the balance more and more in favor of the homologous theory, which states that all life-cycles with an alternation of unequal generations are derived by progressive modi-fication from a type with isomorphic alternation and that this type has been, in turn, derived from haploid organisms simply by suppres-sion of meiosis at the time of germination of the zygote. This theory, originally proposed by Pringsheim, has been elaborated particularly by A. J. Eames (1936) and W. Zimmerman (1955) and has received support from D. H. Scott, F. E. Fritsch (1945), G. Haskell (1949), H. C. Bold (1957), and W. C. Steere (1958). The arguments pre-sented by Eames and Zimmerman are as follows:

1. In the most primitive vascular plants, the Psilotales, the gametophyte and sporophyte resemble each other more closely than they do in either more advanced vascular plants or in any of the Bryophyta. Both generations of these plants consist of radially symmetrical, dichotomously branched, leafless structures, the early stages of which resemble each other still further in being subterranean and rhizome-like.

2. Most of the types which the older morphologists regarded as stages in the intercalary development of the sporophyte—e.g., *Ricciocarpus, Ophio-glossum, Isoetes*—are now, on the basis of several lines of evidence, looked upon as reduced forms associated with specialized habitats.

3. The dependent, apparently "parasitic" sporophytes of the Bryophyta consistently form chloroplasts at least when young, indicating that they have been reduced from more elaborate free living structures.

4. Fossil evidence, admittedly fragmentary, suggests that the modern Bryophyta are no older, and perhaps even younger, than the oldest known vascular plants.

5. The isomorphic type of alternation of generations is the most wide-spread among the algae, which are generally recognized to be ancestral to the higher plants.

6. The heteromorphic type with a smaller sporophyte, which, according to the intercalation theory, should form the beginning of an evolutionary line leading toward Bryophyta, is very rare in algae, and the few genera which have it, such as *Cutleria* (Smith, 1955), are almost certainly descended through reduction of the sporophyte from ancestors with an isomorphic alternation.

7. Genetic and morphogenetic studies have shown that most, if not all, of the morphological differences between the gametophyte and the sporophyte depend not upon a difference in chromosome number but upon morphogenetic changes entirely comparable with those which take place in an organism which goes through several morphologically different stages or "generations" without changing its chromosome number. Thus pieces of moss sporophytes easily produce gametophytes when cultured under certain conditions; and unfertilized eggs can sometimes give rise parthenogenetically to sporophytes which are in appearance exactly like those arising from a fertilized zygote but which have the same chromosome number as the maternal gametophyte. This shows that doubling of the chromosome number in a normally haploid plant would probably lead to a diploid which resembled it in appearance, i.e., either to a diploid race indistinguishable from the original haploid or to isomorphic alternation of generations.

If we accept this theory, our opinion about the evolutionary position of the mosses and liverworts becomes entirely different from that usually stated in textbooks. They are no longer the "amphibians" of the plant kingdom, representing the intermediate stage between aquatic and terrestrial life, but an assemblage of separate evolutionary lines that have come to a dead end, having been derived from ancient, long-extinct primitive land plants which may have resembled the earliest vascular plants (Psilophytales) more nearly than any modern mosslike plants (Steere 1958). As Steere has pointed out, a considerable body of evidence, particularly the fact that spores of land plants occur in strata of early Cambrian age, points to the probability that a well-developed primitive land flora existed for hundreds of millions of years before the first generally recognized fossils of land plants were laid down in the Silurian period.

Although the evolutionary relationships of plants with different types of life-cycles have been much discussed, little attention has been devoted to a problem which has an even broader evolutionary significance. This is the question Why do different groups of plants possess such an array of different chromosomal cycles, while in animals the diploid cycle occurs with such monotonous regularity from the higher Protozoa to man? A partial answer has been given by Haskell (1949) and the present writer (Stebbins, 1950, chap. 5). This is based upon the fact that in haploid organisms interaction between alleles, i.e., dominance and recessiveness, cannot occur except in the zygote, so that all new mutations must immediately be expressed in the phenotype. Populations of diploid organisms, on the other hand, can build up a great store of potential variability in the form of recessive genes maintained in the heterozygous condition and can also benefit from the greater adaptive properties which may be conferred by heterozygosity for certain genes or gene combinations. As Lerner (1954) has pointed out, this heterozygosity exerts its effects briefly through the better buffering of adaptively superior intermediate heterozygous types. Both Lerner (1955) and Dobzhansky (1955) have summarized the abundant evidence from population genetics which supports this concept as applied to animals and cross-fertilizing higher plants. Muller (1949, 1960) disagrees with it, partly on the grounds that the evidence of heterozygote superiority is not convincing to him and partly because he does not believe that rare recessive genes held in the heterozygous condition can increase their frequency quickly enough to play a major role in evolution.

Whether one accepts or rejects Dr. Muller's first objection depends upon one's opinion as to what constitutes adequate evidence to maintain an hypothesis; in the present writer's opinion the evidence is already ample and is rapidly increasing in volume. His second objection, however, does not take into account the point brought out by Mayr (1954), that speciation and other major evolutionary changes are usually accompanied by inbreeding due to reduction in population size, conferring a particular selective advantage on genes which contribute to adaptive combinations in the homozygous condition. In most instances the few individuals of a large population which invade a new habitat will not possess the necessary equipment of recessive genes to raise them to the required new adaptive level, and so will perish. But from time to time such invasions will be made by individuals which do have the necessary genetic equipment, and the colonization of an unoccupied niche by individuals capable of generating quickly a range of new adaptive gene combinations will trigger off a "genetic revolution" having consequences far out of proportion to the rarity of the event.

The evolutionary significance of diploidy to higher organisms resides, therefore, in the greater flexibility which it confers on their populations. The next question which comes to mind is How have many groups of Protozoa, algae, and fungi managed to remain highly successful and to evolve a large number of variously adapted orders, families, genera, and species without benefit of diploidy? The only possible answer to this question would be that in populations of these organisms the selective advantage of evolutionary flexibility is less than it is in most diploids or in plants with predominantly diploid alternation of generations and that this flexibility can be secured by other means than heterozygosity and the storage of potential variability in the form of recessive genes.

This difference can be explained by two characteristics found in all organisms with a haploid life-cycle. First, they multiply rapidly and can build up large populations in a relatively short time. This means that mutations which occur at low frequencies are far more likely to be available for adjustment to new environments than they are in populations of higher organisms with slower reproduction. Second, all of them are relatively undifferentiated morphologically, and, in particular, their period of embryonic development is either completely lacking or very short. Development in both higher plants and animals is controlled by a precisely integrated succession of metabolic processes, each of which is controlled by different enzyme systems and hence by different genes. The facts upon which this generalization is based are reviewed in a general treatment by Waddington (1957), while the succession of enzyme systems which activates cellular differentiation in pea seedlings is well described by Brown and Robinson (1955). The discussions by Lwoff (1950) and Tartar (1956) of differentiation in ciliate Protozoa show that these organisms, in spite of their unicellular condition, have a complexity of development approaching that of higher animals.

On the basis of the one-gene–one-primary-function concept of gene action we must conclude that any chain of developmental processes which is epigenetic, each process depending for its success on the processes which have preceded it, can be activated only by a specific combination of genes which interact in a very precise fashion. Any change in the developmental sequence and hence any change in the adaptive norm of the organism require simultaneous, integrated changes in many or all of the genes which control the sequence. Mutations of individual genes serve merely to throw the system off balance. Hence the selective value to an organism of new gene combinations as compared to individual gene mutations depends principally upon the length and complexity of its developmental or embryonic life.

We are thus led to the conclusion that the prevalence of haploidy in unicellular flagellates and filamentous algae is due to their relatively short and simple developmental period, plus their rapid reproduction, which reduces the selective value in them of complex gene combinations and renders more easy their evoluton through the occurrence and establishment of single mutations. In higher plants and animals, on the other hand, the increasing length and complexity of their developmental period place an ever higher premium on evolution by the acquisition of new integrated gene combinations, which is accomplished much more easily in diploid organisms because of their reserve store of recessive genes.

This hypothesis, however, does not explain the actual origin of diploid life-cycles or of the alternation of generations, since the building-up of complex developmental sequences could not take place until diploidy or alternation of generations had become well established in a group. In several groups of algae and Protozoa there exist forms with diploidy or with isomorphic alternation which are so closely related to forms with haploid cycles that both can be placed in the same genus or at least the same family. So far as the writer is aware, comparisons between the developmental stages of these related types has not yet been made, but it seems hardly likely that really significant differences will be found. A more likely hypothesis is that diploidy or isomorphic alternation became established initially for the same reason that many structural heterozygotes and apomicts have become established more recently in higher organisms, because of the adaptive superiority in a particular environment of certain specific hybrid combinations. Earlier discussions by the writer (Anderson and Stebbins, 1954; Stebbins, 1959b) have emphasized the importance in new environments of those new adaptive combinations which are generated when crossing occurs between populations having very different adaptive properties. In a haploid organism, such combinations are immediately broken up by segregation occurring as the zygote germinates. The accidental preservation of such hybrid combinations by suppression of meiosis may, therefore, have had a very beneficial result in certain situations, and this could have led to the preservation and spread of the gene or gene complex responsible for the suppression. Many organisms may not have evolved any greater complexity at all as a result of this change. But the diploid condition may be looked upon as a preadaptation for the evolution of greater genetic and developmental complexity. This could confer upon the organism an ever increasing range of evolutionary opportunity. Those evolutionary lines able to avail themselves fully of the opportunity thus offered become the dominant organisms in the world today. This explains the fact that diploidy and isomorphic alternation of generations do exist in organisms with rapid reproduction and relatively simple developmental stages but that strictly haploid cycles are never found in organisms with slow reproduction and complex development.

There is little doubt that organisms with a completely diploid cycle, as well as those with an isomorphic alternation of generations, have arisen directly and separately many times from ancestors with the original haploid chromosomal cycle. Instances of the direct origin of diploidy are probably the more numerous, there being at least four in the Protozoa (Ciliophora, Sporozoa, Polymastigina, Radiolaria), plus one or two additional examples in the lines leading to Metazoa, and in plants three orders of green algae, diatoms, and probably certain yeasts. Isomorphic alternation has arisen once in red algae, once in ancestors of brown algae, probably twice in green algae, perhaps also in the common ancestor of the Bryophyta and vascular plants, and once in fungi (*Allomyces*). In multicellular plants which already possessed an environmentally controlled alternation between the production of asexual zoospores and of gametes, as is true in most of the haploid filamentous algae, suppression of meiosis in the zygote would be very likely to give rise to a diploid plant which at maturity would produce asexual spores as a result of meiosis. With the aid of a few modifying genes, natural selection could easily establish an alternation between a diploid spore-forming and a haploid gamete-forming generation. In other types of organisms, however, and particularly in unicellular forms, suppression of meiosis in the division of the zygote would be more likely to lead either directly to a completely diploid cycle or to an irregular alternation of diploid and haploid phases which, by selection of modifying genes, would be quickly adjusted to the diploid condition. Essentially diploid life-cycles have also originated indirectly from heteromorphic cycles with predominant diploidy, as is probably true of the Fucales in the brown algae.

Finally, we must consider the possible selective basis of the evolutionary trend which led to the Bryophyta, in which an original isomorphic alternation of generations appears to have given way to a heteromorphic cycle with the haploid gametophyte predominant. These plants appear to have wantonly cast away the advantage which presumably results from the diploid chromosomal condition and reverted toward the less promising haploid state of their remote ancestors. Can this be explained?

In discussing the origin of diploidy, the point was made that this condition, by enabling the population to store up potential variability in the form of recessive genes, favors evolutionary flexibility at the expense of immediate fitness. Haploidy, on the other hand, favors immediate fitness or evolution by changes in one or a few genes. Now the writer has elsewhere (Stebbins, 1950, 1957, 1959) suggested that in plants which are adapted to rapid colonization as pioneers of new areas, temporary genetic constancy may have a selective advantage because it assures that a single well-adapted initial colonizer will produce a large number of equally well-adapted descendants. Mosses and liverworts are, next to lichens, the most universal and successful pioneers of all organisms. Their evolution toward a greater emphasis on the haploid generation may therefore have been a result of the actual selective advantage of this chromosomal condition in their pioneer habitats.

CHROMOSOMAL CYCLES IN THE FUNGI

Having developed a reasonable working hypothesis to explain the evolution of chromosomal cycles in animals and green plants, our next task is to see whether this hypothesis can be applied to the much more numerous and complex array of cycles found in the fungi. These are well reviewed by Raper (1954). As his chart shows, in addition to the five types of chromosomal cycle found in other organisms, there are three peculiar to fungi, all based upon the dicaryotic condition, in which each cell contains two nuclei of opposite sexes or mating types. Furthermore, "haploid" plant bodies or mycelia can contain two or more genetically different nuclei of the same mating type in the hetero-caryotic condition, by which means they come to possess phenotypic characteristics determined by all of them. Further complications are added by the fact that six different types of heterothallism, which require cross-fertilization, plus homothallism, which usually results in self-fertilization, are distributed among the different chromosomal types with little obvious regularity of pattern. Finally, nearly all fungi except for the more advanced Basidiomycetes have repeatedly given rise to forms which reproduce largely or exclusively by asexual means.

The interpretation of either the evolutionary relationships between or the selective forces which have determined the origin of this welter of different methods of reproduction will require both a thorough knowledge of the fungi as a whole and an intimate acquaintance with numerous individual genera in each one of the major subdivisions of the class. Nevertheless, the review of Raper, plus more restricted studies which have paid particular attention to cytological and genetic phenomena in individual groups, such as that of Emerson (1954) on the Blastocladiales, can provide a basis for detecting some general trends.

Diploid life-cycles are known only in the yeasts, where they are associated with apparent morphological simplicity but great complexity at the biochemical level. In these organisms, diploidy has apparently contributed to a greater biochemical flexibility, since a single genotype of a diploid yeast can become adapted to a great variety of fermentation processes through developing different enzyme systems, each in association with an appropriate host. Consequently, yeasts have become highly successful in their own relatively restricted sphere, but diploidy has not aided this evolutionary line to progress in new directions, perhaps because it was already too specialized when it became diploid.

The only known genus of fungi with an isomorphic alternation of haploid and diploid generations—the water mold *Allomyces* (Emerson, 1954)—is also a small and morphologically relatively simple form, and one which, in addition, has produced highly successful variants of a single pattern but has not been the starting point for any major evolutionary advances. Furthermore, all known species of *Allomyces* are homothallic and predominantly self-fertilized, although the related genus *Blastocladiella,* which Emerson regards as more specialized than *Allomyces,* is dioecious and cross-fertilized. Hence, unless extinct or unknown primitive cross-fertilizing ancestors are postulated, the evolutionary advantage of the diploid generation in *Allomyces* does not appear to consist of heterozygosity, and the reason for its origin is hard to see. Neither of the two best-known examples of nuclear diploidy in the fungi agrees well with the pattern established by this phenomenon in autotrophic plants.

If, however, we broaden our concept of genetic diploidy to include the dicaryotic condition, the pattern becomes more familiar. Since a dicaryotic cell has all the essential genetic properties of a diploid cell, particularly that of interaction between alleles, this broadened concept is fully justified from the standpoint of evolutionary genetics. The distribution of the dicaryotic condition is just what we would expect to find according to the hypothesis that it confers an immediate advantage in preserving adaptively superior hybrid combinations and that it also promotes the development of evolutionary lines characterized by the elaboration of increasingly complex morphological structures, which are built up by correspondingly longer and more complex sequences of development. The dicaryotic condition is impossible in the coenocytic Phycomycetes, which in their morphological structures as well as their mode of life are the most nearly analogous among fungi to the haploid filamentous green algae. In the Ascomycetes, which in their small size and tendency to behave as "weedy" pioneers, are comparable to Bryophyta, it is confined to the reproductive structures. In the Basidiomycetes, which contain the largest, longest-lived fungi with the most complex developmental sequences, it is universal and often exists during the majority of the growth cycle. All the most complex morphological structures, host-parasite relationships, and biochemical phenomena found in Basidiomycetes are associated with the dicaryotic phase of their life-cycle.

In many Ascomycetes, the advantages of heterozygosity and genetic buffering are often secured by the heterocaryotic condition (Stebbins,

1950; Jinks, 1952; Stanier, 1953). Because the different nuclei of a heterocaryon do not divide synchronously, different genetic properties can exist in different parts of the same heterocaryotic mycelium. This produces a most flexible means of adjusting to chemically variable substrates, but it militates against building up integrated sequences of developmental processes. Ascomycetes have evolved a great variety of biochemically complex and diverse types but have retained a relative simplicity of structure except for the reproductive bodies of the most advanced forms.

The diversity and complexity of sexual types in the fungi deserves at least a few brief comments. Raper (1954) agrees with the majority of mycologists in assuming that homothallism, with its predominant self-fertilization, is the primitive condition in the group. His arguments are, first, that it is the most common and widespread condition; second, that it is common in the most primitive fungi, the water molds; and, third, that the various types of heterothallism differ so widely that it is hard to see how they could all have evolved from a single primitive heterothallic type. He recognizes, nevertheless, that the existence of homothallism and heterothallism side by side in many different groups raises great difficulties against the hypothesis that all homothallic types were descended from a common ancestor. He therefore suggests that homothallic fungi are of two types, those directly descended from the primitive homothallic ancestor and those derived secondarily from heterothallic species.

If homothallism and predominant self-fertilization were the original condition in fungi, then this class differs from all other Eucaryota in the evolution of its sexuality. Sonneborn (1957) has given good evidence in favor of the hypothesis that the sequence from primitive cross-fertilization through self-fertilization to asexuality has been the common and perhaps the only one in the higher Protozoa, and in Metazoa self-fertilization and asexuality are always derived conditions. Wherever sexuality has been found in algae, cross-fertilization is the more widespread and probably primitive condition, and the same is obviously true of Bryophyta and vascular plants.

One might remark here that the fungi are unique in other respects, particularly the combination of saprophytism or parasitism with lack of motility and the development of highly complex biochemical systems of nutrition. Nevertheless, the hypothesis that homothallism is their primitive condition requires careful scrutiny, particularly in view of the fact that the system of heterothallism which is most common in the water molds, the most primitive representatives of the class, is essentially the same as that found in green flagellates. Perhaps the phylogenetic succession is even more complex than that postulated by

Raper and has gone from heterothallism to homothallism, then back to a different type of heterothallism, and finally to recently derived homothallism. Since the present situation is without doubt highly complex, the suggestion of an equally complex evolutionary phylogeny seems not unreasonable.

Asexuality in fungi appears to be derived by reduction, and it occurs principally where it would be expected, in forms which develop rapidly, are highly successful colonizers (*Penicillium, Aspergillus*), or are pathogens on a single widespread host (*Fusarium*). All these environments place a premium on temporary constancy at the expense of evolutionary flexibility.

GENETIC SYSTEMS IN HIGHER PLANTS AND ANIMALS

A maximum amount of evolutionary flexibility is produced by genetic systems of diploid or predominantly diploid, sexual organisms with (1) random mating or panmixia, (2) a high chromosome number and consequently a large number of linkage groups, (3) crossing over at a high frequency within these groups, and (4) no other restrictions to genetic recombination. According to the present hypothesis, such systems should predominate in long-lived organisms with slow reproduction and complex sequences of development, which maintain populations relatively constant in size. Actually, this condition exists, so far as is known, in most of the ferns and fern allies, in all the woody gymnosperms, most of the woody angiosperms, the longer-lived herbaceous perennial flowering plants which occupy stable habitats, probably in the majority of the larger brown algae, and in the larger forms of Metazoa, particularly the larger Crustacea and the bulk of the vertebrates. Hence these forms agree with expectation on the basis of the present hypothesis.

In both higher plants and animals, deviations away from the mode of life which would favor maximum flexibility of the genetic system have been frequent. One would expect such deviants to acquire one or more of the modifications which shift the genetic system in the direction of greater immediate fitness. The writer has elsewhere (Stebbins, 1957, 1959) produced evidence to show that this is, in general, true of flowering plants. The principal types of deviations are reversion toward predominant self-fertilization, the development of asexual reproduction by apomixis, and restriction of genetic recombination through reduction of the chromosome number, as well as prevention or restriction of crossing over. These three conditions usually appear in annuals or in perennials which occupy temporary or pioneer habitats, so that they are subject to great fluctuations in population size.

Furthermore, they tend to be mutually exclusive; self-fertilizing groups rarely develop apomixis, and reduction of the basic chromosome number takes place most often in cross-fertilizing species which are annuals or pioneers.

A similar parallelism between changes in the genetic system and the mode of life has been suggested for the higher Protozoa by Sonneborn (1957).

In the Metazoa, deviations in the direction of asexuality, partial or complete inbreeding, reduction of the basic chromosome number, and various restrictions on crossing over have occurred repeatedly in several phyla. As compared to higher plants, however, asexuality and inbreeding are less common devices, and reduction of recombination through reducing the chromosome number and particularly by means of various restrictions on crossing over are much more frequent. As is evident from White's (1954) classic survey, all these deviations are best known in the insects, a class containing many evolutionary lines which have progressed in the direction of shorter life-cycles and great fluctuations in population size. A superficial glance at this class shows that low chromosome numbers are most prevalent in types such as coccids, aphids, and the higher Diptera and that parthenogenesis is likewise most widespread in forms which can be regarded as pioneers. Hence a careful comparison between modes of life and genetic systems in various groups of insects and other invertebrates may yield further evidence in favor of the writer's hypothesis. This, however, is a task which cannot be attempted here but must be left to comparative evolutionists of the future.

Summary

Comparative studies of systems for genetic recombination in all forms of life have shown that they vary in a regular fashion which is correlated with the mode of life of the organism concerned. In bacteria and blue-green algae, which have poorly defined nuclear structures, genetic recombination, when found, takes on several forms which differ from those characteristics of higher organisms and often involve transfer of only part of a genome. This is associated with their small size, their evolution of great biochemical complexity with little structural differentiation, and probably their possession of many genes which act only under certain environments. The hypothesis is advanced that these or similar types of genetic recombination have existed ever since life first appeared and have been gradually modified in the direction of greater precision and integration in association with the evolution of greater structural and developmental complexity in the organisms concerned. Reversion toward asexuality has occurred very often and has been highly successful because the organisms in which it has taken place have become very well adapted to their particular environment and reproduce so rapidly that they can become adapted to new environments by the establishment of rare mutations. Evolution toward increasing integration of the genotype and greater precision in the division of the genetic material finally led to the appearance of the first organisms with true nuclei, chromosomes, mitosis, and meiosis. These organisms are believed to have been sexually reproducing autotrophic green flagellates having the haploid chromosome number except for their zygotes.

These haploid organisms gave rise directly several times to organisms with a diploid life-cycle, of which the only haploid cells are the gametes, as well as to others with an isomorphic alternation of diploid and haploid generations. Reversion to asexuality has also been very common in them. The chromosomal cycles with a heteromorphic alternation of generations, like those in Bryophyta, in which the gametophyte is the dominant generation, and in the Tracheophyta, or vascular plants, in which the sporophyte is dominant, are probably derived secondarily from the isomorphic alternation cycle. Reasons are advanced for the hypothesis that mosses and their relatives do not represent intermediate evolutionary stages between algae and vascular plants, but are reduced forms descended from primitive extinct ancestors which may have resembled the earliest-known vascular plants more nearly than any modern Bryophyta. The homologous theory of the origin of alternation of generations is thus upheld and the antithetic or intercalation theory rejected.

The selective basis for the origin of diploidy is believed to be associated with the immediate advantage which this chromosomal condition gives in buffering genetic heterozygosity, plus long-term advantages in enabling the population to build up a store of potential variation in the form of recessive genes held in the heterozygous condition. This advantage would be greatest in those organisms with relatively long life-cycles and slow reproduction, which require integrated changes in a large number of genes in order to evolve new adaptive systems. Such conditions are realized most completely in the higher Protozoa, the Metazoa, the larger brown algae, and the vascular plants, chiefly because their developmental stages are controlled by a long sequence of precisely integrated epigenetic processes of metabolism. The fungi are more complex than any other class of organisms in both their chromosomal cycles and the relationships between self- and cross-fertilization in them. If, however, the dicaryotic condition is regarded as genetically comparable to diploidy, then the evolution of chromosome cycles in fungi bears much the same relationship to the evolution of structural and developmental complexity that it does in green plants, and it has probably been guided by similar selective pressures. Reasons are given for suggesting that the currently prevailing opinion among mycologists, that homothallism is the primitive condition in the class, needs to be re-examined.

In the higher animals and plants, the commonest genetic system is one which promotes a maximum of evolutionary flexibility by genetic recombination. Reversions toward systems reducing the amount of recombination and therefore increasing immediate fitness at the expense of flexibility have occurred repeatedly in many different groups. These have included reversion to asexuality, toward predominant or exclusive self-fertilization, and restriction of recombination through reducing the number of chromosomes, as well as by various mechanisms which reduce or eliminate crossing over. In higher plants and probably also in animals, such reversions have usually taken place in forms with increased rates of reproduction, reduction in size and complexity of development, occupation of temporary or pioneer habitats, and/or evolution toward a mode of life which involves great fluctuations in the size of the populations.

I am much indebted to my colleague, Dr. A. G. Marr, for helpful criticisms and suggestions regarding the parts of this paper dealing with microorganisms. All ideas and hypotheses, however, are strictly my own responsibility.

BIBLIOGRAPHY

BENZER, SEYMOUR. 1955. "Fine Structure of a Genetic Region in Bacteriophage," *Proc. Nat. Acad. Sci.,* XLI, 344–54.

BOLD, H. 1957. *Morphology of Plants.* New York: Harper & Bros.

BOWER, F. O. 1908. *The Origin of a Land Flora.* London: Macmillan & Co., Ltd.

BOYDEN, ALAN A. 1953. "Comparative Evolution with Special Reference to Primitive Mechanisms," *Evolution,* VII, 21–30.

BROWN, R., and ROBINSON, E. 1955. "Cellular Differentiation and the Development of Enzyme Proteins in Plants," *Symp. Soc. Study of Development and Growth,* No. 12: *Biological Specificity and Growth,* pp. 93–118.

COHEN, S. S. 1955. "Comparative Biochemistry and Virology," *Advances Virus Res.,* III, 1–48.

CROSBY, JACK L. 1955. "The Evolution of Mitosis," *Proc. University of Durham Phil. Soc.,* XII, 73–81.

CROW, W. B. 1924. "Variation and Species in the Cyanophyceae," *Jour. Genetics,* XIV, 397–424.

DARLINGTON, C. D. 1939. *The Evolution of Genetic Systems.* Cambridge: Cambridge University Press.

————. 1958. *The Evolution of Genetic Systems.* 2d ed. New York: Basic Books, Inc.

DOBZHANSKY, TH. 1955. "A Review of Some Fundamental Concepts and Problems of Population Genetics," *Cold Spring Harbor Symp. Quant. Biol.,* XX, 1–15.

DOUGHERTY, ELLSWORTH C. 1955. "Comparative Evolution and the Origin of Sexuality," *Systematic Zoöl.,* IV, 145–169.

EAMES, A. J. 1936. *Morphology of Vascular Plants, Lower Groups.* New York: McGraw-Hill Book Co., Inc.

EMERSON, R. 1955. "The Biology of Water Molds," pp. 171–208 in *Aspects of Synthesis and Order in Growth,* ed. D. RUDNICK. Princeton: Princeton University Press.

FRITSCH, F. E. 1945. "Studies in the Comparative Morphology of the Algae. IV. Algae and Archegoniate Plants," *Ann. Bot.,* N.S., IX, 1–29.

HALDANE, J. B. S. 1954. "The Origins of Life," *New Biol.,* No. 16, pp. 12–27.

HASKELL, GORDON. 1949. "Some Evolutionary Problems concerning the Bryophyta," *Jour. Amer. Bryol. Soc.,* LII, 49–57.

HOROWITZ, N. H. 1945. "On the Evolution of Biochemical Syntheses," *Proc. Nat. Acad. Sci.,* XXXI, 153–57.

HUTNER, S. H. 1955. Introduction. In *Biochemistry and Physiology of Protozoa,* Vol. II. New York: Academic Press.

HUXLEY, J. 1942. *Evolution: The Modern Synthesis.* New York: Harper & Bros.

KLUYVER, A. J., and VAN NIEL, C. B. 1956. *The Microbe's Contribution to Biology.* Cambridge: Harvard University Press.

JINKS, J. L. 1952. "Heterokaryosis: A System of Adaptation in Wild Fungi," *Proc. Roy. Soc. London, B,* CXL, 83–106.

LEDERBERG, J. 1955. "Recombination Mechanisms in Bacteria." In *Symposium in Genetic Recombination, Jour. Cell. Comp. Physiol.,* XLV, Suppl., 2, 75–107.

————. 1957. "Viruses, Genes, and Cells," *Bacteriol. Rev.,* XXI, 133–39.

LERNER, I. M. 1954. *Genetic Homeostasis.* New York: John Wiley & Sons.

————. 1955. "Concluding Survey," *Cold Spring Harbor Symp. Quant. Biol.,* XX, 334–40.

LEWIS, D. 1951. "Structure of the Incompatibility Gene. III. Types of Spontaneous and Induced Mutation," *Heredity,* V, 399–414.

LWOFF, A. 1943. *L'Évolution physiologique: études des pertes de fonctions chez les microorganismes.* Paris: Hermann et Cie.

————. 1950. *Problems of Morphogenesis in Ciliates: The Kinetosomes in Development, Reproduction, and Evolution.* New York: John Wiley & Sons.

MATHER, K. 1943. *"Polygenic Inheritance and Natural Selection,"* Biol. Rev.,* XVIII, 32–64.

MAYR, ERNST. 1954. "Change of Genetic Environment and Evolution." In *Evolution as a Process,* 157–80. London: Allen & Unwin.

MULLER, H. J. 1949. "The Darwinian and Modern Conceptions of Natural Selection," *Proc. Amer. Phil. Soc.,* XCIII, 459–70.

————. 1960. "The Mutation Theory Re-examined," *Proc. Tenth Internat. Cong. Genetics* (in press).

OPARIN, A. T. 1957. *The Origin of Life on the Earth.* Translated from the Russian by ANN SYNGE. 3d ed. Edinburgh: Oliver & Boyd.

PAPENFUSS, G. F. 1957. "Progress and Outstanding Achievements in Phycology during the Past Fifty Years," *Amer. Jour. Bot.,* XLIV, 74–81.

RAPER, J. R. 1954. "Life Cycles, Sexuality, and Sexual Mechanisms in the Fungi." In *Sex in Microorganisms,* ed. D. H. WENRICH, pp. 42–81. ("Publications of the American Association for the Advancement of Science.")

SMITH, G. 1955. *Cryptogamic Botany.* Vol. I: *Algae and Fungi.* 2d ed. New York: McGraw-Hill Book Co., Inc.

SONNEBORN, T. M. 1957. "Breeding Systems, Reproductive Methods, and Species Problems in Protozoa." In *The Species Problem,* pp. 155–324. ("Publications of the American Association for the Advancement of Science," No. 50.)

STANIER, R. Y. 1953. "Adaptation, Evolutionary and Physiological: or Darwinism among the Microorganisms." In *Adaptation in Microorganisms: Third Symposium of the Society for General Microbiology, Held at the Royal Institution,* London. Cambridge: Cambridge University Press.

STEBBINS, G. L. 1950. *Variation and Evolution in Plants.* New York: Columbia University Press.

————. 1956. "Artificial Polyploidy as a Tool in Plant Breeding," *Brookhaven Symp. Biol.,* IX, 37–52.

————. 1957. "Self Fertilization and Population Variability in the Higher Plants," *Amer. Naturalist,* XCI, 337–54.

————. 1959. "Longevity, Habitat, and Release of Genetic Variability in the Higher Plants," *Cold Spring Harbor Symp. Quant. Biol.* (in press).

STEERE, WILLIAM C. 1958. "Evolution and Speciation in Mosses," *Amer. Naturalist,* XCII, 5–21.

TARTAR, V. 1956. "Pattern and Substance in *Stentor.*" In *Symp. Soc. for Study of Development and Growth,* No. 14: *Cellular Mechanisms in Differentiation and Growth,* ed. D. RUDNICK, pp. 73–100.

TYLER, S. A., and BARGHOORN, E. S. 1954. "Occurrence of Structurally Preserved Plants in Precambrian Rocks of the Canadian Shield," *Science,* CXIX, 606–8.

WADDINGTON, C. H. 1957. *The Strategy of the Genes.* London; Allen & Unwin.

WENRICH, D. H. 1954a. "Sex in Protozoa: A Comparative Review." In *Sex in Microorganisms,* ed. D. H. WENRICH, pp. 134–265. ("Publications of the American Association for the Advancement of Science.")

WENRICH, D. H. 1954*b*. "Comments on the Origin and Evolution of 'Sex.' " In *Sex in Microorganisms,* ed. D. H. WENRICH, pp. 335–46. ("Publications of the American Association for the Advancement of Science.")

WHITE, M. J. D. 1954. *Animal Cytology and Evolution.* 2d ed. Cambridge: Cambridge University Press.

WOLLMAN, E. L., JACOB, F., and HAYES, W. 1956. "Conjugation and Recombination in *Escherichia coli* K-12," *Cold Spring Harbor Symp. Quant. Biol.,* XXI, 141–62.

ZIMMERMANN, WALTER. 1955. "Phylogenie des Archegoniaten-Generationswechsels," *Feddes Repertorium,* I, 283–307.

DANIEL I. AXELROD

THE EVOLUTION OF FLOWERING PLANTS

The evolution of flowering plants presented Darwin with a series of problems which could not be answered satisfactorily until an adequate number of fossil floras had been found, described, and analyzed and until certain basic principles of geology, paleontology, ecology, climatology, and evolution had been discovered which would illuminate the relations shown by the fossil floras. Although great progress has been made along these lines during the past century, the data in hand even now provide only partial answers to most of the problems considered by Darwin. In particular, these included the "abominable mystery" surrounding their early evolution, notably their center of origin, their ancestry, and their "sudden appearance" in the Middle Cretaceous as a fully evolved, wholly modern phylum. Together with Gray and Hooker, Darwin also pondered the relations of the temperate deciduous forests of eastern Asia and America and the history of the old Antarctic flora, remnants of which occur now in the Fuegian and Tasman regions. In addition, such problems as the evolution of insular floras and transtropic migration came under his purview. Thus it seems appropriate to review here current ideas on some of these varied aspects of flowering-plant evolution, with emphasis on the development of modern patterns of distribution. Since the topics are diverse, they will be woven into a discussion which parallels the presumed history of the phylum, commencing, first, with certain inferences which may be made with respect to the early history of the group.

PRE-CENOZOIC EVOLUTION

ANTIQUITY

Angiosperms must have had a long history prior to the Middle Cretaceous (Cenomanian), when they first appear in the record in abundance. Not only are numerous and diverse modern families represented

DANIEL I. AXELROD is Professor of Geology at the University of California at Los Angeles. He was trained in botany and then in geology at the University of California (Berkeley), and his research in paleobotany has been sponsored chiefly by the Carnegie Institution of Washington and by the National Science Foundation.

in Middle Cretaceous floras, but apparently many living genera, including *Acer, Amelanchier, Cercidiphyllum, Cornus, Ficus, Magnolia, Platanus, Populus, Quercus, Sassafras,* and *Vitis,* were already established within both primitive and derived groups by this time. Supporting evidence comes from Lower Cretaceous (Aptian) rocks, which have yielded woods that are wholly modern in structural details, with such specialized families as Dipterocarpaceae and Ternstroeemiaceae represented.

These Cretaceous records give us a clue to the probable antiquity of the group. The morphological diversity of Cretaceous plants led Camp (1947) to infer that flowering plants were probably already in existence by the close of the Paleozoic, with divergence of basic family types completed by the Jurassic. Thomas (1936), viewing the slow rates of evolution which have occurred in the phylum since the Cretaceous, also concluded that the group was probably established by the later Paleozoic. More recent evidence, based on rates of evolution of major plant phyla whose histories are reasonably well known, suggests that a group such as the angiosperms probably diverged from its ancestral type no less than sixty to seventy million years prior to its first abundant records. Measuring downward from the Cretaceous, the ancestry of the group would fall in the Permian, and it may be older.

When we turn to pre-Cretaceous rocks to look for ancient angiosperms, we find that there are only a few records of them. One investigator (Krausel, 1957) has taken the extreme position that *none* of the pre-Cretaceous fossils referred to as angiosperms by other investigators represent the group. This view is based chiefly on the fact that most of the characters which are used to identify fossil angiosperms occur in other alliances (i.e., net-veined leaves in the Gnetales and Pteridospermae; vessels in some gymnosperms and ferns; pollen similar to gymnosperms and ferns). Admitting the likelihood that not all the reported pre-Cretaceous angiosperms represent the phylum, some nonetheless appear to be flowering plants. Palmlike plants occur in the Middle Triassic of southern Utah (Brown, 1956): these fossils certainly are not ginkgophytes, as Krausel (1957) supposes. Fossil pollen representing the magnolian and water-lily alliances is recorded in the Jurassic of Scotland (Simpson, 1937) and Scania (Erdtman, 1948), and parts of palmlike leaves occur in the Jurassic of France (Lignier, 1907; Eames, 1953, p. 188). There are several other records which are, at least in my opinion, probably angiosperms (see Axelrod, 1952a; also Krausel, 1957, for review of more recent reports of angiosperms). They support the view that flowering plants had a long and largely unrecorded history prior to the Cretaceous, during which time essentially modern family types had already evolved. Their rarity in the record seems due chiefly to circumstances related to the sites in which they were living and to the nature of their early evolution.

SITE

The belief that early angiosperm evolution took place in upland regions, in areas sufficiently remote from lowland basins of deposition to have precluded their occurrence in the record, is now generally conceded. In the first place, studies of sequences of floras have shown that plants of more complex (advanced) type appeared first in the uplands, long before they entered the lowland record of the region to replace the older flora. For example, conifers and seed ferns, which did not dominate the lowland record until the Late Devonian and Carboniferous, occur in Middle Devonian rocks. Represented by battered trunks and branches suggesting transport from distant highlands to lowland sites of deposition near sea level, they occur in association with the Psilophyte Paleoflora, the simplest known land vegetation. A similar relation must be invoked to explain the existence of Cambrian land plants which are considerably more complex than the psilophytes (Axelrod, 1959a). In addition, typical Permian plants are recorded in the lowlands of Kansas during a relatively drier stage of the Pennsylvanian; they disappeared when conditions became more humid but reappeared again when the drier Permian environment was favorable (Elias, 1936). During the humid interval and earlier, they probably were confined to more distant, well-drained upland slopes remote from the lowland sites of deposition. Further, during Eocene time the temperate Arcto-Tertiary Geoflora occupied upland areas at middle latitudes in North America and Europe, when the lowlands were dominated by subtropical forests. As temperatures were lowered during the succeeding Oligocene epoch, the deciduous hardwoods invaded the lowlands (Reid and Chandler, 1933; Chaney, 1938). Such relations suggest that the rare pre-Cretaceous angiosperms probably represent members of a flora living in upland sites far removed from the plants which were preserved in the lowlands.

Second, an upland area of early angiosperm evolution assumes significance because there is a greater probability that a new adaptive type would become established there rather than in the more equable lowlands near sites of deposition. The existence of a varied environment, both physical and biotic, is necessary for the establishment of a new adaptive type because diversity of environment tends to promote rapid evolution and is probably essential to it. A variety of habitats results in the subdivision of a species into local breeding units, and such fragmentation is favorable for rapid evolution. Furthermore, many more adaptive types—both vegetative and floral—can be accommodated in a diverse, as compared with a more homogeneous, environment. Thus, granting (*a*) a good degree of heterozygosity in the ancestral angiosperms, (*b*) the occurrence of characters (both physiological and morphological) preadaptive in directions of change, and (*c*) a favorable population structure, the probability is high that a new adaptive type, like the flowering plants, would develop in the uplands. It is also apparent that if angiosperms were represented by generally small populations early in their history, they would have even less chance of entering the accumulating lowland record.

Third, we must not forget that the plants which make up the bulk of the record lived at sites of deposition in lowland areas. Although some floras are preserved in such upland basins as mountain lakes, these deposits are comparatively young. As we go farther back in time, fewer upland deposits are encountered in the record because highlands are constantly subject to erosion and the sediments which accumulate there are soon destroyed. Since the older floras almost exclusively represent vegetation bordering lowland basins, they tell us little about ancient upland angiosperms. Thus the rarity of pre-Cretaceous flowering plants is wholly consistent with the thesis that they probably evolved in upland areas, in environments far removed from those which were represented in the lowlands.

ANCESTRY

The ancestral group that gave rise to angiosperms has not yet been identified in the fossil record, and no living angiosperm points to such an ancestral alliance. In addition, the record has shed almost no light on relations between taxa at ordinal and family level. Such a situation is not surprising. If angiosperms evolved chiefly in the distant uplands, ancestral types would not be expected (except very rarely) in a record which accumulated in the lowlands. This explains why Thomas (1936), after reviewing the numerous reproductive structures of Paleozoic and Mesozoic seed plants, concluded that none of the evolutionary schemes hitherto proposed for the dicotyledons, whether from a magnolian or an amentiferan source, seemed to agree with paleontological evidence as to the origin of the carpel. The fossils from the lowland sites, which he felt showed the probable course of evolution of the carpel, represent forms well removed from the "main line" toward the more successful angiosperms. The absence of plants clearly ancestral to angiosperms in the known and abundant record of the lowlands practically demonstrates that they must have been confined to upland areas throughout their history; otherwise we should have records of them.

The geologic record provides little evidence as to the early history of the phylum because the classification and presumed phyletic relations of flowering plants have been founded chiefly on floral structures which are rarely preserved (even in lowland deposits), not on the gross hard parts (leaves, wood) which make up much of the record. By comparison, the relations of the major phyla of vertebrates are far better understood today because they are based on the structural and adaptive significance of hard parts (bones, teeth, etc.). This does not mean that plants cannot be placed in a phyletic scheme. For the lower groups—the ferns, lycopods, horsetails—details of the morphology of the *whole plant* have been used effectively to indicate relationships between modern and fossil forms. In this connection, Bower's monumental study (1923–28) of the ferns will always stand as a guiding beacon to sound methodology in pursuing phyletic problems. In recent years more attention has gradually been focused on the phyletic significance of wood, pollen, and leaves of angiosperms. Continued studies along these lines may be expected to illuminate more clearly the phylogeny of flowering plants, particularly following their early quantum stage of differentiation (see section on "Adaptive Adaptation").

Although the record has provided no evidence to show that the primitive angiosperm was of a woody magnolian type, most botanists now base their phylogeny on this group. The chief difficulty with accepting any living plant as ancestral to the phylum is the tacit assumption that the ancestral type has persisted down to the present in only slightly modified form. However, in other plant phyla such as conifers and ferns—as well as in many groups of animals—the evidence clearly shows that the primitive, ancestral members became extinct early in the history of the alliance and that many of the modern taxa are highly specialized. Furthermore, from what we may infer about the evolution of major categories (orders, classes), it would appear that in the early quantum phase of differentiation there is a great deal of splitting and divergence of many adaptive types. Thus to select any living alliance as ancestral to a group that apparently was already in existence in the Permian—some 240 million years ago—if not earlier, seems a questionable procedure. This is particularly true if the chief evolutionary lines (orders, families) of flowering plants represent a reticulum of numerous interwoven types which hybridized early in the history of the phylum (Stebbins, 1950, p. 508).

A considerable body of evidence supports the idea that, following the early quantum phase of rapid splitting into many basic types, the divergent groups give rise to a series of subparallel major alliances that continue to evolve (Simpson, 1944, 1953; Stebbins, 1950, pp.

508–10; Axelrod, 1952, p. 47). In a recent paper, Němejc (1956) has developed this concept as it applies to early angiosperm evolution. He suggests that, instead of a phyletic tree with roots in the magnolian alliance, we should perhaps visualize the angiosperm phylum as composed of many trunks rising out of an early proangiosperm plexus (Fig. 1). On this basis, the woody magnolian alliance is not ancestral

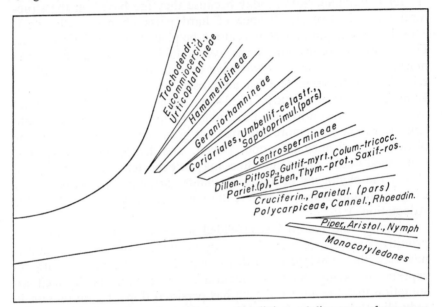

Fig. 1.—Němejc (1956) suggests that a rapid splitting and divergence of numerous basic angiosperm alliances occurred in the Permian. In this scheme the woody magnolian alliance has a collateral, not an ancestral, position.

but represents only one of the divergent groups arrested in an early developmental stage, though still well removed from proangiosperms. Some botanists will no doubt quarrel with the details of Němejc's proposed phyletic branches and hence will probably discredit the idea for this reason alone. Regardless of the details, his basic suggestion seems more sound than any other yet presented: it is wholly consistent with what we may infer about the early stage of evolution of a major alliance.

Several phyla have been considered as possibly ancestral to flowering plants, notably the cycadeoids, gnetales, and even the lycopods. The Mesozoic seed-fern alliance Caytoniales approaches an angiosperm in floral structure more closely than does any other known group (Thomas, 1936) but otherwise differs in leaf and stem structure. Although well removed from the direct line leading to angiosperms, the Caytoniales has provided evidence for the view that flowering plants may have diverged from a seed-fern plexus related to it. More recently, Němejc (1956) has noted that angiosperms possibly evolved from a primitive group intermediate between ferns and seed ferns, basing his views on numerous anatomical features of the groups concerned: leaf, type of branching, vascular system, reproductive organs, and the nature of the flower. Without going into details, he suggests that this "proangiosperm" alliance, which he also feels was evolving in upland areas, probably had the following general characteristics: (*a*) leaf derived from naked phyllophores of a primitive fern or seed-fern alliance which were arrested early in growth, presumably as an adaptation to growing in more exposed upland regions, leaf with open (dichotomous) venation, with a tendency to webbing and reticulation—early form possibly palmate in outline; (*b*) branching originally dichotomous, thence axillary (monopodial) to afford better bud protection; (*c*) woody cylinder massive (eustele) with a tendency to dissection (ataktostele) in herbs and monocotyledons, wood vessel-less, with scalariform pits, with a tendency to form vessels; (*d*) semi-inclosed seeds with a tendency to become inclosed; (*e*) pollen monocolpate, as in ferns or seed ferns, with a tendency to complex sculpturing and ornamentation.

It is amply clear that the earliest angiosperms are far removed in antiquity and that even now it is difficult to infer their probable nature. Thus it is not surprising to find that botanists have differed greatly in their interpretations of the phylogenetic relations of the different alliances in the group. The divergent viewpoints with respect to presumed primitive and advanced characters and with respect to the interrelations of some of the major alliances, as well as the underlying philosophies which have governed these views, have been reviewed recently (Constance, 1955) and need not be probed here. Regardless of the incompleteness of the fossil record, it is the only possible source that may some day reveal at least some of the actual events during early angiosperm evolution. By confining our search for these still undiscovered early angiosperms to rocks in Carboniferous and Permian basins which had bordering highlands, we may discover a few rare angiosperm scraps which were transported into the lowlands. They will illuminate the true nature of early flowering plants more clearly than any philosophy can.

ENVIRONMENT AND AREA

Assuming that the origin and initial differentiation of angiosperms occurred in upland regions of environmental diversity during the later Paleozoic, we may now inquire as to the general geographic area and the nature of the climate under which they evolved. Did this early evolution take place in temperate Holarctica, in temperate austral regions, or was the ancient tropical world the region of primary diversification? This is a fundamental question because, during the course of geologic time, climate has had a crucial role in directing the course of plant evolution.

Since plants are rooted to their environment, climate, as expressed by temperature and water relations, exerts a primary control on both their existence and their persistence within any given area. Major trends of climatic change during spans of geologic time are of prime importance to plant evolution because the expansion and contraction of climatic belts and the appearance of new climates—both of which correspond to shifting adaptive zones—make possible the development within a phylum of many adaptive types. The notion that the general course of plant evolution was guided by climate has been skilfully discussed by Andrews (1913, 1914) in Australia and by Bews (1925, 1927) in Africa. In brief, equable climates have tended to produce wide-ranging groups, whereas differentiation of climates has resulted in the restricted localization of the old and in the origin and spread of new adaptive types. On this basis we may infer that (a) the more ancient and primitive angiosperms, as represented now by ordinal and family categories, may well be in environments generally like those that the ancestral forms occupied and that (b) the more highly evolved taxa of each alliance may occur in the more specialized environments.

The magnolian alliance represents one of the most primitive angiosperm groups now living. In its broadest relations, it is primarily adapted to the tropics and secondarily to the bordering climates (Bews, 1927). The larger families and most of the genera are found in tropical to warm-temperate forests. The families which depart most widely from type occur in extra-tropical areas, and the genera of a given family which differ most from the basic type are also found chiefly in communities of cooler and drier aspects that border tropical forests. Of the two hundred-odd genera in the alliance, scarcely 10 per cent occur in temperate forests: all the latter which have a known fossil record (i.e., *Cercidiphyllum, Eucommia, Trochodendron*) clearly had a more tropical distribution in the Cretaceous and Tertiary than they do today.

It is pertinent that the more primitive living angiosperms occur in upland areas. This applies to the rare relict types in the New Caledonia–Fiji region and to a host of woody ranalian plants that occur in the mountains of Southeast Asia, centering in the subtropical valleys of Yunnan and Upper Burma (see Takhtajan, 1957, for examples). Since they are ancient bradytelic types, they probably have persisted under generally similar conditions for long periods of time. This agrees with fossil evidence, which shows that several of them lived under equable climates from the Middle Cretaceous into the Middle Tertiary, when mild conditions enabled them to have a much wider distribution, particularly across the middle latitudes. It was only during the later Tertiary that these ancient taxa were confined to the regions where they now live. Since the present areas of these relict "primitive" angiosperms comprise only isolated refuges as compared with their earlier distribution and since they have come into existence as mountainous tracts only since the Early Tertiary, neither New Caledonia nor Yunnan can be considered to represent the center of origin of the angiosperm phylum, as has been suggested. But the montane tropical to subtropical environments in which they occur may well resemble, at least in a general way, those under which flowering plants originated.

The data provided by the magnolian alliance thus suggest that (1) primitive angiosperms were probably evolving in montane tropical to subtropical regions, giving rise to basic taxa (orders, families) that were adapted to tropical areas chiefly, and that (2) some of them exploited the cooler and drier upland environments marginal to the tropics, evolving into alliances adapted to temperate and subhumid climates. Should these inferences be correct, then the phylum should provide evidence of it.

The pattern of adaptation shown by the magnolian alliance occurs throughout the whole phylum (Bews, 1927; Axelrod, 1952a). Bews's critical review of the adaptive trends in angiosperms illustrates that, in alliance after alliance, the more primitive forms of a given group commonly occur in tropical regions and that the derived forms are in the more specialized tropical and extra-tropical areas (also see Camp, 1947, 1952, 1956; Tahktajan, 1957). In addition, distributional evidence shows that half the three-hundred-odd families of flowering plants have a tropical occurrence today (Axelrod, 1952a). If we add to this group those families which, while attaining optimum development and diversity in tropical regions, also range into extra-tropical areas, where they are represented largely by derivative types, then fully three-fourths of all angiosperm families must be considered as primarily adapted to tropical regions. Most of the remainder, whether the forty families narrowly confined to the temperate and dry regions marginal to the tropics or the twenty-five cosmopolitan and largely herbaceous families, also appear to have been derived chiefly from tropical alliances.

The data thus suggest that the phylum as a whole is adapted primarily to tropical environments. Primitive tropical taxa of numerous alliances appear to have contributed derived species, genera, and families not only to tropical regions but to border-tropical environments and to the temperate (Holarctic, Antarctic, high-mountain) and drier regions on all the continents during their history. We may conclude that the earliest angiosperms probably were tropical to subtropical in distribution, occupying the uplands of the Permian world.

EARLY EVOLUTION

Permian climates were more extreme than those of succeeding periods. Diverse drier subclimates existed over the western margins of the tropics, and the bordering temperate areas to the north and south were no doubt also varied in character. In montane areas the diversity of habitats would be even more marked. Such environmental relations would be particularly important to early angiosperm evolution because they would tend to promote the geographic differentiation of species and genera and hence the origin of new adaptive types in the initial angiosperm populations. In brief, since conditions would have been propitious for quantum evolution (Simpson, 1944, 1953), we may infer that many alliances (genera, families, orders) evolved in a relatively short time (Stebbins, 1950; Axelrod, 1952a; Němejc, 1956).

We must emphasize that this early evolution took place within the *varied* environments of a broader tropical zone than exists today. These populations were evolving not only in the humid montane tropics but probably also in the diverse subtropical and warm-temperate areas which were then in existence in the uplands. If evolution had commenced at this early date on the cooler and drier margins of the tropics, certain border tropic groups derived from basic tropical stocks may have appeared very early in angiosperm history. This may account for the great antiquity that must be postulated for a number of "peculiar" plant forms that are on the margins of the tropics today. Although it cannot be demonstrated that such plants as *Pachycereus, Dideria, Pachypodium, Idria,* and others are relict, bradytelic plants of the early Mesozoic, the probability is high that they represent their descendants.

Commencing in the Triassic and continuing through the Jurassic, there was moderation of climate. With the restriction of the more diverse and extreme continental climates of the preceding interval, some of the earlier "transitional" types probably became extinct as the more localized environments to which they were adapted tended to disappear. This would produce discontinuities between existing groups, thus delimiting in a random manner taxa of variable magnitude (genera, families, orders) within the surviving types. The latter could now expand and differentiate in upland areas, for there was a broad tropical belt flanked by mild temperate climates at high latitudes, with savannas in existence at middle latitudes.

During the early Mesozoic, therefore, many families probably commenced to evolve in the broad tropical belt. Others, which earlier had also begun to exploit extra-tropical environments to which they were preadapted, probably spread more widely, invading the montane temperate to subhumid regions both to the north and to the south. Some may have entered cooler and drier upland areas lying chiefly in northern extra-tropical regions. Others probably continued to differentiate not only in the montane tropics but also in the southern extra-tropical regions as well. As sketched in Figure 2, these are the inferred *primary* distribution patterns of angiosperm families. They had evolved in upland areas during the Triassic and Jurassic, they were in existence during the Cretaceous and Tertiary, and they are still evident today, though highly modified by late Cenozoic environmental changes (see below).

Adaptive radiation.—Angiosperms were undergoing adaptive radiation in upland areas during pre-Cretaceous time, deploying into different environments, where they were subdividing into numerous adaptive types. The basic type was terrestrial, autotrophic, and probably a shrub rather than a tree if the phylum diverged from a fern or seed-fern plexus. Regardless of its exact nature, widely divergent forms evolved from the generalized prototype which was adapted chiefly to mild, moist upland regions.

To understand the problem, we must recall that living angiosperms are adapted to their environments in different ways. In order, family, and genus, in alliance after alliance, the common adaptive types tree-shrub-herb are found in many environments, with the derived types regularly adapted to the more particular ways of life (Bews, 1925, 1927). Within more narrow alliances, some have developed distinctive responses to different climates. Thus woody species of the same genus may be either evergreen or deciduous, as in magnolia, oak, maple, and cherry. By contrast, some adaptive types are confined to specialized habitats, like the poplars, cottonwoods, and willows, which comprise a family restricted to sites where there is always ample water. A more extreme case is found in the marine littoral belt, which supports mangrove, nipa, and eelgrass, all of divergent orders and families. Floating and submerged plants, such as pondweed and water chestnut, have developed in numerous alliances. Varied and specialized types occur also in dry regions. Some are woody, leafless shrubs of monotypic families (Koeberliniaceae), others are succulent water-storage types (Cactaceae, Aizoaceae), and growing side by side with them are geophytes, drought-deciduous shrubs, and scores of minute

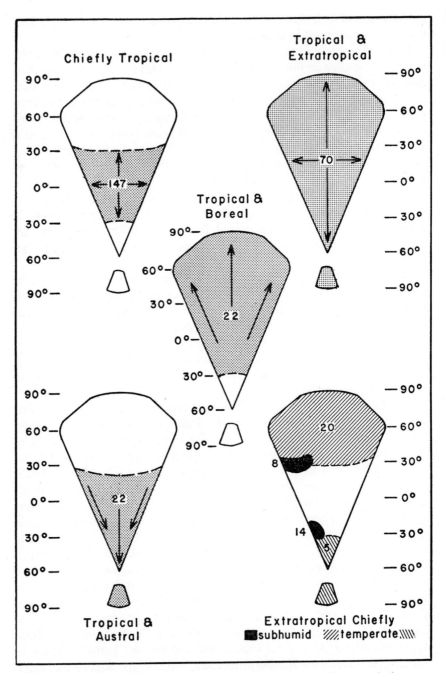

FIG. 2.—Primary distribution patterns of angiosperm families, sketched on an idealized world continent. The figures refer to the approximate number of families in each geographic pattern.

annuals—contributed by many orders and families—which span their life-period in a week or two.

There also are climbers, epiphytes, and halophytes, as well as underground plants, saprophytes, parasites, and insectivorous plants. Approximately sixty angiosperm families are made up almost exclusively of these specialized adaptive types (Table 1). They all have pro-

TABLE 1

ANGIOSPERM FAMILIES MADE UP CHIEFLY OF THE ADAPTIVE TYPES LISTED

Climbers:	*Xerophytes:*	*Hydrophytes:*
Actinidiaceae	Aizoaceae	Alismaceae
Ancistrocladaceae	Cactaceae	Aponogetonaceae
Convolvulaceae	Crassulaceae	Butomaceae
Dioscoreaceae	*Epiphytes:*	Cabombaceae
Lardizabalaceae	Bromeliaceae	Callitrachaceae
Menispermaceae	Marcgravaceae	Ceratophylaaceae
Passifloraceae	(also abundant in Orchida-	Elatinaceae
Sargentodoxaceae	ceae, Eticaceae, Rubia-	Halogoraceae
Vitaceae	ceae)	Hippuridaceae
Parasites (hemi- to holo-):	*Saprophytes:*	Hydrocharitaceae
Balanophoraceae	Burmaniaceae	Hydrostachaceae
Cynomoriaceae	Monotropaceae	Juncaginaceae
Hydnoraceae	Triuridaceae	Lennonaceae
Lennonaceae	*Geophytes:*	Najadaceae
Loranthaceae	Begoniaceae	Nymphaceae
Myzodendronaceae	Podophyllaceae	Pontederiaceae
Orobranchaceae	Taccaceae	Potamogetonaceae
Rafflesiaceae	Zingiberaceae	Rhizophoraceae
Santalaceae	*Insectivorous:*	Sparganiaceae
	Cephalotaceae	Trapaceae
	Droseraceae	Trapellaceae
	Lentibulariaceae	Tristichaceae
	Nepanthaceae	Typhaceae
	Sarraceniaceae	Zanchilliaceae

nounced structural modifications, not only in internal organization, but in external form as well. These specializations for particular ways of life are in the vegetative parts (roots, stems, leaves), the reproductive structures showing only minor variation in each alliance. Many of these families are generically monotypic or else are composed of only a few (less than five) genera.

These specialized adaptive types occur repeatedly throughout the phylum, and many show convergence in terms of the plant body. This plasticity of angiosperms with respect to structural and functional adaptations parallels the vertebrates, in which adaptive types at ordinal and family level also represent marked structural and functional adaptations. The difference between an aquatic pondweed, a climbing morning glory, and a subterranean podophyllum is thus comparable to that between (*a*) an aquatic ichthyosaur, a climbing tree snake, and a fossorial legless lizard in the reptiles; between (*b*) an aquatic grebe, a climbing woodpecker, and a burrowing owl in the birds; or between (*c*) an aquatic dugong, a climbing monkey, and a mole among the mammals.

As discussed in considerable detail by Bews (1925, 1927), the various trends of adaptation in flowering plants appear to radiate from forms basically adapted to the more moist terrestrial habitats. Their derivatives are largely adapted to the more specialized ways of life. Although the phyletic relations of some specialized families are uncertain, the affinities of others seem generally agreed upon, for instance:

Ancestral Type	Derived Adaptive Type
Aristolochiaceae (climbers)	Hydnoraceae (parasitic)
Ericaceae-Pyrolaceae (trees, shrubs, herbs, parasites)	Monotropaceae (saprophytic)
Lythraceae (woody to herbaceous, some aquatic)	Rhizophoraceae (marine aquatic)
Onograceae (shrub, herb, many aquatic)	Trapaceae (aquatic)
Ranunculaceae (herbaceous, mesic to aquatic)	Ceratophyllaceae (aquatic)
Scrophulariaceae (numerous adaptive types, see below)	Orobranchaceae (parasitic)
Ternstroemiaceae (trees, shrubs)	Marcgraviaceae (epiphytic)

It is critical that some families include a number of adaptive types because they suggest the manner in which higher categories may arise. One of the better examples noted by Bews is the large family Scrophulariaceae, comprising over 250 genera and 3,000 species. Widely distributed from the tropics to the cold-temperate regions, they are represented by woody, as well as herbaceous, types. The majority are terrestrial in moist habitats and are especially abundant in the warmer latitudes. Some of the specialized adaptive types in the family include the following:

Prostrate to creeping types	*Veronica, Mazus, Linaria*
Marshy to aquatic	*Ambulia, Hydrotriche*
Hemiparasites (green)	*Euphrasia, Pedicularis*
Parasites	*Lathraea, Harveya, Hyobranche*

The trend toward parasitism in the Scrophulariaceae apparently terminates in the related Orobranchaceae, and, further, the insectivorous Lentibulariaceae probably was also derived from it.

Many other angiosperm families include several divergent adaptive types, a relation also paralleled by the major groups of vertebrates. For instance, the rodents include types adapted for speed (rabbit), digging (ground squirrel), underground (gopher), swimming, (muskrat), climbing (tree squirrel), and flying-gliding (flying squirrel); and the carnivores comprise climbing (jaguar), walking (lion), aquatic (otter), and digging (badger) types. These analogies suggest that the plasticity of flowering plants has led repeatedly to the origin of new taxa during adaptive radiation as divergent types have gradually achieved new adaptive peaks, passing from specific to generic, familial, and, eventually, even to ordinal (Cactales—succulent xerophytes; Podostemonales—aquatic; Santalales—parasitic; Sarraceniales—insectivorous) level.

Figure 3 sketches some of the major adaptive trends in the angiosperm phylum. The lines connecting the different adaptive types do not mean that these are the only ways in which a given type may have evolved; thus parasites may develop from climbers as well as from terrestrial forms. It is instructive to compare Figure 3 with Figure 4,

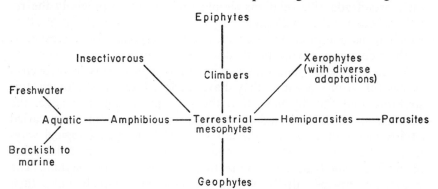

Fig. 3.—Showing the principal adaptive types which have developed in flowering plants (compare with Fig. 4).

which also portrays in an abbreviated way adaptive radiation of the vertebrates (Lull, 1947).

Bews has emphasized that divergent adaptive trends occur repeatedly in most of the larger angiosperm alliances. His belief that phylogeny can be interpreted, at least in part, from an ecological point of view in terms of adaptive trends in radiating groups obviously has much merit. Most botanists, however, have chiefly emphasized the evolutionary significance of reproductive structures in angiosperms. The fact that each angiosperm is an organism which reflects its adaptation to a particular way of life has not been sufficiently exploited from an evolutionary point of view. It seems clear not only that future investigations of the natural alliances of flowering plants in terms of

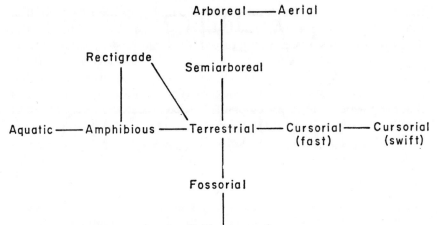

Fɪɢ. 4.—Showing the principal adaptive types which have developed in the vertebrates (from Lull, 1945).

their broad adaptive relations should indicate more precisely the relations between the smaller and larger taxa, but, just as important, they will help us comprehend more clearly the responses of angiosperms to their changing environments during the course of time.

Much has been made of the point that angiosperms have been a successful group because they have inclosed seeds. Although this structure undoubtedly has given the phylum an adaptive edge, the great plasticity of the angiosperm body in terms of meeting varied environments in so many different structural and physiological ways may well account in even larger measure for the fact that flowering plants have ruled the lands more than any other plant phylum. The psilophytes are essentially hydrophytes and are scarcely more than small, tender herbs. Their present representatives are specialized types of tropical regions—*Psilotum,* a slender shrub, and *Tmespteris,* an epiphyte. The arthrophytes are chiefly hydrophytes, with three major adaptive lines, herbaceous (*Equisetum*), arborescent (*Calamites*), and climbing (*Sphenophyllum*). The lycopods are largely mesophytes, also of tree (*Lepidodendron, Sigillaria*) and herbaceous (*Lycopodium, Selaginella*) habit, with some of the latter adapted to arid as well as moist environments. One isolated taxon (*Phylloglossum*) is a geophyte, paralleling tuberous angiosperms, and another (*Isoetes*) is an aquatic or marsh plant. The ferns have displayed but little plasticity of form in their adaptive radiation, with the water ferns a conspicuous exception. Many ferns are epiphytes, some are climbers, but most are in the tree-shrub-herb category, with some of the latter ranging into the alpine regions as well as the desert. Gymnosperms show adaptations somewhat more diverse than the preceding phyla. They include trees, shrubs, and climbers (*Gnetum*) but no herbs. The trees may be deciduous (*Ginkgo, Larix, Metasequoia, Taxodium*), but most are evergreen (*Abies, Araucaria, Cupressus, Picea, Sequoia*). The majority occur in humid regions, and a few are aquatic (*Taxodium, Glyptostrobus*). Many range into the drier regions (*Cupressus, Juniperus, Callitris*), and two are extreme xerophytes, one (*Ephedra*) being essentially an aphyllous shrub, the other (*Welwitschia*) a geophyte. The adaptive types displayed by all the preceding phyla can be found in a number of families of flowering plants, and the latter include many which are not known in any other plant phylum.

In view of the inherent plasticity of the group, we may suppose that numerous adaptive types existed in montane areas during the pre-Cretaceous. If we could take a walk through a Jurassic mountain area, we would probably find a wealth of plant forms, not only trees, shrubs, and herbs in many alliances and in different climatic regions but also specialized aquatics (*Nymphaea* pollen is recorded from the Jurassic), xerophytes, geophytes, climbers, epiphytes, and probably parasites as well. This evolution of plant form in terms of adaptive type must have been taking place concurrently with floral evolution. Saporta was apparently the first to suggest that pollinating insects may have been a significant agent in angiosperm evolution.[1] This relation, which apparently started in the earlier Mesozoic, probably "was the beginning of a partnership which has proved highly successful for both" (Ross, 1956, p. 417). It is no accident that over 67 per cent of the living flowering plants are insect-pollinated and that over 20 per cent of the insects depend on flowers for food during at least some stage of their development. Pertinently, Cretaceous insects were as "modern" as the plants on which they were feeding, and Jurassic insects chiefly represent living families—a relation which we have inferred for most angiosperms. Thus, taking into account the adaptive plasticity of the alliance together with the powerful stimulus provided by pollinating insects and probably also by birds and bats, numerous taxa (families, genera) of modern type had probably already evolved in upland regions during pre-Cretaceous time.

[1] Saporta advanced this idea in a letter to Darwin (*Life and Letters*, II, 458–59). Although Darwin urged him to publish it, so far as I have been able to determine he apparently did not do so.

The evolutionary relation between insect pollination and flowering plants was first discussed seriously by Arber and Parkin (*Jour. Lin. Soc.*, XXXVIII [1907], 29–80). Dr. Verne Grant, who is well acquainted with the history of the idea, has pointed out to me that, since Arber and Parkin cited much of Saporta's work, they almost surely would have credited him with the idea if he had discussed it in one of his numerous papers.

INVASION OF LOWLANDS

Angiosperms assumed dominance over lowland areas during the Early Cretaceous, displacing the Gymnophyte Paleoflora of cycadophytes, conifers, ferns, and seed ferns which had dominated lowland sites of deposition since the Permian. This replacement was gradual, as shown by comparison with the time required for the other paleofloras to rise to dominance. In each case—Psilophyte-Pterophyte in the Late Devonian, Pterophyte-Gymnophyte in the Carboniferous-Permian transition, and Gymnophyte-Angiophyte in the Early Cretaceous— replacement took place during an interval of approximately twenty to twenty-five million years (Axelrod, 1952*a*). Flowering plants did not migrate into the lowlands at all latitudes simultaneously. Rather, they appear to have invaded the higher latitudes gradually from a center of origin at lower, tropical latitudes. This is contrary to the earlier idea that the Early Cretaceous Kome flora of Greenland represents the oldest assemblage containing angiosperms (about 10 per cent) associated with vegetation which otherwise is largely Jurassic in aspect; this relation led to the belief that flowering plants originated in the north and thence migrated southward. More recent stratigraphic evidence (summarized in Imlay and Reeside, 1954) indicates that the Kome is high in the Early Cretaceous, probably transitional Aptian-Albian. Further, the rich, angiosperm-dominated Dakota is now judged Albian, not Cenomanian. These revised age relations cast entirely new light on the problem of invasion of the lowlands by angiosperms. When examined in terms of the percentage of angiosperms in the various Early Cretaceous floras, we find a higher percentage in floras from lower latitudes as compared with those in contemporaneous floras at higher latitudes during the Wealden (Neocomian), Aptian, and early Albian; one or two exceptions (in Alaska) may be local relict areas. In general, angiosperms appear first in small numbers (up to 10 per cent) at lower middle latitudes (35°–40° N.) in Virginia, Portugal, and California during the Neocomian. They reached middle latitudes (40°–55° N.) in moderate numbers during the Aptian (Canada, England, Korea, southern Alaska, Russia), but only replaced the Gymnophyte Paleoflora at high latitudes (60°–80° N.) after the Albian (Axelrod, 1959*c*). It is apparent that age analysis must take into account the time-space factor in the Cretaceous as well as in the Tertiary.

Examination of the first lowland Cretaceous floras containing angiosperms in abundance shows that several major regional floras were already differentiated. Tropical to warm-temperate vegetation characterized the low and lower-middle latitudes, with differences apparent from region to region. These floras include families which are clearly and preponderantly tropical, which have their greatest diversity there, and which probably underwent their early evolution in tropical uplands in earlier times. Since the primary tropical alliances apparently evolved chiefly in the montane tropics, those that now typify the lowland rain forests invaded this zone during the Early Cretaceous. Many of their nearest relatives might therefore be expected in the montane tropics. This agrees with the observation that, of the genera which have fairly broad altitudinal ranges within the tropics, the more primitive living species are usually found on the lower mountain slopes, not in the lowlands (Camp, 1956).

The temperate Cretaceous floras of higher northern and southern latitudes differed greatly from one another. They are composed of plants that presumably had evolved from ancestral tropical forerunners which deployed into temperate montane regions early in the history of the phylum. The plants in the Cretaceous floras of northern Holarctica represent the immediate ancestors of the temperate Arcto-Tertiary Geoflora, whereas those in the south gave rise to species typifying the Antarcto-Tertiary Geoflora.

Taxa ancestral to those that are restricted now to subhumid areas at low-middle latitudes in the western parts of the continents were probably also in existence in the pre-Cretaceous. For example, the Early Cretaceous Shasta flora of California shows that regional climatic and vegetation differences were already in existence in the Far West: it contains small-, thick-leafed plants that are not now known in contemporaneous floras elsewhere. Furthermore, some of the Late Cretaceous and Paleocene floras of western North America include species apparently ancestral to those which typified the drier climates during and following the Eocene (Axelrod, 1958). Since they belong to many different families, we may suppose that the origin of the distinct and isolated families now confined to the drier regions commenced at an earlier date. They probably evolved from ancestral subtropical groups in the drier uplands of the western part of the continent during the pre-Cretaceous. A similar relation may be inferred for the evolution of the dry floras of the other continents.

We may conclude that angiosperms have not had an exclusively holarctic source or a wholly austral center of origin. They appear to have evolved in both regions as basic tropic stocks gradually deployed into extra-tropical montane environments during pre-Cretaceous time. From this standpoint, the temperate regions to the north (holarctic) and south (antarctic) are *secondary* centers of angiosperm evolution, as are the drier areas marginal to them and the hot lowland tropics as well. However, all these regions have been centers of radiation (migration) for major, generalized plant communities (geofloras) during the past hundred million years in which flowering plants have dominated lowland regions. The shifting area occupied by each geoflora—whether of tropical, temperate, or subhumid character—was determined chiefly by the changing pattern of global climate.

CENOZOIC EVOLUTION

TERTIARY GEOFLORAS

Looking to geographical distribution, if we admit that there has been during the long course of ages much migration from one part of the world to another, owing to former climatal and geographical changes and to the many occasional and unknown means of dispersal, then we can understand, on the theory of descent with modification, most of the great leading facts in Distribution [DARWIN, 1859].

By the dawn of the Tertiary, flowering plants of modern aspect covered the earth. Most older Tertiary plants can be referred to existing genera, and many are similar to living species. Close relationships between nearly all fossil and modern species are apparent by the later Oligocene. Although all Tertiary floras resemble modern plant communities, the distribution and composition of Tertiary vegetation differed in many ways from that of the present day. From these relations it is possible to reconstruct the habitats and climates under which Tertiary floras lived, to outline the belts of Tertiary vegetation, and to explain the evolution of modern patterns of distribution.

The modifications in distribution and composition which led to the development of our present regional floras were due chiefly to a climatic trend toward increased continentality. As a result, mild and humid (tropical to warm-temperate) climates became more restricted, drier (subtropic, steppe) and colder (cold-temperate) ones expanded, and wholly new regional climates (mediterranean, desert, tundra, polar) gradually developed. In addition, an ever increasing diversity of subclimates appeared in each major climatic type. These changing global climatic relations correspond to the opening-up of new adaptive zones and to the restriction of older ones. They account in part for the evolution at lower taxonomic levels of new plants adapted to these newer climatic areas and for the development of present-day patterns of distribution. In brief, the trend of Tertiary climate was responsible for the migration of major units of Tertiary vegetation (geofloras) and for changes in the composition and distribution of plant communities due to the effect of changing climate operating on the varying and changing ranges of tolerances of species through time.

Since the general character and distribution of the Tertiary Geo-floras have been summarized elsewhere (Chaney, 1947), attention is focused here chiefly on the evolution of the broader modern patterns of distribution, a topic of particular interest to Darwin and to his contemporaries—Hooker, Wallace, and Gray.

Tropical-Tertiary Geofloras.—World-wide moderation of temperature at the outset of the Tertiary is indicated by a poleward shift of tropical vegetation into middle latitudes on all the continents. The tropical to subtropical forests that migrated northward into Eurasia and southward into Africa and Australia–New Zealand comprise the Paleotropical-Tertiary Geoflora. The closely related forests that ranged into middle latitudes in the Americas represent the Neotropical-Tertiary Geoflora. Their maximum extent is sketched in Figure 5, which shows that they interfingered with the temperate Arcto-Tertiary Geoflora to the north and with the Antarcto-Tertiary Geoflora at the south; the broad ecotone or zone of overlap between the Tropical and Temperate Geofloras is not depicted here.

The Paleotropical-Tertiary Geoflora shows greatest relationship with the modern Old World tropical forests, whereas the Neotropical-Tertiary Geoflora includes many American types. These differences are presumably the result of evolution in these widely separated regions during pre-Tertiary times. There are, however, important resemblances between the floras of the tropics of both hemispheres which have not previously been explained and which must be accounted for. Of the 300-odd plant families, 139 are strictly tropical today, and they apparently have always been confined to tropical regions. Setting aside the 49 endemic families, 54 are pantropic, and most of them comprise the larger and more characteristic alliances of the tropics. The remainder are discontinuous in the tropics, 12 of them linking the American and African tropics, 8 the tropics of America and the Southeast Asian region (hereafter termed "Australasian"), and 16 the tropics of Africa and Australasia. These stronger tropical ties are increased when we add an additional 125 families, which, while represented in the temperate and drier regions by derivative types, reach their optimum development and diversity in the tropics and are largely pantropic in occurrence.

An even larger number of families was common to the tropical region in the past. Thus the Aponogetonaceae, presently confined to the African and Australasian regions, has been recorded in the Cretaceous of South America, the fossil being most nearly like a living African species (Selling, 1947). The Alangiaceae of the Old World tropics has been recorded in North America (Potbury, 1935). Further, the Casuarinaceae of present Australasian distribution occurs in the Ter-

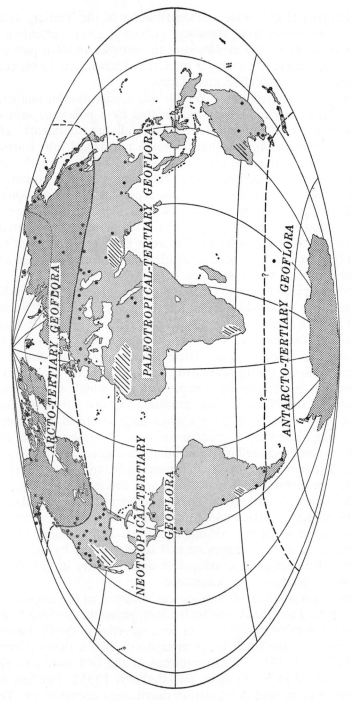

Fig. 5.—Distribution of geofloras in the Early Tertiary (data chiefly from Chaney, 1940; Berry, 1938; Krystofovich, 1957; Couper, 1953, 1954). Floras (*black circles*) above dotted line in far north are cool-temperate; diagonal lines show areas where semiarid geofloras were commencing to appear.

tiary of South America (Frenguelli, 1943). We may suppose that other families which are now restricted had wider occurrences in the past, including the endemic tropical families, of which 20 are now in America, 12 in Africa-Madagascar, and 17 in the Australasian region. In this connection, reference is made to the wood of *Cyclantho-dendron* from the Eocene of India, for it appears to represent the Cyclanthaceae, now confined to the American tropics (Sahni and Surange, 1953).

The generic relations of plants in the New and Old World also suggest stronger intertropical ties. Using Good's (1947) data, there are now 250 pantropic genera, 28 are widely discontinuous, 91 are common to the American and African tropics, and 37 to the American and Australasian tropics. As with the families, the genera show that there were stronger connections across the tropics in the Cretaceous and Early Tertiary and presumably earlier. For example, a number of present-day Old World genera, chiefly of the Indo-Malayan and border areas, occur in the Cretaceous and Early Tertiary of North America, notably *Alangium, Artocarpus, Aleurites, Cinnamomum, Columbia, Mallotus, Nipa, Phytocrene, Raphis,* and others. In the same way, some European floras include living American types—for instance, *Sabal* and *Serenoa* in the London Clay flora. Mention should also be made of the occurrence, in the Eocene of India (Sahni, 1943), of sporocarps similar to those of the water fern *Regnellidium,* now confined to Brazil. It is apparent that a more careful comparison of fossils representing the Tropical Geofloras with modern species throughout the tropics may reveal that there were even greater similarities between the Tropical-Tertiary Geofloras than now appear to be indicated. In any event, the present data are sufficient to show that extensive intertropical migration must be postulated to explain the relations of the Tropical Geofloras and of the modern floras as well.

Past connections between the tropics were not around the higher latitudes during the Cretaceous or Tertiary because those regions were occupied by temperate climates during this hundred-million-year interval. There appear to have been three important connections across the ancient tropics that are no longer present and which may explain the relations noted. First, there was a direct connection between the African and Australasian regions through the dry zone that now effectively separates these provinces and which came into existence only following Eocene time. That migration was readily possible across the lowlands of an extended paleotropical region is shown by Cretaceous and Paleocene-Eocene floras from the Sahara and the Red Sea hills which contain plants whose nearest relatives now live in wet, tropical southeastern Asia (Seward, 1935; Chandler, 1954). Second, there was more land for plant migration in the west Indian Ocean during the Mesozoic and the Tertiary as well. The Indian Ocean is composed of two contrasting parts (Fairbridge, 1948), separated by the Carlsbad–Mid-Indian–Kerguelen Ridge (Fig. 6). To the eastward the basin is deeper, generally "featureless," apparently without continental rocks, and it is aseismic. The median ridge rises to moderate depths and has a general arcuate outline much like present-day alpine systems. Some of the islands on the south part of the ridge contain continental rocks (see Fig. 6)—for instance, Kerguelen (syenite, monzonite, diorite), St. Paul (rhyolite, rhyolite tuff), and Crozet (granite, mica schist) (see Appendix). This suggests that the ridge to the northward is probably sialic, which is consistent with the fact that it is an important seismic zone (Fig. 7). The Indian Ocean west of the median rise is composed of linear ridges and basins, which suggest its continental structure, as do seismic data (Gutenberg, 1951). The nature of the rocks on some of the islands provides additional evidence (Fig. 6). Madagascar, with its granitic and metamorphic rocks, is certainly part of an old land area, connected with Africa in pre-Cretaceous time; the faulting which accounts for truncation and subsidence along its east coast is apparently of Tertiary age. The Seychelles-Mauritius Rise is continental because the Seychelles at the north contain granite and slate and Mauritius at the south has slate (see Appendix). Further, the older Mesozoic and Paleozoic sediments of South Africa (Cape) and East Africa (Natal) were derived from regions east of the present continent; they were not transported from a festoon of offshore volcanic islands but from an ancient (Archean?) terrain of gneiss, granite, and schist which is now largely submerged (Haughton, 1952). The Laccadive, Maldive, and Chagos islands lie on the Maldive Ridge, which has a strong negative anomaly, indicating that downwarped light continental rocks underlie it (Glennie, 1936); further, the ridge is seismically active, which also points to its continental structure (Fig. 7). Since the west coast of India was downfaulted following Eocene time (Lees, 1953), the Maldive Ridge may represent part of a larger Indian subcontinent.

The relations of the fossil marine invertebrate faunas appear to demand land areas separating the Indo-Pacific from the Tethys province during the Late Jurassic (Arkell, 1956, p. 600; Wadia, 1953, p. 287) and in the later parts of the Cretaceous as well (Blanford, 1890, pp. 96–98; Kossmat, 1897; Usher, 1952; Dutoit, 1954; Wadia, 1953, p. 287). The affinities of the flora of Madagascar and bordering islands to the Indo-Malaysian region also indicate stronger ties in the past. In addition, biogeographic evidence provided by birds, insects, land snails, and other animals (excluding placentals) on these islands

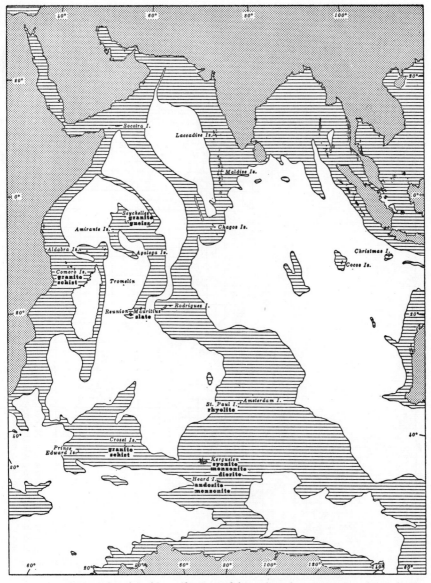

FIG. 6.—Crests of major ridges (*horizontal lines,* less than 4,000 feet deep) in the Indian Ocean represent presumed sites of wider lands in the Mesozoic and Early Tertiary which existed at least as extensive archipelagos. The ridges are largely volcanic (Tertiary-Recent), underlain by older sialic rocks, and are still active seismically (see Fig. 7).

251

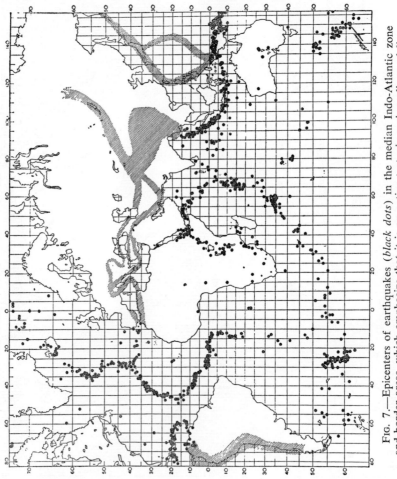

FIG. 7.—Epicenters of earthquakes (*black dots*) in the median Indo-Atlantic zone and border areas, which emphasize that it is an active tectonic region; diagonal lines show active seismic zones on the bordering continents (from Rothe, 1954).

points to faunal interchange with the Indo-Malayan region in the past, probably in the Cretaceous and later, depending on the particular group and their probabilities for dispersal (Blanford, 1890; Wallace, 1895; Darlington, 1957). Wallace thought that migration was chiefly over more extensive archipelagos than exist today, but Blanford visualized an essentially continuous land area in the west Indian Ocean Basin chiefly because dinosaurs (possibly *Megalosaurus; Laplatasaurus,* an amphibious type) occur in the Cretaceous of Madagascar. The absence of primary fresh-water fishes on the islands and the relations of the mammals provide strong evidence for islands in the western half of the Indian Ocean during the later Cretaceous and Tertiary, not a continuous continent. So far as the plants are concerned, the data suggest that the tropical floras of Africa-Madagascar and the Australasian region were essentially continuous during the Mesozoic, bridging both the present dry zone to the northward and land areas in the western half of the Indian Ocean which have largely subsided.

The third area for migration probably was across the Atlantic at low to middle latitudes, utilizing land areas which have since disappeared. The Mid-Atlantic Ridge, which bisects the ocean basin, emerges from a broad, relatively shallow plain north of the Azores, trends southward through the Atlantic, and finally swings eastward into the south Indian Ocean. The higher parts of the ridge form the Main Range, which is 30–60 miles wide. It is typified by a number of closely spaced ridges, many of whose peaks rise to within 2,000 feet of sea level, and several of them emerge to form the islands of the mid-Atlantic. The morphology of the subordinate ridges and their *en echelon* arrangement suggest that they are of diastrophic origin and the result of compression. The Main Range is flanked by a broad plateau, underlain at least locally by 3,000 feet of sediment of unknown age (Tolstoy, 1951). Although the islands of the ridge and much of the ridge itself are largely basalt, they differ in no essential way from basalts which are typical of the continents (Shand, 1949); they are not ultrabasic "oceanites" like those of the Pacific Basin. Some of the Atlantic islands have yielded continental rocks (see Appendix, and Fig. 8), notably Ascension (xenoliths of granite, gneiss, gabbro, granite-jasper conglomerate in basalt), Tristan da Cunha (xenoliths of granite and gneiss in basalt, andesite), and St. Paul's Rocks (dynamically metamorphosed [mylonitized] dunite and peridotite). Continental rocks also have been recovered from dredgings, notably on the south Azores Swell (mylonitized anorthositic gabbro) and on the east slope of the Walvis Ridge (arkose pebble). The granite and gneiss blocks on the coasts of Santa María and Terceria in the Azores have been attributed to transport by icebergs, but rhyolites in the volcanic section suggest

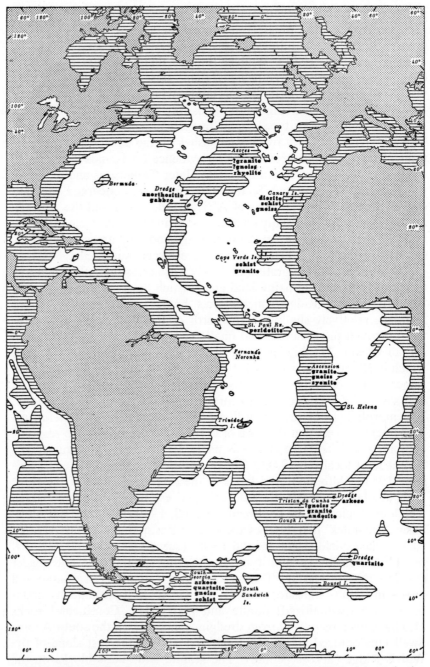

FIG. 8.—Crests of major ridges (*horizontal lines,* less than 4,000 feet deep) in the Atlantic Ocean represent presumed sites of wider lands in the Mesozoic and Early Tertiary which existed at least as extensive archipelagos. The ridges are largely volcanic (Tertiary-Recent), underlain by older sialic rocks, and are still active seismically (see Fig. 7).

254

that the Azores are probably underlain by continental rocks. The presence of quartzite on Meteor Bank indicates its continental structure and suggests that the median ridge south of Africa, which is a continuation of the Mid-Atlantic Ridge and links it with the Mid-Indian Ridge, is sialic in nature. This inference finds support in the occurrence of schist and granite on Crozet, and, further, the area is seismically active (Fig. 7).

The preceding suite of rocks recovered from the Mid-Atlantic Ridge demonstrates that it is an old mobile belt or alpine system because rocks of this type are formed only in such regions. It is pertinent that seismic evidence indicates that sialic rocks underlie the Ridge (Gutenberg, 1951) and the area is still active seismically. Since the loci of the earthquakes which occur along the Ridge are shallow, not intermediate or deep, the processes that built it are no longer active in the sense that it is a young structure comparable to the East or West Indies (Gutenberg and Richter, 1949). The basement rocks have been considered Paleozoic, though they may be older. The present relief is due chiefly to Cenozoic vulcanism and to faulting (Daly, 1938; Shand, 1949; Kuenen, 1950; Kulp and Carr, 1953), the old basement having subsided largely in pre-Tertiary time (see below).

The possible extent of other land areas in the Atlantic Basin during the early history of angiosperms is suggested by Rothe's analysis of the seismic evidence, which, he believes, indicates that all the Atlantic Basin east of the Ridge is continental (sialic). The physical architecture of the east Atlantic, with its basins and ridges, is compatible with such an interpretation. It is also consistent with the fact that much of the west coast of Africa is composed of a Precambrian crystalline basement only thinly veneered with sediment; the basement obviously once extended farther west—into the Atlantic. Further, there is evidence of subsidence off the Guiana coast (Haughton, 1952); off the coast of South Africa, where the Cape Ranges strike into the Atlantic (Umbgrove, 1947); in Nigeria-Cameroon, where the faulted Massif de Ladamqua strikes seaward into the Bight of Biafra, its trace being marked by a series of small islands (Fernando Po-Annobon), and which appears to extend to St. Helena; and the Cape Verde Islands, 500 miles off the coast, contain a granite-schist basement overlain by vertically dipping Jurassic and Cretaceous sediments. This section may be a southwesterly extension of the Atlas fold belt that strikes through the Canaries, where diorite, schist, and gneiss crop out under the younger volcanics.

Although there appears to be good evidence for ancient land areas encompassed within the region occupied by the east Atlantic Basin at generally lower latitudes, little information is available on the nature of the western part of the tropical Atlantic, which extended to at least latitude 40° north-south during the Mesozoic. The western part of the south Atlantic is composed of ridges and troughs, which suggest that they are of tectonic origin. Much of the eastern coast of Brazil is a Precambrian basement that fronts the ocean and clearly extended farther east during the past. Foundering has been postulated for parts of the Caribbean region (Weeks, 1948), and in the far south Gregory (1929, p. cx) has reviewed evidence which suggests that the source for the older sediments along the Scotia Arc probably was in the region of the present deep Brazilian basin. Geophysical evidence has also shown that the Atlantic coastal plain of the United States extended farther east during the later Mesozoic (Ewing et al., 1939, 1950). The Azores in the mid–north Atlantic rest on a broad shallow rise which appears to be continental; mylonitized anorthositic gabbro occurs on the south part of the rise, and rhyolite is on the islands.

That wider lands were available for migration across the Atlantic now seems clear from geologic evidence alone. This is not a new idea but, taken in conjunction with paleontological evidence, has earlier been advocated by Suess, Von Ihering, Neumayr, Blanford, Schwartz, and Gregory (1929, see references and his maps). More recently, Caster (in Mayr, 1952) has again visualized a broad craton (platform) linking South America and South Africa during the Paleozoic and Early Mesozoic. Others have argued for at least a series of islands spaced sufficiently close to allow migration across the region during the Mesozoic and probably later for some groups (see Darlington, Roemer, and Camp in Mayr et al., 1952; Pillsbury, 1911; Schuchert, 1932; Willis, 1932). As far as flowering plants are concerned, trans-Atlantic migration probably was largely completed by the close of the Early Cretaceous (Albian), if not earlier, following which generic and family tropical types seem to have evolved largely independently in the Old and New World tropics.

Much additional information is needed from geophysics, geology, and paleontology before the general distribution and times of subsidence of these wider Atlantic lands can be determined with greater assurance. The data now in hand suggest that subsidence continued in the Atlantic through the Mesozoic and into the Cenozoic. Arguing from the relations of the Triassic faunas and floras, Caster (in Mayr, 1952) believes that important (major?) foundering commenced at the close of the Triassic or in the Early Jurassic; the Upper Triassic dolerites of South Africa and South America, which welled up as a result of crustal tension, appear to be symptomatic of this movement (Caster, op. cit., p. 145). The Atlantic coastal plain seems to have been depressed to abyssal depths following the Early Cretaceous

(Ewing *et al.*, 1939, 1950); the east Brazilian coast (Bahia to Rio du Grand Sul) with its narrow continental shelf is clearly due to Late Tertiary (and earlier?) faulting (De Oliveira, 1956); the occurrence of fresh-water diatoms of Pleistocene age recovered from the slopes of the Mid-Atlantic Ridge at depths of over 10,000 feet suggests quite recent movement there (Kolbe, 1957). The relations of the upland flora of the Macronesian islands to the Pliocene floras of southwestern Europe indicate a Late Cenozoic land connection; that the region has been deformed recently is shown by the occurrence of Miocene marine rocks on Madeira at elevations of 1,200 feet.

As noted earlier, these trans-Atlantic connections which have been discussed briefly are required to explain the similarities which exist between the Cretaceous and the Cenozoic tropical floras of the world, relations which seem to have been established early in the history of the alliance.[2] Marked differences gradually developed between the tropical floras of the New and Old World during the Tertiary, and in each region conspicuous floristic changes also occurred, topics which we shall now consider.

A. The Paleotropical-Tertiary Geoflora gradually shifted to lower latitudes, commencing in the late Eocene, in response to the secular trend toward cooling and drying. The dry climate, expanding across the low-middle latitudes of the Old World, was the forerunner of the present desert, steppe, and mediterranean climates of Eurasia and North Africa. As subhumid climates developed over the lowlands, dry (deciduous) subtropical savanna and scrub gradually replaced the retreating moister forests; the scrub and savanna appear to have originated autochthonously, by the gradual adaptation of ancestral mesophytic types to local drier sites over the region during the later Cretaceous and Early Tertiary. Dry climate thus separated the moister facies of the geoflora into an eastern (Australasian) and a western (African) sector, with isolation largely completed by the close of the

---

[2] Slowly accumulating evidence suggests that the northern Pacific basin may also have provided a route of migration for tropical taxa between the New and Old Worlds. The recently-discovered major lineations (Murray, Mendocino, Clipperton, Clarion fracture zones) in the northeastern Pacific, some of which extend for more than 3000 miles, appear to mark the sites of important earth movement. Topography within the fracture zones is distinguished by large seamounts (which earlier were islands), deep narrow troughs, asymmetrical ridges, and escarpments. Some of the latter are about one mile high and over 1000 miles long (H. W. Menard. 1959. "Minor Lineations in the Pacific Basin," *Bull. Geol. Soc. Amer.*, LXX, 1491–96).

Whether the major features extend also into the northwestern Pacific, or have counterparts there, or whether extensive lands were present in the region during the Mesozoic and Early Tertiary, is not now known. However, the presence of numerous guyots in the north Pacific clearly indicates that volcanic islands were once more common than they are today. The history of the mid-Pacific mountains (Hamilton, 1956) suggests that they may be chiefly of Mesozoic age.

Eocene. These relations bear directly on the fact that the modern floras of the Indo-Malayan and African regions are still rather closely related; 278 genera are common to them and occur nowhere else. Patches of the geoflora persisted into the Miocene in southern Europe on the western side of the expanding dry belt, and some species survived in the western Mediterranean basin down to the close of the Tertiary. A few relicts still occur in the area (palm, laurel, fig, myrtle) and also in the Macronesian islands, where the fog-shrouded highlands in summer are favorable for laurel, dragon tree, avocado, and others.

In the east the Paleotropical-Tertiary Geoflora extended northward to central Japan: its northern margin was at a somewhat lower latitude on the eastern side of the Eurasian land mass, which is consistent with its geographic position (Chaney, 1940). Relicts of the geoflora persisted in northeastern China into the Late Miocene, but most had retreated south of the Yangtze by that epoch (Chaney and Hu, 1942), except probably for the mild coastal strip. Quaternary submergence of the Japanese islands, coupled with warming from the Kuroshio current and heavy rainfall through the year, probably accounts for the occurrence of large numbers of subtropical trees and shrubs in central Japan today: at the same latitude in eastern North America (Maryland to New Jersey), analogous relicts of the Neotropical-Tertiary Geoflora are essentially absent because of their proximity to the glacial border. Owing to the generally low altitude of the east Asian land area and to a broad continental shelf which has only recently been submerged, it seems likely that the Paleotropical-Tertiary Geoflora retreated southward as a unit on this eastern side of the continent, where a severe dry climate did not develop at lower latitudes.

In the southwestern Pacific the Paleotropical-Tertiary Geoflora occupied Australia, most of New Zealand, and also the islands to the northeast. Owing to favorable marine climate, subtropical conditions persisted at middle latitudes into the later Tertiary. The patches of subtropical rain forest on South Island (New Zealand) are remnants of the Tertiary, as are those in New South Wales (Australia), where they have survived in mild, humid, sheltered valleys of the coastal slope.

B. The Neotropical-Tertiary Geoflora, which extended to southeastern Alaska on the west coast, possibly to Nova Scotia on the east coast, and southward into Patagonia, had a closely similar history. In response to cooling in the Oligocene, the geoflora shifted toward the equator. As in southern Eurasia, the expansion of dry climate over the low-middle latitudes in western North America disrupted the earlier, more continuous moist forest belt. Isolated patches of tropical and subtropical forest survived on the Pacific Coast. They extended from coastal Washington into southern California during the Oligocene but were confined to coastal California by the Pliocene, with relicts like palm and avocado persisting down to the close of the Tertiary. Their gradual elimination from the region was due chiefly to the disappearance of summer rain, though lowered temperature was also responsible. Counterparts of the relict subtropic types in the Macronesian islands occur off the Pacific Coast of North America on Guadalupe and Socorro islands.

The fossil floras comprising the Neotropical-Tertiary Geoflora in eastern North America show that tropical to subtropical forests gradually retreated southward during the epoch. In contrast to eastern Asia, the dry climate that developed over the lower latitudes along the western Gulf Coast formed a barrier to its southward movement. Floras from the interior suggest that only a narrow fringe of subtropical forest persisted along the western Gulf Coast during Miocene time, and it probably was supplanted by subtropical scrub in the Early Pliocene. As compared with Japan, where many subtropic relicts have persisted at latitude 35°, only a few of the Neotropical-Tertiary Geoflora survived in the eastern United States, largely close to the seaboard from Cape Hatteras southward. Although numerous woody subtropic plants may have occupied the immediate coastal strip into the Late Tertiary, as judged from the composition of the later Miocene Calvert flora of Maryland, they were probably finally eliminated by the severe glacial climates, and most have not been able to re-establish there except for a few herbs of tropic families (see lists in Cain, 1944, pp. 261–64; Braun, 1950, chap. 15).

To the southward, the geoflora extended into Patagonia during the early part of the Tertiary. The similarity between floras on opposite sides of the Andes in Chile and Patagonia during the Eocene shows that the range was not yet in existence in the Early Tertiary, when a mild, frostless climate typified the middle latitudes. To judge from the Tertiary floras which have been studied (summarized in Berry, 1938), the South American flora included many plants of modern South American alliance; as mentioned above, a careful taxonomic revision of these floras may reveal stronger relations with the Paleotropical-Tertiary Geoflora than Berry suspected. In response to lowered temperature, the geoflora shifted equatorward following the Eocene. During the middle and later Tertiary, the development of dry climates on the west (Chile-Peru) and east (Bahia) coasts gradually confined the tropical flora to its present general region. In South America, Juan Fernández has relicts of the Neotropical-Tertiary Geoflora which persisted there under mild, marine climate well south of the present tropics, a pattern somewhat similar to that of New Zealand and southern Japan.

Floristic evolution of the present regional floras of the New and Old World tropics cannot yet be worked out because of the rarity of Tertiary floras in the tropics which might provide evidence of their later history there. Data available in some critical areas, such as India, coastal Peru, central Africa, Brazil (Bahia), and southern California, suggest that important floristic differences in the tropics developed in the later Cenozoic as new subclimates evolved over the shrinking moist tropical belt and as plants of formerly wide distribution became more restricted in some areas and extinct in others.

Summarizing, the chief distribution patterns of present-day tropical and subtropical floras seem to have evolved along the following general plan:

1. The occurrence of many pantropic families and genera today and of even larger numbers in the past, together with the presence of families and genera discontinuous between America-Africa or America-Australasia, seems explicable only if extensive archipelagos are postulated for the tropical Atlantic during the Mesozoic.

2. In the Old World, expanding dry climate separated the Paleotropical-Tertiary Geoflora into two major sectors—Australasian and African. Important floristic differences seem due to regional restriction of ranges, as well as to independent evolution in these widely separated areas.

3. In the New World, the floras of North and South America show important regional differences which are due chiefly to the contraction of formerly more widespread types and also to evolution in each area.

4. The disappearance of numerous Old World tropical genera and some families from the American tropics following the Eocene was due to unknown factors.

5. Hardy relicts of subtropical forests have survived at low-middle latitudes wherever the maritime climate is favorable (Baja California, Canary Islands, Spain, Juan Fernández).

Temperate-Tertiary Geofloras.—The temperate forests which had become established over the lowlands at higher northern latitudes by the beginning of the Tertiary comprise the Arcto-Tertiary Geoflora, and those in the cool austral regions represent the Antarcto-Tertiary Geoflora. Like the Tropical-Tertiary Geofloras, these temperate forests were in no sense homogeneous but differed from area to area in response to local climate and topography. The Temperate Geofloras closely followed the Tropical Geofloras as they retreated equatorward in response to cooling climate following the Eocene and had largely replaced them over the lowlands at middle latitudes by the Miocene.

During this migration the Arcto-Tertiary Geoflora shifted southward across fully 15° of latitude (Chaney and Hu, 1940). Data are not sufficient to determine the latitudinal shift of the Antarcto-Tertiary Geoflora during this interval, but available evidence suggests that it was of essentially similar magnitude.

A. The Arcto-Tertiary Geoflora was composed of a mixture of temperate conifers and deciduous hardwoods whose closest relatives occur in the forests of widely separated parts of Holarctica, such as western Europe, the Alpine belt, northeastern Asia, western North America, and eastern North America. During the Early and Middle Tertiary the Arcto-Tertiary Geoflora linked all these regions, extending across the tundra, steppe, and desert areas which have come into existence more recently. The latitudinal pattern of distribution shown by the segregate forests of the geoflora developed chiefly in response to changing climate during the Middle and Late Tertiary. The salient floristic evolutionary features of the geoflora in four regions—(1) western Europe, (2) eastern Asia, (3) western North America, and (4) eastern North America—will now be sketched.

1. Already occupying the lowlands of northern Europe during the Early Tertiary, the geoflora gradually invaded central Europe during the Middle Tertiary and had reached the Mediterranean Basin by the Miocene, where it overlapped the Paleotropical-Tertiary Geoflora. In Europe it was composed of several floristic units, the chief ones being (*a*) a European Element, including fossil species related to those that are now typically temperate European; (*b*) a Colchic Element, whose species resemble plants now in southeastern Europe and the adjacent areas to the eastward; (*c*) an East Asian Element, composed of fossil plants allied to species now in the area from Japan and Manchuria southward through temperate China; (*d*) an East American Element, whose species resemble plants now in eastern North America; and (*e*) a Boreal Element, the fossil species of which are related to phylads that now range more or less continuously across northern Holarctica. A rare West American Element, notably *Sequoia,* is present. Another important element, composed chiefly of herbaceous plants in the rich Pliocene seed floras, may be termed "Circumpolar" because the fossil species are very similar to plants that now have a wide distribution in the higher northern latitudes.

Commencing in the later Miocene and continuing through the Pliocene, three major floristic areas can be discerned in Europe. They correspond chiefly to the present areas of Europe (*a*) north of the Alps, (*b*) the Mediterranean Basin, and (*c*) southeastern Europe. Although species of most of the floristic elements were common to these regions, their proportional representation differs, as Szafer

(1946, 1954) has ably shown. Thus the East Asian Element is more prominent in the north, the Colchic in the southeast, and the East American in the Mediterranean Basin. As members of the East American and East Asian Elements continued to decrease during the Pliocene, they were supplanted by species of the European Element. Some species of the former groups are recorded in the first Interglacial north of the Alps and in the Mediterranean Basin, where members of these elements occur in southern France and Italy. They also persisted into the Quaternary in Tunis and Algeria, where species of *Carpinus Eleaganus, Juglans, Pterocarya,* and *Ulmus* of the East Asian and Colchic Elements lived in the lowlands, together with plants which are now typical of central to northern Europe (Arambourg *et al.,* 1953).

The gradual reduction in numbers of species of the eastern elements in Europe during the Pliocene has been ascribed to decreased temperature. However, decreased yearly rainfall over the lowlands may have been the chief factor because most of the "exotic" Pliocene species find their nearest relatives in regions where rainfall is higher than that which now occurs over the lowlands of Europe. The Ice Age also played a role in the final elimination of the "exotic" species from the region, though its influence probably was not so great as has been supposed (i.e., Hooker, 1878; Seward, 1941; Reid and Chandler, 1833). As noted above, some of the "exotics" reinvaded central Europe during the first Interglacial, presumably from refuges to the south or east, where they were already present during the Middle and Late Tertiary. The disappearance of summer rain was the chief factor responsible for their extinction in the Mediterranean refuge, but in the Colchic area to the eastward, where there is ample summer rain, a number of Tertiary relicts have persisted, notably *Acer orientalis, Carpinus orientalis, Castanea vesca, Diospyres lotus, Juglans regia, Pterocarya caucasica, Quercus mongolica, Ulmus parvifolia,* and *Zelkova crenata.* They clearly comprise an outpost of the East Asian Element in the Caucasus. A few species, such as *Carpinus betulus, Fagus sylvatica,* and *Ulmus campestris,* which have been able to reestablish to the northward in Europe, are hardy relicts of genera that now find optimum development in the wetter, eastern parts of the northern continents.

The immediate forerunners of plants typical of the major floristic areas of Europe were admixed in more generalized communities in the Pliocene. Quaternary differentiation of the local floristic areas was due chiefly to the increased climatic and topographic diversity which developed over the region and which segregated out the present floras. The time is now ripe to integrate the numerous local studies of the

Late Cenozoic floras of Europe into a monographic analysis of the evolution of its present floristic areas; an excellent start was made earlier by Depape (1928) and has been extended by Szafer (1946, 1954).

2. In eastern Asia, fossil floras comprising the Arcto-Tertiary Geoflora are not so abundant as in Europe, except in Japan, where widespread vulcanism and tectonic instability provided conditions unusually favorable for the preservation of a rich array of forest vegetation. As compared with Europe, the geoflora in eastern Asia shows important floristic differences. Its species are preponderantly those of the East Asian Element, whose closest modern relatives still live in that region. Fossil species related to plants now typically American are in a minority in all floras, with such species as *Acer rubrum, Juglans cinerea, Liquidambar stryciflua, Nyssa sylvatica,* and *Taxodium distichum,* comprising derivatives of the East American Element, and *Sequoia sempervirens,* of the West American, having fossil counterparts there. Fossil species representing the European Element are apparently absent. However, the discovery of new seed floras and future pollen studies may disclose their presence there, particularly since the Boreal Element has a good representation, notably in the widespread phylads of *Alnus, Betula, Crataegus, Picea, Populus, Prunus,* and *Salix.*

Occupying the higher latitudes of eastern Asia during the Early Tertiary, the Arcto-Tertiary Geoflora migrated southward as temperatures decreased during the period. It had reached the latitude of central China by the Miocene and ranged farther south during the later Tertiary. Near the close of Miocene time and continuing into the Pleistocene, the Alpine-Himalayan axis and the East Asian land mass to northward were rapidly elevated. This brought a drier and colder climate to central Asia, as shown by Pliocene floras which demonstrate that the rich Oligocene and Miocene summer-green forests had largely been eliminated from the lowlands (Chaney, 1935). They were replaced by hardier stream- and lake-border trees and shrubs, which regularly have smaller leaves than their Miocene relatives and which have persisted down to the present in the mountains of interior Asia in scarcely modified form.

The floristic changes which occurred in eastern Asia during the later Tertiary are not readily explicable. For example, *Sequoia,* which had persisted down to the end of the Tertiary in Japan, was eliminated there. Conditions suitable for the survival of most of its East Asian associates continued; yet redwood now lives in the coastal strip of northern California, where mild (frostless) yearly temperature, coupled with winter rain and summer fog, characterizes its environment, as compared with freezing winters and ample summer rain in Japan. The East American species of walnut, tupelo, red maple, and others also disappeared during the Pleistocene, but for reasons which are difficult to grasp, since they survive in an area of generally similar climate. Another problem pertains to the segregation of the floras of China and Japan. A large number of plants typical now of central China had close relatives in Japan during much of the Tertiary, and they persisted there well into the Pliocene. These included several genera which are no longer in the archipelago, such as *Carya, Eucommia, Fortunearia, Glyptostrobus, Metasequoia, Meliodendron, Pseudolarix,* and *Stephania,* as well as a number of species in genera such as *Gleditschia, Ilex, Mahonia, Melia, Pterocarya, Prunus, Sapium, Tilia,* and *Ulmus.* Reasons for their elimination are difficult to suggest, especially since many of their associates in China, which have close fossil relatives in the Late Tertiary of Japan, persisted in both areas. Glacial climates probably cannot wholly explain the relationship, since submergence of the continental shelf gave Japan a mild maritime climate and glaciation did not greatly affect the southern part of the area. Furthermore, conditions were more severe on the Asian land mass, where the plants which were eliminated from Japan now survive. Since the Pliocene species lived under climates milder than those in which their nearest descendants occur, it is possible that the plants in Japan were coastal ecotypes of otherwise continental species; but, even so, the reasons for their local extermination are not known.

The Late Cenozoic evolution of the modern forest provinces of eastern Asia is a problem difficult of solution. The fossil floras now in hand provide critical information, but they are few in number outside Japan. Another handicap is that the natural forest communities of much of eastern Asia have been destroyed, and the original associations are not easy to reconstruct in terms either of their composition or of the areas they occupied. Paleobotanical interpretations can best be accomplished if the investigator is able to tramp through the modern counterparts of the forests of the past.

3. In western North America the Arcto-Tertiary Geoflora occupied the lowlands stretching from high latitudes to southeastern Alaska and thence across central Montana during Paleocene time. By mid-Oligocene time it had reached northern California and Nevada and central Colorado. It ranged somewhat farther south over the lowlands during the Miocene, but the rapid spread of dry climate over the southwestern part of the continent following the Middle Oligocene prohibited its southward migration over the lowlands there (Axelrod, 1939, pp. 76–78). With respect to composition, it included (*a*) many members of the East Asian Element, (*b*) numerous plants of the West American

Element, (c) many species of the East American Element, and (d) species of the Boreal Element related to phylads that still range across the middle-high latitudes. With one or two possible exceptions, members of the European Element are not recorded.

In the Pacific coastal region, species of the East Asian Element had a prominent to dominant place in the forests of the later Oligocene, indicating important migration around the northern Pacific Basin. The East Asian Element gradually became subordinate to species of the East American Element during the Miocene, due possibly to lowered precipitation. It was during the Miocene that increasing numbers of the West American Element are recorded. These included species of *Abies, Chamaecyparis, Libocedrus, Picea, Pinus, Pseudotsuga, Sequoia, Thuja,* and *Tsuga* whose modern derivatives now dominate the western conifer forests, as well as close counterparts of many of their typical associates, for example, in *Acer, Alnus, Amelanchier, Cornus, Fraxinus, Populus, Prunus, Quercus, Rhamnus, Ribes,* and other genera. Commencing in the later Miocene and continuing through the Pliocene, species of the East Asian and East American Elements were gradually reduced in numbers as summer rains decreased in frequence and in amount. Disappearing first in the interior, a few relicts survived in the mild coastal strip down to the Pleistocene, notably species of *Ailanthus, Castanea, Pterocarya, Trapa,* and *Ulmus.* Asa Gray (1846, 1859) long ago noted that there are links between the temperate floras of eastern Asia and the Pacific Coast of North America. These relations extend to a number of identical species in the two areas, as well as to several genera which occur in both areas but find their optimum development in eastern Asia, notably *Castanopsis, Gaultheria, Lithocarpus,* and *Photinia.* In addition, there are a number of related species, particularly in the conifers *Abies, Libocedrus, Pseudotsuga, Picea, Taxus,* and *Torreya.* All of them clearly are relics of the Arcto-Tertiary Geoflora that formerly linked both areas.

As members of the eastern elements decreased, they were replaced by species of the West American Element, which rose to dominance. Members of this group were still admixed in rather generalized communities during the Pliocene. Segregation of the three major forest provinces—Coast, Sierra-Cascade, and Rocky Mountain—was chiefly in response to increasing Late Cenozoic environmental (topographic-climatic) diversity. Species of the Coast Forest were confined to the mild coastal strip of high rainfall and summer fog, those of the Sierra-Cascade to a mountain axis of high precipitation and cool winters, and the Rocky Mountain to the central cordilleran area of cold snowy winters and summer showers (Axelrod, 1956). Many species (and varieties) are still common to these forests, which show zonal differentiation in response to altitude and floristic differences from north to south—all of which were accentuated during the Quaternary (Axelrod, 1957, 1959*b*).

4. Records of the Arcto-Tertiary Geoflora are not abundant in eastern North America (see Berry, 1937, for references; Traverse, 1955). Judging from available evidence, the geoflora shows some important floristic differences here as compared with the other sectors. Dominant in the area were species of the East American Element whose nearest descendants now typify the forests of the region, in genera such as *Castanea, Carya, Fagus, Gordonia, Ilex, Liquidambar, Magnolia, Morus, Nyssa, Parthenocissus, Persea, Planera, Quercus, Rhododendron, Rhus, Taxodium, Tilia, Ulmus,* and *Vaccinium.* Representatives of the East Asian Element are present, but in small numbers, including *Engelhardtia, Glyptostrobus, Illicium, Pterocarya,* and *Trapa.* Pollen studies of the Oligocene formations of the central Atlantic coastal plain may show that they were more abundant during that epoch than in the Miocene. Species of the West American Element have not been recorded in the region; the reports of *Sequoia* need verification.

The fact that there is a strong East American Element in eastern North America and in western Europe during the Tertiary and that it has only a poor representation in eastern Asia demonstrates important and effective migration around the North Atlantic for the geoflora during the Early Tertiary. This is consistent with the composition of the older Tertiary floras of Greenland, Iceland, and Spitzbergen, for they contain numerous species of the East American Element, as well as the East Asian. Although there were many resemblances between the temperate forests on opposite sides of the Atlantic during the Middle and Late Tertiary, the forests of these regions differ markedly today. Widespread elimination of close ancestors of American forest trees and shrubs in western Europe during the later Pliocene partly explains the relation. But it does not account for the absence of derivative species of the European Element in North America: perhaps they are largely of European origin, much like the West American Element, which appears to have evolved chiefly in that sector of the Arcto-Tertiary Geoflora.

The northern margin of the geoflora on the eastern side of the land mass during the Early Tertiary has not been placed accurately. The Early Tertiary floras of Greenland are temperate to warm-temperate, indicating that the temperate-tropical ecotone lay farther south. It may have been at the latitude of Nova Scotia, to judge from the character of the Miocene Brandon flora of Vermont, which includes some subtropical relics (*Alangium, Cinnamomum, Engelhardtia, Illicium, Mimusops,* and *Phellodendron*), and from the fact that the Eocene marine faunas of New Jersey are tropical. In any event, the geoflora penetrated southward along the uplands of the low Appalachian axis during the Eocene, as judged from a few records of it in the Wilcox flora in the Tennessee region, where they were carried into the subtropical lowlands (Brown, 1944).

Factors responsible for the elimination of members of the East Asian Element from the region are obscure, unless glacial climate is invoked. Even so, one would raise the question as to why the climate was so selective of this one element, when apparently all their East American associates persisted. The problem seems comparable to the disappearance of the East American species from eastern Asia at the close of the Tertiary: the same factors can probably explain both relations.

Evolution of the modern forest communities in the eastern United States has been synthesized by Braun (1950), who properly relates it to community readjustment in response to the diverse topographic-climatic subprovinces which developed in the region during the Late Cenozoic, segregating out associations adapted to more restricted environments.

It has been widely stated that the longitudinal ranges of North America enabled the Arcto-Tertiary Geoflora to extend southward into the mountains of Mexico and Central America (Guatemala, Costa Rica). Several authors have recently summarized the plant evidence which points to past connections between the Appalachian region and the Mexican highlands. The affinities are shown by the disjunct occurrence of identical trees and shrubs (*Berchemia scandens, Carpinus caroliniana, Hamamelis virginiana, Liquidambar styraciflua, Nyssa sylvatica, Ostrya virginiana, Rhus radicans*), paired-species, some scarcely distinct (*Acer negundo-orizabense, Fagus americana-mexicana, Illicium floridum-mexicanum, Tilia heterophylla-longipes*), and plants that are probably varieties (*Cornus florida* var. *urbiniana, Ilex vomitaria* var. *chiapensis*). The relations extend also to ferns, mosses, and fungi.

Owing to the absence of an adequate fossil record in Mexico, there is little agreement as to the historical interpretation of the disjunction. Deevey (1949), Dresseler (1954), and Sharp (1953) believe that southward migration took place in the Pleistocene, as suggested earlier by Harshberger (1911). However, it has been demonstrated that the connection must be older (Berry, 1926; Axelrod, 1939; Braun, 1950, 1955; Martin and Harrell, 1957). There is no evidence to suggest that the present dry belt of thorn scrub and semidesert grassland was replaced by humid temperate forests in the Pleistocene. Most of the data point now to only moderate change south of the glacial border; the Pleistocene faunas and floras from the drier parts of North America suggest that rainfall increased only 10–15 inches in these areas during the pluvials. If the humid Appalachian types extended across a moist corridor into Mexico during the Pleistocene, then numerous small forest animals should have accompanied them; however, they are largely absent from the montane forests of Mexico that are typified by the Appalachian disjuncts (Martin and Harrell, 1957). At a maximum, there probably was only an interchange of prairie-border woodland and savanna biota between Texas and northern Mexico during the pluvials, allowing such xeromesophytes as *Cercis, Juniperus, Juglans,* and *Prunus* to bridge the gap (Braun, 1955; Martin and Harrell, 1957).

The disjunctions seem to predate the development of the dry zone, Braun favoring an Oligocene (possibly Eocene) date, Martin and Harrell the Miocene. As noted in earlier discussions (Axelrod, 1939, pp. 76–78; Clements, 1936, p. 136), the connections are older because the Madro-Tertiary Geoflora already occupied the intervening region during the Miocene and Oligocene and in the later Eocene as well (Axelrod, 1958). Evidence supporting the idea that the connection dates well back into the Eocene or Paleocene, if not even into the Cretaceous (Berry, 1926; Steyermark, 1950) is supplied by the strong Arcto-Tertiary element in the hills bordering the subtropic Green River Basin of the central Rocky Mountains. The Paleocene floras of the western interior also show that warm temperate plants were rather numerous on slopes bordering the lowlands, and they were even more abundant in the Cretaceous. Significantly, the Cretaceous (Albian) Dakota flora of Kansas and Nebraska includes a number of near-modern species, some closely allied to the Appalachian-Mexican–Central American disjuncts, particularly in the genera *Carya, Fagus, Hamamelis,* and *Magnolia,* as well as *Sassafras,* which apparently is not disjunct. Many other warm-temperate species of essentially modern type are represented in the Dakota flora, including *Platanus* (cf. *lindeniana*), *Quercus* (cf. *magnoliaefolia*), and *Persea* (cf. *hartwegii*), all of which occur with the Appalachian disjuncts in Mexico. In Mexico the disjuncts regularly live with warm-temperate to subtropic plants, a relation typical of the Arcto-Tertiary–Neotropical-Tertiary ecotone, an ecotone which has persisted from the Middle Cretaceous.

The ecotone probably extended southward into Mexico during the Cretaceous and Early Eocene, occupying the scattered low mountains of the region. High mountains are not required for migration because climatic zonation was much weaker than it is today. Since the high latitudes were mild (temperate to cool-temperate) and the northern margin of the tropics was farther north, the Cretaceous and Eocene tropical zone would have had to be somewhat cooler than it is today in order to maintain the normal heat budget of the earth. This explains not only why warm-temperate types could have penetrated well southward along low mountain axes during the Cretaceous and Eocene but also why so many of the older floras have been described as representing an ecotone between tropical and temperate climates.

The inference that the present disjunctions probably developed during the Eocene and were largely completed by the middle of the epoch can be tested only when fossil floras of appropriate age are found in Mexico and bordering areas. In any event, it is apparent that, while subsequent evolution of these ancient bradytelic types has in some cases produced minor differences between widely separated relict populations, many appear to have survived essentially unchanged in these regions which probably have been disjunct for at least forty million years.

Summarizing, the Temperate Arcto-Tertiary Geoflora was composed of conifers and deciduous hardwoods which were grouped into diverse forest communities, depending on local differences in topography and climate. The geoflora displayed important regional differences across Holarctica during the Tertiary, as follows:

1. An East Asian Element was well represented in Europe, eastern Asia, and western North America but was poorly developed in eastern North America; this points to important migration around the North Pacific.

2. The East American Element was prominently developed in eastern and western North America and in western Europe but was rare in eastern Asia; this suggests migration around the North Atlantic.

3. Autochthonous elements appear to have evolved in western North America and in western Europe, to judge from the fact that their species are not recorded elsewhere except for a few conifers.

The chief climatic changes during the later Cenozoic that seem to account for the present distribution and composition of the living derivative forests include the following:

4. On the western sides of the continents, gradually diminishing rainfall over the lowlands appears to explain the progressive reduction in numbers of species of the eastern elements in the Pliocene floras. But the factors responsible for the elimination of species of the East American Element from eastern Asia and of the East Asian from eastern North America are not now known.

5. By the close of the Tertiary, most species of the eastern elements

had disappeared from western North America and from the Mediterranean Basin, owing not only to lowered rainfall but to the elimination of effective summer precipitation over the lowlands as well. Relics of these elements disappeared from central and northern Europe during the glacials, but they reinvaded the region from the southeast during the early (and later?) Interglacials and also in postglacial time.

6. Species of the autochthonous elements gradually assumed dominance as members of the eastern elements became extinct. During the Late Cenozoic the surviving generalized communities were differentiated into more narrowly restricted associations as climatic and topographic diversity increased, the species responding according to their varying ranges of tolerance.

B. The Antarcto-Tertiary Geoflora covered Antarctica and the southern parts of South America and New Zealand during the Cretaceous and Early Tertiary, having apparently evolved in upland austral regions from ancestral tropical and border tropical alliances during pre-Cretaceous time. Collections—generally small—have been recovered from widely scattered areas, notably in Patagonia, southern Chile, Seymour Island (west Antarctica), Kerguelen Island, New Zealand, Tasmania, and southeastern Australia. Although most of the older reports need extensive systematic revision, it is nonetheless clear that Hooker was correct in his assertion that Antarctica formerly harbored a distinctive forest, remnants of which now lie in lands widely separated. In his words:

> . . . The three great land areas in the southern hemisphere (New Zealand, Australia-Tasmania, temperate South America) . . . [show] a botanical relationship . . . which is not to be accounted for by any theory of transport or variation, but which is agreeable to the hypothesis of all being members of a once more extensive flora, which has been broken up by geological and climatic causes [Hooker, 1853, II, Part 1, xxxvi].

The geoflora shows relationships with the temperate and cool-temperate rain forests of southern Chile and adjacent Patagonia and with the closely similar forests of the Tasman region, including New Zealand, Tasmania, southeastern Australia, and New Caledonia. Species of the Fuegan Element include plants related to those in the *Nothofagus* and bordering forests of temperate South America, in genera such as *Araucaria, Saxegothea, Lomatia, Fitzroyia, Eucryphia, Libocedrus, Podocarpus, Laurelia, Embothrium, Wintera,* and their associates. The Tasman Element comprises fossil species related to plants now in the general area bordering the Tasman Sea. They are distributed in genera such as *Acompyle* (recorded in western Antarctica, Patagonia), *Arthrotaxis* (recorded in Patagonia), *Dacrydium* (apparently fossil in western Antarctica), *Agathis, Phyllocladus, Podocarpus,* numerous ferns, *Nothofagus, Knightia* (in western Antarctica), *Laurelia, Coprosma,* and many other angiosperms (see Couper, 1953; Couper and McQueen, 1954).

The floristic unity of the Antarcto-Tertiary Geoflora (Fig. 3) demonstrates that its continuity was due not to long-distance migration over broad stretches of sea but to migration over extensive archipelagos which have since subsided. These connections were probably between Antarctica and South America along the Scotia arc and between Antarctica and the Tasman area along the Macquarie Swell and the New Zealand Plateau (Fig. 9). This migration route coincides with the circum-Pacific Mesozoic and Tertiary fold belt (Fairbridge, 1949; Davies, 1956), which seismic evidence shows is still active (Gutenberg and Richter, 1949) and is marked by active and recently active volcanoes of the Atlantic type. Further, the Antarctic Shield (eastern Antarctica) is apparently separated from the fold belt that comprises western Antarctica by a major fault system which is relatively young—apparently Middle to Late Cenozoic—and strikes northward toward New Zealand. Thus it is no accident that there are highly folded and faulted rocks on Macquarie. Between Macquarie

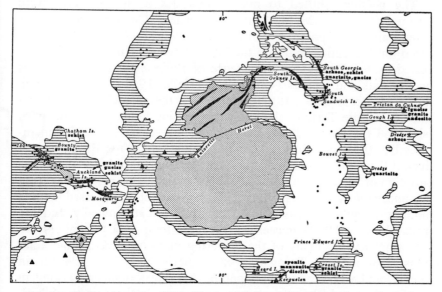

Fig. 9.—Crests of major ridges (*horizontal lines*) in circum-Antarctic regions represent possible sites for wider, discontinuous land connections during the Mesozoic and Early Tertiary. The ridges are largely volcanic (Tertiary-Recent) but are floored locally with sialic rocks. Epicenters of earthquakes shown as black dots; Late Cenozoic volcanos as ▲'s; Mesozoic-Tertiary fold belt as sinuous lines.

and Adelie there is a major fork in the submarine relief, one branch leading to Tasmania-Australia, the other to New Zealand: significantly, this topographic division also coincides with a major branch in the seismic belt. Waters along all these tracts are of only moderate depth today, and at distances of 200–300 miles the higher parts now rise to within 1,000 feet of sea level. The submarine ridges on which these islands are situated were probably the sites of extensive archipelagos during much of the Cretaceous and Tertiary and thus permitted the migration of the geoflora across the region at a time when climate was favorable (Axelrod, 1952b). This conclusion is consistent with evidence of the vertebrate faunas, which indicates that water barriers (probably small) largely hindered faunal interchange between South America and Australia during the Tertiary (Simpson, 1939). It agrees also with evidence of the brachiopod faunas of the Antarctic and subantarctic islands, which suggests that shallow seas existed between Australia, New Zealand, Kerguelen, Antarctica, and South America during the Early Tertiary (Thomson, 1918). Additional evidence for wider lands is provided by the biogeographical relations of the spider fauna, earthworms, millipedes, and many groups of insects in these austral regions (see data summarized by Skottsberg, 1920–56, Vol. I, Paper 5).

The geoflora shifted to middle latitudes as temperatures were lowered during the Middle and Late Tertiary. Cold-temperate forest communities composed of hardier trees and shrubs may have persisted on Antarctica well into the later Pliocene. This relation is suggested by the Quaternary occurrence of *Podocarpus* and *Libocedrus* on the Falkland Islands (Gonthan, in Halle, 1911), an area where no forests occur today. It agrees also with the paleoclimatic implications of a Late Tertiary shallow-water marine fauna from Cockburn Island off the Palmer Peninsula, which suggests sea surface temperatures like those now in southern Patagonia, where the Fuegan forest lives at the shore. Climatic factors that were responsible for the differentiation of the modern floras of the Tasman and Fuegian areas from the ancestral Antarcto-Tertiary Geoflora cannot be assessed until a number of the more critical floras are revised taxonomically. Judging from Florin's (1940) masterly revision of the southern conifers, we may suppose that many of the flowering plants showed similar relations: that modern Tasman types formerly had close relatives in Fuegia, and vice-versa. It is apparent that paleobotanists working in the Fuegian and Tasman regions must consult the forests of both areas for living descendants of their temperate Tertiary species.

Apart from the Late Cenozoic floristic changes which tended materially to differentiate the forests of the Feugian and Tasman regions, there were also important changes in distribution in these more local sectors. Couper (1953) notes that certain species of Proteaceae, Fagaceae, and Podocarpaceae were common to Australia and New Zealand in the Early Tertiary and Cretaceous but now have more restricted distributions. For example, *Beaupurea* from the Cretaceous and Oligocene of New Zealand and Australia now occurs only in New Caledonia; genera of Proteaceae represented in the Upper Cretaceous and Eocene of New Zealand occur today in Australia and areas to the northward; *Nothofagus* in the Cretaceous and Tertiary of New Zealand is allied to subtropic species now in New Caledonia and New Guinea and to others that are in South America. *Dacyridium,* from the Cretaceous and Eocene of New Zealand, Australia, and Kerguelen, is now found only in Tasmania; *Microcachrys* shows similar relations.

As in Holarctica, it is apparent that many plants were more widely distributed in the Southern Hemisphere than are their descendants today. Such occurrences point up the futility of assembling statistical data as to the modern relations of floras (or faunas: see Ekman, 1953) and then drawing conclusions from them as to their center of origin, their routes of migration, or the stability of continents. In biogeographical discussions of this type it is usually assumed that the absence of a species (or genus) from any area means that it was never there—a supposition that can in many cases be demonstrated to be false. The composition of floras (and faunas) changed continuously through the Tertiary and at a particularly rapid rate in the Late Cenozoic. No biogeographic discussion can ignore the fossil record.

Summarizing, the history of the Antarcto-Tertiary Geoflora generally parallels that of its boreal counterpart, the Arcto-Tertiary Geoflora:

1. Both geofloras appear to have evolved from basic tropic stocks, one at the north, the other at the south.

2. Both geofloras intially had circumpolar distributions and migrated from high to middle latitudes in response to a cooling climate following Eocene time.

3. Both show Late Tertiary floristic evolution into distinctive, though closely related, forests, with differentiation in response to changing climate operating on the varying ranges of tolerance of the respective species.

4. Forests derived from these geofloras now have a latitudinal distribution in each hemisphere.

Semiarid-Tertiary Geofloras.—In response to the expansion of regional dry climate following the Eocene, semiarid vegetation typified by small, thick-leafed plants appeared over the low-middle latitudes in the western parts of the continents. These semiarid geofloras evolved on the drier margins of the subtropic savannas during Cretaceous (or pre-Cretaceous) and Eocene times. Their species were apparently derived chiefly from alliances in the tropical geofloras, though the temperate geofloras contributed to them as well.

In terms of area they formed generally smaller units than the Tropical- or Temperate-Tertiary Geofloras, which accounts in part for the fact that they are still poorly known. The Mediterrano-Tertiary Geoflora gave rise to the present woodland, macchie, dry grassland, and related vegetation of the Mediterranean Basin. A sufficiently large number of fossil floras is now known in that area so that its history should be reconstructed. Ecologically similar geofloras evolved independently in southern Australia, central Chile, and southwestern Africa, but their history cannot now be worked out because only a few fossil floras are known from those regions. In southwestern North America, however, where widespread vulcanism during the Tertiary provided conditions particularly favorable for the preservation of fossil plants, a number of fossil floras have been recovered which give us some insight into the evolution of the Madro-Tertiary Geoflora of that region (Axelrod, 1950, 1958).

The Madro-Tertiary Geoflora was composed of plants whose nearest living relatives contribute to the semiarid live-oak woodland, conifer woodland, chaparral, arid subtropic scrub (thorn forest), desert grassland, and subdesert to desert vegetation of southwestern North America. From a survey of the taxonomic and adaptive relations of its plants it has been concluded that it was derived chiefly from subtropical to warm-temperate alliances that evolved in response to the expansion of a new adaptive zone—dry climate. The geoflora had an origin in southwestern North America because taxa that appear to be ancestral to Madro-Tertiary lineages occur in the Upper Cretaceous and Paleocene subtropical floras of that region; they are not represented in the temperate Arcto-Tertiary Geoflora to northward, nor are they recorded in the humid phases of the Neotropical-Tertiary Geoflora.

Geologic and paleoclimatic data indicate that during the Cretaceous and Early Tertiary southwestern North America was generally a lowland region, characterized by tropic savanna climate. During this interval ancestral Madro-Tertiary plants apparently were evolving chiefly in sites away from the moist lowland floodplains, particularly in scattered drier areas provided by sandy and rocky stretches and in dry sites to leeward of low ranges. With a strong linear component to selection imposed by a gradual trend toward increased aridity, these scattered isolated phylads of subtropic and warm-temperate affinity were probably undergoing quantum evolution during the Cretaceous, giving rise to numerous, highly specialized taxonomic and adaptive types. This may well account for the fact that when they are first recorded in moderate numbers in the Eocene and Early Oligocene, they are closely similar to modern species.

The geoflora migrated widely over southwestern North America as dry climates expanded during Miocene and Pliocene times. In the Pliocene it ranged from central California and southern Oregon to the High Plains on the east and probably to Montana at the north. Its communities were of generalized composition, including mixtures of species that now typify the varied communities in the different semi-arid climates of the region. For example, thorn-scrub vegetation that ranged northward into the southern Great Basin during the Miocene included species related to those in the thorn scrub now in Baja California, in Sonora-Sinaloa, and in Tamaulipas–Nuevo León. Similarly, woodland vegetation in California, Nevada, Utah, Colorado, Nebraska, and Oklahoma included close relatives of species that occur now only to the southward, chiefly in the Sierra Madre of Mexico and in the structurally continuous ranges to the northward in adjacent Arizona, New Mexico, and western Texas. Studies of the later Tertiary floristic evolution of vegetation represented in the geoflora show that the various woodland, chaparral, thorn-scrub, and subdesert communities were derived from more generalized ancestral Tertiary communities by climatic selection and segregation during the Late Cenozoic as environmental diversity increased. In general, plants of wide distribution became more restricted in area as temperatures were lowered, as precipitation decreased over the developing desert area, and as summer rainfall disappeared from the Far West. This Late Cenozoic restriction in range of numerous species was largely responsible for the origin of certain highly endemic areas.

The history of the modern flora of the Cape Region of Baja California provides a good example. A number of highly distinctive endemics occur in the oak-piñon woodland, which has a patchy distribution in the mountains and also in the thorn forest of the dry tropic lowlands. Fossil species closely similar to the endemics characterizing both communities occur to the northward at a number of localities in rocks ranging from Oligocene to Pliocene in age (Fig. 10). They could not have occupied the present Cape Region at any time from the Cretaceous into the Middle Miocene, because the southern part of the peninsular region where they now occur was submerged during this interval. In Late Miocene time, however, a series of volcanoes came into existence, aligned north-south close to the present eastern coast, thus linking the northern and southern parts of the peninsula.

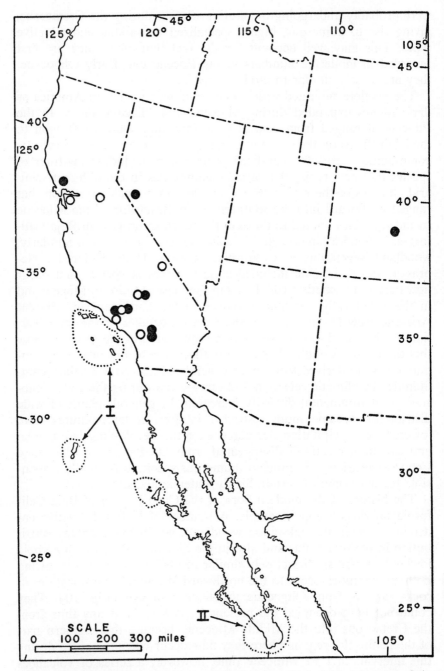

FIG. 10.—Showing the occurrences of fossil plants closely related to some of the highly distinctive endemics now confined to insular regions. Open circles show occurrences of species similar to those now in the Californian Islands (*I*); solid circles to those in the Cape Region (*II*).

They probably afforded a southward route for the migration of woodland vegetation in the uplands and thorn scrub in the lowlands. Elimination of summer rainfall to the northward explains the disappearance of the immediate ancestors of the Cape woodland endemics there and their persistence in the summer-wet uplands of the southern peninsular region. The disappearance of summer rain and increasing winter cold seem responsible for the confinement of the thorn forest to the southward. The marked endemics typifying the woodland of the Cape Region have thus survived in an extremely isolated part of the continent. The Cape woodland is separated from the related California woodland to the northward by some 500 miles of desert which came into existence more recently (Axelrod, 1950). It is isolated from the related woodland in the Sierra Madre of northwestern Mexico by the 150-mile stretch of the Gulf of California and by the dry subtropic plains in the lowlands of Sonora and Sinaloa.

The flora of the archipelago off the coast of southern California and adjacent Baja California also includes a number of distinctive woody plants that have close fossil relatives in rocks of Miocene and Pliocene age on the mainland (Fig. 10). Evidence shows that the insular woodland and chaparral were segregated from the Madro-Tertiary ancestral communities in response to several factors (Axelrod, 1939, 1958). Numerous plants which had lived with them, both of thorn-scrub (*Acacia, Acalypha, Bursera, Erythea, Ficus, Karwinskia, Pithecolobium, Randia*) and woodland (*Arbutus, Condalia, Ilex, Persea, Quercus, Robinia, Sapindus, Ungnadia*) communities, disappeared from California during the later Pliocene as summer rainfall was eliminated. The surviving California woodland was then differentiated into northern and southern communities in response to moisture-temperature relations. In southern California, further differentiation into insular, coastal, and interior associations was due to the development during the Pleistocene of different subclimates in each of these localized areas. The insular segregate, which includes the peculiar endemics, significantly has a few scattered outposts on the mild coastal slope. It is apparent that the insular archipelago has served as a refuge for ancient types and is not their center of origin. However, insular varieties of mainland species—some woody, but mostly herbaceous—seem to have evolved in the insular area during the later Cenozoic.

THE ORIGIN OF INSULAR FLORAS

"To assume that insular conditions originate new forms is to overlook what has taken place on the continents." This observation by William A. Setchell (1935) might serve as theme for the present section—a topic of perennial interest to students of evolution.

Darwin became interested in the problem of insular floras as a result of his experiences in the Galapagos Islands. In his *Origin of Species* he noted that (1) the total species inhabiting oceanic islands is small as compared with continental areas of equal size; (2) although few in species, the proportion of endemics is often large in insular areas; and (3) the representation of taxa is unbalanced, for important groups (orders, families) common on the continents are often absent in insular regions. Thus Darwin was the first to recognize the problem of the origin of insular floras and introduce their relation to paleogeography.

John Dalton Hooker (1867), following his studies of Darwin's Galapagos plants and a comparison with insular floras in other tropical regions, expressed the opinion that the peculiar endemics of insular floras are "relicts of a far more ancient vegetation than now prevails on the mother continent." He felt that they had largely evolved on the continents because some of the narrow endemics (epibiotics) of the Macronesian flora occur as fossils in the Miocene and Pliocene of Europe in essentially their present form—for instance, *Ilex canariensis, Laurus canariensis, Oreodaphne foetens,* and *Persea indica.* And how did they reach these islands? Certain dispersal difficulties prevented him from fully accepting Darwin's view that various agents could carry most plants across wide expanses of sea, and he finally concluded that the peculiar species in the uplands of the Madeira and Canary Islands which have close relatives in the Late Tertiary floras of Europe could be explained only with the help of "intermediate masses of land" which have since subsided. This was not a new idea to Hooker, for he had earlier utilized it to account for the similarities between the temperate floras of the Fuegan and Tasman regions which are "agreeable to the hypothesis of all being members of a once more extensive flora, which has been broken up by geological and climatic causes" (1853, II, Part I, xxxvi).

It was Wallace (1876) who distinguished between the biota of continental and oceanic islands, and in *Island Life* (1895) he clearly demonstrated their connection with geological history. Continental islands represent fragments of continents, some detached but recently (Great Britain, Borneo), others long ago (Madagascar, New Zealand). Oceanic islands, both volcanic and coral islands built on volcanic foundations, lie within the ocean basin and have never been directly connected with the continents. Nonetheless, since "volcanic islands are subject to subsidence as well as elevation . . . some islands may have intervened between them and the coast, and have served as stepping stones by which the passage to them of various organisms would be greatly facilitated" (1895, p. 285). Wallace noted that evolution has taken an enormously long time and that on the continents nothing of a truly revolutionary nature has occurred since the Cretaceous (except the placentals). Families, genera, and in some cases species still living date back to the earlier Tertiary and even into the Cretaceous. However, he felt that a great deal of evolution took place on isolated islands during the Tertiary and that, in general, the older the island, the more distinct its inhabitants, whether plant or animal.

By the close of the third decade of this century, widely divergent views had been presented on the problem of insular endemics by men such as Arldt, Campbell, Edwards, Gregory, Gulick, Guppy, Hedley, Irmscher, Sarasin, Setchell, Skottsberg, and Von Ihering. As for migration to distant islands, one group maintained that the continents and the ocean basins are wholly stable, that plant dispersal is essentially unlimited, and that the peculiar insular endemics are largely ancient relicts carried to the islands by long-distance transport. Another group, denying effective transport, erected land bridges almost at will —in any direction and for any epoch of time—to explain nearly every isolated fact of distribution. A third, small group of the Hooker-Wallace school recognized essentially stable continents and ocean basins but maintained that migration to remote islands, using island steppingstones which have since become submerged, could explain most of the facts. Today there is much new evidence from geology that lends strong support to the latter belief.

As for evolution in insular regions, the initial problem still remains: Did the highly peculiar endemics evolve in insular areas due to the isolation (Wallace), or do they merely represent ancient types which have survived largely unchanged in insular regions, following a long continental history (Hooker)? So far as plants are concerned, there is much evidence to suggest that (*a*) the highly distinctive insular endemics (epibiotics) of both continental and oceanic islands are largely relicts of ancient continental floras which have survived in isolation and that (*b*) clusters of endemic species on islands which do not differ greatly from one another, or from their nearest continental relatives, probably have evolved in isolation. The data supporting these conclusions come from geology, plant geography, paleoclimate, evolution, and paleobotany. This evidence will now be summarized in a series of brief statements; some require little or no comment, but for others some documentation is necessary. With these guiding principles in mind, it will then be possible to view the problem of plant evolution in insular regions in clearer perspective.

EVIDENCE FROM GEOLOGY

1. The continents and ocean basins stand at different altitudes because of differences in their density and hence in their rocks. The continents are composed chiefly of quartz-rich (or sialic) rocks, the ocean basins of basaltic (or simatic) types.

2. The relative geographic positions of these major crustal segments have remained stable throughout the history of angiosperms and probably throughout the time that life has been in existence.

This statement is at variance with current studies which have led some geophysicists to conclude that the geographic and magnetic poles, which are presumed to stay in near-coincidence, have wandered widely across the globe during the geologic past (i.e., Runcorn, 1956) and that the continents also have been drifting in one form or another (i.e., Wegener; Creer *et al.*, 1958; King, 1958). At the present time there does not appear to be any paleontologic evidence that *demands* drifting continents or wandering geographic poles; in fact, the evidence seems to militate against major movement of either sort. The evidence for stability is provided by the distributional and climatic implications of Tertiary floras (Chaney, 1940), shallow-water Tertiary molluscan faunas (Durham, 1952), and Permian (Stehli, 1957) and Jurassic (Arkell, 1956) marine faunas, all of which are consistent with the poles and continents in their present positions. My preliminary studies of Permian, Triassic, Jurassic, and Cretaceous floras also indicate that the geographic poles have been stable during this interval because the paleoclimates they indicate had a symmetrical arrangement similar to that of the present day: cool climates are clearly indicated for latitudes that are presently high; warm climates occupy a central position; and dry climates occur over the western parts of the continents. Such a distribution is reconcilable only with polar and continental stability, not drift. In addition, the distribution of cycadophytes, coniferophytes (Pinaceae, Araucariaceae, Taxodiaceae, Polocarpaceae) and ferns (Dicksoniaceae, Marattiaceae, Matoniaceae, Dipteraceae) during the Triassic, Jurassic, and Cretaceous is also consistent with the arrangement of the poles and continents much like that of the present. Finally, if continents such as Australia have drifted from high (polar) to low latitudes since the Carboniferous (Creer *et al.*, 1958), then the fossil floras should record a trend from cold-temperate to tropical vegetation and climate during the Late Paleozoic and Mesozoic. However, the comparatively complete sequence of fossil floras in southeastern Australia represents tropical vegetation throughout this 230-million-year interval apart from the Late Tertiary. Such a relation, which is consistent only with stability, not drift, is shown also for other continents that are presumed to have drifted.

3. The outlines of the continents have changed during geologic time, owing to slight subsidence which has permitted shallow seas to invade them temporarily or for longer intervals.

4. Continental foundering has occurred, representing a loss of lands to oceanic regions. Examples include the fragmentation of the North Atlantic basalt plateau in post-Eocene time (Barrell, 1927); the subsidence of the Atlantic coastal plain to abyssal depths following the Early Cretaceous (Ewing *et al.,* 1939, 1950); the subsidence of parts of Eria off the coast of northwestern Europe in the middle Paleozoic (Holtedhal, 1927); the formation of the eastern Arabian Sea by subsidence of the Deccan traps of peninsular India following the Eocene (Barrell, 1927; Lees, 1953); the submergence of land areas between Australia and Fiji–New Caledonia during the Late Mesozoic (Reed, 1949, p. 686); the disappearance of lands off South Africa in the earlier Mesozoic (Umbgrove, 1947; King, 1953); the subsidence of lands in the East Atlantic off the Congo Basic following the Cretaceous (Umbgrove, 1947; Haughton, 1952; Lees, 1954); the foundering of land areas off the Pacific coast of the Andes (Eardley, 1954); the disappearance of land west of Macquarie, apparently the source for the glacier that picked up boulders on the west coast and carried them across the summit of the island (alt. 1,200 ft.) to the east coast (Mawson, 1943); and the occurrence of beds of fresh-water diatoms of Pleistocene age recovered from deep-sea cores at depths of 10,700 feet in the eastern slope of the central Mid-Atlantic Ridge (Kolbe, 1957; Rigby, Burckle, and Kolbe, 1958).

5. Subsidence has also taken place within the ocean basins, which appear to have been deepening since the mid-Mesozoic at least. This is suggested by the relations of the deep-sea fauna which preserves a Mesozoic facies (Walther, 1911); by the drilling results at Eniwetok and Bikini, which show that shallow-water Eocene reef corals are now at depths of 3,000 and 4,000 feet (Ladd *et al.,* 1948, 1953); by the widespread occurrence of flat-topped, marine-planed volcanos (guyots) in the Pacific Basin which lie at varying depths (Hess, 1946) and which have terraces—presumably wave-cut—on their flanks; by the occurrence of shallow-water fossils (including reef corals) of Cretaceous and Eocene age on the guyots of the Mid-Pacific Mountains at depths of 6,000 feet (Hamilton, 1956); by geophysical evidence which indicates subsidence through elastic yielding of the crust, as shown by oceanic islands and archipelagos of volcanic origin (Woollard, 1954); and by the fact that the rising continents during

the Middle and Late Tertiary were accompanied by a deepening of the ocean basins in order to maintain isostatic equilibrium.

6. This evidence of subsidence (4, 5 above) indicates that the islands within the present oceanic regions comprise three major types.

a) *Continental islands,* composed of continental rocks, are parts of old continental areas but are now separated from them, owing to subsidence in the intervening region (Wallace, 1895). Some of these connections were severed recently (i.e., British Isles from Europe, Sunda Islands from Asia, Tasmania from Australia, Japan from Asia, etc.), but others have considerable antiquity (i.e., New Zealand–Fiji, Madagascar, Seychelles, Philippines, South Georgia, etc.).

b) *Oceanic islands* have been built up as volcanos or as volcanic ranges from the floor of the ocean basin (Wallace, 1895). Included here are (i) the present high volcanic islands, (ii) low coral archipelagos built on the foundations of old, beveled, subsided volcanic islands, and (iii) submerged archipelagos which were the sites of high islands during the Mesozoic and Early Tertiary. The latter are of the utmost significance for the problem of insular evolution, particularly in the Pacific Basin.

The Mid-Pacific is marked throughout its length by a Swell composed of basaltic rocks (Menard, 1958). The Swell averages 1 km. shallower than the ocean basin and has a cross-section of a broad arch, parts of which (East Pacific Rise) are 1,000 miles wide. Numerous high and low archipelagos on the Swell are now above sea level, and many others are submerged. When the latter were islands, they comprised extensive archipelagos. At the same time the ridges of the Swell were shallow banks, possibly emergent locally, ranging from 1,000 to 2,000 miles long and up to 1,000 miles wide. The Swell is judged to be an impermanent feature (Menard, 1958) because (*a*) seismic evidence shows that part of it (Easter Rise) is a major earthquake zone; (*b*) high heat-flow measurements (twice those of continents and ocean basins) suggest active subcrustal processes and instability; (*c*) numerous volcanos on it are in various stages of evolution; (*d*) submerged volcanos (seamounts, guyots) occur at different subsea levels, indicating several stages in the evolution of the Swell; and (*e*) evidence of Cretaceous and Tertiary subsidence is shown by shallow-water coral reefs and other fossils recovered from guyots in the Mid-Pacific Mountains (Hamilton, 1956) and at Bikini (Ladd *et al.,* 1948) and Eniwetok (Ladd *et al.,* 1953).

Mechanisms that explain such regional earth movements are not clearly understood today, though they are of high interest because of their ultimate bearing on the problem of evolution in oceanic regions. There are two current theories that may account for the elevation and subsidence of large tracts of basaltic lands in ocean basins. The convection theory postulates that movement in the mantle exists in the form of rising (warm) and sinking (cool) currents. Rising currents that diverge may result in the elevation, and their waning in the subsidence, of broad regions. Rising currents that converge apparently account for the full geosynclinal cycle that culminates in mountain-building (Griggs, 1939). The phase-change theory suggests that the Mohorovičić discontinuity (which marks the base of the crust) may not represent a boundary between different rock types but a zone in which basaltic material is transforming into a high-pressure equivalent similar to eclogite (Lovering, 1958). This would provide a mechanism for changing the earth's surface relief whenever there is a change in temperature at the base of the crust. A rise in temperature would displace the Mohorovičić downward, and a certain amount of high-density (eclogitic) material would transform into a less dense—and hence higher-standing—rock (basalt), with a corresponding volume increase of about 15 per cent. A decrease in temperature would cause a depression of the earth's surface over the region. Since basaltic plateaus and archipelagos are of widespread occurrence in the ocean basins, both theories are of high interest. We must emphasize that these possible mechanisms for transient land areas within the ocean basin involve oceanic (simatic), not continental (sialic), rocks; altering a continent into an ocean basin means lowering the surface by more than 5 km. and changing 35 km. of sial into 5 km. of sima. As suggested earlier by Stearns (1945): "Some of the conflict in thought regarding these land connections has resulted from considering them to be continental rocks. Perhaps these early bridges . . . were extensive basaltic plateaus." Regardless of the exact mechanism of earth movement, which we hope will soon be clarified by geophysical research, it is nonetheless amply clear that numerous transient island steppingstones of the type visualized by Hooker and Wallace and discussed at length by Zimmerman (1948), together with extensive (subcontinental) shallow banks and emergent swells, were available for migration into the Pacific during the Mesozoic and Early Tertiary, being linked to the nearest continents by subordinate ridges. These data seem clearly to vindicate many earlier investigators who have pleaded in vain for wider lands in the Pacific because the organisms they were considering—land snails, earthworms, millipedes, spiders, numerous and varied forest insects, many land plants—do not migrate over broad stretches of open ocean.

c) Composite islands—a type not previously defined—have had a dual history, first as continental islands and then as oceanic islands. They occur today chiefly on the ridges of the Atlantic and west Indian oceans. As discussed above (pp. 249 ff.), sialic rocks are sufficiently common on these ridges to suggest that the west Indian and Atlantic oceans are floored with sial, which agrees with seismic evidence as to their general character. Early in their history, probably during the Mesozoic and earlier, they were apparently the sites of large islands (subcontinents?) or archipelagos. Accompanying and following subsidence, they have been areas of more recent volcanic activity. Comparatively shallow water now exists along the ridges of these oceans which earlier supported numerous islands. Of those remaining, probably none is as old as Eocene, and most are probably of later Cenozoic age. It must be particularly emphasized that the subsidence of ancient lands in these oceans has been continuing through time, as indicated by the evidence of foundering in the Atlantic during the Jurassic, Cretaceous, and Tertiary and by generally similar relations in the western half of the Indian Ocean (see pp. 255, 278–79).

EVIDENCE FROM PLANT GEOGRAPHY

7. Plant dispersal (transport) goes on continuously, providing essentially an infinite number of chances for migration during the history of a species.

8. Distance does not impose an insuperable barrier to migration for plants adapted to ready carriage. The greater the distance, the stronger the winnowing effect on the migrants, resulting in a higher degree of imbalance in the flora. Plants with ineffective mechanisms for dispersal do not migrate over broad stretches of sea.

9. Migration is rapid and highly effective at times of favorable climate. For example, the arctic islands were populated by an essentially homogeneous flora since the last glacial and in some cases (Franz Joseph Land, Spitzbergen, Iceland) over 100–200 miles of water. Likewise, the subantarctic islands were glaciated, yet they also have been populated by plants and over considerable distances; of the 30 vascular plants on Kerguelan (fully glaciated), 26 occur in Fuegia, and 12 are on Macquarie (fully glaciated). Further, a number of cool-temperate herbs now range down the cordillera from British Columbia to Fuegia, occurring at lower latitudes chiefly on the high volcanos of Plio-Pleistocene age.

10. The critical factors limiting migration and accounting, therefore, for absence are (a) the nature of the climate and (b) closed plant communities.

a) Migration is impossible unless climate is favorable for establishment. For example, depending upon the kinds of plants involved, whether of desert, tropical rain forest, or temperate deciduous communities, opportunities for migration varied during the Tertiary because of the secular trend toward drying and cooling (Axelrod, 1952*b*). Whereas probabilities for migration were high for tropical plants in the Early Tertiary, they are lower today because tropical climates are more restricted in area and diverse in subtype. Conversely, arid types have a higher probability for dispersal today than at any time during the history of angiosperms because dry climates are more extensive now.

b) Plant competition in closed communities is an important factor in determining whether or not the migrants will become established. In the case of oceanic islands (volcanic) rising out of the sea, closed communities probably develop within only a few hundred years. Hence the likelihood of establishment by migrants is rapidly reduced in a brief time and probably accounts for the unbalanced character of these floras as much as the accidental transport of waifs.

EVIDENCE FROM PALEOCLIMATE

11. Climatic zonation is more marked today than that at any other time since flowering plants have been in existence. Climates were broadly zoned from the later Paleozoic into the Oligocene, with the tropical belt ranging generally between latitude 45°–50° north and south and with mild, continuously moist temperate climates reaching into the polar regions.

12. There was a gradual trend toward cooling and drying in the latter half of the Tertiary, owing largely to rising continents and increased mountain-building. Diverse climatic subtypes developed over the broad tropical and temperate belts, and wholly new regional climates (polar, tundra, desert, mediterranean) came into existence at the close of the period.

The climatic trend toward increased continentality has an important bearing on the concept of evolution in insular regions. In particular, it must be emphasized that the great climatic diversity now found on some oceanic islands is a comparatively recent development. For example, during the Late Cenozoic, trees that are now confined to moist upland forests lived in the lowlands on the lee side of Oahu, where precipitation is now much lower (Stearns and Vaksvik, 1935). Further, many of the islands that have pronounced endemics occur off the western coasts of the continents, where there is upwelling of cold water, as expressed by the California, Canary, and Humboldt currents. To judge from molluscan evidence, these cold currents are of later Cenozoic age, as are the dry land climates associated with the islands that occur in these regions. Whereas some of these islands display great environmental diversity today, like Teneriffe, which rises from a dry subtropic lowland to a subalpine summit, these environmental differences are a comparatively recent development. A small Pleistocene flora from sea level at St. Jorge, Madeira, represents chiefly the laurel forest that is now found only in the uplands there (Heer, 1855). This is an important point, for many of the peculiar endemics of the insular floras of drier regions (Californian, Revillagigedo, Galapagos, Canary, Madeira, Cape Verde islands) occur chiefly in the moister uplands in climates that are relict from the Late Tertiary and which typified the lowlands at that time. By contrast, the drier (often desert to subdesert) climates of the lowlands are comparatively new and harbor most of the "weak" endemics which show affinities to nearby mainland forms, or else clusters of "new" insular species or "weak" genera (*see below,* item 17).

EVOLUTIONARY PRINCIPLES

13. Evidence from Cretaceous and older rocks indicates that many of the larger taxa (orders, families) of flowering plants were already differentiated by the Jurassic.

14. Most living woody species have existed essentially unchanged since the Oligocene, many go back to the Eocene, and some even to the Middle Cretaceous. Hence the isolating mechanisms accounting for them were in operation largely during the Cretaceous and earlier Tertiary.

15. Tertiary Geofloras show that, although spatial isolation of populations has existed since the Oligocene for temperate forest species and probably since the Middle Eocene for tropical types, these isolated species have not diverged sufficiently to become very distinct, and some are scarcely unchanged. This may be explained by their persistence in relatively stable, unchanging environments.

16. Diversity of environment promotes rapid evolution and is essential to it, whereas relatively unchanging conditions lead to evolutionary stagnation. The major taxa of flowering plants that comprise our great forest belts evolved in diverse upland environments, but since invading the lowlands in the Cretaceous they have largely been bradytelic. Only in the case of the newly expanding, broad lowland environments—tundra, desert, steppe, mediterranean—which are geologically young (post-Miocene), is there evidence for rapid evolution in the lowlands. With few exceptions, this has resulted chiefly in minor change, notably in new varieties, species, and "weak" genera in some families, such as the grasses and composites.

17. Continents and continental islands provide conditions far more diverse and subject to change by both climatic and tectonic factors than do oceanic islands, which, for the most part, are small in area

and were typified by mild marine conditions during the Mesozoic and most of the Cenozoic (see item 11, above). On the continents the reticulate nature of plant evolution during epochs of time has led to taxa far removed from their ancestral types, to taxa highly specialized and peculiarly adapted to a wide array of environmental (both biotic and physical) conditions.

But low environmental diversity on oceanic and composite (volcanic part) islands during most of the Tertiary has tended to preserve plants arriving there rather than to accentuate evolutionary rates: all migrants regularly become established in environments to which they are already highly adapted. In the absence of ecologic opportunities, these small populations have diverged chiefly through the accumulation of non-adaptive characters by genetic drift.

To judge from the species which have clearly evolved on existing islands, the process appears to have resulted in change chiefly at low taxonomic levels. As we have noted (item 11 above), these "weak" endemics and species clusters occur usually in the lowlands in climates which, to judge from the evidence supplied by the fossil floras on the continents and by the marine invertebrate faunas, are comparatively recent (Late Cenozoic). They largely comprise species that are related to those on the nearby mainland, and their usual associates are common, widely distributed types on the nearby continents. But the peculiar endemics of the Canary, Revillagigedo, Cape Verde, and Galapagos islands occur chiefly in the milder, moister climates of the uplands that are relict from the Middle and Late Tertiary and which, in general, resemble climates under which they evolved. The chief difference is that the summer fogs which shroud the highlands tend to compensate for the lowered summer rainfall as compared with that of the Tertiary. The nearest relatives (if any) of these endemics are usually found in distant regions: (*a*) the peculiar endemics in the uplands of the Revillagigedo Islands (i.e., Socorro) find their affinities (often obscure) with plants on the wet eastern side of Mexico, Central America, and in the West Indies, not on the nearby Mexican mainland; (*b*) the Canaries show a similar relation, preserving a number of moister types that have their nearest relatives in Africa and the Indo-Malayan region; (*c*) Juan Fernández has relicts whose nearest affinities are in Polynesia and on the wet eastern slopes of the Andes to the northward. Since evolution takes place in response to a changing organism-environmental relation, the "weak" lowland endemics appear largely to be new taxa that evolved in response to new (drier) Late Cenozoic lowland climates, whereas the distinctive endemics of the uplands seem chiefly to represent relicts of floras that were more widely distributed at times when milder, more equable climates were extensive over the lowlands, at which times they migrated to these insular regions.

The problem of endemism of insular floras is therefore tied up inextricably with migration. As Setchell (1935) and Skottsberg (1956) note, although the assumption has frequently been made that rapid and divergent evolution leads to the development of highly peculiar types in insular regions, there is much evidence to the contrary, as Hooker (1867) originally pointed out. Setchell's chief arguments are sufficiently persuasive to be reiterated here. They will be reinforced with data provided by the Tertiary Geofloras, for they give critical evidence as to the origin of endemic areas, both of the continents and of islands.

EVIDENCE FROM TERTIARY GEOFLORAS

In the first place, Tertiary Geofloras provide evidence which shows that the grades of difference between widely distributed plants and the narrowest endemic, whether at the level of species, genus, or family, may develop very quickly from a geological standpoint, during which time the taxon remains essentially unchanged. As for species, there exists today across Holarctica a series of closely related, nearly continuously distributed species in genera such as alder, birch, poplar, and haw. They appear to have become differentiated only since the Miocene from more widespread ancestral species. On the other hand, some closely related species have wide disjunctions, as between eastern Asia and eastern North America in the case of *Alnus japonica-maritima, Carya chinensis-ovata, Hamamelis orientalis-virginiana, Liquidambar formosana-stryciflua,* and *Nyssa chinensis-sylvatica.* Fossil species scarcely distinguishable from them ranged widely over the intervening region during the Early and Middle Tertiary, becoming restricted in area largely following the Miocene, as dry and cold climates expanded and as mediterranean climates gradually developed on the western coasts. Today some of these modern species have a restricted occurrence in one area but are quite narrow in the other. Further restriction of range in the latter areas would soon lead to extinction, and the surviving species would be relict endemics.

As for genera, most of those in the Arcto-Tertiary Geoflora had a wide distribution, and many of them still do—for instance, *Acer, Alnus, Corylus, Crataegus, Populus, Quercus, Rhus, Rosa, Salix,* and a host of others. Some, however, are discontinuous, as between Europe-Asia–North America for *Aesculus, Castanea, Cercis, Fagus, Ostrya,* and *Ulmus,* or between eastern Asia and eastern America in the case of *Berchemia, Cladrastris,* and *Gordonia.* Yet all of them occupied much of the intervening region as late as the Miocene and into the Early Pliocene. Others which are now relict endemics also formerly had wide distributions. *Cercidiphyllum*, one of the most abundant and widespread plants in the Arcto-Tertiary province, is confined now to isolated areas in China and to Japan. It survived in western Europe into the Late Pliocene and in western North America into the Mio-Pliocene transition (and probably later). During the Pliocene the flora of Japan included a number of genera that are now found exclusively in China, notably *Eucommia, Glyptostrobus, Melio-dendron*, and *Stephania*. Furthermore, genera such as *Ailanthus, Pterocarya*, and *Trapa*, which are now confined largely to the Asian land mass, occurred in California in the Late Pliocene. Western Europe had species of *Cercidiphyllum, Eucommia, Keteleeria, Glyptostrobus*, and *Pseudolarix* down to the close of the Pliocene, but their modern derivatives are largely monotypes, confined today to restricted areas in eastern Asia. Evidence provided by the Antarcto-Tertiary Geoflora has shown that a number of genera presently discontinuous between the Tasman and Fuegian regions occupied intermediate regions during the Early and Middle Tertiary. Some which are confined now to restricted areas in Fuegia had close relatives on Antarctica, Kerguelan, Tasmania, New Zealand, and southeastern Australia during the Cretaceous and Early Tertiary. Further, close ancestors of narrow endemics of the Tasman area ranged across Antarctica to Fuegia at the same time. We have also mentioned that a number of genera now typical of the Indo-Malayan region have been recorded in America in rocks of Cretaceous and Eocene age. Likewise, typically tropical American plants are known from Europe and from India.

With respect to families, the monotypic Leitneriaceae, confined now to three small areas in the southern United States, has been recorded from the Miocene of Oregon. Other monotypic families in the Arcto-Tertiary province, including Actinidaceae, Cercidiphylaceae, Eucommiaceae, and Trochodendronaceae, were restricted to temperate eastern Asia very recently; all of them have Late Pliocene records in Europe. We have also seen that some families now in the paleotropics have Early Tertiary records in North America and that others in the Antarcto-Tertiary province are much more restricted today than they were in the Tertiary.

It is apparent that on the continents many of the distinctive endemics, whether species, genera, or families, are due to restrictions of range in response to rapidly changing Late Tertiary climate following a long continental history during which they were widespread and abundant and differed in no essential respects from living types. We may conclude that the more extreme endemics (epibiotics) are often due only to recent environmental change which has restricted them to favorable relict areas, and not to evolution in the isolated regions where they now occur.

Second, it must be recalled that pronounced endemism is not peculiar to insular areas but occurs in segregated parts of the continents. The developmental history of the Arcto-Tertiary Geoflora has shown that close ancestors of endemic species in the temperate forests of eastern Asia, the Caucasus, the Appalachians, and the Klamath-Siskyou Mountains of California had a wide distribution across temperate Holarctica in the Middle and Early Tertiary, following which they were confined to the present areas—they did not evolve in these regions. We have also seen that the history of the Madro-Tertiary Geoflora illustrates that in the drier parts of western North America marked endemism developed chiefly in the Late Cenozoic as plants of wider occurrence became restricted, as the climates to which their antecedents responded tended to shrink in area and to change in character. The highly endemic flora in the uplands of the Cape Region of Baja California did not evolve *in situ:* it migrated into the region during the latter half of the Tertiary and has survived there in isolation largely unchanged. The Antarcto-Tertiary Geoflora shows that the endemics in southern Chile, New Zealand, Tasmania, and adjacent areas are relicts of a southern temperate flora that formerly ranged across Antarctica. We may conclude that on the continents highly endemic areas—fully comparable to those of some insular regions—came into existence as changing later Tertiary climates restricted species of formerly wide distribution to localized relict areas of favorable climate, where they have persisted.

Third, the degree of endemism found in certain archipelagos is not unique but can be duplicated in continental areas as well. In California there are numerous small endemic areas that now harbor highly distinctive plants (both species and genera) derived from the Arcto-Tertiary and Madro-Tertiary Geofloras. Pertinently, the degree of endemism in the various mountain ranges of the area generally parallels that of insular regions. Many of the present mountains that comprise the Coast Ranges formed an archipelago during Miocene and Pliocene times, and generally similar relations are indicated for most of the mountain ranges of the Mediterranean Basin and its borders. In terms of age, these mountains are as old as many existing islands that harbor endemics. Yet there is no evidence that rapid and widely divergent evolution occurred on the islands that were isolated by shelf seas in California and the Mediterranean region during the Miocene and Pliocene. This is a significant point, especially since some of these islands were isolated for as long a time as the present Canary and Californian archipelagos have been separated from their bordering continents. Furthermore, many of the immediate ancestors of the peculiar endemics of these insular regions did have a long continental history, during which time they ranged widely on the nearby continents. These relations are well documented not only for the California and Canary-Madeira islands but also for the distinctive endemics of New Zealand. As we have noted, these peculiar living endemics occur now chiefly in the uplands, where they have persisted in generally moister—and relict—climates; their nearest relatives usually occur in distant areas. By contrast, the "weak" endemics of the lowlands regularly show relationships with species on the nearby continent. The latter have apparently evolved in response to climates generally similar to those in which we now find them, in climates of later Cenozoic age.

Fourth, the rate of evolution demanded by rapid and divergent change in insular areas poses another inconsistency which makes the process seem unlikely for the distinctive endemics. We have mentioned that most woody angiosperms have changed but slowly during their recorded history. Whether we consider fossil relatives of insular endemics that have a recorded history or the more numerous endemics that comprise relicts of continental floras, in each case it is clear that Miocene and Pliocene species can scarcely be distinguished from plants now living and that most Eocene and Oligocene species are similar to living types. Yet the peculiar insular endemics are commonly isolated morphologic types, often with no near living relatives, and they are found in environments that are clearly relict. As Skottsberg (1956) cogently notes, to evolve *in situ* one of the peculiar endemics that occurs today on Hawaii, St. Helena, Mauritius, or Juan Fernández would take a far longer time than these islands have been in existence.

Finally, if the pronounced insular endemics are largely relicts of tropical geofloras, then the existing relations of the present floras of continental, composite, and oceanic islands should be consistent with this interpretation. The relations of the floras of some islands do provide evidence supporting this relationship. For example, in the western part of the Indian Ocean the flora of Mauritius is well known for its high endemism. This composite island is made up of comparatively young volcanics that accumulated on an old, subsiding slate basement. By contrast, Christmas Island on the opposite side of the Indian Ocean is of about the same age as Mauritius but is an oceanic island built up from the floor of the deep ocean. Endemism is generally low in this flora, which is composed chiefly of widely distributed plants of the East Indies that were transported to it in later Cenozoic time. If insular isolation promotes rapid and divergent evolution, then we may appropriately ask: Why is it that Mauritius has many peculiar endemics, yet Christmas—closely similar in age, soil, and climate—has very few? An answer to this question is suggested by the relations in the Seychelles archipelago north of Madagascar. Most of these continental islands are composed of granite, and they have been in existence throughout the Tertiary and probably the Mesozoic as well. They are well known for their high endemism, and they parallel Mauritius in this respect. If we accept the thesis that the endemics of Mauritius and the Seychelles evolved in isolation, then it must follow that evolution was truly explosive on Mauritius because it is so much younger than the Seychelles.

Actually, it seems more probable that Mauritius and the Seychelles have only preserved a number of relics of an ancient flora that occupied these sites when they were large continental islands during the Mesozoic and Early Tertiary. As volcanism built up the modern island of Mauritius in the later Tertiary, the continental basement subsided isostatically, and the ancient relics then occupied a composite island. Thus the differences in the endemism of Mauritius and Christmas are due chiefly to the relative ages of the areas concerned and not to more rapid evolution on one island as compared with another. Closely similar relations exist in the Atlantic Ocean. Fernándo Noronha, a volcanic island situated 200 miles off Cape San Roque, Brazil, has few marked endemics, which is consistent with the fact that it is a newly populated oceanic island of later Cenozoic age. Across the ocean the composite Canary Islands lie 250 miles from Africa and are highly endemic. Subsidence in the later Cenozoic isolated the Canaries from the mainland together with many peculiar endemics that no longer have continental records, though a number of them have close counterparts in the Miocene, Pliocene, and Early Pleistocene floras of southwestern Europe and adjacent Africa.

SUMMARY OF INSULAR FLORAS

Data from geology, paleoclimate, evolution, and paleobotany provide evidence supporting John Dalton Hooker's belief that the highly distinctive plant endemics of insular regions probably evolved in continental areas and that they either migrated to insular sites, where they have been preserved in isolation, or else insularity developed over areas of their former occurrence.

In terms of their geological history, three major types of islands may be distinguished: (1) Continental islands have been connected with the continents, some recently but others long ago (Wallace). Within the tropics and on its margins these islands (i.e., Madagascar, Seychelles, New Zealand, Japan, Philippines, etc.) harbor many relics of Cretaceous and Tertiary Geofloras that reached them at various times over lands which have since subsided. (2) Oceanic islands (and archipelagos) rise from the depths of the ocean basins and are composed of basaltic rocks (Wallace). In the Pacific they were connected with bordering continents and continental islands by emergent basaltic swells and archipelagos, over which migration occurred in the Mesozoic and Early Tertiary. Some of these islands, like Hawaii, harbor peculiar relict endemics that apparently are survivors of these migrations. (3) Composite islands occur chiefly on the ridges of the Atlantic and Indian oceans. They were sites of wider continental lands early in the history of flowering plants and seemingly account for the many similarities that still exist between the floras of the tropics. The younger volcanic islands on these ridges (i.e., Azores, Cape Verde, St. Helena, Mauritius, Reunion, etc.) were populated by species from the subsiding continental lands, and they have thus persisted as ancient relicts in isolation under mild marine climate.

That the highly distinctive endemics did not evolve on oceanic or composite islands is suggested by the fact that the islands are far younger than the peculiar species that occupy them, and some of them had close relatives on the continents. Although a number of the peculiar endemics are not now known to have fossil relatives, the fact that many of them belong to families and genera which have been bradytelic since the beginning of the Tertiary, if not earlier, also suggests that they may be relicts rather than the result of evolution in isolation.

The numerous insular endemics that do not differ greatly from those on nearby continents as well as the species-clusters that distinguish certain archipelagos have apparently evolved in isolation. To judge from geologic and paleoclimatic evidence, this insular evolution took place chiefly during Pliocene and Pleistocene times.

These conclusions concerning evolution in oceanic regions can now be tested. Oceanic and composite islands are composed chiefly of basaltic flows which are often separated by old soils or by fine tuffs. Since the latter regularly contain pollen and spores, they can provide us with evidence concerning the trends of changing vegetation and climate in these insular areas during the Tertiary. This information should enable us not only to determine the age of the islands but also to judge the nature of plant evolution there more clearly than has heretofore been possible. For those islands on the median oceanic ridges which contain acid to intermediate volcanic rock, radiogenic methods are now available (e.g., K-A dating) which make it possible to determine age more precisely.

APPENDIX

Selected References to Continental Rocks of Oceanic Regions *

ATLANTIC OCEAN

Ascension Island: Granite, gabbro, syenite, granite-jasper conglomerate in a wacke matrix, all included as xenoliths in the volcanics.

DALY, R. A. 1925. "The Geology of Ascension Island," *Proc. Amer. Acad. Arts and Sci.,* LX, No. 1, 1–80.

DARWIN, C. 1900. *Geological Observations on Volcanic Islands and Parts of South America Visited during the Voyage of H.M.S. "Beagle,"* pp. 48–53. 3d ed.

RENARD, A. 1899. "Report on the Rock Specimens Collected on Oceanic Islands during the Voyage of H.M.S. 'Challenger,' during the Years 1873–1876," *Challenger Rept., Physics and Chemistry,* Vol. II.

SHAND, S. J. 1949. "Rocks of the Mid-Atlantic Ridge," *Jour. Geol.,* LVII, 89–92.

SMITH, W. C. 1930. "Notes on the Rocks Collected on Ascension Island," in *Report of Geological Collections Made during the Voyage of the "Quest"* . . . *in 1921–1922,* pp. 108–16. London: British Museum (Nat. Hist.).

Azores Islands: Granite, gneiss (some authorities report the blocks may be iceberg-rafted); Miocene limestone, rhyolite.

GAGEL, C. 1919. "Die Mittelatlantischen Vulkaninseln," *Handb. regionalen Geol.,* Heft 4, VII, No. 10, 9–12.

Azores Swell: Anorthositic gabbro (mylonitized); dredged at 30°06' N., 42°08', W., 800 fathoms.

SHAND, S. J. 1949. "Rocks of the Mid-Atlantic Ridge," *Jour. Geol.,* LVII, 89–92.

Canary Islands: Diorite, schist, rhyolite, syenite, gabbro, Cretaceous limestone.

COTTREAU, J., and LEMOINE, P. 1910. "Sur la présence du Crétace aux Iles Canaries," *Bull. Géol. Soc. France,* 4th ser., X, 267–71.

FURON, R. 1950. *Géologie de l'Afrique,* pp. 171–72. Paris: Payot.

Cape Verde Islands: Syenite, quartzite, granite, diorite, andesite, Jurassic and Cretaceous vertically dipping limestones.

FURON, R. 1950. *Géologie de l'Afrique,* pp. 172–74. Paris: Payot.

PART, G. M. 1930. "Report on the Rocks Collected from St. Vincent, Cape Verde Islands," in *Report of Geological Collections Made during the Voyage of the "Quest"* . . . *in 1921–1922,* pp. 117–25. London: British Museum (Nat. Hist.).

* A general bibliography to the literature cited in this chapter follows the present section, pp. 298–305.

PIRES SOARES, J. M. 1948. "Observations géologiques sur les Iles du Cap Verde," *Bull. Géol. Soc. France,* 5th ser., XVIII, 383–89.

Meteor Bank: Quartzite; dredged at 48°14′ S., 8°22′ E.

MACHATSCHEK, F. 1955. *Das Relief der Erde,* II, 505. Berlin-Nikolassee: Gebrüder Brontraeger.

Rockall Island and Bank: Granite, andesite, micaceous sandstone.

SABINE, P. A. 1955. "Specimens Collected from Rockall, in the North Atlantic," *Proc. Geol. Soc. London, Session 1955–1956,* Nos. 1530–41, November 2, 1955, p. 3.

ANONYMOUS. "Notices of Memoirs, 1899," *Geol. Mag.,* N.S., Decade IV, VI, 163–67.

St. Paul's Rocks: Mylonitized dunite and peridotite.

DARWIN, CHARLES. 1900. *Geological Observations on the Volcanic Islands and Parts of South America Visited during the Voyage of H.M.S. "Beagle,"* pp. 36–39. 3d ed.

PRATJE, OTTO. 1950. "Geologische und morphologische Beobachtungen an den St. Pauls-Felsen in Atlantischen Ozean," *Mitt. Geog. Gesellsch. Hamburg,* XLIX, 143–57.

RENARD, A. 1889. "Report on the Petrology of the Rocks of St. Paul," in *H.M.S. Challenger,* Narrative, Vol. II Part I, Appendix B.

WASHINGTON, HENRY S. 1930. "The Petrology of St. Paul's Rocks (Atlantic)," in *Report on the Geological Collections Made during the Voyage of the "Quest"* . . . *in 1921–1922,* pp. 126–41. London: British Museum (Nat. Hist.).

South Georgia: Quartz-diorite, granite, gabbro, peridotite, schist, quartzites, Paleozoic quartzose-greywacke-slates, Mesozoic shales, tuffs.

TYRRELL, G. W. 1918. "Additional Notes on the Petrography of South Georgia," *Geol. Mag.,* N.S., Decade VI, IV, 483–89.

————. 1930. "Petrography and Geology of South Georgia," in *Report on the Geological Collections Made during the Voyage of the "Quest"* . . . *in 1921–1922,* p. 29. London: British Museum (Nat. Hist.).

South Orkneys: Greywacke, greywacke-slate, quartzite, arkosic conglomerate, conglomerate, slate, altered diabase, spilite.

STEWARD, DUNCAN, JR. 1937. "Petrography of Some Rocks from the South Orkney Islands and the Antarctic Archipelago," *Amer. Mineralogist,* XXII, 178–82.

TYRRELL, G. W. 1918. "Additional Notes on the Petrography of South Georgia," *Geol. Mag.,* N.S., Decade VI, IV, 489.

South Shetlands: Pre-Mesozoic basement of crystalline schists and gneiss; mid-Tertiary (?) andesites, diorite dikes, phyllites.

FERGUSON, DAVID. 1921. "Geological Observations in the South Shetlands, the Palmer Archipelago, and Graham Land, Antarctica," *Trans. Roy. Soc. Edinburgh,* Vol. LIII, Part I, No. 3, pp. 29–55.

THOMAS, HERBERT H. 1921. "On the Innes Wilson Collection of Rocks and Minerals from the South Shetland Islands and Trinity

Island," *Trans. Roy. Soc. Edinburgh,* Vol. LIII, Part I, No. 5, pp. 81–89.

TYRRELL, G. W. 1921. "A Contribution to the Petrography of the South Shetland Islands, the Palmer Archipelago, and the Danco Land Coast, Graham Land, Antarctica," *Trans. Roy. Soc. Edinburgh,* Vol. LIII, Part I, No. 4, pp. 57–79.

WORDIE, J. M. 1921. "Shackleton Antarctic Expedition, 1914–1917; Geological Observations in the Weddell Sea Area," *Trans. Roy. Soc. Edinburgh,* Vol. LIII, Part I, No. 2, pp. 3–25.

Trinidad, South: Radiolarian chert. Significance open to question.

PRIOR, G. T. 1900. "Petrographical Notes on the Rock Specimens Collected in the Little Island of Trinidad, South Atlantic, by the Antarctic Expedition of 1839–1843, under Sir James Clark Ross," *Mineral. Mag. and Jour. Mineral. Soc.,* XII, 317–23.

Tristan d'Acunha: Augite andesite, hornblende andesite. Gneiss block (some question as to whether it is a xenolith carried up by the lavas, or whether it was part of a ship's ballast).

SMITH, W. CAMPBELL. 1930. "Petrography of the Tristan da Cunha Group," in *Report of Geological Collections Made during the Voyage of the "Quest"* . . . *in 1921–1922,* pp. 72–87. London: British Museum (Nat. Hist.).

TIZARD, T. H., *et al.* 1885. In *Narrative of the Cruise of H.M.S. "Challenger,"* . . . 1, Part 1, pp. 252, 262, 264.

SCHWARZ, E. H. L. 1905. "The Rocks of Tristan d'Acunha, Brought Back by H.M.S. 'Odin,' 1904, with Their Bearing on the Question of the Permanence of Ocean Basins," *Trans. South African Phil. Soc.,* XVI, 9–51.

Walvis Ridge: Arkose pebble. Dredged at 35°40′ S., 5°1′ W.; 1,942 fathoms.

DOUGLAS, A. V. 1930. "Deep-Sea Deposits and Dredgings," in *Report of Geological Collections Made during the Voyage of the "Quest"* . . . *in 1921–1922,* pp. 145–56. London: British Museum (Nat. Hist.).

INDIAN OCEAN

Comores: Schist, granite, granodiorite monzonite, andesite.

LACROIX, A. 1922. "La Constitution lithologique de l'Archipel des Comores," *Compt. rend. Internat. Geol. Cong.,* XIII, Part 2, 949–79.

Crozet (Possession) Island: Granite, mica-schist, trachyandesite.

PRIOR, G. T. 1898. "Petrographical Notes on the Rock Specimens Collected in Antarctic Regions during the Voyage of H.M.S. "Erebus" and "Terror" under Sir James Clark Ross, in 1839–1843," *Mineral. Mag. and Jour. Mineral. Soc.,* XII, 75–79.

TYRRELL, G. W. 1937. "The Petrology of Possession Island," *B.A.N.Z. Antarctic Research Expedition, 1929–1931, Reports,* Ser. A, Vol. II, Part 4, pp. 65–66.

Heard Island: Micromonzonite, biotite andesite, crystalline limestone.

AUBERT DE LA RUE, A. 1929. "Un Voyage d'exploration dans les mers australes," *Rev. géog. phys. et géol. dynamique,* II, Fasc. II, 127–35.

Kerguelen: Rhyolite, syenite, monzonite, diorite, aplite.

AUBERT DE LA RUE, A. 1932. "Étude géologique et géographique de l'Archipel de Kerguelen," *Rev. géog. phys. et géol. dynamique,* V, Fasc. I, II, 1–231.

EDWARDS, A. B. 1938. "Tertiary Lavas from the Kerguelen Archipelago," *B.A.N.Z. Antarctic Research Expedition, Reports,* Ser. A, II, Part 5, 72–100.

Mauritius: Clay-slate

HAIG, H. DE HAGA. 1895. "The Physical Features and Geology of Mauritius," *Quart. Jour. Geol. Soc. London,* LI, 463–71.

SHAND, S. J. 1933. "The Lavas of Mauritius," *Quart. Jour. Geol. Soc. London,* LXXXIX, 1–13.

Seychelles: Granite, syenite, slate, hornfels.

GARDINER, J. S. 1931. *Coral Reefs and Atolls.* London: Macmillan Co.

REED, F. R. C. 1949. *The Geology of the British Empire,* pp. 544–45. 2d ed. London: Edward Arnold & Co.

St. Paul: Rhyolite, rhyolite tuff.

AUBERT DE LA RUE, A. 1929. "Un Voyage d'exploration dans les mers australes," *Rev. géog. phys. et géol. dynamique,* II, 7–105.

NORDENSKJÖLD, O. 1913. "Antarktis," *Handb. regionalen Geol.,* VIII, Part 6, 25.

SOUTHWEST PACIFIC

Auckland Islands: Granite, olivine gabbro, schist, gneiss, andesite.

MARSHALL, P. 1911. "New Zealand and Adjacent Islands," *Handb. regionalen Geol.,* Vol. VII, Part 1, No. 5, p. 62.

Bounty Islands: Granite.

MARSHALL, P. 1911. "New Zealand and Adjacent Islands," *Handb. regionalen Geol.,* Vol. VII, Abt. 1, Heft 5, p. 61.

Campbell Island: Mica schist, quartz conglomerate, sandstone, chert.

MARSHALL, P. 1911. "New Zealand and Adjacent Islands," *Handb. regionalen Geol.,* Vol. VII, Abt. 1, Heft 5, pp. 63–64.

PRIOR, G. T. 1900. "Petrographical Notes on the Rock Specimens Collected in Antarctic Regions during the Voyage of H.M.S. 'Erebus' and 'Terror,' under Sir James Clark Ross, in 1839–1843," *Mineral. Mag. and Jour. Mineral. Soc.,* XII, 73–75.

Chatham Islands: Mica schist, micaceous andesite.

MARSHALL, P. 1911. "New Zealand and Adjacent Islands," *Handb. regionalen Geol.,* Vol. VII, Abt. 1, Heft 5, p. 61.

REED, J. J. 1952. "Sediments from the Chatham Rise," *New Zealand Jour. Sci. and Technol.,* XXXIV, 176–80.

Fiji Archipelago: Granite, quartz diorite, quartzite, schist, arkose, andesite, rhyolite.

MARSHALL, P. 1911. "Oceania," *Handb. regionalen Geol.,* Vol. VII, Abt. 2, pp. 19–22.

Kermadec Island: Hornblende granite, as xenoliths in andesite.

MARSHALL, P. 1911. "Oceania," *Handb. regionalen Geol.,* Vol. VII, Abt. 2, p. 23.

Macquarie Island: Granite, hornfels, hornfels cataclasite, gabbroic cataclasite, sandstone, arkose and marble occur as erratics on the beaches in the northern part of the island. Source in doubt. Mawson suggests (1) transport by land ice sheet from an area (to the west) now submerged; (2) transport by icebergs to island; (3) ballast from shipwrecks on the island.

MAWSON, D. 1943. "Macquarie Island, Its Geography and Geology," *Australian Antarctic Expedition, Sci. Repts.,* Ser. A, Vol. 5.

LITERATURE CITED

ANDREWS, E. C. 1913. "The Development of the Natural Order Myrtaceae," *Proc. Linn. Soc. New South Wales,* XXXVIII, 529–68.

———. 1914. "The Development and Distribution of the Natural Order Leguminosae," *Jour. Roy. Soc. New South Wales,* XLVIII, 333–407.

ARAMBOURG, C., ARENES, J., and DEPAPE, G. 1953. "Contribution à l'étude des flores fossiles Quaternaires de l'Afrique du Nord," *Arch. Mus. Nat. Hist. Naturelle,* 7th ser., Vol. II.

ARKELL, W. J. 1956. *Jurassic Geology of the World.* Edinburgh: Oliver & Boyd.

AXELROD, D. I., 1939. *A Miocene Flora from the Western Border of the Mohave Desert.* ("Publications of the Carnegie Institution of Washington," No. 516.)

———. 1950. *Evolution of Desert Vegetation in Western North America,* pp. 217–306. ("Publications of the Carnegie Institution of Washington," No. 590.)

———. 1952a. "A Theory of Angiosperm Evolution," Evolution, VI, 29–60.

———. 1952b. "Variables Affecting the Probabilities of Dispersal in Geologic Time," *Bull. Amer. Mus. Nat. Hist.,* Vol. XCIX, art. 3, pp. 177–88.

———. 1956. *Mio-Pliocene Floras from West-central Nevada.* ("University of California Publications in Geological Science," Vol. XXXIII.)

———. 1957. "Late Tertiary Floras and the Sierra Nevadan Uplift," *Bull. Geol. Soc. America,* LXVIII, 19–45.

———. 1958. "Evolution of the Madro-Tertiary Geoflora," *Bot. Rev.,* XXIV, 433–509.

———. 1959a. "Evolution of the Psilophyte Paleoflora," *Evolution,* XIII, 264–75.

———. 1959b. "Late Cenozoic Evolution of the Sierran Bigtree Forest," *ibid.,* pp. 9–23.

————. 1959c. "Poleward Migration of the Early Angiosperm Flora," *Science,* CXXX, 203–7.

BARRELL, J. 1927. "On Continental Fragmentation, and the Geologic Bearing on the Moon's Surficial Features," *Amer. Jour. Sci.,* CCXIII, 283–314.

BERRY, E. W. 1926. *Pleistocene Plants from North Carolina,* pp. 97–119. (U.S. Geol. Surv. Prof. Paper 140-C.)

————. 1937. "Tertiary Floras of Eastern North America," *Bot. Rev.,* III, 31–46.

————. 1938. *Tertiary Flora from the Rio Pichileufu, Argentina.* (Geol. Soc. America Spec. Paper 12.)

BEWS, J. W. 1925. *Plant Forms and Their Evolution in South Africa.* New York: Longmans, Green & Co.

————. 1927. "Studies in the Ecological Evolution of Angiosperms," *New Phytol.,* XXVI, 1–21, 65–84, 129–48, 209–48, 273–94.

BLANFORD, W. T. 1890. Anniversary Address of the President, *Proc. Geol. Soc. London, 1889–1890,* pp. 59–110.

BOWER, F. O. 1923–28. *The Ferns.* 3 vols. Cambridge: Cambridge University Press.

BRAUN, E. L. 1950. *Deciduous Forests of Eastern North America.* Toronto: Blakiston Co.

————. 1955. "The Phytogeography of the Unglaciated Eastern United States and Its Interpretation," *Bot. Rev.,* XXI, 297–375.

BROWN, R. W. 1944. "Temperate Species in the Eocene Flora of the Southeastern United States," *Jour. Washington Acad. Sci.,* XXXIV, 349–51.

————. 1956. *Palmlike Plants from the Dolores Formation (Triassic), Southwestern Colorado,* pp. 205–9. (U.S. Geol. Surv. Prof. Paper 274-H.)

CAIN, S. A. 1944. *Foundations of Plant Geography.* New York: Harper & Bros.

CAMP, W. H. 1947. "Distribution Patterns in Modern Plants and Problems of Ancient Dispersals," *Ecol. Mono.,* XVII, 159–83.

————. 1952. "Phytophyletic Patterns on Lands Bordering the South Atlantic Basin," *Bull. Amer. Mus. Nat. Hist.,* Vol. XCIX, art. 3, pp. 205–12.

————. 1956. "The Forests of the Past and Present, in *A World Geography of Forest Resources,* pp. 13–47. (Amer. Geog. Soc. Spec. Pub. 33.)

CARR, D. R., and KULP, J. L. 1953. "Age of a Mid-Atlantic Ridge Basalt Boulder," *Bull. Geol. Soc. America,* LXIV, 253–54.

CHANDLER, M. E. J. 1954. "Some Upper Cretaceous and Eocene Fruits from Egypt," *British Mus. (Nat. Hist.), B., Geol.,* II, 149–87.

CHANEY, R. W. 1935. "The Kucha Flora in Relation to the Physical Conditions in Central Asia during the Late Tertiary," *Geog. Ann., Ann. Svensk. Sällsk, Antropol. och Geog.,* XVII, 75–105.

————. 1938. "Paleoecological Interpretations in Cenozoic Plants in Western North America," *Bot. Rev.,* IV, 371–96.

CHANEY, R. W. 1940. "Tertiary Forests and Continental History," *Bull. Geol. Soc. America,* LI, 469–88.

————. 1947. "Tertiary Centers and Migration Routes," *Ecol. Mono.,* XVII, 141–48.

CHANEY, R. W., and HU, H. H. 1942. *A Miocene Flora from Shantung Province, China,* Part II. ("Publications of the Carnegie Institution of Washington," No. 507.)

CLEMENTS, F. E. 1936. "Origin of the Desert and Desert Climax," in *Essays in Geobotony in Honor of W. A. Setchell.* Berkeley: University of California Press.

CONSTANCE, L. 1955. "The Systematics of Angiosperms," in *A Century of Progress in the Natural Sciences, 1853–1953,* pp. 405–83. San Francisco: California Academy of Sciences.

COUPER, R. A. 1953. "Distribution of Proteaceae, Fagaceae, and Podocarpaceae in Some Southern Hemisphere Cretaceous and Tertiary Beds," *New Zealand Jour. Sci. and Technol., B,* XXXV, 247–50.

COUPER, R. A., and MCQUEEN, D. R. 1954. "Pliocene and Pleistocene Plant Fossils of New Zealand and Their Climatic Interpretation," *New Zealand Jour. Sci. and Technol., B,* XXV, 398–420.

CREER, K. M., IRVING, E., NAIRN, A. E., and RUNCORN, S. K. 1958. "Palaeomagnetic Results from Different Continents and Their Relation to the Problem of Continental Drift," *Ann. géophys.,* XIV, 492–501.

DALY, R. A. 1938. *Architecture of the Earth.* New York: D. Appleton–Century Co.

DARLINGTON, P. J., JR. 1957. *Zoogeography: The Geographical Distribution of Animals.* New York: John Wiley & Sons.

DAVIES, W. E. 1956. "Antarctica Stratigraphy and Structure," in *Antarctica in the International Geophysical Year,* pp. 44–51. (American Geophysical Union, Geophys. Mono., Vol. I.)

DEEVEY, E. S., JR. 1949. "Biogeography of the Pleistocene," *Bull. Geol. soc. America,* LX, 1315–1416.

DE OLIVEIRA, A. I. 1956. "Brazil," in *Handbook of South American Geology,* ed. W. F. JENKS, pp. 1–62. (Geol. Soc. Amer. Mem., No. 65.)

DEPAPE, G. 1928. "Le monde des plantes à l'apparition de l'homme en Europe occidentale," *Ann. Soc. Sci. Bruxelles, B, Sci. phys. et naturelles,* Vol. XLVIII, Part 2, 39–101.

DRESSLER, R. L. 1954. "Some Floristic Relationships between Mexico and the United States," *Rhodora,* LVI, 81–96.

DURHAM, J. W. 1952. "Early Tertiary Marine Faunas and Continental Drift," *Amer. Jour. Sci.,* CCL, 321–43.

DUTOIT, A. L. 1954. *Geology of South Africa.* 3d ed., rev. London: Oliver & Boyd.

EAMES, A. J. 1953. "Neglected Morphology of the Palm Leaf," *Phytomorphology,* III, 172–89.

EARDLEY, A. J. 1954. "Tectonic Relations of North and South America," *Bull. Amer. Assoc. Petroleum Geologists,* XXXVIII, 707–73.

EKMAN, S. 1953. *Zoogeography of the Sea.* London: Sidgwick & Jackson.

ELIAS, M. K. 1936. "Late Paleozoic Plants of the Midcontinent Region as Indicators of Time and Environment," *Internat. Geol. Cong., Rept. 16th Session, U.S.A., 1933*, I, 691–700.

ERDTMAN, G. 1948. "Did Dicotyledonous Plants Exist in Early Jurassic Time?" *Geol. fören. Stockholm förhandl.*, March–April, pp. 265–71.

EWING, M., WOOLLARD, G. P., and VINE, A. C. 1939. "Geophysical Investigations in the Emerged and Submerged Atlantic Coastal Plain," Part 3: "Barnegat Bay, N.J., Section," *Bull. Geol. Soc. America*, L, 257–96.

EWING, M., WORZEL, J. L., STEENLAND, N. C., and PRESS, F. 1950. "Geophysical Investigations in the Emerged and Submerged Atlantic Coastal Plain," Part 5: "Woods Hole, New York, and Cape May Sections," *Bull. Geol. Soc. America*, LXI, 877–92.

FAIRBRIDGE, R. W. 1948. "The Juvenility of the Indian Ocean," *Scope* (Sci. Union, Univ. Western Australia), I (3): 29–35.

———. 1949. "Antarctica and Geology," *ibid.*, I (4): 25–33.

FLORIN, R. 1940. "The Tertiary Fossil Conifers of South Chile and Their Phytogeographical Significance," *Kgl. Svensk. Vetenskaps. Handl.*, 3d ser., Vol. XIX, No. 2.

FRENGUELLI, J. 1943. "Restos de *Casuarina* en el mioceno de El Mirador, Patagonia central," *La Plata Univ. Nac. Mus., Notas*, Vol. VIII, Paleont. No. 56, pp. 349–54.

GLENNIE, E. A. 1936. "A Report on Values of Gravity in the Maldive and Laccadive Islands," *Brit. Mus. (Nat. Hist.) John Murray Expedition, Sci. Rept.* I, No. 4, 95–107.

GOOD, R. 1947. *The Geography of Flowering Plants.* London: Longmans, Green & Co.

GRAY, ASA. 1846. "Analogy between the Flora of Japan and That of the United States," *Amer. Jour. Sci. and Arts*, LII, 135–36.

———. 1859. "Diagnostic Characters of New Species of Phaenogamous Plants, Collected in Japan by Charles Wright, with Observations upon the Relations of the Japanese Flora to That of North America, and Other Parts of the Northern Temperate Zone," *Amer. Acad. Arts and Sci. Mem.*, VI, 377–452.

GREGORY, J. W. 1929. "The Geological History of the Atlantic Ocean," *Proc. Geol. Soc. London*, XXV, lxviii–cxxii (bound as appendix with *Quart. Jour. Geol. Soc. London*, Vol. LXXXV).

GRIGGS, D. T. 1939. "A Theory of Mountain Building," *Amer. Jour. Sci.*, CCXXXVII, 611–50.

GUTENBERG, B. 1951. "Crustal Layers of the Continents and Oceans," *Bull. Geol. Soc. America*, LXII, 427–40.

GUTENBERG, B., and RICHTER, C. F. 1949. *Seismicity of the Earth.* Princeton, N.J.: Princeton University Press.

HAMILTON, E. L. 1956. *Sunken Islands of the Mid-Pacific Mountains.* ("Geol. Soc. America Mem. 64.)

HALLE, T. G. 1911. "On the Geological Structure and History of the Falkland Islands," *Bull. Geol. Inst. Upsala*, XI, 215.

HARSHBERGER, J. W. 1911. *Phytogeographic Survey of North America.* New York: G. E. Stechert & Co.

HAUGHTON, S. H. 1952. "The Karroo System in the Union of South Africa," *19th Internat. Geol. Cong., Algeria, Symposium . . . Gondwana,* pp. 254–55.

HEER, O. 1855. "Ueber die fossilen Pflanzen von St. Jorge, in Madeira," *Neuv. Mém. Soc. Helvet. Sci. Nat. Hist.,* XV, 1–40.

HESS, H. H. 1946. "Drowned Ancient Islands of the Pacific Basin," *Amer. Jour. Sci.,* CCXLIV, 772–91.

HOLTEDHAL, O. 1920. "Paleogeography and Diastrophism in the Atlantic-Arctic Region during Paleozoic Time," *Amer. Jour. Sci.,* XLIX, 1–25.

HOOKER, J. D. 1853. *Botany of the Antarctic Voyage of H. M. Discovery ships "Erebus" and "Terror" in the years 1831–1843,* Vol. II: *Flora Novae-Zelandiae,* Part 1, Introductory Essay.

———. 1867. "Insular Floras," *Gard. Chron. and Agr. Gaz.,* XLIII, 6–7, 27, 50–51, 75–76.

———. 1878. "The Distribution of the North American Flora," *ibid.,* XLIV, 140–42, 216–17.

IMLAY, R. W., and REESIDE, J. B., JR. 1954. "Correlation of the Cretaceous Formations of Greenland and Alaska," *Bull. Geol. Soc. America,* LXV, 223–46.

KING, L. C. 1953. "Necessity for Continental Drift," *Bull. Amer. Assoc. Petroleum Geologists,* XXXVII, 2163–77.

———. 1958. "Basic Paleogeography of Gondwanaland during the Late Paleozoic and Mesozoic Eras," *Quart. Jour. Geol. Soc. London,* CXIV, Part 1, 47–77.

KOLBE, R. W. 1957. "Fresh-Water Diatoms from Atlantic Deep-Sea Sediments," *Science,* CXXVI, 1053–56.

KOSSMAT, F. 1897. "The Cretaceous Deposits of Pondicherri," *Records of Geol. Surv. India,* XXX, Part 2, 51–110.

KRAUSEL, R. 1956. "Zur Geschichte der Angiospermen," *Bot. Mag., Tokyo,* LXIX, 537–43.

KRISHTOFOVICH, A. N. 1957. *Paleobotanika.* 4th ed. Leningrad: Gosudar. Nauch.-Tech. Izd. Neft. i. Gorono-Topliv. Lit.

KUENEN, P. H. 1950. *Marine Geology.* New York: John Wiley & Sons.

LADD, H. S. *et al.* 1948. "Drilling on Bikini Atoll, Marshall Islands," *Science,* CVII, 51–55.

———. 1953. "Drilling on Eniwetok Atoll, Marshall Islands," *Bull. Amer. Assoc. Petroleum Geologists,* XXXVII, 2257–80.

LEES, G. M. 1953. "The Evolution of a Shrinking Earth," *Quart. Jour. Geol. Soc. London,* CIX, 217–57.

———. 1954. "The Geological Evidence on the Nature of the Ocean Floors," *Proc. Roy. Soc. London, A.,* CCXXII, 400–402.

LIGNIER, O. 1907. "Nouvelles recherches sur le *Propalmophyllum liasinum,*" *Mém. Soc. Linn. Normandi,* XXIII, 1–15.

LOVERING, J. F. 1958. "The Nature of the Mohorovičić Discontinuity," *Trans. Amer. Geophys. Union,* XXIX, 947–55.

LULL, R. S. 1947. *Organic Evolution.* New York: Macmillan Co.

MARTIN, P. S., and HARRELL, B. E. 1957. "The Pleistocene History of Temperate Biotas in Mexico and Eastern United States," *Ecology,* XXXVIII, 468–80.

MAYR, E., *et al.* 1952. "The Problem of Land Connections across the South Atlantic with Special Reference to the Mesozoic," *Bull. Amer. Mus. Nat. Hist.,* Vol. XCIX, Art. 3.

MENARD, H. W. 1958. "Development of Median Elevations in Ocean Basins," *Bull. Geol. Soc. America,* LXIX, 1179–85.

NĚMEJC, F. 1956. "On the Problem of the Origin and Phylogenetic Development of the Angiosperms," *Sborn. Nat. Mus. Prase, Acta Mus. Nat. Pragae,* XII, 65–143.

PILSBURY, H. A. 1911. "Notes upon the Characteristics and Origin of the Non-marine Mulluscan Fauna of South America," in W. B. SCOTT (ed.), *Reports of the Princeton University Expeditions to Patagonia, 1896–1899,* Vol. III (No. 2): *Zoology,* Part 5: "Non-marine Mollusca of Patagonia," pp. 611–33.

POTBURY, S. S. 1935. *The LaPorte Flora of Plumas County, California,* pp. 29–81. ("Publications of the Carnegie Institution of Washington," No. 465.)

REED, F. R. C. 1949. *The geology of the British Empire.* 2d ed. London: E. Arnold Co.

REID, E. M., and CHANDLER, M. E. J. 1933. *The London Clay Flora.* London: British Museum (Nat. Hist.).

RIGBY, J. K., BURCKLE, L. H., and KOLBE, R. W. 1958. "Turbidity Currents and Displaced Fresh-Water Diatoms," *Science,* CXXVII (No. 3313), 1504–05.

ROSS, H. H. 1956. *A Textbook of Entomology.* New York: John Wiley & Sons.

ROTHE, J. P. 1954. "La Zone seismique médiane Indo-Atlantique," *Proc. Roy. Soc. London, A,* CCXXII, 387–97.

RUNCORN, S. K. 1956. "Paleomagnetism, Polar Wandering, and Continental Drift," *Geol. en Mijnbouw,* XVIII, 253–56.

SAHNI, B. 1943. "Deccan Intertrappean Series," in "Paleobotany in India," *Jour. Indian Bot. Soc.,* XXII, 171–82.

SAHNI, B., and SURANGE, K. R. 1953. "On the Structure and Affinities of *Cyclanthodendron Sahnii* (Rode) Sahni and Surange from the Deccan Intertrappean Series," *Paleobotanist,* II, 93–100.

SCHUCHERT, C. 1932. "Gondwana Land Bridges," *Bull. Geol. Soc. America,* XLIII, 875–916.

SELLING, O. H. 1947. "Aponogetonaceae in the Cretaceous of South America," *Svensk. Bot. Tidskr.,* XLI (No. 1), 182.

SETCHELL, W. A. 1935. "Pacific Insular Floras and Pacific Paleogeography," *Amer. Naturalist,* LXIX, 289–310.

SEWARD, A. C. 1935. *Leaves of Dicotyledons from the Nubian Sandstone of Egypt.* ("Pub. Geol. Surv. Egypt.")

———. 1941. *Plant Life through the Ages.* Cambridge: Cambridge University Press.

SHAND, S. J. 1949. "Rocks of the Mid-Atlantic Ridge," *Jour. Geol.,* LVII, 89–92.

SHARP, A. J. 1953. "Notes on the Flora of Mexico: World Distribution of the Woody Dicotyledonous Families and the Origin of the Modern Vegetation," *Jour. Ecol.,* XLI, 376–80.

SIMPSON, J. B. 1937. "Fossil Pollen in Scottish Jurassic Coal," *Nature,* CXXXIX, 673.

SIMPSON, G. G. 1939. "Antarctica as a Faunal Migration Route," *Proc. 6th Pacific Sci. Cong.,* pp. 755–68.

———. 1944. *Tempo and Mode in Evolution.* New York: Columbia University Press.

———. 1953. *The Major Features of Evolution.* New York: Columbia University Press.

SKOTTSBERG, C. (ed.). 1920–56. *The Natural History of Juan Fernández and Easter Island.* 2 vols. Uppsala: Almquist & Wiksells Boktryckeri.

STEARNS, H. T. 1945. "Late Geologic History of the Pacific Basin," *Amer. Jour. Sci.,* CCXLIII, 614–26.

STEARNS, H. T., and VAKSVIK, K. N. 1935. *Geology and Ground Water Resources of the Island of Oahu, Hawaii.* (Div. of Hydrography, T.H., Bull. 1.)

STEBBINS, G. L., JR. 1950. *Variation and Evolution in Plants.* New York: Columbia University Press.

STEHLI, F. G. 1957. "Possible Permian Climatic Zonation and Its Implication," *Amer. Jour. Sci.,* CCLV, 607–18.

STEYERMARK, J. A. 1950. "Flora of Guatemala," *Ecology,* XXXI, 368–72.

SZAFER, W. 1946. *The Pliocene Flora of Kroscienko in Poland,* Vol. I: *General Part.* Polska Akad. Umiej., Rozprawy t. 72, dzial B (s. 3, t. 32), no. 1. (In Polish, English Summary, pp. 90–162.)

———. 1954. "(Pliocene Flora from the Vicinity of Czorsztyn [West Carpathians] and Its Relationship to the Pleistocene)" (Polish, with long English summary). *Prace. Inst. Geol. Warszawa,* XI, 1–238.

TAKHTAJAN, A. 1957. "(On the Origin of the Temperate Flora of Eurasia)," *Bot. Mag.,* XLII (11), 1635–53 (in Russian, with English summary).

THOMAS, H. H. 1936. "Paleobotany and the Origin of the Angiosperms," *Bot. Rev.,* II, 397–418.

THOMSON, J. A. 1918. *Brachiopoda.* (Australian Antarctic Expedition, 1911–1914. Sci. Repts., Ser. C, Vol. IV, Part 3.)

TOLSTOY, I. 1951. "Submarine Topography in the North Atlantic," *Bull. Geol. Soc. America,* LXII, 441–50.

TRAVERSE, A. 1955. *Pollen Analysis of the Brandon Lignite of Vermont.* (U.S. Dept. Interior, Bur. of Mines, Rept. of Investigation, No. 5151.)

UMBGROVE, J. H. F. 1947. *The Pulse of the Earth.* The Hague: M. Nijhoff.

USHER, J. L. 1952. *Ammonite Faunas of the Upper Cretaceous Rocks of Vancouver Island, British Columbia.* (Canada Dept. Mines and Tech. Surv., Geol. Surv. Canada Bull. 21.)

WADIA, D. N. 1953. *Geology of India.* 3d ed. London: Macmillan & Co.

WALLACE, A. R. 1876. *Geographical Distribution of Animals.* 2 vols. London: Macmillan & Co.

————. 1895. *Island Life.* 2d ed., rev. London: Macmillan & Co.

WALTHER, J. 1911. "The Origin and Peopling of the Deep Sea," *Amer. Jour. Sci.,* CLXXXI, 55–64.

WEEKS, L. G. 1948. "Paleogeography of South America," *Bull. Geol. Soc. America,* LIX, 249–82.

WEGENER, A. 1924. *The Origin of the Continents and Oceans.* English translation by J. G. A. SKERL. New York: E. P. Dutton & Co.

WILLIS, B. 1932. "Isthmian Links," *Bull. Geol. Soc. America,* XLIII, 917–53.

WOOLLARD, G. P. 1954. "Crustal Structure beneath Ocean Islands," *Proc. Roy. Soc. London, A.,* CCXXII, 361–87.

ZIMMERMAN, E. C. 1948. *Insects of Hawaii,* Vol. I: *Introduction.* Honolulu: University of Hawaii Press.

ALFRED E. EMERSON

THE EVOLUTION OF ADAPTATION
IN POPULATION SYSTEMS

The vast body of evidence used to establish the concept of organic evolution and to analyze the processes that bring about evolutionary change is derived from study of individual organisms, whether the individual be acellular, cellular, multicellular, or colonial.

The evolution of integrated systems composed of two or more individual organisms is recognized by early and recent biologists (Lerner, 1954; Wright, 1956; Nicholson, 1957; Dobzhansky, 1957, 1958). However, some investigators have not conceived of the population (intra-species or interspecies) as an inclusive entity with emergent characteristics that transcend the summation of the attributes of the component individuals (Thompson, 1956; Muller, 1958). Louis Agassiz (1860), who did not agree with his contemporary, Darwin, on the theory of evolution, said: "If species do not exist at all . . . how can they vary and if individuals alone exist, how can the differences which may be observed prove the variability of species?"

It is my intention in this essay to emphasize the evolution of adaptation (Allee *et al.,* 1949, p. 630) in population systems without, however, negating the data or the major interpretations of the roles of individuals in evolutionary history or processes. Individual organisms seem to have been maintained as living entities since the origin of life. The large majority of living individuals show definitive boundaries that can be easily recognized, although the boundaries of the individual in colonial animals and in many plants are not sharp or clear. Our information must be interpreted as indicative of the tremendous importance of individual integration in the existence and transformation of life.

Every known living individual organism has been produced by the division or by the fusion of parts of parental individuals. As repro-

ALFRED E. EMERSON is Professor of Zoology at the University of Chicago. He has conducted research in America, Europe, and Africa as a Guggenheim Fellow. Formerly the editor of *Ecology,* a past president of the Ecological Society of America, and a past president of the Society of Systematic Zoology, he is currently President of the Society for the Study of Evolution.

duction seems to be a basic potential of all living biological systems, it follows that the attributes of any individual in large part have been derived from its ancestors. The individual thus is dependent upon other individuals for its existence and its characteristics. Through the long course of evolution, there has been persistence, accumulation, change, and elimination of genetic elements. Each contemporary individual in large measure is literally a product of its ancestors and their genetic constitutions organized to survive under past and present conditions. It is also obvious that every population system is dependent upon its component individuals for its existence and its properties. There have been philosophical concepts in the past (and several are powerful determiners of present attitudes) that either emphasize the individual to the exclusion of the group entity or emphasize the group system to the exclusion of the individual entity. In my opinion, both extremes are scientifically untenable, whether applied to biological or to human systems. Dichotomies are often treated as mutually exclusive, but in this instance there is much evidence of complex transactions between the individuals associated in more inclusive group systems and between the whole inclusive population and its component individuals.

Many scientists during the post-Darwinian century have written on the subject of "levels of integration" (Redfield, 1942). Here I shall not deal with the individual levels from the molecular or cellular systems to the numerous types of multicellular organisms. Suffice it to say that the individual organism possesses protoplasmic or molecular continuity or contiguity which in large part determines the mechanisms and types of transactions taking place between its parts. On the other hand, population systems are largely limited to integrating factors that must pass through a non-living medium between individuals. Interindividual relations thus tend to be based upon stimulus and response mechanisms. Relatively simple interindividual biochemical mechanisms may integrate populations of plants and also of primitive cellular animals, but the evolutionary emergence of sensory stimulus and response by means of the nervous system greatly augmented the unity of animal populations. The story of organic evolution gives every indication that the direction of evolution of the more advanced animals is intimately correlated with functional behavior in various types of populations (Roe and Simpson, 1958).

The above statement should not be interpreted as indicating a sharp boundary between physiological and behavior mechanisms, nor yet a sharp differentiation between single-celled plants and animals, multicelled organisms, or populations of organisms. Moscona (1959) says: "The cell is an immensely complex elementary body; its integration in tissues is as much a matter of behavior as of architecture." Cells, organisms, and integrated populations illustrate many common biological principles, even though the mechanisms of these integrative levels may be fundamentally different and therefore functionally analogous and separately evolved (Redfield, 1942). Different levels of integration may be phylogenetically related. For example, nearly all true social animals with division of labor between adults of the same sex, have non-social ancestors organized in family systems, and all family systems emerged from integrated sexual adjustments. However, the same organizational level may not be phylogenetically related to another in the same category. The family system of birds has little evolutionary relation to that of mammals, and the societies of ants and termites evolved independently from non-social ancestral wasps and roaches, respectively. Evolutionary convergence of analogous function is often exhibited by these various population systems, but genetic homology also is characteristic of phylogenetically allied group systems. There has doubtless been much evolutionary modification of adaptive integration of populations during long periods of time.

Although much of Darwin's information was based upon the biology of individual organisms, he included group systems in his theory of evolution. He dealt rather extensively with the species population without being able to define the concept operationally with the degree of precision that we can today. He gave much thought to the question of sexual behavior and display, but explained such interindividual attraction and stimulation largely through sexual selection by the individuals of opposite sexes. He discussed competition and combat between males for the possession of the female as an important part of sexual selection at an interindividual, but intra-sexual, level. He discussed the behavioral interaction between the mother and her offspring, particularly among suckling mammals. He did not attempt, however, to discuss the family unit as a whole, nor did he interpret the evolutionary processes that might have led to the establishment of the family—a system composed of interacting parents and offspring with properties that transcend those of the individuals. Darwin came fairly close to the modern interpretation of the group system of the social insects when he pointed out that the "neuter" or sterile castes must have arisen through the selection of the whole entity. He acknowledged that the evolution of the non-reproductive castes was the greatest special difficulty that his theory of natural selection had encountered and that this case also refuted Lamarck's concept of the inheritance of acquired characters. He did not, however, adequately apply natural selection to whole group or population units in contrast to his theory of natural selection of individuals.

The attempt is made here to re-evaluate some aspects of the role of populations in modern evolutionary theory. Only a summary treatment of adaptive population systems is attempted, but even a cursory abstract may afford us a better-balanced understanding of modern evolutionary theory and provide indications of the direction of some future investigations.

The word *population* means a grouping of individual organisms. *Population system* means an orderly arrangement of the individuals in a population. The order may be spatial—what is often called "population structure"—or it may be temporal—an orderly sequence in time. The temporal dimension may involve a short reaction time to stimuli between individuals. This may be as short as the time lapse in the production of the stimulus plus the time lapse in its reception and transmission to effectors. Or the time may be still comparatively short, but involve reactions to thresholds that result from a gradual cumulation to the point of activation. Such a reaction may result from cumulative substances that reach an activation threshold at a biochemical or biophysical level, or it may be the cumulative effect through associative memory, reinforced conditioned behavior, and learning.

Contrasted with the relatively short times involved in stimulus and response of physiological and neurological interactions between individuals, there is a longer time axis in the development and growth of a population. This may be analogized with the development (embryological and postnatal growth and differentiation) of the individual organism. Populations often exhibit a life-cycle that is superimposed upon the life-cycle of each component individual. In extreme cases, particularly among the social insects and aphids, the individuals in the population may exhibit morphological, physiological, and behavioristic polymorphism not directly resulting from genetic polymorphism. In contrast, sexual dimorphism among most higher animals is genetically or cytogenetically triggered. Well-known examples of polymorphism in the life-cycle of the populations are found in the rust fungi, the sporozoan malarial parasites, the parasitic cestodes and trematodes, and the aphids.

The word *evolution* has been applied to various sorts of changes during time sequences, but *organic evolution* is now commonly confined to the results of changes in the genetic constitution and their phenotypic consequences during long geological time. Evolution may involve microevolutionary genetic changes in local populations in relatively short periods, or macroevolutionary changes in major systematic categories of animals and plants. Organic evolution, in other words, always involves changes, both great and small, in the genetic constitution of natural populations—changes in part determined by the survival of each organized individual or group system.

Developmental or temporal changes that are not the consequence of genetic change in evolutionary time are not discussed here, but we need to emphasize the well-known fact that genetic factors may operate comparatively directly in the so-called inherited characters, or genetics may be basic to the capacity to react at certain physiological or ecological thresholds. Genetic factors may set the stage for divergent responses that may not be directly activated by differences in the genetic constitution. The investigation of organic evolution concentrates on the genetic determiners rather than the subsequent determiners of differential responses. To give a simple illustration, organic evolutionary inquiry deals with the inherited capacity of man to speak—not with non-genetic developmental or physiological impairment of speaking ability or with the acquired vocabulary and grammatical form with which he speaks. This statement does not interfere with the parallel investigation of *cultural evolution* that is based upon a social inheritance by means of symbolic communication. Organic evolution and cultural evolution are distinctive in their fundamental mechanisms, but certain principles of change in time are applicable to both these contrasting types of evolution (Emerson, 1954).

The word *system* in the title may be broadly taken to signify an orderly relatedness between parts of a whole entity with a definitive boundary. Boundaries may be recognized by the prevention of certain factors from crossing the border from the inside or outside or by a quantitative change in the factor as it crosses the border. All living systems are open systems with transactions occurring across boundaries, but so long as some transactions are stopped or changed in rate at the boundary, a system can be delimited and treated as a scientific entity.

A population system, then, is composed of individuals with inter-individual transactions of various types, but with a population boundary across which certain types of transactions do not occur or do not occur at the same rate that they would without the boundary. Many studies on the dynamics of contemporary populations with statistical analysis have been made. A fairly recent summary by Thomas Park is published in Allee *et al.* (1949, p. 263; also see *Cold Spring Harbor Symposia on Quantitative Biology*, Vol. XXII [1957]). Many of these data on population biology have yet to be interpreted in evolutionary terms, and it is predicted that the statistics of the contemporary populations and the evolving populations will be harmonized within a unified theory.

A further restriction of subject for the purposes of this essay is also necessary. All living systems exhibit evolutionary adaptation—adaptation for reproduction, adaptation for maintaining metabolic function in the living state, and adaptation of the whole system to its physical and biotic environment (for discussions of the concept of adaptation, see Allee *et al.*, 1949, p. 630; Simpson, 1953, p. 160; Wright, 1956; Waddington, 1957; Lewontin, 1957; Pittendrigh, 1958). Orders within and between population systems that are the products of the chance impact of modifying forces, but without any indication of adaptive trend resulting from natural selection, do not immediately concern us here. (For a discussion of the role of chance and random factors in evolution, see Wright's essay elsewhere in this volume.) Other important investigations deal with an analysis of relations of living systems, whether adaptive or not, and in many instances such inquiries help us to understand aspects of evolutionary processes and evolutionary adaptation. In no sense should such researches be disparaged, but the evolution of population systems here disussed is confined to the origin and progress of their functional adaptations.

One controversial concept repeatedly brought up in the literature I should like to mention very briefly. Some authors postulate that the advancing organization of living systems is negative entropy or negentropy (Patten, 1959). Others (Blum, 1951) do not consider that organic evolution or increase in biological organization runs counter to the Second Law of Thermodynamics. I share Blum's viewpoint on this matter. As I have indicated before (in Allee *et al.*, 1949, p. 598), the order of the dissipation of energy from great concentration in bodies like the sun is not counteracted, in my opinion, by the short- or even long-time capture, storage, and use of energy by living systems within the narrow temperature range of the earthly habitat. Negentropy would, in my opinion, be illustrated by the reconcentration of energy into newly formed atoms and these into energy-producing bodies like the stars. Life seems to have nothing to do with the production of such physical processes. So I am inclined to avoid building a principle of organic evolution around the concept of negentropy. An attempt to postulate a cosmic function of life has been made by Williamson (1958), but I fail as yet to see the effect of life outside the confines of the planets upon which it occurs, even at the dawn of the "space age," when some products of earthly life extend to other parts of our solar system.

ANIMAL AGGREGATIONS

Many interesting studies of various types of animal aggregations have been made (Allee, 1931; Allee *et al.*, 1949, p. 393). Co-operative adjustments between individuals are evident with many different mechanisms, both physiological and behavioristic. Allee experimented with group survival values and demonstrated their existence in a wide variety of animals. He concludes (Allee *et al.,* 1949, p. 419):

> The evolution of truly social animals such as termites, bees, and ants on the one hand and man on the other, has occurred independently in widely separated divisions of the animal kingdom. These could hardly have arisen so many times and from such diverse sources if a strong substratum of generalized natural proto-cooperation—call it physiological facilitation, if you prefer—were not widespread among animals in nature. Such tendencies precede and condition the formation of animal concentrations, the existence of which is prerequisite for the development of group organization.

There is probably some basic truth in this quotation, but we should also remember that aggregation and social mechanisms are often analogous and not homologous and that emergent properties with some degree of functional similarity may arise independently during the course of evolution.

Contacts between individuals in the areas occupied by populations is by no means always co-operative. Much conflict, aggressiveness, combat, individual dominance in a group, and territorial limitation exist. Such lack of co-operation is thought to be antisocial by some (Schneirla, 1946). Allee *et al.* (1949, p. 691) consider territorialism to have survival value for the group, and the capacity to establish territories through fighting and threat has been naturally selected through the more efficient spacing of breeding, nesting, and feeding functions. Fisher (1954) says that both land and water birds that gather in "sociable" aggregrations are the most successful. Both flocking and territoriality are considered "social" by Fisher, although it is well known that conflict between individuals is found among such groups. Huxley (1942) has pointed out that, once aggregations enjoy an advantage over non-aggregated individuals, "selection will encourage behavior making for aggregation and the aggregation itself will become a target for selection."

MENDELIAN POPULATIONS

Dobzhansky (1951) defined a Mendelian population as a reproductive community of sexual and cross-fertilized individuals that share a common gene pool. Population geneticists have been actively engaged in investigating the evolutionary implications of interbreeding populations. Other essays in this volume and its companion—"Evolution of Man"—summarize aspects of population genetics, including such matters as gene incidence, polygenic characters and their establishment, coadaptation of genes and chromosomes within local populations, selection of heterozygosity over homozygosity in some instances, heterosis or "hybrid vigor," the relation of numbers in local populations to genetic change, and interpopulational competition (Park, 1954) and selection (for some modern references to this active field of study see Wright, 1932, 1956; Sheppard, 1954; Lerner, 1954, 1958; Dobzhansky, 1957; Waddington, 1957).

Dobzhansky (1957) summarized his conclusions that were based upon a large amount of experimental evidence gathered by himself and several other authors in the following words:

A genotype may be favored when it is rare in the population but it may lose its selective advantage as its frequency increases, or *vice versa*. A Mendelian population will then tend to become so balanced in its composition that the average adaptive value for the population as a whole is maximized. . . . The interactions of the genotypes in a population may be in the nature of facilitation at some frequencies, and of inhibition at other frequencies. . . . Coadaptation leads to an integration of the gene pool which makes the population an organic system rather than an assemblage of individuals.

Dobzhansky (1957, p. 392) further amplifies his interpretations of the evolution of Mendelian populations. The interdependence of cooperating individuals in sexual reproduction and the dependence of the genotype of the individual upon the composition of the breeding community to which the parents of this individual belong

lead to natural selection acting to shape the genotype of the population itself successfully in its environment. Hence the apparent paradox which baffles some evolutionists: Natural selection operates through differential survival and differential fertility of individuals, and yet it sometimes brings about such forms of integration of the gene pool of the population which lead to the sacrifice of some of the individual members of the population. The phenomenon of balanced polymorphism, with highly fit heterozygotes contrasting with less fit homozygotes, is one of such forms of genetic integration of Mendelian populations.

It is the opinion of numerous modern authors that genetic variability produced both by mutation and by recombination is in part a self-regulatory property of the population. It has been called "genic equilibrium," "genetic inertia," and "genetic homeostasis" (Jones, 1958). I personally prefer the term *homeostasis* for self-regulatory adjustments with feedback mechanisms in organic systems. Homeostasis includes the regulation of dynamic functional disequilibrium (Emerson, 1954, 1955). A great many homeostatic functions establish differentials, gradients, polarizations, asymmetries, and periodic fluctuations. A rigid interpretation of *stasis* was avoided by Cannon (1932, 1941), when he coined the word *homeostasis,* but some contemporary biologists avoid the term because of a misunderstanding of the original meaning.

It is also fairly obvious that there is an evolutionary feedback from functional effects to genetic causations by means of natural selection of whole systems at various levels. The properties of the genes and genetic systems are a product in part of their contribution to the fitness or adaptation of the more inclusive organic systems.

One emerging concept of considerable import is that competition, in the process of selection, is advantageous at optimal intensity and disadvantageous at maximal or minimal intensities. Probably optimal competition is itself adaptive and regulated in successful integrated populations. We need, however, much more information before we can be sure that this is so (see Neyman, Park, and Scott, 1956).

Before the impact of the rediscovery of Mendelian genetics in 1900, Weismann (1893) indicated not only that he recognized the reality of inclusive population units but that selection could act upon adaptive breeding structure of populations—a concept that has been mathematically elaborated during the last two decades by Wright (1946, 1949, 1950). Natural selection produces a balance between inbreeding and outbreeding within many local and species populations (Stone, 1959).

The Evolution of Sex

A wealth of detailed information is available on the genetics, cytogenetics, physiology, development, structure, behavior, and function of sex in simple organisms and complex plants and animals. Much of this information allows comparisons of phylogenetically closely related species and genera. And yet there seems to be no comprehensive review of the evolution of sex processes together with an up-to-date evaluation of the principles that have guided the evolution of sexual adaptation.

There is a fairly general agreement among critical sex biologists that the primary function of sex is not that of reproduction but is rather the balance between recombination as a source of genetic variation (Lewontin, 1957) and the predominant conservative role of inheritance. The establishment of a complex coadapted gene system by means of a balance between inbreeding and outbreeding has profound evolutionary effects. Partial or complete reproductive isolation is both the dividing factor in the phylogenetic tree and the consolidating factor for the interadapted genetic complex. Lederberg (1956) has expressed the opinion that "the recombination of genes stands on a par with mutation and selection as a cardinal element of biological variation." Recombination generates

a multitude of different combinations which are then sifted by natural selection. Until recently, genetic recombination has been closely identified with sexual reproduction: indeed geneticists consider it to be the principal biological function of sexuality, but other processes are now recognized as alternative means to the same end [see also Raper, 1959]. . . . In sexual reproduction, the fertilization of one intact cell or gamete by another precedes the formation of the new zygote and assures the union of a full complement of genes from each of two parents. In *Genetic transduction,* by contrast, one cell receives only a fragment of the genetic content of another . . . we should not insist on genes as self-reproducing units, but as units or markers of a more complex self-reproducing system.

Numerous highly competent geneticists have recently discussed the influence of sexual recombination on the evolution of integrated populations (Lerner, 1954; Dobzhansky, 1957). Here I wish to emphasize a few interpretations that seem to be misunderstood by some modern students of evolution. Also I include some speculations that are controversial because of lack of sufficient evidence.

Sexual adaptation is certainly a major factor of population integration in the majority of living organisms. Probably sex evolved some time after primary asexual reproduction had appeared (White, 1945), presumably with the origin of life. Gene mutation was probably an earlier source of genetic variation than sexual recombination. Genetic transduction may have been an intermediate step in the evolution from primary asexual reproduction to gametic sexual recombination. Some authors in the present volume (e.g., Stebbins) suggest the possibility of sexual fusion in the earliest organisms. The data at present are insufficient to form a well-substantiated conclusion regarding the origin of sexuality with the origin of life or at a later period, as here suggested. The reproductive process itself integrated populations of different generations, while sexuality integrated contemporary populations as well as temporal sequences of populations. Secondary asexual reproduction, of course, evolved from earlier sexuality. The evolution of apomictic plants is summarized by Stebbins (1950).

Following the gradual origin of sexual adaptations, there is no question that selection continued to direct further complex adaptive changes toward the efficiency of sexual union in an almost infinite number of ways. Waddington (1957) has summarized his concept of *genetic assimilation* and has indicated that physiological adaptibility may later be replaced by genetic precursors alongside of developmental and physiological factors. This evolutionary "feedback" would seem to be clearly illustrated by the evolution of sex mechanisms.

Many primitive organisms are either hermaphroditic or have physiological (also ecological and behavioristic) thresholds that determine the alternative development of males or females. In these cases, there is no genetic determination of sex, although we must not forget that the capacity to develop sexual organs or sexual dimorphism is doubtless a polygenic character of great genetic complexity.

In the higher animals (i.e., insects and vertebrates) sex may be determined in the zygote by cytogenetic and genetic mechanisms. These certainly arose in evolutionary time long after physiological determination of sex differentiation had become established. The phylogenetically older physiological mechanisms were not eliminated or replaced, but certain "trigger" mechanisms became genetic (switch genes). Comparative studies of species and higher systematic categories indicate that both the later genetic mechanisms of sex determination and the earlier physiological mechanisms underwent considerable modification after their evolutionary origin. It would seem that Waddington's (1957) concept of *genetic assimilation* together with its profound philosophical and biological implications is the only tenable hypothesis to explain major features in the evolution of sex. There are recent attempts to invoke Lamarckian inheritance of acquired somatic characters as an alternative hypothesis for the evolution of sexuality (Martin, 1956), but the overwhelming evidence from modern studies makes such an explanation scientifically unacceptable (see Waddington's essay elsewhere in this volume).

Cleveland (1947, 1950, 1951) has made an exacting and brilliant study of cytological events in a series of related species of flagellates (some within the same genus) inhabiting the hind gut of wood-eating roaches. Gradations between mitotic and meiotic cell division are described in some detail and were followed during the last decade by numerous further studies. Cleveland (1950, p. 199) concludes:

> These facts indicate that in some of the flagellates of *Cryptocercus* we are seeing either the primitive beginnings of sexual cycles in which no firmly established behavioral pattern has been set, or a degeneration has reduced the sexual behavior of these organisms to a primitive, protean level. The former seems more logical.

Personally, I think general biological considerations would indicate evolutionary regression of sexuality rather than its origin in these examples. First, if sex originated in these flagellates through speciation of closely related forms, it seems to have been a blind alley of evolution. The systematically related flagellates living symbiotically with termites are all asexual so far as is known, and the termites, together with their protozoan faunules, were derived from ancestral roaches with their faunules. Second, the gradations indicate that cytological processes and sexuality are complex polygenic characters with highly adapted complex functions. The origin of intricate adaptations is likely to be a macroevolutionary process of long duration rather than a microevolutionary process involving drastic functional changes during the origin of related species. In contrast, regression of complex adapted characters may take place through simple gene mutation (or may even occur by physiological inhibition without mutation as in the case of some neoteinic salamanders). Sexuality is too complex a character from the standpoint of genetics and evolution to expect its origin in a speciation process or to expect a large number of separate origins of meiosis, but there are a great many known instances among plants and animals of the evolutionary regression of sexuality within a species and between species derived from closely related sexual ancestors.

Intersexual relations are not the only integrating adaptive mechanisms of population systems, but they are certainly one of the most important and very often are antecedent to the evolution of other factors that co-ordinate more inclusive levels, such as the family or the intra-specific society. In the case of the flowering plants and the pollinating insects, birds, and bats, intra-specific sexual adaptations also are basic to the integration of the interspecific ecological community. Sex involves relationships of individuals in populations that transcend the properties and evolution of the individual organism, so that nearly every population geneticist recognizes the population entity as a unit in biological evolution (Wright, 1932; Lerner, 1954, 1958; Dobzhansky, 1957). Other investigators emphasize the intra-adaptiveness of population systems and may refer to such entities as whole superindividual units (Tinbergen, 1954; Bonner, 1955), epiorganisms (Gerard, 1940, 1942), superorganisms (Emerson, 1939*a, b*), or supra-organisms (Emerson, 1942, 1952, 1958). The organismic analogies between the individual organism and the population system have been recognized and discussed for centuries, and these significant analogies are still emphasized in modern literature in spite of much skepticism and open opposition. One fear expressed by a few authors, with some admitted documentation, is that a label like *supra-organism* may give a false sense of explanation and consequently may inhibit further analytical investigation (Schneirla, 1946). However, there is no reason why a concept of this sort should not challenge an investigation and evaluation of the causes underlying the organization and stimulate new penetrating researches.

FAMILY SYSTEMS

Kendeigh (1952) gives a wealth of data on the details and evolutionary sequences of family organization and parental care among birds. The evidence is clear that the sexes are integrated and show much reciprocal behavior (Huxley, 1938). The care of the eggs and young, together with nest building, brooding, feeding, and protection, strongly indicates adaptive interaction on the part of every individual in the family system, and the selection of a beneficial trait of one individual is accompanied by the selection of reciprocal responding traits in the other individuals of the family group (Tinbergen). The phylogenetic modifications of these activities and their accompanying morphological, color, and behavior patterns seem quite inexplicable on the basis of selection either by individuals or through individual survival alone. The unit of selection must be the system composed of both sexes and the young, so that the adaptation of one individual to another is analogous to the adaptation of one part of the body to another part within an individual organism.

Although it seems clear that natural selection acts upon the group system represented by the parents and offspring in the family, this does not mean that no selection of the individual organism occurs relatively independent of other individuals. There seems to be no reason to suppose that the unit of selection must be exclusively confined to a single system of organization, either at the individual, sexual, family, or social level of integration.

The evolution of increased care of the offspring, both in the embryonic state and in young stages of development, seems to be clearly associated with the provision of more optimal conditions for the survival of the young and the species, but sometimes at an increase in hazards to the individual parent. It is difficult to account for this evolutionary progress, involving co-ordination between the physiology and behavior of the parents with the physiology and behavior of the early stages of development of the following generation, without recognizing the increase in homeostasis at the group level (Lewontin, 1957) but often involving a decrease in individual homeostasis (Allee *et al.*, 1949). It would be extremely difficult to explain the evolution of the uterus and mammary glands in mammals or the nest-building instincts of birds as the result of natural selection of the fittest individual.

SOCIAL SYSTEMS

The term "social" has been applied very broadly to almost all groupings of animals and plants and has been used simply to imply living together. I am not opposed to such broad usage, but here I am using the word in a very narrow sense. In order to separate the distinctions within the concept of social, I use the term "true society" when I refer to those animal groupings in which a division of labor occurs between adults of the same sex. This separates the social insects and human society from the family and sexual systems that preceded them and from various types of animal aggregations. It should be noted that insect societies are based upon genetics and undergo organic evolution, while human societies are integrated largely by symbolic communication. The capacity of man to think, to associate, to learn, to symbolize, and to speak undoubtedly has genetically evolved, but, without further genetic change, cultural evolution can and does occur relatively independently of continuing organic evolution. Cultural evolution is therefore fundamentally different in its mechanisms from organic evolution. Although cultural evolution is not the result of direct genetic changes, the unit symbols and symbolic systems are subject to variation, isolation, and selection, and thus show convergent functions and phenomena parallel to organic evolution.

Most social insects seem to have arisen from ancestors that were highly organized into family systems. In the case of the bees, however, Michener (1958) gives convincing evidence that the societies evolved through "associations of adults to form semisocial groups and ultimately true societies." Even bees have an adult-larval relationship, but, through mass-provisioning, it may be separated in time so that the adult may have no direct contact with its own offspring as it does in the primitive ancestors of the other social insects. There is thus a temporal family unit in the non-social bees, but often no contemporary family unit occurs.

The sterile castes of termites are bisexual, with regressed ovaries or testes. In some genera of advanced termites soldiers may be males only (Noirot, 1955), but in the primitive termites without adult workers, the soldiers are both regressed males and females. In the Hymenoptera, where males are nearly always haploid and the females are diploid, the sex of the sterile castes is always female. In the termites, the advanced genera have sterile adult workers and soldiers that never reproduce and are probably incapable of reproduction. In the advanced genera of the social wasps, bees, and ants, the workers often lay eggs. These may be fed to the larvae in the ants, but occasionally they may develop into functional males.

The effect of haplo-diploidy on the evolution of populations in the social Hymenoptera has been discussed by numerous authors (Snell, 1932; Flanders, 1946; Kerr, 1950; Michener, 1958), but it is not yet clear how differences in the cytogenetics or genetics of social Hymenoptera and termites affect the social evolution. The social insects are remarkably convergent in spite of the difference in the sex-determining mechanisms.

Details of the social structure and behavior of insects have been summarized in numerous publications (Wheeler, 1928; Allee *et al.*, 1949, p. 419; Michener and Michener, 1951; Emerson, 1959). The evolution of behavior in social insects has also received some attention (Emerson, 1958). Following the astonishing discoveries of the methods of communicating the distance, direction, quantity, and quality of discovered food by the common honeybee (Frisch, 1958), Lindauer (Lindauer and Kerr, 1958) has compared the communication systems in phylogenetically related species and higher categories of social bees. These studies are giving us a picture of the evolutionary sequences of complex social behavior.

POPULATION LIFE-CYCLES

Several groups of organisms have developed a sequence of generations with different forms and responses that are adapted to different environments. In addition to the life-cycle of the individual, we also have a life-cycle of the entire population composed of numerous generations. The aphids illustrate such temporal population systems. During the yearly life-cycle of many generations (sometimes about forty), some generations are winged and some wingless, some are egg-laying and others viviparous, some are sexual with males and females and others are composed of parthenogenetic females only, some may feed on one plant species and others feed on a different host, and some may make galls and others not. These population life-cycles vary from species to species and indicate phylogenetic relationships (Allee *et al.*, 1949, pp. 612, 703).

Populations of one generation may be separated in seasonal time from the populations of other generations, and yet they are obviously coadapted within the temporally integrated species population. Other well-known organisms that exhibit temporal polymorphism and co-adaptation are the malarial sporozoans, the flukes, and the tapeworms. Among the plants, the rust fungi illustrate this same phenomenon, and there are many other examples, both plant and animal. Alternation of sexual and asexual individuals in the life-cycle has been called *metagenesis* for many years (see Lewontin, 1957). Alternation of diploid and haploid generations are often found, particularly in the plants. Temporal polymorphism, however, occurs in sequences of generations with or without metagenesis or cytogenetic change. The development of the different forms may be triggered by the environment or in the case of parasites, by the biochemistry or physiology of the host. Thresholds of reaction, however, are based upon genetic potentialities. Otherwise there would be far less consistency in the sequence of forms from generation to generation within the same species.

The evolution of the relations of parasites to their hosts allows us to make certain logical postulates. The host in which the parasitic sexual generation occurs is regarded as the original or primary host. For example, the mosquito rather than the vertebrate host is regarded as the original or primary host for malarial sporozoans (Huff, 1938, 1945; Allee *et al.*, 1949; Lewontin, 1957). It is also noteworthy that the pathogenic effects upon the original host commonly are less marked than they are upon the secondary host—an indication of the evolution of toleration in the host-parasite interspecies system over long periods of time.

REGRESSIVE EVOLUTION

One may find numerous vestigial structures associated with different levels of population integration. For example, sexual homologues may be regressed in one sex and developed in the opposite sex. The vestige may be inhibited in one sex, or the normal development in the other sex may be activated by known physiological agents such as the sex hormones. If sex is genetically determined, the subsequent physiological activity may be considered to be initiated by genetic factors in many cases. In evolutionary sequences, the sexual differentiation may be less in more primitive animals (i.e., oviducts in male frogs). In several instances the male sex itself becomes rare or entirely eliminated in an evolutionary sequence. Evolutionary loss of the male is known among fishes, and many examples of independent evolutionary elimination of males are known among insects. Sexuality may be lost in apomictic plants (Stebbins, 1950) and secondarily asexual animals.

At the family level, the so-called parasitic birds indicate an evolutionary sequence in the gradual elimination of nesting behavior and care of the young (Friedman, 1929; Kendeigh, 1952).

At the social level a great many instances of regression of social adaptations occur, some associated with the augmentation of other functions in the social division of labor among the castes in a colony, and some involve the complete loss of the sterile castes in the so-called "social parasites" found among the wasps, bees, and ants. What appear to be known evolutionary gradations have been described among related species within a genus and among closely related genera.

A few instances of regression of structure in one caste of a social insect without regression in another caste of the same species may be given. The soldier caste is the primitive sterile caste in the termites, as is evidenced by its presence in the structurally most primitive forms such as *Mastotermes* (Mastotermitidae), *Archotermopsis* (Hodotermitidae), *Kalotermes* (Kalotermitidae), *Psammotermes* (Rhinotermitidae), etc. The soldier caste has been wholly lost in two related advanced genera, *Anoplotermes* and *Speculitermes* (Amitermitinae of the Termitidae). The worker caste appears as an adult sterile caste only in the more advanced derivative termites with one exception (*Hodotermes* and related genera). No adult sterile worker is found in the more primitive and presumably ancestral types.

Compared with the primary reproductive caste of its own species (its parents), the soldier shows vestigial gonads (a few exceptions among the primitive genera), absence of wings (wing buds among primitive genera), and vestigial eyes. (Some intercastes are known that doubtless result from abnormal physiological thresholds in the mechanisms of caste development but usually are not socially functional or important in evolution.) The compound eyes in particular show a gradation of regression in phylogenetic series from reduced eyes with visible external facettes and pigmentation, through eyespots without facettes or pigment, to complete absence of external indications of the eye. The numbers of species and genera in this series are so large and so many other characters of phylogenetic significance are correlated with the reduction of the eye that the data may safely be assumed to indicate an evolutionary reduction of the eye in the soldier caste. The small steps of gradation indicate that the reduction of the compound eyes is a polygenic character. At the same time, the functional compound eye with no indications of reduction is found in every winged reproductive of either sex. And winged reproductive males and females are found in every species of termite. It may then be assumed that the full complement of genes that initiate normal eye development is present in every soldier with partially or completely reduced eyes.

All the modern experimental evidence on caste development in termites indicates that caste differentiation is not based upon distinctive genetic differences between the castes. It is rather the result of differential development probably resulting from a different trophic (food) intake and trophallactic exchange from the other castes (usually sterile workers or worker-like nymphs) which procure the food, imbibe secretions and excretions from all the castes and young, and themselves produce secretions and excretions that may be digested by the young or other adult castes. It may thus be stated that the eggs are genetically alike so far as caste differentiation is concerned. In some instances

(Noirot, 1955) the soldiers may have vestigial gonads of either males or females, and in other instances all the soldiers of a species may have vestigial gonads of males only, so that soldier development may be partially influenced by the genetic sex-determining mechanism. But, on the whole, we may liken the caste differentiation to the physiological rather than to the genetic differentiation mechanisms of the individual organism. Each caste has essentially the same genetic and chromosome components analogous to the genetic identity of each cell that multiplies by equational mitosis in an individual organism.

That genetic mechanisms are involved in the physiological determination of the castes is apparent by the phylogenetic sequences of soldier types, both in the adaptive progression of the defensive mechanisms and in the non-adaptive regression of such organs as the compound eyes.

In a number of instances a phylogenetic sequence is apparent in the reduction of a portion of an organ. For example, primitive soldiers of certain subfamilies of the family Termitidae (Amitermitinae, Termitinae, and Nasutitermitinae) have a conspicuous sharp tooth (a large projection from the inner edge of the biting mandible). This tooth is absent in the adult soldier of derived genera. The contemporaneous socially non-functional soft-bodied soldier nymph in these derived genera exhibits a clearly defined tooth homologous with that of its primitive adult soldier relatives. I should be inclined to regard this non-functional nymphal tooth as a recapitulation of the once functional tooth of the adult soldier in the ancestral genera. It is, however, homologous with one of the marginal teeth of the reproductive cast and also of the worker caste. The mandibles in the worker or worker-like nymph function in chewing food and other cellulose products. The soldier cannot gather food but functions exclusively in the defense of the colony against predatory invaders. The recapitulated marginal tooth of the soldier nymph is quite clearly of the protective type of the ancestral adult soldier and not of the feeding type of the reproductive or worker castes. One must remember, however, that the adult soldier is sterile and does not produce offspring, so that the genetic as well as the physiological and growth mechanisms of the sterile castes are inherited through the reproductive castes only.

It will be noted that these examples of regressive evolution in the termite society system can be explained as the outcome of a number of principles that are applicable to regressive evolution of the individual, and a number of principles are likewise applicable to population systems that transcend the level of individual integration.

Those principles that apply to the regressive evolution of both the society and the individual organism may be listed as follows: (1)

pleiotropy of genes; (2) polygenic characters; (3) genetic assimilation; (4) gene mutation at a statistically predictable rate; (5) biochemical stability of some genes and genetic systems over long periods of evolutionary time (surely as far back as the Mesozoic and probably much farther back); (6) variation by means of sexual recombination; (7) emergence of novelty by means of new associations of genes and parts; (8) selection of whole organizational units with the genetic, biochemical, physiological, developmental, and adult functional attributes which slowly evolve an internal adjustment or coadaptation between the multiple functions of the living system; and (9) incorporation of physiological, ontogenetic, and phylogenetic time dimensions into the contemporary living system.

It follows that selection for any complex function will result in a shifting around of the elements in a genetic complex that served former adaptations that have lost importance, so that positive selection pressures for new functions and compensatory adjustments will inevitably reduce the structures that have lost their adaptive significance under changing conditions, both internal and external. Because many persistent genes and portions of genes involved in the growth of an organ also serve other functions in the organism, we should expect to detect the functionless vestigial structures over long geological periods. We have eliminated Darwin's errors in his theory of use and disuse in the evolution of rudiments and have substituted a far more satisfactory explanation of the evolution of vestigial organs recapitulated in embryos or larvae or present in adults. The data on the regressive evolution among termites (and other social insects) are understandable on the basis of the processes occurring in the evolution of the individual organism, but only if we consider the whole social colony population as a unit analogous to the individual organism. This conclusion does not mean that populations have all the functional attributes of organisms. For example, innate senescence leading to death is not exhibited by species or other populations, while it is an innate characteristic of most individuals. However, data on the evolution of population systems gives us much better understanding of the evolution of individual systems.

EVOLUTION OF INDIVIDUAL DEATH

Among the attributes of the individual organism that would seem to be explicable only through the selection of whole population systems is the intrinsic limitation of the life-span and the incorporation of innate death mechanisms.

Death has often been assumed to be the result of abnormality, disease, or accident. Of course, death of many individuals results from these factors together with chance survival in what is often referred to as the "hostile environment." Probably most individuals in nature meet their end before the aging process has advanced far, and long before they have attained their potential age limit under favorable conditions of life.

There are, however, numerous indications that innate factors produce a characteristic life-span for each species and that the evolution of death mechanisms cannot be understood by confining selection to the welfare and survival of the individual alone.

The best example of a characteristic short adult life is found in the insect order Ephemeroptera (commonly called "mayflies"). After passing through a series of nymphal stages in fresh-water habitats, during which the individuals are adapted for feeding and for escaping from predatory enemies, the winged stage emerges into the air. The adult is adapted to see with its compound eyes (often with ommatidia differentially adjusted to day and night vision), to fly with its wings, and to mate with its specialized genitalia. The mouthparts, however, are reduced and non-functional in contrast to the mouthparts of the young stages, and no food is sought or eaten by adults. Also no protective or escape adaptations are apparent, and no resistance to predators is manifest. The adult life is very short. A species of the genus *Callibaetis* leaves the water one day, lives as a subimago for about 24 hours, transforms to an imago, mates, oviposits, and dies on the second day (Needham, Traver, and Hsu, 1935). A number of other mayflies have a shorter adult life, and a few live a day or two longer (two or three weeks in extreme cases), but the adult of each species has a characteristically short period of life, and each individual dies soon after mating and oviposition. Most genera also indicate a genetic continuity of the causal factors that result in the phylogenetically correlated short adult life typical of each species.

Other examples of the evolutionary reduction of mouthparts in the adult insect and inability to feed or store energy during a fairly short adult existence are to be found among the caddis flies or Trichoptera (Ross, 1944), the bagworms and clothes moths in the order Lepidoptera (Comstock, 1924; Austen and Hughes, 1935), and the worm-lions in the order Diptera (Wheeler, 1930; Hafex and El-Moursy, 1956).

Five species of the Pacific salmon of the genus *Oncorhynchus* regularly die within a week or two following their first spawning. Several other fishes likewise die after their first reproduction (Robertson, 1957). O. H. Robertson and B. C. Wexler have published some investigations of the innate factors associated with the death of the

Pacific salmon (Robertson, 1955, 1956, 1957; Robertson and Wexler, 1957). Further researches on the causes of this sudden death are in progress. This genus of salmon migrates from the sea into fresh-water rivers prior to spawning and does not feed after entering fresh water. Degenerative changes occur in the adrenal cortical tissue and in the pituitaries of the fishes as they spawn and approach death. At full sexual maturity other internal organs and tissues show extensive degeneration which seems incompatible with continued life. Although the physiology of death is not fully known, there seems to be a strong indication that death mechanisms are innate and characteristic of related species of Pacific salmon.

It appears that the limitation of the life of the individual has a genetic basis in these insects and fishes that die soon after their first reproduction and that the death mechanisms are adaptive, not to individual survival but to group survival. Adaptive death has been called *beneficial death* (Allee *et al.*, 1949, p. 692). No adequate explanation of the evolution of individual death seems possible without assuming a function in the population system and selection of populations as whole units. Pearl (1930) said: "No death of an individual occurring in . . . the post-reproductive period can possibly be selective, in the sense of having any effect upon the race." In the instances cited above and in the evolution of the sterile castes of the social insects, selection of postreproductive characters or characters of non-reproductive individuals can be selected and can effect the evolution of the race because the unit of selection is not wholly confined to the individual organism but may and often is the more inclusive population system.

Williams (1957) assumes initially that senescence is an unfavorable character and that its development is opposed by selection. He explains the evolution of senescence by theorizing that natural selection will frequently maximize vigor in youth at the expense of vigor in old age. "The rate of senescence shown by any species will reflect the balance between this direct, adverse selection of senescence as an unfavorable character, and the indirect, favorable selection through the age-related bias in the selection of pleiotropic genes."

There is a great need for the study of the evolution of physiological mechanisms and adaptations in general (see the essay by Prosser elsewhere in this volume). Williams (1957) is on sound ground in postulating the evolution of balance between advantageous and detrimental characters by means of pleiotropy. It is also entirely reasonable to assume that pleiotropic effects and polygenic effects may occur at different stages of development. Homeostatic mechanisms often represent compromise solutions of somewhat incompatible functions (for example, the general temperature regulation of the body of most mammals, including man, is optimal for many functions but too high for spermatogenesis, necessitating the evolution of the scrotum), and certainly perfection of adaptation is not to be expected for any organism or any biological system. However, it is important to recognize the selection of population systems as entities and not to confine selection to individual organisms alone.

Innate aging, innate senescence, and innate death mechanisms would seem to show phylogenetic consistency and may, therefore, indicate a genetic basis. Selection may well operate on pleiotropic, polygenic, and homeostatic balance of many functions in the temporal development of an individual organism or an individual cell. But selection may also operate on population systems that evolve functional adaptation of the integrated group of individuals. A harmful effect upon an individual which has lost its group function may well be beneficial for the population as a whole and be selected through long periods of evolutionary time. Williams (1957) points out: "The selective value of a gene depends on how it affects the total reproductive probability." Among the social insects that have evolved adult sterile castes, genes have been selected that eliminated the reproductive probability of the individual but, at the same time, probably enhanced the total reproductive capacity of the social system which contained specialized reproductive castes receiving food and protection from the non-reproductive castes. In such an instance, the integrated population must have been the unit of selection, a surmise clearly stated by Darwin in the *Origin of Species,* and even more clearly emphasized by Weisman (1893).

Wright (1945) has developed a mathematical genetic theory to account for the fixation of a character valuable to the population but disadvantageous at a given time to the individual organism. He postulates some form of intergroup selection for the establishment of socially advantageous, but individually disadvantageous, mutations. Conditions for such creative evolution of social units seem to be met among the social insects with close inbreeding within small, partially isolated populations with occasional crossing between reproductives from different colonies and intercolony competition within the same species. The selection of population systems as unit entities is by no means confined to the social insects but is a principle of evolution for all living systems which reproduce in such a manner as to integrate one generation to the next by genetic mechanisms which have themselves evolved through this primary selective value.

The evolutionary analysis of individual death is of great philosophical importance. Particularly with regard to human death, some have thought that "death is an incomprehensible event" (Dempster,

1959). Others, back to the beginnings of abstract human thought, have rationalized death by means of mystical and supernatural concepts. Natural science now is beginning to find some evidence that indicates that death can be considered a natural event capable of scientific analysis and interpretation. Evolutionary processes must be considered along with the physiological analysis of aging and death mechanisms. A rapid advance in our knowledge of these events can be predicted in the early future.

SELECTION OF REPRODUCTIVE POTENTIAL

It is very common to find statements in the literature to the effect that maximum reproductive capacity of individuals is *always* selected in competition with individuals of less reproductive capacity (Simpson, 1944, p. 180, 1949, 1953, p. 161; Pitelka, 1951, p. 82; Lack, 1954). Waddington (1957, p. 64) says that ". . . 'survival' does not, of course, mean the bodily endurance of a single individual. . . . That individual 'survives' best which leaves most offspring." Critical data on this contention are difficult to find, and it is likely that much new investigation is needed before the point is either verified or refuted. Williams (1959) shows that the evidence among fishes does not support the contention that evolutionary development of parental care entails a reduced fecundity. The evidence among birds, however, seems to support the concept of an evolutionary trend toward decreased numbers in clutches of eggs in many tree-nesting birds, with associated increase in parental and natural protection of the young. Egg numbers, it must be remembered, are not closely proportional to numbers of surviving reproductive adults. I suggest that some other hypotheses than selection of the individual be considered in future research.

It is fairly obvious that maximal numbers of cells and maximum size of an individual are not selected but that growth and cell division is inherently inhibited at varying thresholds to produce what is presumably an optimum number of cells and an optimum size. Evolution of organisms has certainly produced homeostatic regulation of the size of adult individuals, the size of each ontogenetic stage, and the relative size of each organ in the balanced functional organism. If this be true for individuals, by analogy there is a suggestion that it is possibly true to some degree for integrated and adapted populations. Furthermore, it may be postulated that either minimal or maximal numbers in a population in a finite environment may be deleterious to the species in comparison to optimal numbers (Allee *et al.*, 1949, p. 418). Numbers are often determined by environmental factors, but there is also an obvious control of population numbers by means of genetic factors influencing natality, growth form, maintenance, and dispersion.

One might, therefore, expect to find an evolution of population increase if the optimum is higher than the actual number and likewise an evolutionary decrease if the optimum is below the actual number (see the essay by Wright elsewhere in this volume). Evolution of increase in population size is illustrated by many examples, among them the phylogenetic increase in size of colonies and number of colonies of termites. It is much harder to find examples of an adaptive evolution of decrease in numbers.

There has been an evolution of decrease in numbers with a change in ecological niches (see Simpson, 1953, p. 161; Pitelka, 1951, p. 82). For example, large predators at the top of the Eltonian pyramid of numbers usually have smaller numbers than the small predators that represent their ancestral condition and that doubtless fed upon different species of prey. Slave-making ants of the genus *Polyergus* have small populations and are comparatively rarer in a given habitat than species of the genus *Formica* from which they presumably originated. The separation of genetic from ecological control of population size has not been determined as yet for *Polyergus*. Parasitic ants that have lost their worker caste are usually both rare and have small populations, in contrast to their hosts, which are often more primitive and ancestral in their type of social life and structure. In this case there is surely a genetic component in the determination of population numbers. These are examples of a change in trophic level or ecological niche. Social parasites are generally evolutionary blind alleys, but they have nevertheless arisen many times under the guidance of natural selection.

Is there an evolution of genetic mechanisms resulting in a decrease in numbers because the population efficiency might be impaired by larger numbers in similar habitats? Would individuals with less reproductive capacity survive better than those with a larger reproductive capacity because of the greater survival value of optimal, compared to maximal, numbers of the population as a whole? Data on this point are meager, although it is generally agreed that overpopulation of humans is detrimental to the advance of civilization (cultural rather than organic evolution).

Mather and Harrison (1949) report decreasing fertility of *Drosophila melanogaster* under experimental selection of either high or low numbers of abdominal chaetae. Natural selection for fertility lowered chaeta number in the same way that artificial selection for chaeta number lowered fertility. The association between chaeta number and fertility was broken in reselections from mass lines and was therefore not simple pleiotropy of genes but involved linkage relations of polygenic systems. Fertility is only one component of reproductive potential, but these experiments do indicate the possibility of selection for one character influencing other characters, such as reproductive capacity and vice versa. Selection is most probably operating on the whole balanced functional system, of which reproductive potential is one important characteristic, but not by any means the only one.

Salt (1936) provides data on the effect of host density on parasite density under experimental conditions. The chalcid egg parasite, *Trichogramma evanescens,* and its host, the eggs of the moth, *Sitotroga cerealella,* were investigated. Five females, capable of depositing 108 eggs, produced 84.4 progeny per 100 available hosts, while 50 females capable of depositing 1,080 eggs, produced only 29.8 progeny (some abnormal) per 100 available hosts because of the competition for food when several parasite eggs were laid in the same host egg. Ullyett (1936) showed that another chalcid, *Microplectron fuscipennis,* indicated some ability to discriminate between parasitized and unparasitized host larvae, *Diprion polytomum* (sawfly), a sensory capacity that probably has been naturally selected. Discrimination by the ovipositing parasite occurred only when moving parasitic larvae were present in the host larvae and not when immobile parasitic eggs were present.

Naylor (1959) points out that feeding and egg-laying gravid female flour beetles (*Tribolium confusum*) tend to select niches of low population density and will spend time in niches in inverse relationship to occupancy. He concludes that "the survival value to the species is obvious" and that few suitable sites "would be so crowded by the hatching larvae that their chances of surviving to adulthood would be impaired."

Thomas Park and David B. Mertz (personal communication) have a series of experiments currently in progress using four genetic "strains" for each of two species of flour beetles (*T. confusum* and *T. castaneum*). These eight strains, developed by a program of interbreeding and selection, affect numbers. Thus strain-1 (of both species) produces maximal population density, and strain-4 minimal population density, when each is husbanded in an identical, controlled environment. Each of the four strains of the one species has been placed in interspecies competition with each of the four strains of the other species, resulting in 16 combinations. Strain-1 of *T. castaneum* was consistently successful when placed in competition against all four strains of *T. confusum.* But in *single-species* cultures, two strains (1 and 2) of *T. confusum* produced larger populations than did strain-1 of *T. castaneum* during the early census history of the experiment, while the two other strains (3 and 4) produced smaller populations. In short, strain-1 of *T. castaneum* invariably bests its rival. This remains true even though the rival has the potential to build larger populations. The survival of strain-1 of *T. castaneum* appears to be grounded in the fact that its inherent rate of development (egg to adult) substantially exceeds that of the other beetles. In certain different species-strain combinations, *T. confusum* is the successful competitor. In these latter instances developmental rate is not the critical factor, and one must look to such parameters as natality, mortality, and cannibalism.

It should be emphasized that these are laboratory strains of beetles and may not be similar to any natural populations of either species. Since we have no knowledge of competition or selection of these beetles under natural conditions, the evolutionary implications of these experiments must remain hypothetical. However, we are dealing with different genetic attributes of populations living in a carefully controlled identical environment, feeding on the same food, and utilizing the same space.

We may conclude that a biological possibility exists, namely, populations of different species with genetic control over relatively small population numbers can be selected in competition with populations in the same habitat that have a larger reproductive potential.

The following hypothesis is worthy of consideration and testing. Selection and progressive adaptation of population systems involves a balance between many functions, of which reproductive potential is only one aspect of adaptation, although admittedly an important one. It is further postulated that this balanced integration of population systems involves optimal, rather than maximal or minimal, numbers in the system. However, the concept of optimal numbers with greater efficiency of population interaction and adjustment—external or internal—has yet to be adequately tested. The data available at present only hint at the possibility of homeostatic control of population numbers and an organic evolution of decrease as well as increase in numbers of individuals in successful species and intraspecies populations.

Ecological Communities and Ecosystems

The general conclusion is drawn that an understanding of ecological communities in their physical and biotic environment must include the analysis of the component species and factors that are correlated with the contemporary ecological structure and interrelations. The biotic relations usually did not originate suddenly but are products of long periods of evolutionary time under the guidance of natural selection and should be viewed in the light of evolutionary processes. It seems obvious that the environment has an evolutionary influence upon the organisms and the species populations and that, in turn, the individuals and the species influence and modify the environment (see essay by Bates elsewhere in this volume). This modification also occurs gradually in geological time as well as in the shorter time sequences of ecological succession and even in the still shorter time of more immediate physiological or behavioristic effects. The actions of organisms upon their habitat may be comparatively simple physical, chemical, and mechanical influences, but they may also involve highly complex physiological and behavioristic activities, themselves the products of evolutionary factors operating over long periods. Each individual and each species has a greater or less lasting selective effect upon the other individuals and species with which it is associated. The genetic constituents of the individuals are the product of an almost infinite series of effects that have impinged upon them from the environment and in turn have produced environmental modification at both simple and complex levels of activity. The large number of orderly effects within the communities and their ecosystems have many feedbacks. In order to understand any individual, any species, or any interspecies unity, one must analyze the system into its component factors, but analysis is not sufficient, nor does it limit scientific method. Together with analysis, we must also recognize the wholes and their emergent properties. We must synthesize as well as analyze.

The analytic and synthetic aspects of interspecies population systems and ecosystems that incorporate the physical and biotic environment have been discussed in recent literature and placed in an evolutionary perspective (Allee et al., 1949, pp. 695–729; Emerson, 1946, 1952; Bray, 1958; Weber, 1958). Some recent authors have not accepted the reality of an interspecies supra-organismic system during long evolutionary time (Bodenheimer, 1953, 1958; Muller, 1958).

The reciprocal evolution of interspecies systems over long periods of geological time is indicative of the modification of the genetic characters of one species by another (Seevers, 1957). The relations of species in the community is often that of unilateral exploitation. Overexploitation would be deleterious to the exploiting species by removing its food from the environment, so that the evolution of a more tolerable adjustment between predator and prey, or parasite and host, seems to have occurred (Huff, 1938; Huffaker, 1958). Balance between populations of exploited species and exploiter species, either parasite-host or predator-prey, may evolve, even though the individual host or prey is killed (see Emerson in Allee et al., 1949, p. 709). The adjustments that may evolve between such species include individual defensive adaptations, reduction of mortality to a tolerable rate, increase in reproductive potential to balance the mortality, an ecological association that makes it difficult for the predator or parasite to find the prey or a food-web that provides other available nutrition that relieves some of the pressure on the exploited species. In any given instance of interspecies relationship, all these adjustments have not necessarily evolved, but one or another may be sufficient. It is important from the standpoint of evolutionary analysis to determine which may result from chance and which are the result of guidance by means of natural selection of genetic traits.

Hutchinson (1959) concludes that the main cause of diversity of the terrestrial fauna is the diversity of the terrestrial flora. He further concludes that the diversity of the whole system is probably due to the greater stability of a food-web of many levels over one of few levels. Interspecies adjustments may have a very long evolutionary history, and in some instances the species have so modified the environment in a favorable direction that the interspecies system and its physical and biotic environment seem to have evolved as a unit—an ecosystem.

Coadaptations between species within the same ecological community have received considerable attention during the last two decades, particularly by the ornithologists (Lack, 1947, 1954; MacArthur, 1958). The general rule is that different related species in the same general habitat evolve somewhat different feeding and other ecological adaptations that reduce the competition to the point that allows coexistence. Each competing species will become involved in the natural selection that guides the evolution of its competitors. There seems to be instances of closely allied species occupying the same habitat with no known adaptive divergence. Such is the case with some of the flagellates living in the hind gut of single species of roach or termite (Cleveland *et al.*, 1934; Cleveland and Day, 1958). The circumstantial evidence also indicates that evolution of some of these species of asexual protozoans has been extremely slow and that some genera now living were already in existence at the end of Permian or the beginning of Triassic times before the origin of the termite order (Isoptera) from its primitive Blattoid ancestry.

Symbiotic mutualism has been studied by many investigators (Allee *et al.*, 1949, p. 710). A recent review of some interesting cases of symbiosis has been written by Lederberg (1952). Mutualism is the clearest illustration of community integration, but many more subtle types of interdependence have also evolved.

Less obvious, but capable of experimental approach, is the tendency for closely related sympatric species to evolve genetic mechanisms that prevent crossbreeding and enhance reproductive isolation

(Crane, 1941; Allee *et al.*, 1949, pp. 620, 710; Stone, 1959). Mating preferences have been demonstrated for both laboratory and natural strains within the same species of *Drosophila* (Santibañez and Waddington, 1958). Although sexual selection by each individual may play an important role in the evolution of mating preferences, we must not forget that a stimulus by one individual must usually initiate a response by another individual and that the totality of sex physiology, sex anatomy, and sex behavior initiated by complex genetic systems demands a mutuality of adaptation between the sexes (see Tinbergen, 1954; Bonner, 1958). Such intricate adjustment, much of it without directly involving individual choice or mate by means of allaesthetic characters, can hardly have arisen solely from individual sexual selection as postulated by Darwin. A better hypothesis is the selection of the sex pairs as units (Marshall, 1936) coadapted to the sexuality of other sex pairs and other species in the ecosystem (see Huxley, 1938).

Evolutionary Increase and Decrease In Integration and Homeostasis

One may well ask why there is a general trend toward a looser organization and decreased self-regulation of optimal conditions in the more inclusive population unit systems compared to the more primitive systems at lower levels of integration. Within a particular level—for example, the family unit or the social unit—an evolutionary increase in homeostasis seems to occur, but at the same time the included part (such as the individual or the sex pair) seems to have an evolutionary decrease in homeostasis as it becomes more dependently incorporated in the more inclusive, but comparatively less integrated, organization. This negative correlation of the curve of the advanced emergence of population levels with the curve of integrative self-sufficiency of parts is not uniform but does seem to be a broad general trend. The indications of improved homeostasis of the whole inclusive population unit compared to its parts decrease as the population level advances from the asexual to the sexual and subsequently to the family and to the society within the genetically integrated species, or from the biocoenose to various types of more inclusive ecological communities and ecosystems. The looser organization and less apparent self-regulation of the more inclusive systems has led many to doubt the reality of such units.

In a few instances, more inclusive systems have preceded the evolution of more tightly organized and regulated component systems. The interspecies system of cellulose-digesting flagellates with their roach or termite hosts seems to have preceded the later evolution of the intraspecies termite society, and the most advanced termite societies are no longer dependent upon cellulose-digesting flagellates. The interspecific mutualism between the flowering plant and the pollinating insect evolved earlier than the evolution of the intra-specific contemporaneous integrated family and society of bees. But, in general, self-regulation of optimal conditions of existence and perpetuation is more obvious in the contemporaneous protoplasmically connected individual organism than in the population and is more obvious in the sexually adapted pair than in the family. The family units are more closely bound together both physiologically and behavioristically than are the later evolved emergent societies of insects or man.

The seeming contradiction that an increase in the homeostasis of a holistic system is usually accompanied by a decrease in the homeostasis of a unit part of the system is really no contradiction at all. Regressive evolution of aspects of self-sufficiency of a less inclusive unit occurs with the incorporation of the once relatively independent unit into a more inclusive system, with its increase of division of labor, increase in integration between parts, and improved homeostasis of the whole system. In other words, a part of an individual may lose some of its homeostatic function with the gain of homeostatic function within the larger whole unit with which it becomes incorporated.

One can account for these trends by tentative explanations based upon somewhat sketchy information. Ultimately these hypotheses must be much more fully substantiated. Possibly the best-documented theory of one aspect of the evolution of population integration is that emerging from modern population genetics and summarized in the paper by Dobzhansky (1957). He has demonstrated the role of selection in Mendelian populations and also adds (p. 392): "An array of asexually reproducing or of obligatorily selfing individuals may in a certain sense be regarded as an ecologically meaningful system. If these individuals live sufficiently close to each other in space and in time, they may be parts of each other's environments."

It would seem that adaptive integration of a system may be more easily attained by means of complex biochemical and biophysical contact than by means of the simple physical or chemical interaction through non-living space. It seems fairly well established that more complex biochemical and biophysical interactions are possible within a part of a cell than between its parts or between cells with limiting membranes.

The fact that biological processes are largely dependent upon enzymes composed of very large and complicated protein molecules may be the major factor in this trend. The molecules that easily pass through intracellular and intercellular permeable membranes are usually comparatively small and simple, although some biochemically complex large molecules are known to pass through membranes that are probably highly adapted to such a function. There are many reasons to suppose that the biochemical and biophysical agents passing between individual units separated by a non-living medium in a population system are, on the whole, simpler than those agents that can pass through cell and tissue membranes within a multicellular organism.

Although the agents may be simple, the response mechanisms may be highly complex. In the higher cellular and multicellular organisms, some complex protoplasmic interactions become restricted to the asexual or sexual reproductive systems (continuity of the "germ plasm"). In population systems, behavioral mechanisms of stimulus and response predominate by means of communication through a non-living medium between protoplasmically separated individuals. The divergence of integrating mechanisms within and between organisms is one of degree as well as of kind. Certainly there is a trend toward simpler mechanisms of interactions through non-living media than through living protoplasms and their complex organic constituents. This does not mean that the sending and receiving mechanisms within the living organisms are organically simpler and earlier in evolutionary origin, but only that the energy waves and chemical substances transmitted from organism to organism are likely to be physically and chemically simpler than the physicochemical factors transmitted between organelles within a living cell or between cells in a living multicellular organism.

This general tendency toward more simplified mechanisms of exchange does not negate the increased complexity of the total stimulus and response interaction. I suspect that the mechanisms of genetic duplication and optimal variation are more complicated in most existing organisms than they were at the dawn of life on earth. I suspect that sexual fusion of gametes is a more complicated process than cell division. And once sound waves were sent and received by different individuals in a population, they were elaborated in evolutionary sequences of communication along with the functional advances of the stridulatory and vocal organs, together with the auditory receptor organs and interadapted nervous systems.

One may make the general statement that the later evolved and so-called higher integrative systems in linear evolutionary sequences have increased the homeostasis of the whole system at the expense of a reduced homeostasis of a part that was relatively more independent and self-sufficient in an earlier stage of evolution. The clearest example of this trend is to be found among the social insects. The increase in division of labor and in social integration results in an improved social regulation of optimal conditions of existence and reproduction (Emerson, 1956). This trend is accompanied by the evolution of sterility in the worker (and soldier) castes. The sterile individuals of derivative termites have less ability to withstand the periodic dry atmosphere outside the socially constructed nests and passageways than their non-social ancestors, the primitive roaches. In other words, as social homeostasis increases, certain parameters of individual homeostasis tend to decrease. Regressive evolution is commonly accompanied by a compensatory progressive evolution, often through adaptation within a more inclusive organismic level.

It seems probable that this similar trend is occurring in the evolution of human society. As division of labor between specialists evolves, integration into higher unit systems also advances, and, as social homeostasis evolves, the individual human loses some portion of his self-regulation and becomes more dependent for his existence upon the division of labor and integration of the social system. The fact that advanced human society is more optimal for existence and perpetuation than primitive society and that primitive man had a greater control over the conditions of existence than his presocial primate ancestors seems fairly obvious, at least to the author. In other words, as conditions of existence and survival improve for the social group, numerous aspects of the homeostasis of the individual component of the society decrease, but natural selection, as well as intelligent selection, operates to increase the group homeostasis over the homeostasis of the individual within the group system (see Muller in our companion volume—"The Evolution of Man").

EVOLUTIONARY "FEEDBACK"

The foregoing considerations indicate the necessity of recognizing circularity or web relations from effects back to causes. The survival of the phenotype of any biological unitary system selects the genotype in succeeding generations. In due time, the attributes of the genes and the genetic pattern as a whole are, in a sense, determined by the effectiveness of the genetic system in the phenotype. Function thus becomes a cause of mechanism.

It seems illogical to some to conceive of a later result as having an effect upon a preceding cause. In biological and human systems we find a continuity and repetition of causation (the order of nature particularly exemplified by genetic replication), so effects quite commonly precede the repeated cause in time and obviously are able to modify causes by means of feedback mechanisms. The term "feedback" is usually applied to automation and to physiological and behavioristic systems, but natural selection is an evolutionary influence of effects upon causative mechanisms; so, for want of a better term, we may possibly extend the usual usage of "feedback" to include evolution by means of natural selection (see Waddington elsewhere in this volume).

Common errors in scientific interpretation involve oversimplifications, the treatment of a single factor as *the* important factor, and in arranging events in a linear one-way cause-to-effect sequence when feedbacks from effects to causes are apparent. Duplication by reproduction units always involves metabolism, maintenance, and self-regulation over periods between reproduction. Life also always includes growth and differentiation of parts. Any given system is composed of parts with special functions integrated in space and time into a unit whole in which division of labor serves the entire system. The problem of basic causation is not whether the genetic units are the cause of the organism in a linear relationship or whether the organism is the cause of the genetic attributes in a linear relationship—in popular language, the old question of which came first, the hen or the (hen's) egg—but includes the interrelatedness of the fundamental properties of living systems. Dobzhansky (1957) says: "An individual is a system of exquisitely co-ordinated parts and processes in which thousands or tens of thousands of different kinds of self-replicating molecules are associated together in a pattern which undergoes orderly changes in the process of living." This statement is also true for supra-individual populations. Organic evolution always involves changes in the genetic systems. The genetic systems are interwoven with mechanisms of growth, differentiation, integration, and homeostasis within various levels of organismic and population systems. I think it is necessary to recognize the interrelationships of the associated internal and external aspects of every living system, of which one, but only one, highly important attribute is the reproductive and genetic capacities. With specialized skills of investigation and well-substantiated principles, each subscience may advance and may even temporarily seem to dominate other subsciences, but it cannot be overemphasized that biology consists of knowledge of multidimensional living processes that are intricately interdependent. An organism is not wholly composed of its genetic attributes alone or of its physiological, its developmental, its ecological, or its behavioristic aspects alone.

One of the most important mechanisms that integrate populations—and possibly the initial mechanism in the evolutionary history of population systems—is the genetic mechanism. It may be said with no possibility of refutation or exception that every individual organism is integrated by means of reproduction and genetic descent with its parental generation, whether the reproduction is asexual or sexual. The function of reproduction itself has a large component of population adaptation, because the survival value of reproduction is measured in terms of advantage to the population. Reproduction is often associated with death or deleterious effects upon the individual that is reproducing.

In addition to replication by means of DNA (deoxyribonucleic acid) duplication in the best-established reproductive mechanisms, we also have good indications of other genetic mechanisms associated at least at times with replication by means of RNA (ribonucleic acid) nucleoproteins, plasmagenes, and some cytoplasmic inheritance. Although we may find it possible largely to concentrate on the repetitive capacity of DNA, together with its mutational capacity and capacity to recombine, we must also take into account other mechanisms of inheritance that might be of importance in at least some cases in integrating ancestral generations with their descendants. A mechanism of great importance to the evolution of the human species is the ability to symbolize and to pass along experience and value-concepts to other individuals and to other generations by means of symbolic communication. This capacity, that seems to be mainly confined to the human species, gives rise to cultural evolution based on symbolic inheritance that is analogous in many ways with organic evolution based upon genetic inheritance (Emerson, 1954).

EVOLUTIONARY PROGRESS

Natural selection within diverse habitats for efficient maintenance and reproduction of unitary systems at various levels of organization seems to be the only directing factor in organic evolution. Genetic mutation and recombination are the factors of variation upon which selection must work. Reproductive isolation is the dividing factor in the origin of species and in the branching of the phylogenetic tree. Reproductive isolation, either partial or complete, effects inbreeding, and it is only through inbreeding or asexual reproduction that complex genetic systems with complex functions can be perpetuated and become characteristic of many individuals in population systems.

Natural selection operates at each level of integration from the gene and complex polygenic characters within the individual, to the whole individual, and to various levels of intraspecific population systems and interspecific interadapted community systems and ecosystems. Selection may operate on the physical habitat through the genetically initiated modification of the environment by some organisms (i.e., beavers, social insects, etc.).

Selection does not act only on the contemporary system in its contemporary environment but also upon the time dimensions of living systems exemplified particularly in feedback mechanisms characteristic of physiological, developmental, and evolutionary temporal adjustments. The circularity of cause and effect—with effects often influencing repeated causes—enables mechanisms to evolve that are directed toward future function. Natural selection is sometimes thought to operate without "foresight" or at least to be "short sighted." It is true that adaptations to oft repeated events are more obvious, but rare events repeated only after the lapse of many years can also be shown to influence selection pressures. And the capacity to respond to new and even to unique events can evolve in the physiological body and the intelligent animal. For example, antibodies against completely new protein poisons can be generated by the cells and tissues. All of this means that the organic systems incorporate time dimensions and that end-directions are apparent in ontogenetic and phylogenetic time. Pittendrigh (1958) refers to such end-directedness as *teleonomy*, without implying Aristotelian teleology as an efficient causal principle. Waddington (1957, and elsewhere in this volume) discusses the evolution of adaptation toward future functions at some length, with a modern genetic explanation of the evolutionary processes involved. Population systems have such teleonomic properties as well as individual organisms, and the basic evolutionary processes are similar.

Progressive evolution of individual organisms and of population systems seems to tend toward an increase in homeostatic regulation of relatively optimal internal and external conditions. The fluctuating external environment of lower levels of organization becomes the internal homeostatic milieu of higher levels. Progress also is in the direction of adaptation to habitats that exhibit a degree of relative stability of important factors, thus reducing the problem of self-regulation. Evolutionary trends toward greater organization, greater integration, increased co-operation, more efficient habitat selection, and increased internal and external adaptation and balance may be equated in large measure with an evolutionary increase in homeostasis at each level of organization from the molecular units of life to the ecosystem. When function requires disequilibrium, fluctuation, periodicity, and divergence, these often become homeostatic. Physiological homeostasis may be improved by the evolution of mechanisms involving the sacrifice of certain cells and tissues. Social homeostasis may increase in evolutionary time with the sacrifice of certain individuals.

Ecological homeostasis may involve the extinction of species and large systematic groups during progressive evolution.

The "goal" of human evolution, organic and cultural, is sometimes given in terms of individual or social adaptation, welfare, fulfilment, and happiness (see the essays by Huxley in this volume and Muller in "Evolution of Man"). Some of these overlapping terms allow for a certain degree of comparative evaluation, but it is important for the biologist, the psychologist, the social scientist, the humanist, and the religionist to attempt a more adequate analysis, synthesis, and comparative evaluation of the meaning of these terms. Some of the suggested directions of organic and cultural evolution are expressed in terms that are too vague, too subjective, too anthropomorphic, and too mystical. In my opinion, dynamic homeostasis is substantiated by much evidence at both the biological, the social, and the ecological level; the concept allows measurements and cross-comparisons between widely different living systems with drastically different homeostatic mechanisms and resultant regulations. All homeostatic regulation involves feedbacks and incorporates time dimensions within the physiological, developing, and evolving system. But, like all comprehensive concepts, further researches into the minutiae of the processes are necessary. Understanding of the incompatibilities between optimal conditions for optimal functions must be sought. But, a hundred years after the great book by Darwin, we have an enhanced motivation for inquiry, a hint of profound rapport between the natural sciences, social sciences, and humanities, and a vision of the possibility of a greater wisdom in dealing with the present and future problems of man within his ecosystem.

SUMMARY

Different levels of population integration, including the asexual reproducing organisms, the sexually reproducing organisms, various forms of aggregations, families, societies, and, finally, various types of ecological communities are considered as unitary systems that may be naturally selected as whole entities during evolutionary time.

By the incorporation of biological time dimensions into each system, adaptive evolution by means of natural selection involves a feedback from effects to repeated causes.

Populations, like organisms, exhibit self-regulation of optimal conditions of existence and survival (homeostasis), and this basic adaptation is convergent and analogous in many cases, or it may exhibit homology through genetic persistence in evolutionary sequences. Homeostatic regulation may be the maintenance of functional unbalance as well as the maintenance of functional balance and equilibrium. Evolutionary progress is equated with improved homeostasis.

Regressive evolution (loss of ancestral adaptations) commonly is correlated with progressive evolution of larger, more inclusive systems, together with an advance in homeostasis of the whole unitary level. The innate regulation of numbers in unitary populations involves the evolution of death mechanisms in individuals. Death and extinction may be the product of the natural selection of progressively evolving population systems.

The physical environment, as well as the internal and external living environment, of organisms evolves adaptively and progressively, but perfection of adjustment is unattainable in any living organism or population of organisms.

An evolution of adaptive behavior between individuals in a population is significantly analogous in function to the evolution of adaptive integration and divergent functions at the molecular and physiological level within individual organisms.

It is concluded that evolution of function directed toward ends can be demonstrated and that modern biological analysis and synthesis give us some understanding of these teleonomic processes. At the same time, our present tentative hypotheses need much further investigation and substantiation.

The author acknowledges his indebtedness for critical comments resulting in some modifications of the manuscript from Sir Julian Huxley, Dr. William K. Baker, Dr. David Pimentel, Dr. Herbert Ross, and his wife, Eleanor Fish Emerson.

BIBLIOGRAPHY

AGASSIZ, LOUIS. 1860. "Professor Agassiz on the Origin of Species," *Amer. Jour. Sci.* (2d ser.), XXX, 142–54.

ALLEE, W. C. 1931. *Animal Aggregations: A Study in General Sociology.* Chicago: University of Chicago Press.

ALLEE, W. C., EMERSON, A. E., PARK, O., PARK, T., and SCHMIDT, K. P. 1949. *Principles of Animal Ecology.* Philadelphia: W. B. Saunders Co.

AUSTEN, E. E., and HUGHES, A. W. 1935. *Clothes Moths and House Moths.* Edited by A. W. MCK. HUGHES, and H. STRINGER. ("Econ. Ser.," No. 14.) 2d ed. rev. London: British Museum.

BODENHEIMER, F. S. 1953. "The Concept of Biotic Organization in Synecology," *Bull. Res. Council Israel,* III, 114–21.

———. 1958. *Animal Ecology Today.* ("Monographae Biologicae," No. 6.) The Hague: W. Junk.

BODENHEIMER, F. S., and SWIRSKI, E. 1957. *The Aphidoidea of the Middle East.* Jerusalem: Swizmann Sci. Press of Israel.

BLUM, H. F. 1951. *Time's Arrow and Evolution.* Princeton, N.J.: Princeton University Press.

BONNER, J. T. 1955. *Cells and Societies.* Princeton, N.J.: Princeton University Press.

———. 1958. *The Evolution of Development.* Cambridge: Cambridge University Press.

———. 1959. *The Cellular Slime Molds.* Princeton, N.J.: Princeton University Press.

BRAY, J. ROGER. 1958. "Notes toward an Ecologic Theory," *Ecology,* XXXIX, 770–76.

CANNON, W. B. 1932. *The Wisdom of the Body.* New York: W. W. Norton & Co.

———. 1941. "The Body Physiologic and the Body Politic," *Science,* XCIII, 1–10.

CLEVELAND, L. R. 1947. "The Origin and Evolution of Meiosis," *Science,* CV, 287–89, 546.

———. 1950. "Hormone-induced Sexual Cycles of Flagellates. II. Gametogenesis, Fertilization, and One-Division Meiosis in *Oxymonas,*" *Jour. Morphol.,* LXXXVI, 185–214.

———. 1951. "Hormone-induced Sexual Cycles of Flagellates. VII. One-Division Meiosis and Autogamy without Cell Division in *Urinympha,*" *ibid.,* LXXXVIII, 385–439.

CLEVELAND, L. R., and DAY, M. 1958. "Spirotrichonymphidae of Stolotermes," *Ark. Protistenk.,* CIII, 1–53.

CLEVELAND, L. R., *et al.* 1934. *The Wood-feeding Roach Cryptocerus, Its Protozoa, and the Symbiosis between Protozoa and Roach.* ("Mem. Amer. Acad. Arts and Sci.," No. 17.)

COLE, L., *et al.* 1957. "Population Studies: Animal Ecology and Demography," *Sym. Quant. Biol.,* Vol. XXII. New York: Biol. Lab., Long Island Biol. Assoc.

COMSTOCK, J. H. 1924. *An Introduction to Entomology.* Ithaca, N.Y.: Comstock Publishing Co.

CRANE, JOCELYN. 1941. "Crabs of the Genus *Uca* from the West Coast of Central America," *Zoologica,* XXVI, 145–208.

DEMPSTER, W. T. 1959. Book review of *Human Dissection* by A. M. Lassek (1958), *Science,* CXXIX, 204.

DOBZHANSKY, TH. 1951. "Mendelian Populations and Their Evolution." In *Genetics in the 20th Century,* pp. 573–89. New York: Macmillan Co.

———. 1957. "Mendelian Populations as Genetic Systems," Cold Spring Harbor Symp. Quant. Biol., XXII, 385–93.

———. 1958. "Evolution at Work," *Science,* CXXVII, 1091–98.

EMERSON, A. E. 1939*a.* "Social Coordination and the Superorganism," *Amer. Midland Naturalist,* XXI, 182–209.

———. 1939*b.* "Populations of Social Insects," *Ecol. Mono.,* IX, 287–300.

————. 1942. "Basic Comparisons of Human and Insect Societies," *Biol. Sym.,* VIII, 163–76.

————. 1946. "The Biological Basis of Social Cooperation," *Trans. Illinois Acad. Sci.,* XXXIX, 9–18.

————. 1952. "The Supraorganismic Aspects of the Society." In *Structure et physiologie des sociétés animales: Colloques internat. centre nat. recherche scient. XXXIV,* pp. 333–54.

————. 1954. "Dynamic Homeostasis: A Unifying Principle in Organic, Social, and Ethical Evolution," *Scient. Monthly,* LXXVIII, 67–85.

————. 1956. "Regenerative Behavior and Social Homeostasis of Termites," *Ecology,* XXXVII, 248–58.

————. 1958. "The Evolution of Behavior among Social Insects." In ANNE ROE and G. G. SIMPSON (eds.), *Behavior and Evolution,* chap. 15, pp. 311–35. New Haven: Yale University Press.

————. 1959. "Social Insects," *Encyclopaedia Britannica,* XX, 871–78.

FISHER, JAMES. 1954. "Evolution and Bird Sociality." In J. HUXLEY, A. C. HARDY, and E. B. FORD (eds.), *Evolution as a Process,* pp. 71–83. London: Allen & Unwin.

FLANDERS, S. E. 1946. "Haploidy as a Factor in the Polymorphic Differentiation of the Hymenoptera," *Science,* CI, 245–46.

FRIEDMANN, H. 1929. *The Cowbirds: A Study in the Biology of Social Parasitism.* Springfield, Mass.

GERARD, R. W. 1940. "Organism, Society, and Science," *Scient. Monthly,* L, 340–50, 403–12, 530–35.

————. 1942. "Higher Levels of Integration," *Biol. Symp.,* VIII, 67–87.

HAFEX, M., and EL-MOURSY, A. A. 1956. "On the General Biology of *Vermileo vermileo* L.," *Bull. Soc. Entomol. Egypte* (333), 333–48.

HUFF, C. G. 1938. "Studies on the Evolution of Some Disease-producing Organisms," *Quart. Rev. Biol.,* XIII, 196–206.

————. 1945. "A Consideration of the Problem of Evolution of Malarial Parasites," *Rev. Inst. Salubridad Enferm. Trop.,* VI, 253–58.

HUFFAKER, C. B. 1958. "Experimental Studies on Predation: Dispersion Factors and Predator-Prey Oscillations," *Hilgardia,* XXVII, 343–83.

HUTCHINSON, G. E. 1959. "Homage to Santa Rosalia or Why Are There So Many Kinds of Animals," *Amer. Naturalist,* XCIII, 145–59.

HUXLEY, JULIAN. 1938. "The Present standing of the theory of Sexual Selection. In G. R. DEBEER (ed.), *Evolution,* pp. 11–42. Oxford.

————. 1942. *Evolution the Modern Synthesis.* New York and London: Harper & Bros.

JONES, D. F. 1958. "Heterosis and Homeostasis in Evolution and in Applied Genetics," *Amer. Naturalist,* XCII, 321–28.

KENDEIGH, S. CHARLES. 1952. *Parental Care and Its Evolution in Birds.* ("Illinois Biol. Monographs," No. 22.)

KERR, W. E. 1950. "Evolution of Caste Determination in the Genus *Melipona,*" *Evolution,* IV, 7–13.

LACK, DAVID. 1954. "The Evolution of Reproductive Rates." In J. HUXLEY,

A. C. HARDY, and E. B. FORD (eds.), *Evolution as a Process,* pp. 143–55. London: Allen & Unwin.

LEDERBERG, J. 1952. "Cell Genetics and Hereditary Symbiosis," *Physiol. Rev.,* XXXII, 403–30.

————. 1956. "Genetic Transduction," *Amer. Scientist,* XLIV, 264–80.

LERNER, I. M. 1954. *Genetic Homeostasis.* Edinburgh and London: Oliver & Boyd.

————. 1958. *The Genetic Basis of Selection.* New York: John Wiley & Sons. 298 pp.

LEWONTIN, R. C. 1957. "The Adaptations of Populations to Varying Environments," *Cold Spring Harbor Symp. Quant. Biol.,* XXII, 395–408.

LINDAUER, M., and KERR, W. E. 1958. "Die gegenseitige Verständigung bei den stachellosen Bienen," *Zeitschr. vergl. Physiol.,* XLI, 405–34.

MACARTHUR, R. H. 1955. "Fluctuations of Animal Populations, and a Measure of Community Stability," *Ecology,* XXXVI, 533–36.

————. 1958. "Population Ecology of Some Warblers of Northeastern Coniferous Forests," *ibid.,* XXXIX, 599–619.

MARSHALL, F. H. A. 1936. "Sexual Periodicity and the Causes Which Determine It," *Phil. Trans. Roy. Soc., London, B.,* CCXXVI, 423–56.

MARTIN, C. P. 1956. *Psychology, Evolution, and Sex.* Springfield, Ill.: Charles C Thomas.

MATHER, K., and HARRISON, B. J. 1949. "The Manifold Effect of Selection. I," *Heredity,* III, 1–52.

MICHENER, C. D. 1958. "The Evolution of Social Behavior in Bees," *Proc. Tenth Internat. Cong. Entomol. (1956),* II, 441–47.

MICHENER, C. D., and MICHENER, MARY H. 1951. *American Social Insects.* New York: D. Van Nostrand Co.

MOSCONA, A. A. 1959. "Tissues from Dissociated Cells," *Scient. American,* CC, 132–34, 136–39, 141–42, 144.

MULLER, CORNELIUS H. 1958. "Science and Philosophy of the Community Concept," *Amer. Scientist,* XLVI, 294–308.

NAYLOR, A. F. 1959. "An Experimental Analysis of Dispersal in the Flour Beetle, *Tribolium confusum,*" *Ecology,* XL, 453–65.

NEEDHAM, J. G., TRAVER, JAY R., and HSU Y. 1935. *The Biology of Mayflies.* Ithaca, N.Y.: Comstock Publishing Co.

NEYMAN, J., PARK, T., and SCOTT, E. L. 1956. "Struggle for Existence. The Tribolium Model: Biological and Statistical Aspects," *Proc. Third Berkeley Symp. on Mathematical Statistics and Probability,* IV, 41–79.

NICHOLSON, A. J. 1957. "The Self-Adjustment of Populations to Change," *Cold Spring Harbor Symp. Quant. Biol.,* XXII, 153–73.

NOIROT, C. 1955. "Recherches sur le polymorphisme des termites supérieurs (Termitidae)," *Ann. sci. nat. zool.* (11th ser.), XVII, 399–595.

PARK, THOMAS. 1954. "Experimental Studies of Interspecies Competition. II. Temperature, Humidity, and Competition in Two Species of Tribolium," *Physiol. Zoöl.,* XXVII, 177–238.

PATTEN, B. C. 1959. "An Introduction to the Cybernetics of the Ecosystem: The Trophic-Dynamic Aspect," *Ecology,* XL, 221–31.

PEARL, R. 1930. "Requirements of a Proof that Natural Selection Has Altered a Race," *Scientia,* XLVII, 175–86.

PITTENDRIGH, C. S. 1958. "Adaptation, Natural Selection, and Behavior." In ANNE ROE and G. G. SIMPSON (eds.), *Behavior and Evolution,* pp. 390–416. New Haven: Yale University Press.

RAPER, J. R. 1959. "Sexual Versatility and Evolutionary Processes in Fungi," *Mycologia,* LI, 107–24.

REDFIELD, R. (ed.). 1942. "Levels of Integration in Biological and Social Systems," *Biol. Symp.,* VIII, 1–240.

———. 1955. *The Little Community: Viewpoint for the Study of a Human Whole.* Chicago: University of Chicago Press.

ROBERTSON, O. H. 1955. "Science, Salmon, and Trout," *Trans. Assoc. Amer. Physicians,* LXVIII, 33–41.

———. 1956. "A Study of the Cause of Death of the Pacific Salmons after Spawning," *Year Book Amer. Phil. Soc., 1956,* pp. 215–18.

———. 1957. "Survival of Precociously Mature King Salmon Male Parr (*Oncorhynchus tshawytscha* Juv.) after Spawning," *California Fish and Game,* XLIII, 119–29.

ROBERTSON, O. H., and WEXLER, B. C. 1957. "Pituitary Degeneration and Adrenal Tissue Hyperplasia in Spawning Pacific Salmon," *Science,* CXXV, 1295–96.

ROE, ANNE, and SIMPSON, G. G. (eds.). 1958. *Behavior and Evolution.* New Haven: Yale University Press.

ROSS, H. H. 1944. "The Caddis Flies or Trichoptera of Illinois," *Bull. Illinois Nat. Hist. Survey,* XXIII, art. 1, 1–326.

SALT, G. 1936. "Experimental Studies in Insect Parasitism. IV. The Effect of Superparasitism on Populations of *Trichogramma evanescens," Jour. Exper. Biol.,* XIII, 363–75.

SANTIBAÑEZ, S. K., and WADDINGTON, C. H. 1958. "The Origin of Sexual Isolation between Different Lines within a Species," *Evolution,* XII, 485–93.

SCHNEIRLA, T. C. 1946. "Problems in the Biopsychology of Social Organization," *Jour. Abnormal and Social Psychol.,* XLI, 385–402.

SEEVERS, CHARLES. 1957. "A Monograph on the Termitophilous Staphylinidae (Coleoptera)," *Fieldiana: Zoology,* XL, 1–334.

SHEPPARD, P. M. 1954. "Evolution in Bisexually Reproducing Organisms." In J. HUXLEY, A. C. HARDY, and E. B. FORD (eds.), *Evolution as a Process,* pp. 210–18. London: Allen & Unwin.

SIMPSON, G. G. 1944. *Tempo and Modes in Evolution.* New York: Columbia University Press.

———. 1949. *The Meaning of Evolution.* New Haven: Yale University Press.

———. 1953. *The Major Features of Evolution.* New York: Columbia University Press.

SNELL, G. D. 1932. "The Role of Male Parthenogenesis in the Evolution of the Social Hymenoptera," *Amer. Naturalist,* LXVI, 381–84.

STEBBINS, G. L., JR. 1950. *Variation and Evolution in Plants.* New York: Columbia University Press.

STONE, D. E. 1959. "A Unique Balanced Breeding System in the Vernal Pool Mouse-Tails," *Evolution,* XIII, 151–74.

THODAY, J. M. 1953. "Components of Fitness," *Symp. Soc. Exper. Biol.,* VII, 96–113.

THOMPSON, W. R. 1956. "The Fundamental Theory of Natural and Biological Control," *Ann. Rev. Entomol.,* I, 379–402.

TINBERGEN, N. 1954. "The Origin and Evolution of Courtship and Threat Display." In J. HUXLEY, A. C. HARDY, and E. B. FORD (eds.), *Evolution as a Process,* pp. 233–49. London: Allen & Unwin.

ULLYETT, G. C. 1936. "Host Selection by *Microplectron fuscipennis* Zett. (Chalcidae Hymenoptera)," *Proc. Roy. Soc. London, B,* CXX, 253–91.

WADDINGTON, C. H. 1957. *The Strategy of the Genes.* New York: Macmillan Co.

WEBER, NEAL A. 1958. "Evolution in Fungus-Growing Ants," *Proc. Tenth Internat. Cong. Entomol.,* II, 459–73.

WEISMANN, A. 1893. "The All-Sufficiency of Natural Selection: A Reply to Herbert Spencer," *Contemporary Rev.,* LXIV, 309–38.

WHEELER, W. M. 1928. *The Social Insects—Their Origin and Evolution.* New York: Harcourt, Brace & Co.

———. 1930. *Demons of the Dust.* New York: W. W. Norton & Co.

WHITE, M. J. D. 1945. *Animal Cytology and Evolution.* Cambridge: Cambridge University Press.

WILLIAMS, G. C. 1957. "Pleiotrophy, Natural Selection, and the Evolution of Senescence," *Evolution,* XI, 398–411.

———. 1959. "Ovary Weights of Darters: A Test of the Alleged Association of Parental Care with Reduced Fecundity in Fishes," *Copeia,* 1959, pp. 18–24.

WILLIAMSON, A. A. 1958. *The Cosmic Function of Life.* New York: Vantage Press.

WRIGHT, S. 1932. "Roles of Mutation, Inbreeding, Crossbreeding and Selection in Evolution," *Proc. Sixth Internat. Cong. Genetics,* I, 356–66.

———. 1945. "Tempo and Mode in Evolution: A Critical Review," *Ecology,* XXVI, 415–19.

———. 1946. "Isolation by Distance under Diverse Systems of Mating," *Genetics,* XXXI, 39–59.

———. 1949. "Population Structure in Evolution," *Proc. Amer. Phil. Soc.,* XCIII, 471–78.

———. 1950. "Genetical Structure of Populations," *Nature,* CLXVI, 247–49.

———. 1956. "Modes of Selection," *Amer. Naturalist,* XC, 5–24.

ERNST MAYR

THE EMERGENCE OF EVOLUTIONARY NOVELTIES

There are fashionable problems and there are neglected problems in any field of research. The problem of the emergence of evolutionary novelties has undoubtedly been greatly neglected during the past two or three decades, in spite of its importance in the theory of evolution. No more auspicious occasion can be envisioned for a renewed consideration of this problem than the centenary of the publication of Darwin's *Origin of Species*. Darwin was fully aware of the importance of this question and devoted a great deal of attention to it. Indeed, his analysis in the sixth edition of the *Origin of Species* is superior to anything published during the ensuing thirty or forty years, and is still worth reading. Yet, in retrospect, it is evident that such a complex scientific problem could not have been solved in Darwin's day. It was necessary first to break it down into individual components and to find solutions for these components. This was not possible until we had gained an understanding of the nature of the genetic material and of the relation between genotype and phenotype.

The emphasis in Darwin's day was on the negative aspects of natural selection, that is, on its power to eliminate the unfit. This certainly could not account for new structures. But, even if one granted natural selection the power to improve existing organs, it would still leave us with the problem of the first origin of these organs. "How can natural selection explain the origin of entirely new structures?" asked Darwin's opponents. Is not evolution characterized by the continuous production of complete novelties, such as the lungs of vertebrates, the limbs of tetrapods, the wings of insects and birds, the inner ear of mammals, and literally thousands of structures in all the phyla of animals and plants? To explain this by a sudden saltation is unsatis-

ERNST MAYR is Agassiz Professor of Zoology at Harvard. His studies in ornithology, begun in his native Germany, brought him to the American Museum of Natural History, New York City, in 1931; he rose to the position of curator (1944–53). He is a past president of the Society for the Study of Evolution and former editor of *Evolution*. Of his extensive writings, perhaps his best-known text is *Methods and Principles of Systematic Zoology* (with E. G. Linsley and R. L. Usinger, 1953).

factory, because a major mutation would surely disturb the harmony of the type. Yet, it was asked, how can an entirely new structure originate without complete reconstruction of the entire type? And how can a new structure be gradually acquired when the incipient structure has no selective advantage until it has reached a considerable size and complexity?

These were some of the questions that bothered Darwin and that have continued to occupy the minds of evolutionists to the present day. Darwin, halfheartedly, took recourse to Lamarckian [1] explanations, and it is not surprising that during the remainder of the nineteenth century the origin of evolutionary novelties was ascribed to Lamarckian causes by the majority of evolutionists. Yet, as time went on, the fallacy of Lamarckian explanations became obvious, and the mutationism of De Vries and Bateson, no matter how wrong it was, was in a way a wholesome reaction against Lamarckism. At that period it seemed somehow impossible to find an interpretation that avoided the opposing evils of Lamarkism and saltationism.

The situation has changed greatly during the past fifty years. The saltationism of the early Mendelians has been refuted in all its aspects. Indeed, most of the evolutionary literature of recent decades has been devoted to the description and documentation of the gradual nature of all kinds of evolutionary changes. Hence the emphasis on allometry, on clines (in space and time), on polygenic systems, on genetic and developmental homeostasis, and on other manifestations of gradual change and of factors favoring it. This period, somehow, did not provide quite the right intellectual climate for the question "How does an evolutionary novelty emerge?" This question seemed, to antimutationist ears, to demand a mutationist answer. As a result, the problem of the emergence of evolutionary novelties has been almost completely neglected during the past two or three decades. However, with the advances in evolutionary theory that were being made during that same period, it is profitable to consider this question once again. It is now possible to give an answer not in conflict with the synthetic theory of evolution and, more specifically, an answer not requiring the occurrence of macromutations.

The treatment in a new attack on this problem will have to be somewhat exploratory at this stage, in view of the recent neglect of this area. I hope that my discussion will encourage more work and more thought on the problem of the origin of evolutionary novelties, permitting eventually a more balanced and definitive treatment.

[1] For the sake of simplicity I shall combine under the term "Lamarckian" all theories that postulate the occurrence of "induction" of directed genetic changes by the environment, by use, or by various other finalistic and vitalistic forces.

In order not to become diffuse, I shall deliberately ignore in my discussion certain aspects which have played a considerable role in previous discussions of the emergence of evolutionary novelties. One of these is the relation of non-genetic modification to changes of the phenotype. Another one is the problem of the role of developmental and age stages in evolutionary change. Like Rensch (1947), I feel that novelties can be incorporated into any stage and that the attempts to "explain" genetic and selective processes by all sorts of fancy terms like "pedogenesis," "palingenesis," "proterogenesis," and whatnot has had a stultifying effect on the analysis. The less said about this type of literature, the better. We can also eliminate from our discussion the entire large group of evolutionary phenomena dealing with regression and the loss of structures. They are entirely consistent with the synthetic theory of evolution.

What Are "Evolutionary Novelties"?

Our discussion will gain in precision if I state at the very beginning what I include in the category "evolutionary novelties." I include any newly arisen character, structural or otherwise, that differs more than quantitatively from the character that gave rise to it. Consequently, not every change of the phenotype qualifies, because change of size or of pigmentation would be a change of phenotype not necessarily qualifying as "emergence of an evolutionary novelty." What particular changes of the phenotype, then, would qualify? Certainly any change that would permit an organism to perform a new function. Tentatively, one might restrict the designation "evolutionary novelty" to any newly acquired structure or property which permits the assumption of a new function. This working definition must remain tentative until it is determined how often it is impossible to decide whether or not a given function is truly "new."

The exact definition of an "evolutionary novelty" faces the same insuperable difficulty as the definition of the species. As long as we believe in gradual evolution, we must be prepared to encounter immediate evolutionary stages. Equivalent to the cases in which it is impossible to decide whether a population is not yet a species or already a species, will be cases of doubt as to whether a structure is already or not yet an evolutionary novelty. The study of this difficult transition from the quantitative to the qualitative is precisely one of the objects of this paper. Unwillingness to face such a difficult situation is one of the reasons so many authors have adopted a saltationist interpretation.

The origin of new taxa, from species to higher categories, will be considered as lying outside the scope of this discussion. Even though, admittedly, the origin of new higher categories is often correlated with the emergence of a new structure or other character, the natures of the two problems are sufficiently different to necessitate separate treatment.

Even so, our scope is wide. In the days of classical comparative anatomy, the term "evolutionary novelty" referred unequivocally to a new structure. With the broadening of biology, attention has been directed to evolutionary novelties that are not morphological or at least not primarily morphological. New habits and behavior patterns are very often as important in evolution as are new structures. Their origins will not be dealt with, since so little is known about the evolution of behavior, even though it seems that the evolution of behavior patterns obeys the same laws as the evolution of structures. The study of cellular physiology (biochemistry of metabolic pathways) and of microorganisms has likewise demonstrated the occurrence of important evolutionary novelties which do not involve the origin of gross new structures such as lungs, extremities, or brood pouches. The uric acid and fat metabolism of the cleidoic egg of the terrestrial vertebrates is such an example. These are chemical innovations at the cellular level. Such cellular inventions have improved the efficiency of almost every organ. Granick (1953) has investigated some of the inventions necessary for the efficient functioning of iron metabolism in organisms possessing hemoglobin: (1) the change of a portion of the intestinal tract into an acid state (by HCl secretion) to permit the reduction of the inorganic iron in the food from the insoluble ferric to the soluble ferrous state; (2) an invention regulating uptake of ferrous iron by the mucosal cells of the intestines; (3) the invention of a special protein—siderophilin—which transports the iron from the capillaries of the intestinal tract to various storage places in the liver, spleen, and bone marrow; (4) the invention of still another protein—ferritin—which serves as a storage mechanism, for times of need (hemorrhage).

Smith (1953) described the numerous inventions characterizing excretion in the various classes of vertebrates. Sharks (elasmobranchs), for instance, prevent water loss to the surrounding sea water by reducing the renal excretion of urea whenever the urea concentration in the blood drops to as low as 2–2.5 per cent. This involves acquisition of special properties by two separate sets of cells: (a) The respiratory epithelium of the gills must become impermeable to urea so that it does not permit the urea molecules to diffuse into the surrounding sea water, and this without seriously impairing the permeability of this epithelium to oxygen and carbon dioxide. (b) The property of the cells of the renal tubules to recover the urea from the glomerular filtrate by tubular reabsorption. About 90 per cent of the urea lost from the blood by the renal glomeruli is thus saved from excretion.

Many similar biochemical inventions are recorded in the literature. They may have played a great role in the replacement of the major classes and phyla of the animal kingdom throughout geological history, but no one knows. Our knowledge of comparative physiology is still so elementary that we do not know, for instance, whether or not the cellular biochemical pathways of the mollusks give them superiority over the brachiopods, as one might suspect from a study of the geological record of these phyla. There is a wide field for comparative physiology and comparative biochemistry.

Evolutionary novelties on the cellular level tend to differ quite drastically, in several respects, from structural novelties. First of all, the genetic basis is usually simpler—indeed, a single gene mutation may be the primary basis of the novelty. Second, the new function may not require any reconstruction of the "type." No lengthy developmental pathway is involved which would necessitate an adjustment in the harmonious interaction of numerous genes. With the individual cell being the phenotype, the pathway from gene to phenotype is short and direct. Third, such a cellular invention more often than not will lead to an improvement of "general adaptation," whether it concerns respiration, digestion, excretion, or environmental tolerance, while a new structure frequently results in an adaptation to a more specialized situation. These average differences between "cellular" novelties and "structural" novelties are recorded in full cognizance of considerable overlap. For instance, new structures may also, on occasion, rest on a single primary mutation, and they may also lead to general rather than special adaptation. Yet the two classes of novelties are, as classes, rather different from each other. And the major evolutionary problem concerns the origin of new structures, since the preservation of gene mutations that permit adaptive improvement on the cellular level is no problem for the modern geneticist. Our discussion, then, will center on the origin of new structures.

THE ORIGIN OF NEW STRUCTURES

The comparative anatomist and paleontologist, when comparing related taxa, occasionally find what appears to be an entirely new structure. Examples that come readily to mind are the bird feather, the ear bones of mammals, the swim bladder of fish, the wings of insects, and the sting of aculeate Hymenoptera. As we shall presently see, one might argue in the case of most of these structures whether or not they are "really" new, and this is even more true for numerous other structures cited in the literature. The line between a quantitative and a qualitative change is not always sharply defined; indeed, to anticipate the outcome of our analysis, this border line is always indistinct. Far more structures were labeled as "entirely new" in Darwin's day, when the fossil record was less completely known and when far less was known, than today, about homologies among distant relatives. The "sudden" origin of new structures as indicated in Darwin's day by the evidence appeared quite incompatible with gradual improvement of the type through natural selection. And yet gradual improvement was the interpretation which Darwin continued to advance in the face of all the attacks by antiselectionists. It soon became evident that ultimately there were only two alternative interpretations: appearance of evolutionary novelties by sudden saltation or by gradual emergence. Dispute over these alternatives has continued to the present day.

THE ORIGIN OF NOVELTIES BY SALTATION

The saltationists' theories in evolution have many roots, some of them going as far back as Plato's ideology (Mayr, 1959). Indeed, all saltationists have been typologists, and most typologists have been saltationists of one sort or another. Genuine variation and gradual change are, of course, incompatible with the typological viewpoint. One of the usual arguments of the typologists is that organs and structures form a harmonious whole, characterizing an entire morphological type, like the mollusks, coelenterates, or vertebrates, and that new structures could have arisen simultaneously only with the origin of these new, major types. Furthermore, the typologist argues, since the origin of these types goes back to the early Cambrian or pre-Cambrian (antedating the fossil record), it will never be possible to explain the origin of new structures. Admittedly, it may never be possible to reconstruct the origin of the chordates or of the arthropods on the basis of their fossil record, but this is no reason for defeatism. Some of the "minor" types, such as birds or mammals, differ strikingly in many structures from the groups from which they have arisen, and yet we have a fairly good fossil record indicating the pathway of the changes. There is already sufficient material available to describe the way in which many "evolutionary novelties" have come into being.

The theory of the origin of new structures by saltation was strong in Darwin's day and was an important component in the antiselectionist argument of his opponents. Chief among these was Mivart (1871), who devoted an entire volume, *The Genesis of Species,* to a point-by-point refutation of Darwin. The problem of the origin of new structures is one of Mivart's major concerns. This is of special interest to the student of Darwin, because most of the major revisions which

Darwin made in the sixth edition of the *Origin of Species* (1872) were rebuttals of Mivart's arguments. Mivart was a saltationist who assumed, for instance, that the differences between the extinct, three-toed *Hipparion* and the horse (*Equus*) had arisen suddenly. He thought it difficult to believe that the wing of a bird "was developed any other way than by a comparatively sudden modification of a marked and important kind," and he applied the same explanation to the wings of bats and pterodactyls. Darwin (1872, p. 261) opposed this assumption quite emphatically: "This conclusion, which implies great breaks or discontinuity in the series, appears to me improbable in the highest degree." He supports his objection by arguing: "He who believes that some ancient form was transformed suddenly through an internal force or tendency, into, for instance, one furnished with wings, will be almost compelled to assume . . . that many individuals varied simultaneously." The absurdity of believing in the simultaneous appearance of numerous "hopeful monsters" was far more clearly appreciated (p. 265) by Darwin than by some recent evolutionists, and yet such a multiple origin would be a necessity in sexual organisms. That the saltationist theory produces far more difficulties than it explains was pointed out by Darwin in the following words (p. 265):

He will further be compelled to believe that many structures beautifully adapted to all the other parts of the same creature and to the surrounding conditions, have been suddenly produced; and of such complex and wonderful co-adaptations, he will not be able to assign a shadow of an explanation. He will be forced to admit that these great and sudden transformations have left no trace of their action on the embryo. To admit all this is, as it seems to me, to enter the realms of miracle and to leave those of science.

Darwin's contention is fully supported by modern genetics. If one had to rely on mutation pressure as the only evolutionary factor, one would need such a high rate of mutation that it would result in an enormous production of "hopeful monsters." All available evidence is opposed to such an assumption. Indeed, most mutations appear to have only a slight, if not an invisible, effect on the phenotype. More penetrant mutations are usually disruptive and produce disharmonious phenotypes, as correctly implied by Darwin, and will therefore be selected against. The real function of mutation is to replenish the gene pool and to provide material for recombination as a source of individual variability in populations.

It took a long time until this role of mutation was clearly appreciated. The "one character–one mutation" reasoning, implicit in much thinking of the Darwinian period, was made the basis of a major evolutionary theory, the mutationism of the early Mendelians (De Vries,

Bateson). According to this theory, any new character, any new species, any new higher category, comes into being through mutation. The genetic work of the last four decades has refuted mutationism (saltationism) so thoroughly that it is not necessary to repeat once more all the genetic evidence against it. Most important, of course, is realization that the phenotype (in higher organisms) is the product of a long developmental pathway and that any part of it, any "character," depends on the harmonious interaction of many, if not all, of the genes of the organism. A mutation affecting one of the numerous genes contributing to the phenotype of a character will have only a minor effect, or, if it has a major one, such drastic interference with the harmony of development will almost certainly be deleterious.

There has been much confusion in the literature on the purely semantic problem of how to define a "big" mutation. It seems to me that this must be measured not in terms of visible change but in terms of adjustment to the environment. When speaking of the "bigness" of a mutation, we must specify whether we are speaking of the level of the gene (amount of reorganization of the DNA), the level of the phenotype, or the level of the resulting fitness. A mutation which affects a growth pattern, such as branching in a plant or a sessile invertebrate, may produce drastic visible changes in the phenotype without much effect on fitness. Individuals of corals with different types of septa could well coexist in a single, interbreeding population, as could graptolites, with different systems of branching, or ammonites, with different patterns of lobe formation. A sinistral and a dextral snail are conspicuously different from each other, and yet the slight shift in the direction of the mitotic spindle causing this shift, as well as the ultimate difference in phenotype, is not likely to have drastic effects on selective values, unless the shift interferes with the interbreeding of dextral and sinistral individuals. Such changes in growth pattern may have a very small differential on the cellular level and be of negligible selective significance, regardless of the considerable phenotypic difference. It would seem to me that it is on the cellular level that a single mutation may be of the greatest effect. The emergence of evolutionary novelties due to a single mutation will occur most likely among microorganisms or, indeed, all unicellular organisms of simple structure.

This conclusion does not deny that a single mutation may add to the fitness of an organism or make it better adapted for a slightly different environmental niche. Huxley (1942, pp. 52, 118, 449) has cited numerous mutations which affect temperature tolerance, growth rate, fecundity, seasonal adjustment, and other components of fitness. The recent literature on balanced polymorphism has added many other cases. Industrial melanism (Kettlewell, 1959) is a specially well-analyzed example of the fitness-enhancing property of single genes. Wherever soot darkens the bark of trees, the melanic moths gain a cryptic advantage over the normally pale-colored individuals of the species. If one is so inclined, one may call the incorporation of any such mutation into a population an emergence of an evolutionary novelty. To me it seems, however, that this would dilute beyond all usefulness a legitimate phenomenon, that of the emergence of new structures. The stated genetic changes lead usually only to what I have called (Mayr, 1956) "ecotypic adaptation," not to a shift of phylogenetic significance.

THE GRADUAL ACQUISITION OF NEW STRUCTURES

The evidence, whether genetic, morphological, or functional, is so uniformly opposed to a saltationist origin of new structures that no choice is left but to search for explanations in terms of a gradual origin. The role of natural selection in evolution would indeed be a very inferior one if, as was believed by the saltationists, it did nothing but weed out "hopeless monsters" in favor of "hopeful monsters." Darwin was fully aware of this situation: "If it could be demonstrated that any complex organ existed which could not possibly have been formed by numerous, successive, slight modifications, my theory would absolutely break down. But I can find out no such cases" (p. 191). Yet the problem remains of how to push a structure above the threshold where it has a selective advantage. The problem of the emergence of evolutionary novelties then consists in having to explain how a sufficient number of small gene mutations can be accumulated until the new structure has become sufficiently large to have selective value. Or is there an explanation which avoids this troublesome threshold problem? This has been discussed by a number of authors, usually under the heading "the origin of adaptations." The publications of Sewertzoff (1931), Huxley (1942), Rensch (1947), and Davis (1949) might be mentioned as recent works devoting special attention to this problem. The following possibilities of the origin of new structures are apparent:

The new structure originates (*a*) as a pleiotropic by-product of a changing genotype, (*b*) as a result of an intensification of function, or (*c*) owing to a change of function.

Pleiotropic by-product.—This hypothesis assumes that not all phenotypic expressions of pleiotropic genes have a definite selective value but that a "natural" character may subsequently acquire selective value under certain circumstances. Darwin suggests (p. 94) that plants may excrete some sweet liquid accidentally from the flower and that this would in time lead to a well-organized system of pollination by insects. The secretion of nectar may well have such an accidental origin; yet Darwin seems to have forgotten that the collecting of pollen was undoubtedly the original reason for the visit of flowers by insects. Nectar is merely an additional "bonus." The first bump in the frontal region of rhinoceroses and titanotheres which subsequently led to their elaborate horns may have been such a pleiotropic by-product. Davis (1949) suggests another case:

In the carnivora the panniculus carnosus muscle inserts in the axilla, along with the pectoral musculature, as in other mammals. The mustelids (weasels and their allies) differ from all other carnivores in having a slip of the panniculus pass to the outer surface of the upper arm. No functional advantage can be assigned to this mustelid aberration. In the badger (*Taxidea*), which is a powerful burrowing mustelid, this slip is larger, ties the elbow down to the body, and inserts on the acromion process of the scapula. It thus aids in tying the scapula down, an important consideration in the absence of a clavicle. The condition of the panniculus in other mustelids is obviously preadaptive for the functional arrangement in the badger [p. 85].

Darwin suggests that some of the variation in the structure of the spines of sea urchins may have led to the development of the pedicellarias (p. 249). Even though it is very probable that neutral genes do not exist, there is no reason for denying the possibility of neutral aspects of the phenotype, that is, "neutral characters." The many differences among phenotypes which are independent but equivalent selective responses to the same functional needs (see below under "Multiple Pathways") indicate the existence of a certain amount of morphological leeway in the selective response. To be sure, it may be impossible to prove whether or not a minor structure has selective significance.

Intensification of function.—Most evolutionary changes take place without the origin of new structures. Even when we compare birds or mammals with their strikingly different reptilian ancestors, we are astonished at how few are the truly new structures. Most differences are merely shifts in proportions, fusions, losses, secondary duplications, and similar changes which do not materially affect what the morphologist calls the "plan" of the particular type. An intensification of the running function has led to a conversion of the five-toed mammalian foot (or hand) to the two-toed foot of the artiodactyls or the one-toed foot of the perissodactyls. Many glands are the result of intensified function and local concentration of previously scattered secretory cells. The intensification of function in these cases does not lead to the emergence of anything that is basically new, and yet it may result in a reorganization of the phenotype so drastic that the first impression is that of the emergence of an entirely new organ. Of importance to the evolutionist is the fact that no essentially new selection pressure is involved but merely the intensification of a previously existing selection pressure. At no time is there a stage in which "the incipient structure is not yet of selective value," to cite a frequently heard objection of the antiselectionists. Sewertzoff (1931, pp. 183–236) has made a special analysis of this process of intensification of function. Darwin was fully aware of it. In fact, he used this principle to explain the origin of what is, perhaps, the most complex of all structures, the eye.

"To suppose that the eye, with all its inimitable contrivances for adjusting the focus to different distances, for admitting different amounts of light, and for the correction of spherical and chromatic aberration, could have been formed by natural selection, seems, I freely confess, absurd in the highest degree" (p. 187). But then he shows, step by step, that this "difficulty" should not be considered "insuperable." The evolution of the eye ultimately hinges on one particular property of certain types of protoplasm—photosensitivity. This is the key to the whole selection process. Once one admits that the possession of such photosensitivity may have selective value, all else follows by necessity. And if one visualizes the enormous number of extinct organisms—we know only the smallest fraction of them— "the difficulty ceases to be very great in believing that natural selection may have converted the simple apparatus of an optic nerve, coated with pigment and invested by transparent membrane, into an optical instrument as perfect as is possessed by any member of the Articulate Class" (p. 189).

It is somewhat oversimplified to explain the origin of the eye in terms of an intensification of the function of a piece of optic nerve. Yet there is a correct nucleus in this claim. In other cases the situation is far more clear-cut. The improvement of a single key component of a structure may result in an "evolutionary avalanche." Schaeffer (1948), for instance, showed that an improvement in the mechanical efficiency of the tarsal joint in a group of Condylyarthra, occurring during a period of about 15 million years, gave rise to the highly characteristic foot structure of the artiodactyl ungulates. No really new structure originated, only a shift of proportions and positions, accompanied by an ever increasing efficiency of function.

A similar improvement of a structure is the conversion of an orthodox mammalian claw in one line of taeniodont mammals into an efficient digging claw. This resulted in sufficient adaptive shift and increased success to set off a whole series of correlated changes in dentition and skull structure (Patterson, 1949, p. 262). Yet this taeniodont digging claw is not an entirely new structure.

It is often difficult to say to what extent a structure is new or merely an improvement on an old one. Let us take, for instance, the evolution of the cleiodoic egg, which enabled the reptiles to complete the shift initiated by the amphibians, from water to land (Needham, 1931, p. 1132). This shift is characterized not only by the acquisition of a hard shell and of new embryonic membrance (amnion, allantois) but also by certain changes in the metabolism of the egg. The uric acid catabolism permits an easy elimination of waste products without poisoning the embryo. Likewise, the shift from a largely protein to an essentially fat metabolism has numerous obvious advantages for a cleiodoic egg. As stated above, clear-cut shifts, such as in these metabolic processes, are most often observed on the cellular-molecular level.

The area indicated by the term "intensification of function" is large and ought to be subdivided. However, I am not entirely certain that the subdivisions proposed by Sewertzoff are the best possible ones. What is needed at the present time, more than anything else, is the collecting of many cases falling under this category from all groups of animals and plants, preparatory to a more detailed analysis.

Change of function.—By far the most important principle in the interpretation of the origin of new structures is that of the "change of function." The discovery of this principle is usually ascribed to Anton Dohrn (1875), but it was clearly recognized and sufficiently emphasized by Darwin, whom Dohrn cites in his essay, in the sixth edition of the *Origin of Species* (1872). Two subsequent authors who have made a special analysis of this principle are Plate (1924) and Sewertzoff (1931). The latter distinguishes no less than seven subdivisions or separate forms of change of function, a scheme which does not seem to add appreciably to an understanding of the problem. Indeed, it makes it appear more complex than it is.

Darwin recognized quite clearly that the possibility for a change of function usually depended on two prerequisites. The first of these is that a structure or an organ can simultaneously perform two functions. "Numerous cases could be given amongst the lower animals of the same organ performing at the same time wholly distinct functions" (p. 191). The other one is the principle of duplication. "Again, two distinct organs, or the same organ under two very different forms, may simultaneously perform in the same individual the same function, and this is an extremely important means of transition" (p. 192). As an example he quotes the fish that were ancestral to the tetrapods and had two separate organs of respiration—gills and primitive lungs.

A change of function is easily explained on the basis of these two premises, either a simultaneous multiple functioning of a single structure or the performance of the same function in different or duplicated organs. For this there are several alternative possibilities. The second structure may secondarily acquire a new function, and this new accessory function may eventually become the primary function. Or if two structures have two simultaneous functions from the beginning, one of them may become the primary and eventually exclusive function for one of the structures, and the other function in the second structure. This second structure is in many cases a simple duplication of the first. The duplication of structures is a frequent phenomenon in segmented, as well as in radially symmetrical, organisms. Morphologists, however, know that it can also take place independently of segmentation. "It occurs quite often, that a primarily undivided organ, a part of the skeleton, a muscle, or a nerve, is divided in the course of phylogeny and that several more or less independent organs originate in this manner" (Sewertzoff, p. 232). Sewertzoff's "similation" and Gregory's (1934) "polyisomerism" are related phenomena.

Dohrn (1875, p. 62) cites the gizzard (muscular stomach) of birds to illustrate the principle of change of function. An unspecialized vertebrate stomach has two functions—the secretion of stomach juice (containing digestive enzymes, etc.) and the mixing of the stomach contents to facilitate digestion. Secretory glands and muscle fibers are thus the functionally important structural elements of this "multipurpose" organ. Dohrn says:

Let us now imagine a differentiation of this stomach, so that the glands and their secretion would greatly increase in one part of the stomach, while the musculature would be strengthened in another part, so that pressure could be exerted against the larger food particles. We would have the first beginning of a change of function in such a differentiation. Let us now assume that the purely mechanical function of moving food around, already present in the original stomach, became so dominant in this second part of the stomach, that the primary function of secreting stomach juice became increasingly pushed into the background in this part of the stomach. We would have a stomach in due time which would correspond to the gizzard of seed-eating birds in which the main function is no longer its chemical task, but rather the mechanical comminution of the ingested seeds. Even the mucous membrane will change under the impact of this new primary function. It no longer secretes stomach juice, but its epidermis becomes horny and firm, permitting the grinding of seeds. A secondary structural element has thus been added to the primary one of the muscles.

And he continues by emphasizing that in this whole division of the originally single stomach into a glandular and a muscular stomach no really new element had arisen. The entire conversion was made possible by a modification of pre-existing structural elements. I have quoted this case in full, to permit an insight into the thinking of the pioneers in this field.

How the duplicated structure arose initially is not always completely clear. The origin of the mammalian middle ear may be a case in point. The location on the prearticular bone of a tympanic ring in a South American Triassic mammal-like reptile indicates that this organism had, simultaneously, two tympanic membranes. One of these was the original reptilian tympanic membrane; the other, lying in front of it, was a secondary window, the presence of which may have facilitated sound transfer in these rather heavy-boned creatures. The origin of the second window was part of a slow reconstruction of the jaw and ear region in this branch of the reptiles, one change leading, by necessity, to the next. It appears that the functional value and hence selective significance of the primary (reptilian) tympanic membrane deteriorated at a subsequent stage following the reorganization of the jaw articulation. The stage was now set for a gradual obliteration of the primary tympanic membrane and the transfer of its function to the secondary membrane.

In all the cases known to us, in which there is a transfer of function from one structure to a duplicate one, there is always a transitional stage during which both structures function simultaneously. This is, for instance, well established for the transfer of respiration in the fish-amphibian series from the gills to the lungs. It has recently been demonstrated for the double jaw articulation of birds (Bock, 1959).

Not only was Darwin aware of the principle, but he cites several illustrations of such a change of function. Perhaps the most frequently quoted one in the evolutionary literature is the shift of function between swim bladder and lungs. Darwin, like the majority of writers since his time, assumed that the swim bladder was the original condition.

"The illustration of the swimbladder in fishes is a good one, because it shows us clearly the highly important fact that an organ originally constructed for one purpose . . . may be converted into one for a widely different purpose" (p. 192). Recent discoveries among fossil fishes have shown that diverticles of the respiratory tract first functioned in them as primitive lungs and only secondarily, in some fishes, as swim bladders. This, however, does not affect the correctness of Darwin's statement that this organ is involved in a transfer of function.

Darwin continued: "In considering transitions of organs, it is so important to bear in mind the probability of conversion from one function to another, that I will give another instance" (p. 193). He then cites the case of egg-carrying folds in one family of cirripedes which become respiratory gills in another family, owing to a change of function.

One would never have been able to trace the pathway of this change if the more primitive family had become extinct. "If all pedunculated cirripedes (with the egg-bearing folds) had become extinct . . . who would ever have imagined that the branchiae (gills) in this latter family had originally existed as organs for preventing the ova from being washed out of the sack?" (p. 194).

Such cases of a change in function are legion. The cited cases are given merely as illustrations of the stated principles. To give a complete catalogue would mean listing a good portion of all animal structures. The change of the ovipositor of bees into a sting, the development of the thyroid from the endostyle, of teeth from scales, and of various parts of the angiosperm flower are other examples. The electric organs in fish, so puzzling to Darwin, also belong here. Lissman (1958) presents suggestive indirect evidence that the electric field created by the contracting muscles is utilized in orientation, gradually evolves into a regular series of pulses, and eventually to the shock discharges, which in some species have such powerful offensive and defensive effects. The muscles are converted during this evolution into electric organs, as the subsidiary function becomes the primary function.

Another celebrated case of a change of function is that of the first dorsal ray of the angler fishes, described by Gregory and Conrad (1936) and by Günther and Deckert (1950) primarily on the basis of the work of Regan and Trewavas (1932). In some of these species it becomes a lure, but in the deep-sea anglers a most interesting sexual dimorphism evolves. In the females this ray becomes a luminescent organ, a lantern; in the males, however, it moves forward until it is incorporated in a character complex with the teeth of the upper jaw or becomes entirely functionless. To the same category belong all structural changes resulting in sexual dimorphism. The pedipalps of male spiders, the chelae of certain crustaceans (e.g., fiddler crabs), the plumes of birds of paradise, and the copulatory organs of fishes with internal fertilization are well-known examples.

Let me describe one further shift of function (Cowles, 1958). In all vertebrates there is a good deal of cutaneous vascularization. In the fishes and particularly in the amphibians this system is involved in dermal respiration and accounts, particularly in the amphibians, for a major component of the oxygen uptake. In the ectothermal reptilians it serves as an organ of heat uptake and heat discharge. Finally, in the warm-blooded animals it plays an important role in the maintenance of a constant body temperature. Here is an organ system which has undergone comparatively little morphological change but has several times acquired a new major function because it was preadapted for this new function in the new environment.

The case of cutaneous vascularization proves also that a change of function is not always tied to a duplication of structures. This is also true if a structure serving locomotion undergoes a change in function or a shift to a new primary function. The anterior extremity of unspecialized mammals serves several functions. In addition to its primary function of ordinary terrestrial locomotion, it may be used for digging, swimming, or, in arboreal gliders, for gliding (with the help of a patagium). The intensification of such a secondary function has led to such greatly modified structures as the shovel arm of the moles (*Talpa,* etc.), the flipper whales (with secondary polyisomerism), and the wing of bats.

The two situations here described differ only in minor detail. In one case the structure exists in duplicate, and a new function is acquired by the duplicated structure. In the other case a secondary function is added to the primary function without duplication of structure. Both cases have the essential feature in common: that an existing structure is preadapted to assume a new function without interference with the original function. This is preadaptation, as now understood (Bock, 1959).

The term "preadaptation" has been applied to diverse concepts. It was coined by Cuénot during the heyday of mutationism. All evolutionary change at that time was believed to be due to major saltations, and the new "hopeful monster" (as Goldschmidt later called it) was either preadapted for a new niche or doomed to immediate extinction. Preadaptation in the modern theory of gradual evolution is something quite different from the concept held by the mutationists.

Discussions on the significance of preadaptation will gain greatly in precision if a distinction is made between preadaptation for a functional shift and that for a habitat shift. In the first case, a single structure is involved which can assume a new function while still carrying out the primary function. Illustrations of this are the wing of a diving bird, preadapted to become a paddle; or the primitive lungs of the early fishes are adapted to become a hydrostatic mechanism (swim bladder); or the large antennae of the cladocerans, preadapted to become paddles.

On the other hand, an organism, as a whole, may be preadapted to undertake a major habitat shift. The aquatic branch of the vertebrates that gave rise to the first partially terrestrial amphibians must not only have had a crawling locomotion, but must also have been partially air-breathing and have had other characteristics of skeleton, epidermis, and sense organs which preadapted them for the habitat shift. The Proavis must have had a considerable number of structural characteristics, such as a light body build and partial bipedalism along with well-developed anterior extremities, to have been preadapted for flight. Admittedly, the preadaptation of a whole organism for an entirely new adaptive zone grades rather insensibly into the limited preadaptation for a single new function; yet it may be useful to distinguish categorically between these two kinds of preadaptations.

The selective value of incipient structures.—This discussion of the multiple function of structures and of the consequent preadaptation of structures for new functions has prepared us for a consideration of an old antiselectionist objection. It claims that many structures could not possibly have had any selective value until these structures were sufficiently large and elaborate to perform the function that gives them selective advantage. If selection is not responsible for getting them through this "incipient stage," what else can it be but some kind of "internal force?" This claim of an absence of selective value in an incipient structure was one of the strongest arguments in Mivart's (1871) attempt to refute Darwin. He devotes the entire second chapter of his book on the *Genesis of Species* to the "incompetence of natural selection to account for the incipient stages of useful structures." This is an eminently reasonable account, which cites many structures like the baleens of large plankton-feeding whales and the milk glands of mammals, a gradual origin of which is indeed not easily imagined. Darwin was struck by the strength of these arguments and went to great lengths to refute them in the sixth edition of the *Origin of Species*. The debate between the two authors is still of interest in our day, even though it is very apparent that both contestants were misled by their belief in blending inheritance and by a lack of appreciation of the statistical nature of natural selection.

It is now easy to see that two different types of phenomena are involved. Some new structures are advantageous from the very beginning. Darwin (p. 230) counters quite effectively Mivart's claim that the lengthening of the neck in the giraffe could not have been brought about by natural selection. Darwin shows that an ability to reach higher branches would be most useful in a continent like Africa that is overrun by grazing and browsing ungulates. One might add that, no doubt, the detection of lions in the high grass is likewise facilitated by the lengthening of the neck. That this could have come about gradually and that every increase might well have been of selective advantage can be asserted with good reason. Indeed, this example of Mivart's is not particularly well chosen because only a rather slight modification of an already existing structure is involved, and not the origin of a new structure.

An immediate selective value is, however, evident even in some cases of genuinely new organs. Let us consider this in connection with the lungs of fishes. Their earliest recorded occurrence is in the Antiarchi (Denison, 1941), in which a pair of sacs with a common duct grows out from the floor of the pharynx. *Polypterus,* one of the most primitive actinopterygians, and some of the choanichthyians also have ventral "lungs." These are obviously primitive structures, preceding in time the dorsal swim bladder of the advanced actinopterygian fishes (Goodrich, 1930). How were the first ventral lungs of fishes developed? It can be assumed that oxygen uptake took place in the lowest fishes through all membranes, external skin, gills, and intestinal tract. As the outer skin became increasingly unsuitable for gas exchange (partly owing to the development of dermal armor) and, even more importantly, as the gills became temporarily rather useless in oxygen-poor stagnant swamps during Devonian drought periods, active air uptake by "air-swallowing" became at times the most important source of oxygen. At this stage, any enlargement of the surface of the inner throat or esophagus, any formation of diverticles, etc., was favored by natural selection. It is apparent that such a ventral diverticle from the floor of the pharynx was the beginning of the respiratory system of the higher vertebrates. At this early stage, however, it was not truly a new organ, but merely an enlargement (an "intensification," as Sewertzoff would say) of an existing organ: the total internal membranaceous surface used for oxygen uptake. This rather rudimentary organ was exposed to a renewed and increased selection pressure when the tetrapods became truly terrestrial. This shift of habitat resulted in the elaborate lungs of mammals and birds.

In a similar manner it can be shown for many structures that they must have been useful from the very beginning. This is true for almost any of the improvements of the digestive apparatus and all mechanisms having to do with heat regulation. It is presumably true for the majority of improvements on the cellular level. It is, however, also true for certain aspects of the general phenotype. Experimental work on mimicry and warning coloration have shown that exceedingly slight changes may be of selective value. It would seem inconceivable that the elaborate "eyes" on the hind wing of certain moths, serving so effectively as warning patterns, could be the result of selection. Yet Blest (1957*a, b*) has shown that the sudden revelation of a very simple contrasting spot on the hind wings has considerable protective value.

Opposed to these evolutionary novelties which add to fitness from the very beginning are others which one cannot consider useful until they have reached a certain size or perfection. Many of the novelties which we have discussed above under "Change of Function" belong in this category. Allowing for the various auxiliary assumptions mentioned above, it becomes apparent in one case after another how an incipient structure could have continued to evolve until it was large enough to assume a new function. Mivart's argument that natural selection is incompetent to account for the early stages of useful structures has now lost most of its force.

One of the questions of Darwin's opponents was Why are not more "transitional stages" of new structures found in nature? Darwin was able to counter this objection rather easily (p. 183):

Animals displaying early transitional grades of the same structure will seldom have survived to the present day, for they will have been supplanted by their successors, which were gradually rendered more perfect through natural selection. Furthermore we may conclude that transitional states between structures fitted for varying habits of life will rarely have been developed at an early period in great numbers and under many subordinate forms.

We would say, nowadays, that adaptive radiation will not take place until after the evolutionary novelty has reached a certain degree of perfection. Furthermore, until after such adaptive radiation and increase in numbers have taken place, it is unlikely that forms representing intermediate stages will be sufficiently common to be encountered in the scanty fossil record.

The Environmental Situation

With the fossil record preserving only the morphology of organs, it is natural that the morphological aspects are always stressed in the discussion of the origin of new organs. However, as Sewertzoff has said so correctly, "The morphological change of structure in an organ is important for a species only to the extent that it achieves an improvement in the function of this organ" and thus adds to the fitness of the species. Yet a change in function may precede a structural reorganization, or the selective value of a structure may change, owing to a change in selection pressures caused by a change in the environment. No discussion of the emergence of evolutionary novelties can be considered exhaustive which does not include a treatment of the environmental situation. Indeed, most evolutionary changes of structures cannot be fully understood without an analysis of the accompanying environmental changes. What categories of environmental change may be important in the origin of evolutionary novelties? And what type of adaptive change would occur most frequently in response to each class of environmental change?

CHANGES IN THE PHYSICAL OR BIOTIC SURROUNDINGS

The environment is never constant. There are always climatic changes, among which long-term climatic trends are particularly important. There are general vegetational trends, as well as specific extinctions or invasions of individual species. There is the steady coming of new sources of food, new competitors, and new enemies and the steady loss of old ones. The organism is, more or less passively, exposed to all these changes and must be prepared to cope with them. Our knowledge of historical ecology is still too slight to permit detailed description of the effects of such changes on individual species and their adaptations. As a general rule, one might suggest that broad, general adaptations will prove most useful in coping with secular changes of the environment. Darwin has already commented on the superior fitness of the species that live on continents in the midst of ever changing faunas and floras. This is not the place to follow up the nature of this adaptation to broad tolerance and ever changing conditions.

THE INVASION OF A NEW NICHE OR ADAPTIVE ZONE

The active shift of an organism into a novel niche or entirely new adaptive zone will set up a powerful array of new selection pressures. An organism must have a special set of characteristics to cope with the demands of the new environment. It must be "preadapted" for the new world in which it will henceforth live. The change from water-living to land-living is a particularly instructive illustration of this. Indeed, the combination of properties permitting terrestrial locomotion and respiration and preventing desiccation is sufficiently improbable or unique to have been mastered only a very few times. The number of independent invasions of land by animals (vertebrates, several arthropods, and mollusks) is incredibly small in spite of the rich opportunities of the plant-covered land, opportunities made particularly apparent by the prodigious adaptive radiation of those animals that successfully accomplished the shift. Among all the marine animals, only benthonic ones, because they already lived a somewhat "terrestrial" life underwater, were able to emerge onto land. The peculiar pedunculated fins of the crossopterygian fishes, presumably used in part for moving along rocks and over the bottom, were ideally preadapted for locomotion along land. A similar situation is probable for the arthropods (Manton, 1953).

The adaptation of the extremities for a shift from aquatic to terrestrial environments is a case in which a structure may be able to function in two adaptive zones in an essentially similar manner. In the case of the heavily vascularized skin of amphibians, reptiles, and warm-blooded vertebrates (Cowles, 1958), an organ acquires a new function without any drastic reconstruction.

Perhaps most astonishing is the relative slightness of reconstruction that seems to be necessary for successful adaptation to rather drastic shifts of adaptive zones.

There is every reason to believe that the group of reptiles ancestral to the birds already had feathers, even though they had been acquired either for temperature control, as an epigamic character, or in some other way not connected with flight. These Proaves were furthermore preadapted in being arboreal, bipedal, and furnished with well-developed, functional anterior extremities. They had all the necessary equipment for becoming a flying machine, and not a single major new structure has appeared in the birds since they branched off from the reptiles. This, of course, does not belittle the many modifications in the bird skeleton, musculature, central nervous system, and sense organs. All these are avian modifications of the reptilian heritage, not the origin of entirely new structures.

No niche is too aberrant or too forbidding to preclude invasion. The bathypelagic niche is one of the most specialized and in some ways most demanding habitats open to living organisms; its fauna comes from two sources, surface pelagic and deep-sea bottom (bathy-benthonic). That the deep-sea-bottom fauna should produce pelagic descendants seems particularly unexpected; yet it has been clearly established as the source of some of the most extraordinary inhabitants of the oceans, such as pelagic holothurians and octopuses.

Whenever a novel type of ecological niche is explored by naturalists, a new fauna is discovered in it. The more aberrant the niche, the more extraordinary its fauna. The psammofauna of the interstitial spaces in sea-bottom sand, discovered by Remane, is a typical example. Who would have expected to find a jellyfish in such a habitat?! And yet this medusa (*Halammohydra*) has become completely adapted to this niche, which would at first sight appear to be totally unsuitable for it. Any textbook of ecology will give further examples of such niches, like hot springs, alkali flats, oil puddles, shifting sand dunes, and caves, that have been successfully colonized by organisms.

Each of these major shifts of habitat is a major evolutionary experiment. Each of the successful branches of the animal kingdom, e.g., the insects, the tetrapods, the birds, is a product of such a shift. However, not all such shifts are equally successful. No spectacular adaptive radiation has followed the invasion of the sand niche by a coelenterate. The shift of a carnivore to a herbivorous diet (Giant Panda) has not led to a new phylogenetic breakthrough (Davis, 1949, p. 84). The tree kangaroos, the return of a specialized line of terrestrial marsupials to arboreal life, likewise seems to have reached an evolutionary dead end. The penguins, on the other hand, in a really extraordinary conquest of the aquatic niche by birds, may be considered reasonably successful, to judge from the enormous size of the penguin populations.

Potentialities of primitive and specialized types.—There has been much speculation in the evolutionary literature as to whether a "primitive" or a "specialized" creature has a higher evolutionary potential. Cope (1896, p. 172) proposed the "law of the unspecialized," according to which every specialization is a dead-end street and true evolutionary advance is to be expected only from amorphous, unspecialized forms. This generalization is certainly not supported by the known evolutionary facts. Most major evolutionary advances depended on a shift into a new adaptive zone, and the feasibility of this shift, in turn, depended on available preadaptations. There is certainly nothing "unspecialized" about the earliest fishes and particularly about those that gave rise to the tetrapods. And those reptiles that gave rise to the mammals and birds were certainly as specialized in their way, or more so, than branches of the reptiles which did not give rise to successful offshoots or are still surviving. On the other hand, some of the nonspecialized "primitive" groups seem to be so successful in surviving that their evolutionary potential is questionable. For example, the opossum (*Didelphis*) represents an ancient group that goes back to the Eocene or earlier and that gave rise to most of the marsupial fauna of Australia and Tertiary South America. Yet many, if not most, of these specialized derivatives have become extinct while *Didelphis* continues to survive and to be quite successful, even though it has remained essentially unchanged. It is therefore completely correct to stress the success of many unspecialized forms, but it is wrong to claim that they are the only forms with a future. Amadon (1943) and Romer (1946) have correctly emphasized the importance of specialization for evolutionary progress. This, of course, does not mean that every specialization will preadapt to the conquest of new adaptive zones. One may state that most specializations lead into dead-end alleys; yet new conquests could not be made without incessant experimentation.

One of the reasons for the former insistence on the "unspecialized" was archetypal thinking. When reconstructing the common ancestor of several evolutionary lines, those who are addicted to archetypal thinking tend to eliminate all specializations. As a result, all their putative ancestors are in every respect generalized and unspecialized. It never seems to have occurred to these students that the creatures they reconstructed in this manner could never have existed in nature. Nor did it ever occur to them that this method would lead to the establishment of phylogenies in which all fossils were always aberrant side lines. Osborn's (1936) phylogenetic tree of the proboscidians is a typical example of this way of thinking.

To sum up the evolutionary aspects of a shift into a new niche or adaptive zone: such a shift can occur only if the organism is pre-adapted for it. However, as soon as the shift has been achieved, a whole new set of selection pressures will tend to modify all those structures that are particularly concerned with life in the new environment. The more drastic the change in environment, the more rapid will be the evolutionary change and the more far-reaching, in general, the structural reorganization.

A CHANGE IN BEHAVIOR

A shift into a new niche or adaptive zone requires, almost without exception, a change in behavior. In the days of mutationism (De Vries, Bateson), there was much heated argument over the question whether structure precedes habit or vice versa. The choice was strictly between saltationism and Lamarckism. The entire argument has become meaningless in the light of our new genetic insight. It is now quite evident that every habit and behavior has some structural basis but that the evolutionary changes that result from adaptive shifts are often initiated by a change in behavior, to be followed secondarily by a change in structure (Mayr, 1958). It is very often the new habit which sets up the selection pressure that shifts the mean of the curve of structural variation. Let us assume, for instance, that a population of fish acquires the habit of eating small snails. In such a population any mutation or gene combination would be advantageous that would make the teeth stronger and flatter, facilitating the crushing of snail shells. In view of the ever present genetic variation, it is virtually a foregone conclusion that the new selection pressures (owing to the changed habit) would soon have an effect on the facilitating structure.

Darwin was fully aware of this sequence of events. The parasitic wasp *Polynema natans,* in the family Proctotrupidae, lays its eggs mostly in the eggs of dragonflies. Most of its life-cycle, including copulation, takes place underwater. "It often enters the water and dives about by the use not of its legs, but of its wings, and remains as long as four hours beneath the surface; yet it exhibits no modification in structure in accordance with its abnormal habits" (Darwin, 1872, p. 185). Other aquatic species of parasitic wasps have since been discovered in the families Chalcididae, Ichneumonidae, Braconidae, and

Agriotypidae. As Darwin stated correctly, none of them has undergone any major structural reorganization following the shift into a new adaptive zone.

The shift from water to land, as mentioned above, was likewise made possible by a prior shift in habits, in this case, in locomotor habits. There is agreement about this between the students of vertebrates (Westoll, 1958) and of the arthropods (Manton, 1953). With habitat selection playing a major role in the shift into new adaptive zones and with habitat selection being a behavioral phenomenon, the importance of behavior in initiating new evolutionary events is self-evident. A study of behavior differences among related species and genera is apt to throw much light on the sequence of events that trigger the emergence of evolutionary novelties.

Man's civilization provides many new habitats into which numerous animals have shifted successfully. Chimney swifts (*Chaetura*) nest in chimneys instead of hollow trees; nighthawks (*Chordeiles*) on the flat roofs of homes and factories instead of on the ground; house martins (*Delichon urbica*) on house walls instead of on cliffs, to cite a few avian examples. In most of these cases there is merely an expansion of the old habitat, resulting in an increase in population size, rather than a shift into a truly new niche requiring a functional readjustment.

A CHANGE IN THE STRUCTURAL ENVIRONMENT

Many functions are performed, not by simple structures, but by a combination of structures. For an articulation, for instance, a minimum of two bones is needed, as well as the muscles that move these bones and the ligaments which help to bind them. To achieve efficient vision, a highly complex organ is needed, consisting of a receptor and its nervous connections, a lens and other focusing devices, pigments, etc. It is probable that some evolutionary novelties have emerged as the result of a more or less incidental coming-together of such components. This may happen either because each component has a primary function and developed in response to the selection pressure exerted in connection with this primary function or because the components are potentialities which are realized singly in various related species or genera but cannot perform with full efficiency until brought together in a single individual. It is probable that the improvement of a primary structure through accessory organs is usually delayed until the proper gene combination arises which permits the accessory structure to emerge. Without the primary structure, there would be no selective value in the secondary structure. This is true, for instance, of many of the accessory structures of the eye.

Let us now consider a specific case of the quasi-accidental coming-together of two structures, resulting in a new character complex with a unified function of high selective advantage. This is the case of the secondary jaw articulation in birds, discovered and beautifully analyzed by Bock (1959). In certain types of birds, in which the open jaw (particularly the mandible) is exposed to heavy impact during the pecking of food or catching of prey, there is a strong selection for a heavy musculature permitting the rapid raising of the mandible (closing of the bill) against considerable resistance. To permit the insertion of the increased muscle mass, a bony spur grows out at the inside of the mandible toward the skull. When this process has grown so long that it comes in contact with the skull, the stage is set for the development of a new character complex composed of previously independent organs (part of the mandible and part of the skull). This new character complex serves as a new articulation which functions simultaneously with the primary articulation. The new articulation has considerable value in all species with feeding habits that expose the jaw to possible dislocation. The secondary jaw articulation reaches its highest perfection in the skimmer (*Rhynchops*), which skims along the surface of the water with its mandible submerged until striking an object, which is then grasped. This secondary jaw articulation is an almost ideal illustration of the formation of a new structure as a result of a coming-together of two structures formed for entirely independent reasons.

The origin of the mammalian ear may well be another example. During the development of the new jaw articulation of the mammals (Olson, 1959; Simpson, 1959), the contact of the quadrate bone to the skull became loosened, and it acquired, at least in the South American forms, the stapes as a medial brace. This simple structural change initiated the establishment of the mammalian chain of ossicles. Natural selection utilized the accidental proximity of these ossicles and the second tympanic membrane and fused them into a vastly improved new character complex. Not all the steps of this process are yet entirely apparent, but I think that little doubt is left as to the principle involved (see also Watson, 1953; Tumarkin, 1955).

Such a fusing-together of individual characters into a new character complex is not restricted to structural characters. It may also play a role in the emergence of complex new behavior patterns. Let me discuss a specific case. Goldschmidt (1948) described the extraordinary behavior complex of the larvae of a New Zealand cave gnat (*Araschnocampa luminosa*) of the family of Mycetophilidae. These larvae live on the ceiling of caves in self-spun webs, and lower trapping threads covered with sticky droplets on which they catch midges (Chironomidae) as they emerge in large numbers from the cave waters. To make their "trapping system" more effective, they have evolved bio-luminescence. Goldschmidt asks, How could such a combination of characters have evolved gradually by the selection of favorable genetic variants? These fungus gnats have eight adaptations, says Goldschmidt, none of which would be of selective value to them without all the others. Actually, most of the eight prerequisites cited by Goldschmidt are fairly widespread among fungus gnats or among animals in general, e.g., an ability of habitat selection, and the list reduces to three essential components of this interesting habit: (1) a carnivorous instead of fungus diet, (2) the ability to spin the sticky trapping threads, and (3) luminescence. Subsequent researches have shown Goldschmidt's belief that none of these characters could occur without the others to be mistaken. There are other carnivorous fungus gnats, luminescence is not unique in the family, and, as Goldschmidt himself mentions, there are even other species which spin slimy trapping threads. There is little difficulty in seeing how these various potentialities of the family could have become concentrated into a single, highly effective device. Indeed, it seems to me that the assumption that all these adaptations could have appeared simultaneously as a single, efficient, new behavior complex in a single orthodox fungus gnat would be infinitely harder to understand. We do not know what the key invention of the New Zealand fungus gnat was, but it is possible that the new behavior complex started with a species which varied its fungus diet by scavenging, that is, by eating dead insects that had become stuck to the moist cave wall. Once such an extension of food habits had occurred, a high selection pressure for all the other components of the character complex would be obvious.

The three cited cases have in common the essential feature of pre-existing building blocks, which, when pieced together, give rise to an "improbable" new character complex of high selective value. The particular organisms are preadapted to acquire the new character complex because they already possess the potentiality for it, that is, the individual building stones. The role of natural selection in these cases is apparently not the bringing-together of the individual units; this is done by forces independent of the prospective new structure. Natural selection enters the scene as soon as the pieces have been combined into a new complex which can function as a unit and can respond to natural selection as a unit.

Multiple pathways.—These cases of the "piecing-together" of character complexes illustrate most graphically the ever ready opportunism of evolution. Whenever the need for a new structure arises, a high premium is placed on anything that satisfies this need. If the same need arises independently in unrelated organisms, independent solutions may be found. There is perhaps no better way to learn how evolutionary novelties emerge than by carefully comparing similar structures that have evolved independently in response to similar selection pressures. The fact that so many independent answers may be found to satisfy a single need proves three points: (a) the ever present pressure of selection, (b) the opportunism of evolution, and (c) the potential variability of any structure. Whichever structure is the first to vary in a desirable direction will be the one on which natural selection can work. That component of the variation of accessory structures will be favored by natural selection which best fits with the modification of the primary structure. The almost innumerable ways by which beetles stridulate is a good illustration. Poison organs throughout the animals kingdom are another one. Any specialist can give numerous examples from the group with which he is most familiar, whether it be web construction in spiders, plume development in birds of paradise, floating devices in pelagic animals, or whatnot. At least five families of songbirds have independently discovered the usefulness of mud in nest-building—the South American ovenbirds (*Furnariidae*), the *Hirundo* group among the swallows, the nuthatches (Sittidae), certain thrushes (Turidae) (for the inside of the nest), and the Australian Grallinidae. Methods for passing cellulose-rich plant food repeatedly through the intestinal tract have been invented by herbivorous mammals independently four times—the ruminating artiodactyls, certain kangaroos (marsupials), the beavers (rodents), (Richard, 1959), and some, if not all, lagomorphs.

One would imagine that social bees with their colonies full of honey and larvae would be exceedingly vulnerable to raids by various nest robbers if they were not protected by their stings. And yet the stings have been lost in one group of social bees, the Meliponinae. Lindauer (1957) has described the numerous methods by which various species of stingless bees in the genus *Trigona* defend their nests. Most of them do it by biting; thousands of bees attack the intruder and make it very uncomfortable for him. *Oxytrigona* has acquired an accessory gland to the mandibles to pour an acid and very painful secretion into the wound. *Trigona droryana* of South America immobilizes the intruder by covering him with small pellets of a very sticky resin, and the South African *Trigona braunsii* by pouring honey over him! The very generalized need—protection against intruders—is achieved by exceedingly different, yet equally efficient, methods.

Natural selection comes up with the right answer so often that one is sometimes tempted to forget its failures. Yet the history of the earth is a history of extinction, and every extinction is in part a defeat for natural selection, or at least it has been so interpreted. Natural selection does *not* always produce the needed improvements.

Darwin was fully aware of this situation, not in the least because Mivart used it skilfully in an argument, restated by Darwin as follows (p. 260): "It has often been asked, if natural selection be so potent, why has not this or that structure been gained by certain species to which it would apparently have been advantageous?" The answer which Darwin gives still appears to be the right one: "It may often have happened that the requisite parts did not vary in the right manner or to the right degree." And this is still our interpretation. Natural selection can operate only when it has a choice between alternate phenotypes. If a gene pool of a population does not contain the right genes, that is, genes that would permit an advantageous variation of the phenotype, natural selection is helpless. To Mivart's question: "If high browsing be so great an advantage, why has not any other hoofed quadruped acquired a long neck and lofty stature, besides the giraffe?" One can no more give an answer to it than to the well-known question: "Why are not all animals as intelligent as man, if intelligence and a large brain are of as great an evolutionary advantage as is claimed by students of human evolution?" In this case, however, it is far more probable that the selective premium for increased brain size was not sufficient in other groups to set up a selection pressure anywhere near as large as that which occurred in the hominid line.

Let us not forget that the phenotype is a compromise between conflicting selection pressures and that every specialization is bought at a price. In many groups of organisms an increase in brain size may not give sufficient selective advantage to compensate for the anatomical and physiological unbalancing which it inevitably causes. Brain size is correlated in many subtle ways with the whole mode of life. Among songbirds (*Oscines*), for instance, a relatively large brain seems to be found only among omnivorous groups. All specialized feeders seem to have relatively small brains. Far more comparative anatomical work is needed, however, before this suggested correlation can be considered established.

GENETIC ASPECTS

The refutation of the mutationist claim that mutations create new structures does not imply that the problem of the emergence of evolutionary novelties has no genetic aspects. In the discussion of multiple pathways, we have already mentioned how the contents of the gene pool may determine the phenotypic response to selection pressure. Another, perhaps even more important, question is to what extent the genotype may be able to respond to selection pressures. A combination of genetic and developmental homeostasis may give the phenotype such uniformity and stability that it may not be able to respond phenotypically to a change in the environment. The case of sibling species, which, in spite of an obvious genetic reconstruction, show no phenotypic difference, is an apt illustration of the stability of the phenotype. The butterfly *Maniola jurtina,* one of the commonest and most widespread of butterflies of the British mainland, is another. In spite of great climatic, geographic, and vegetational differences, there is no phenotypic geographic variation in the south of England east of western Devonshire (Dowdeswell *et al.,* 1957). I have previously (Mayr, 1954) emphasized this phenotypic stability of common, widespread, mainland populations and have ascribed it to strong selection favoring stabilizing mechanisms in the face of a continuous flow of alien genes into every local population. The stronger these stabilizing mechanisms, the less opportunity for evolutionary change. The breakdown of phenotypic stability and uniformity in peripherally isolated populations of such species is testimony to the strength of these stabilizing devices. I am inclined to ascribe the phenotypic stability of "old" genera (G. G. Simpson would call them "bradytelic phyletic lines") to similar internal stabilization. It is evident that too great a stability of the phenotype would be a handicap in a newly arising situation where there is a premium on the development of a new structure. A peripherally isolated population, or any other population in which the stabilizing mechanisms are temporarily weakened, may occasionally be in an especially favorable situation with respect to the emergence of evolutionary novelties. However, in view of the change of function and other mechanisms discussed above, the origin of evolutionary novelties is by no means limited to such peripherally isolated populations.

Conclusion

The tentative answer to our question "What controls the emergence of evolutionary novelties" can be stated as follows: Changes of evolutionary significance are rarely, except on the cellular level, the direct results of mutation pressure. Exceptions are purely ecotypic adaptations, such as cryptic coloration. The emergence of new structures is normally due to the acquisition of a new function by an existing structure. In both cases the resulting "new" structure is merely a modification of a preceding structure. The selection pressure in favor of the structural modification is greatly increased by a shift into a new ecological niche, by the acquisition of a new habit, or by both. A shift in function exposes the fully formed "preadapted" structure to the new selection pressure. This, in most cases, explains how an incipient structure could be favored by natural selection before reaching a size and elaboration where it would be advantageous in a new role. Mutation pressure, as such, plays a negligible role in the emergence of evolutionary novelties, except possibly on the cellular level. Yet the structure of the gene complex is important: too great a genetic and developmental homeostasis will result in too stabilized a phenotype and will tend to prevent a response to new selection pressures. Any population phenomenon that would tend to counteract excessive stability of the phenotype may favor evolutionary changes.

A draft of the manuscript was read by W. Bock, Julian S. Huxley, B. Patterson, G. G. Simpson, and C. H. Waddington, all of whom made valuable suggestions for which I am deeply indebted to them.

LITERATURE CITED

AMADON, DEAN. 1943. "Specialization and Evolution," *Amer. Naturalist,* LXXVII, 133–41.

BLEST, A. D. 1957a. "The Function of Eyespot Patterns in the Lepidoptera," *Behavior,* XI, 209–56.

———. 1957b. "The Evolution of Protective Displays in the Saturnioidea and Sphingidal," *ibid.,* pp. 257–309.

BOCK, WALTER. 1959. "Preadaptation and Multiple Evolutionary Pathways," *Evolution,* XIII, 194–211.

COPE, E. D. 1896. *The Primary Factors of Organic Evolution.* Chicago: Open Court.

COWLES, RAYMOND B. 1958. "Possible Origin of Dermal Temperature Regulation," *Evolution,* XII, 347–57.

DARWIN, CHARLES. 1872. *Origin of Species.* 6th ed. Oxford University Press reprint. Oxford.

DAVID, D. DWIGHT. 1949a. "Comparative Anatomy and the Evolution of Vertebrates." In *Genetics, Palaeontology, and Evolution,* ed. G. L. JEPSEN, G. G. SIMPSON, and ERNST MAYR, pp. 64–89. Princeton, N.J.: Princeton University Press.

———. 1949b. "The Shoulder Architecture of Bears and Other Carnivores," *Fieldiana, Zoology,* XXXI, 385–405.

DENISON, R. H. 1941. "The Soft Anatomy of *Bothriolepis,*" *Jour. Palaeontol.,* XV, 553–61.

DOHRN, ANTON. 1875. *Princip des Functionswechsels.* Leipzig: Englemann.

DOWDESWELL, W. H., FORD, E. B., and McWHIRTER, K. G. 1957. "Further Studies on Isolation in the Butterfly. *Maniola jurtina* L., *Heredity*, XI, 51–65.

GOLDSCHMIDT, RICHARD. 1948. "Glow Worms and Evolution," *Rev. Sci.*, LXXXVI, 607–12.

———. 1951. "Eine weitere Bemerkung über Glühwürmer und Evolution," *Naturwiss.*, XIX, 437–38.

GOODRICH, E. S. 1930. *Studies on the Structure and Development of the Vertebrates*. London: Macmillan & Co., Ltd.

GRANICK, S. 1953. "Inventions in Iron Metabolism," *Amer. Naturalist*, LXXXVII, 65–75.

GREGORY, WILLIAM K. 1934. "Polyisomerism and Anisomerism in Cranial and Dental Evolution among Vertebrates," *Proc. Nat. Acad. Sci.*, XX, 1–9.

GREGORY, W. K., and CONRAD, G. M. 1936. "Pictorial Phylogenies of Deep-Sea Isospondyli and Iniomi," *Copeia*, No. 1, pp. 21–36.

GÜNTHER, KLAUS, and DECKERT, KURT. 1950. *Wunderwelt der Tiefsee*. Berlin-Grünewald: Herbig.

HUXLEY, J S. 1942. *Evolution, the Modern Synthesis*. New York: Harper & Bros.

KETTLEWELL, H. B. D. 1959. "Industrial Melanism in the Lepidoptera and Its Contribution to Our Knowledge of Evolution," "Amer. Soc. Zool. and Nat. Assoc. Biol. Teachers Refresher Course in Evolution," pp. 25–40. (Mimeographed.)

LINDAUER, MARTIN. 1957. Zur Biologie der stachellosen Bienen: Ihre Abwehrmethoden. "*Tagungsbericht*," *Deutsche Akad. Landwirtschafts, Berlin*, No. 11, pp. 71–78.

LISSMAN, H. W. 1958. "On the Function and Evolution of Electric Organs in Fish," *Jour. Exper. Biol.*, XXXV, 156–91.

MANTON, S. M. 1953. "Locomotory Habits and the Evolution of the Larger Arthropodan Groups," in *Symp. Soc. Exper. Biol.*, No. 7: *Evolution*, pp. 339–76.

MAYR, ERNST. 1954. "Change of Genetic Environment and Evolution." In *Evolution as a Process*, ed. HUXLEY, HARDY, and FORD, pp. 157–80. London: Allen & Unwin.

———. 1956. "Geographical Character Gradients and Climatic Adaptation," *Evolution*, X, 105–8.

———. 1958. "Behavior and Systematics." In *Behavior and Evolution*, ed. ANN ROE and G. G. SIMPSON, pp. 341–62. New Haven, Conn., Yale University Press.

———. 1959. "Darwin and the Evolutionary Theory in Biology." In *Evolution and Anthropology: A Centennial Appraisal*, pp. 3–12. Washington, D.C.: Anthropological Society of Washington.

MIVART, ST. GEORGE. 1871. *Genesis of Species*. London: Macmillan & Co., Ltd.

NEEDHAM, J. 1931. *Chemical Embryology*. 3 vols. Cambridge: Cambridge University Press.

OLSON, E. C. 1959. "The Evolution of Mammalian Characters," *Evolution,* XIII, 344–53.

OSBORN, HENRY FAIRFIELD. 1936–42. *Proboscidea: A Monograph of the Discovery of Evolution, Migration of the Mastodonts and Elephants of the World.* 2 vols. New York: American Museum of Natural History.

PATTERSON, BRYAN. 1949. "Rates of Evolution in Taeniodonts." In *Genetics, Palaeontology, and Evolution,* ed. G. L. JEPSEN, G. G. SIMPSON, and ERNST MAYR, pp. 243–78. Princeton, N.J.: Princeton University Press.

PLATE, L. 1924. *Allgemeine Zoologie und Abstammungslehre.* Jena: Fischer.

REGAN, C. T., and TREWAVAS, E. 1932. "Deep-Sea Angler-Fishes (Ceratioidea)." In *Rep. Carlsberg Ocean. Exped., 1928–30,* Vol. II.

REMANE, ADOLF. 1951. "Die Besiedelung des Sandbodens im Meere und die Bedeutung der Lebensformtypen für die Ökologie," *Verh. Deutsch. Zool. Gesellsch.,* pp. 327–59.

RENSCH, BERNHARD. 1947. *Neuere Probleme der Abstammungslehre.* Stuttgart: Enke.

RICHARD, PAUL-BERNARD. 1959. "La Caecotrophie chez le castor du Rhône (*Castor fiber*)," *Compt. rend., Séances de l'Académie des Sciences,* No. 9, pp. 1424–26.

ROMER, A. S. 1946. "The Early Evolution of Fishes," *Quart. Rev.,* XXI, 33–69.

SCHAEFFER, BOBB. 1948. "The Origin of a Mammalian Ordinal Character," *Evolution,* II, 164–75.

SEWERTZOFF, A. N. 1931. *Morphologische Gesetzmässigkeiten der Evolution.* Jena: Fischer.

SIMPSON, G. G. 1953. *The Major Features of Evolution.* New York: Columbia University Press.

————. 1959. "Mesozoic Mammals and the Polyphyletic Origin of Mammals," *Evolution,* XIII, 405–14.

SMITH, HOMER. 1953. *From Fish to Philosopher.* Boston: Little, Brown & Co.

TUMARKIN, A. 1955. "On the Evolution of the Auditory Conducting Apparatus: A New Theory Based on Functional Considerations," *Evolution,* IX, 221–43.

WATSON, D. M. S. 1953. "Evolution of the Mammalian Ear," *Evolution,* VII, 159–77.

WESTOLL, S. T. 1958. "The Lateral Fin-Fold Theory and the Pectoral Fins of Ostracoderms and Early Fishes." In *Studies on Fossil Vertebrates,* pp. 180–211. London: University of London.

All quotations from foreign languages were translated by the author.

C. H. WADDINGTON

EVOLUTIONARY ADAPTATION

The subject of this paper is the origin of adaptation, still an issue one hundred years after Darwin, and recently characterized by George Gaylord Simpson as the "primary problem of evolutionary biology" (Roe and Simpson, 1958).

The assemblage of life-sciences that are usually classed together as "biology" form a group at least as complex and diversified as the whole group of the physical sciences. Within this enormous range one can discern three main foci toward which the individual sciences tend to be oriented. One of these is analytical biology—the attempt to determine the ultimate constituent units upon which the character of living things depend. Analytical biology investigates development and heredity through the analysis of genes and subgenic units and so to the macrochemical entities such as the DNA, RNA, and protein of the chromosomes. The whole group of such studies plays the same role in the biological field as does atomic physics in the physical sciences.

Another major focus of interest is what may be called "physiological biology"—the study of the mechanisms by which organisms carry on their existence. This corresponds perhaps to chemistry and engineering in the physical role.

Finally, there is what may be called "synthetic biology," which is concerned with providing an intellectually coherent picture of the whole realm of living matter. In the structure of biology this fulfils the same role as cosmology does in the physical sciences; and just as in the physical realm we find that cosmology and atomic physics have very close connections with one another, so in biology the analytical and synthetic approaches to the world of the living employ very similar concepts.

In the hundred years since Darwin wrote, it has become universally

C. H. WADDINGTON is affiliated with the Institute of Animal Genetics, a department of the University of Edinburgh. Prior to coming to Edinburgh, where he has conducted important research in embryology and genetic processes, Prof. Waddington served as Lecturer in the Department of Zoology, Cambridge, and as Embryologist at the Strangeways Laboratory.

accepted that the only synthetic biological theory which needs serious consideration is that of evolution. In an appraisal of evolutionary biology as it stands now in this centenary year, it is perhaps well to begin by reminding ourselves of the fundamental reasons for mankind's interest in this subject. During the century of intensive work which has been devoted to its study, so many detailed problems have emerged which have a great fascination of their own that one is sometimes inclined to be carried away by enthusiasm for these puzzles; however, they are really attractive only to those who have already taken their first steps toward this direction of study. The enormous impact of Darwin's theories on the whole intellectual life of his own day—and, indeed, on that of all later generations—arose not from details but from the relevance of the broad outline of his thinking to one of the major problems with which mankind is faced.

That problem is presented by the appearance of design in the organic world. Animals and plants in their innumerable variety present, of course, many odd, striking, and even beautiful features, which can raise feelings of surprise and delight in the observer. But over and above this, a very large number of them give the appearance of being astonishingly well tailored to fit precisely into the requirements which will be made of them by their mode of existence. Fish are admirably designed for swimming, birds for flying, horses for running, snakes for creeping, and so on, and the correspondence between what an organism will do and the way it is formed to carry out such tasks often extends into extraordinary detail.

It is clear from the oldest literatures that man has always been impressed by this correspondence. The simplest explanation—and the one almost universally accepted in prescientific times—is that this appearance reflects the activities of an intelligent Being who has designed each type of animal and plant in a way suitable for carrying out the functions assigned to it. It is the challenge presented to this explanation that constitutes the major interest of the theory of evolution. A really convincing alternative account of the origin of biological adaptation is the major demand which must be made of it.

The essential feature of an evolutionary theory is the suggestion that animals and plants, as we see them exhibiting an apparently designed adaptedness at the present day, have been brought to their present condition by a process extending through time and were not designed in their modern form. This does not, as many of Darwin's contemporaries thought it did, necessarily deny the existence of any form of intelligent designer. It means only that any designing activity there may be has operated through a process extending over long periods of time and has not brought suddenly into being each of the biological forms as we now see them. The question of theism or atheism, which played such a large part in the public discussions of Darwin's day, is, we now recognize, not critically answered by the acceptance or rejection of an evolutionary hypothesis but must be settled—if it ever can be—in some other way. We need not, therefore, be further concerned with it in this discussion.

Evolutionary theories had, of course, been put forward some time before Darwin wrote *Origin of Species*. The most famous of these earlier discussions is that associated with the name of Lamarck. It has suffered a most surprising fate. Lamarck is the only major figure in the history of biology whose name has become, to all intents and purposes, a term of abuse. Most scientists' contributions are fated to be outgrown, but very few authors have written works which, two centuries later, are still rejected with an indignation so intense that the sceptic may suspect something akin to an uneasy conscience. In point of fact, Lamarck has, I think, been somewhat unfairly judged.

Lamarck's theory involved two main parts, and each of these has encountered some essentially spurious difficulties in gaining acceptance. The first part supposed that the initial step toward an evolutionary advance involves something which Lamarck characterised as an act of will. Clearly, in this form the postulate applies only to animals and not to plants. Lamarck was, I take it, suggesting that the organism's own behaviour is involved in determining the nature of the environmental situation in which it will develop and to which its offspring will become adapted. In this form his theory could perhaps be generalized to cover the plant kingdom also if one accepts a wide enough definition of the concept of behaviour. However, let us leave that on one side: Lamarck himself was concerned primarily with animal evolution.

Now a concept such as an act of will was for a long time very unfashionable in the scientific study of biology. It is only relatively recently that biologists have shown any confidence in tackling the problems presented by the study of animal behaviour. Most students of behaviour still avoid such terms as "act of will," but the concept of a choice between alternative modes of behaviour or conditions of life is by now quite respectable, and one must make allowances for the terminology used by someone writing in the eighteenth century.

If a certain sympathy is shown in interpreting Lamarck's words, the second phase of his theory also appears less unacceptable than it is usually considered to be. This is the well-known hypothesis of the inheritance of acquired characters. Conventionally at the present time this is interpreted as though Lamarck used the word "inheritance" as we should now use it, that is to say, to mean transmission of a char-

acter from a pair of parents to their offspring in the next or immediately subsequent generation. But, at the time Lamarck wrote, no
distinction had yet been made between heredity over one or two generations, as we study it in genetical experiments, and heredity over
much longer periods of time, as we encounter it in evolution. Nor was
there any discrimination between the genetics of individuals and what
we now call "population genetics." Lamarck's theory could quite well
be interpreted to mean not that an individual organism which acquires
a character during its lifetime will tend to transmit this to its immediate offspring, but that, if members of a population of animals undergoing evolution in nature acquire a character during their lifetime, this
character will tend to appear more frequently in members of a derived
population many generations later. In this form it is not so easy to
reject his view. In fact, in a later part of this lecture I shall produce
some evidence in favour of it.

Lamarck's words were, however, not interpreted in the way that
I have suggested. His postulated "act of will" was rejected as something vitalistic and non-scientific. His doctrine of the inheritance of acquired characters was interpreted in terms of individual genetics and
not population genetics. Even with this interpretation it has frequently
been accepted by comparative anatomists and naturalists as providing
the simplest explanation for the occurrences which they can observe in
the natural world. However, practically all experimentalists have rejected it. I need not summarise the well-known experiments which
have failed to demonstrate an effect of environmental conditions on
the hereditary qualities which are passed on from parent to offspring.

In quite recent years the situation has changed somewhat. We have
now obtained abundant evidence of the induction of hereditary changes
—in the form of gene mutations, chromosome aberrations, etc.—by
external agents such as ionising radiation and highly reactive chemicals. But these changes are non-directional; and induced mutagenesis
as we normally encounter it in the laboratory does not provide any
mechanism by which relatively normal environments could induce
hereditary changes which would improve the adaptation of the offspring to the inducing conditions. Directional hereditary changes have,
indeed, also been induced, but, so far, only in very simple systems such
as bacteria, and by the use of highly specific inducing agents—for instance, the transforming principles. A more general mechanism of
biological alteration, which does not depend on such exceptional inducing agents, is the induction of the synthesis of specific enzymes
related to particular substrates. The changes produced in enzyme induction are for the most part not hereditarily transmissible, but it
seems in principle not inconceivable that under suitable conditions

actual gene mutations could be induced by some such mechanism.

Finally, one should notice some recent evidence which has been produced to support the hypothesis that variations of the normal environment may in some cases induce hereditarily transmissible changes. This evidence relates largely to plants, and most of it has emanated from Russia and is regarded with considerable scepticism in other countries, where attempts to repeat the experiments have been rather uniformly unsuccessful. Nevertheless, evidence of a not entirely dissimilar character has begun to appear in Western countries also—for instance, in the studies of Durrant (1958) on the hereditary transmission of the effects of manurial treatment of flax, the work of Highkin (1958) on the effects of alternating temperature on peas, and a few others. It is not clear in any of these cases that the hereditary effects produced, if any, are of a kind that improves the adaptation of the organism to the inducing conditions. The field of work is clearly one of great inherent interest, but it remains true that the vast majority of changes in the environment do not directly produce any hereditary modifications in the organisms subjected to them, and we are certainly very far from being able to provide a general explanation of evolutionary adaptations in terms of the type of effects which have just been mentioned.

The development of evolutionary theory in the last hundred years has in fact proceeded along quite other lines. Darwin's major contribution was, of course, the suggestion that evolution can be explained by the natural selection of random variations. Natural selection, which was at first considered as though it were a hypothesis that was in need of experimental or observational confirmation, turns out on closer inspection to be a tautology, a statement of an inevitable although previously unrecognized relation. It states that the fittest individuals in a population (defined as those which leave most offspring) will leave most offspring. Once the statement is made, its truth is apparent. This fact in no way reduces the magnitude of Darwin's achievement; only after it was clearly formulated, could biologists realise the enormous power of the principle as a weapon of explanation. However, his theory required a second component—namely, a process by which random hereditary variation would be produced. This he was unable himself to provide, since the phenomena of biological heredity were in his day very little understood. With the rise of Mendelism, the lacuna was made good. Heredity depends on chromosomal genes, and these are found in fact to behave as the theory requires, altering occasionally at unpredictable times and in ways which produce a large, and, it is usually stated, "random" variety of characters in the offspring bearing the altered genes. On these two foundations—natural selection operating on variation which arises from the random mutation of Mendelian genes—the present-day neo-Darwinist or "synthetic" theory of evolution has been built up.

This theory has brought very great advances in our understanding of the genetic situation in populations as they exist in nature, of the ways these genetic systems may change, and of the differences between local races or between closely related species. The question discussed in this paper is the adequacy of its treatment of the major problem of the "appearance of design," or biological adaptation. In dealing with this problem, neo-Mendelian theory relies essentially on the hypothesis that genes mutate at random; that is to say, if one waits long enough, an appropriate gene mutation will occur which will modify the phenotypic appearance of the organism in any conceivable way that may be required. It is pointed out that, however rare such a mutation may be, the mechanism of natural selection is eminently efficient at engendering states of high improbability, so that, from rare and entirely chance occurrences, an appearance of precisely calculated design may be produced.

This explanation is a very powerful one. It could, in fact, explain anything. And there is no denying that the processes which it invokes —random gene mutation and natural selection—actually take place. I should not dream of denying it—as far as it goes—but I wish to argue that it does not go far enough. It involves certain drastic simplifications which are liable to lead us to a false picture of how the evolutionary process works, whereas, if we take into account certain factors which have been omitted from the conventional picture, we shall not only be closer to the situation as it exists in nature but will find ourselves with a more convincing explanation of how the appearance of design comes about.

Let us consider some examples of the type of biological adaptedness which we are trying to understand. In many cases in which we speak of an animal as being adapted, the adaptation is comparatively trivial and its precise character is not critical. As an example, one may take the phenomenon of industrial melanism in Lepidoptera, which is one of the best-studied examples of natural selection in the field. In industrial areas of Great Britain several species of moths which a century ago most commonly appeared in fairly light-coloured forms have in recent years shown increasing numbers of dark melanic varieties; in several instances these have now become by far the most common type in regions contaminated by industrial fumes. A typical region where this replacement of light by dark forms has occurred has earned the nickname "The Black Country." It was natural to suppose that the blackening of the moth is connected with the darkening of the general vegetation by contamination with industrial smoke.

One of the earliest investigators to examine the subject in some detail was Heslop-Harrison (1920). He held somewhat Lamarckian views about the origin of the melanic form and, indeed, claimed at one time to show that it could be induced by feeding larvae on leaves which had been contaminated by various metallic salts. This claim has not found general acceptance in later years. However, Heslop-Harrison also made a further and more important contribution to the subject. He demonstrated that natural selection operates differentially on dark and light forms of the moth *Oporabia autumnata,* the melanics being favoured in regions with a dark background whereas the light forms were favoured in the presence of light-coloured vegetation. He was able to show this with particular clearness by studying a wood in which one section had been separated in about 1800 by the cutting of a wide gap, later grown up with heather. A considerable number of years later, in 1885, the southern section of the wood was planted with light-coloured birch trees, while in the northern portion nearly all the trees were dark pines. By 1907 the populations of moths in the two sections of the wood showed a quite different proportion of dark to light forms. In the birch part of the wood only 15 per cent were melanics; in the pine section about 96 per cent were dark. Moreover, Heslop-Harrison showed that in the dark pinewood section, where by far the majority of the moths were melanics, the majority of the wings found isolated on the ground—representing remnants left after the insect's body has been eaten by a predator—were actually light. Thus it was clear that the pale-coloured forms were at a disadvantage in the dark wood.

A similar situation has been re-examined in a much more thorough form quite recently by Kettlewell (1955). He found that the predation is in this case, at least to a large extent, carried out by birds, and he has been able to demonstrate very clearly the reality of the natural selective advantage enjoyed by an insect which blends reasonably well with its background. We have here, then, a well-studied example of an evolutionary process in which a species acquires a characteristic— namely, melanism—which can be considered to adapt it to its surroundings. However, in this example the adaptive character is of the very simplest kind. It is a mere darkening of the wings, and it does not seem at all likely that the precise pattern in which the blackening is laid down can have any great importance. The effective change probably involves nothing more elaborate than a markedly increased producton of the melanic pigment. It is perhaps satisfying enough in such

a case to attribute the appearance of the relevant new hereditary variation simply to a random gene mutation.

But the adaptations which have tempted man to think of design are
rather more far-reaching. For instance, Figure 1 shows the skeleton

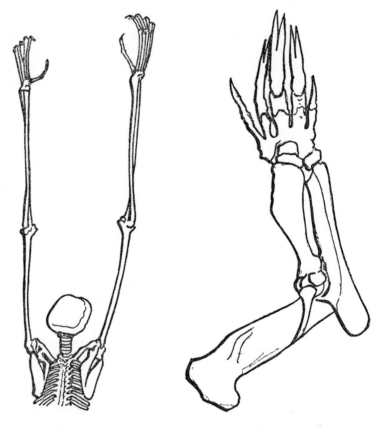

FIG. 1.—The skeleton forelimbs of a gibbon (*left*) and of a pangolin.

forelimbs of a gibbon and a pangolin. The former uses its arms for
climbing in trees, the latter for digging in hard soil. The limb bones
are very precisely modeled in relation to the functions they will carry
out, and the difference between them involves something more than a
simple over-all change comparable to the blackening of a moth's
wing. A mere lengthening of the pangolin's arm would not turn it into
that of a gibbon. We are dealing here with a precise set of carefully
co-ordinated changes involving several different bones of the limb and
the shoulder girdle. Now we know that during the lifetime of any
single individual the use of the limb muscles in a particular way will
increase the size and strength of those muscles, and if the operations

take place early enough, they have some effects on the associated bony structures, these effects being of a co-ordinated kind, such as those which distinguish the two forelimbs illustrated. In conventional neo-Mendelian theory, these effects of the use of an organ, exerted during the organism's own lifetime, are dismissed as irrelevant to the evolutionary process. They are "acquired characters" and are not genetically inherited. Insofar as the individual exhibits them, his phenotype is likely to deceive us as to the characters which he will pass on to his offspring. The acquired characters act, the neo-Mendelian theory asserts, merely as genetic "noise," in the information-theory sense of that term. We have to find the explanation for such evolutionary changes in random gene mutations, to whose occurrence the physiological processes which lead to the formation of adaptive ontogenetic changes are completely irrelevant.

However, that explanation leaves us with two major points on which we may feel some lack of satisfaction. One is that we have no specific explanation for the co-ordinated nature of the changes as they affect the different bones or other subunits in the system. Can we do no better than fall back on the very general explanation in terms of the efficiency of natural selection in engendering highly improbable states? Since we see similar co-ordinated changes being produced by physiological adaptation within a lifetime, this highly abstract principle seems a little inadequate.

Second, we are bound, both for practical reasons and on the basis of fundamental theory, to regard all forms, functions, and activities of an organism as the joint product of its hereditary constitution and its environmental circumstances; the exclusion of acquired characters from all part in the evolutionary process does less than justice to the incontrovertible fact that they exhibit some of the hereditary potentialities of the organism. All characters of all organisms are, after all, to some extent acquired characters, in the sense that the environment has played some role during their development. Similarly, all characters of all organisms are to some extent hereditary, in the sense that they are expressions of some of the potentialities with which the organism is endowed by its genetic constitution.

This point is one which has only recently forced itself firmly into the attention of geneticists, perhaps largely through current interest in characters to whose variation hereditary differences contribute only a small fraction, such as the milk yield of cattle. It is still not always kept in mind in all contexts in which it is relevant, and in the earlier days of genetics it was very frequently ignored. To take a relevant example from the very early years of this century, Baldwin and Lloyd Morgan pointed out that a capacity for carrying out adaptive changes during their lifetimes might enable organisms to survive in environments in which they would otherwise be inviable and that they could in this way exist until a suitable hereditary variation occurred which could be seized upon by natural selection and enable a genuine-evolutionary adaptation to take place. They did not point out that there was any hereditary variation in the capacity for forming such ontogenetic adaptations. Mayr, writing in 1958, actually describes their view as "the hypothesis that a non-genetic plasticity of the phenotype facilitates reconstruction of the genotype." But a plasticity of the phenotype *cannot* be "non-genetic"; it *must* have a genetic basis, since it must be an expression of genetically transmitted potentialities. It is conceivable, of course, that in any given population there will be no genetic variation in the determinants of this plasticity, but our experience of natural populations shows that this is a very unlikely state of affairs. When wild populations have been investigated, they have, I think, always exhibited some genetic variation in respect of any character that has been studied.

There is actually no need to rely on purely a priori arguments in this respect. Experiments have recently been made in which *Drosophila* populations were searched for the presence of genetic variation in the capacity to respond by ontogenetic alterations to the stimuli produced by various abnormal environments, and the effectiveness of selection on this genetic variation was studied. Both the characters involved and the environmental stimuli applied were of rather diverse kinds in the different experiments in the series, but in all cases genetic variation in capacity to response, utilisable by selection, was revealed.

Perhaps the simplest of these experiments was actually the last to be performed (Waddington, 1959). It attempted to bring about the adaptation of a population of *Drosophila* to a high concentration of sodium chloride in the medium in which the larvae live. The larvae possess anal papillae on either side of the anus (Fig. 2), and these are known to play some part in regulating the osmotic pressure of the body fluids (Gloor and Chen 1950). The size of the papillae can be measured most accurately just after pupation when the hardening of the puparial skin prevents distortion by the muscular movements of the body. Three stocks were employed. One was a wild-type "Oregon K"; the other two, sp^2 bs^2 and al b c sp^2, each contained the gene speck in which the anal area is pigmented in the pupa, making it somewhat easier to see the anal papillae. From the Oregon wild-type stock two selected lines were set up, known as "Oregon L" and "Oregon E," while for each of the other two stocks one selected line was maintained. These selected lines were carried on by growing the larvae

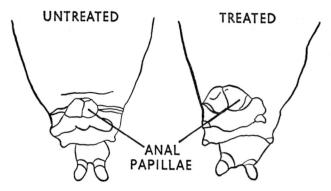

UNTREATED   TREATED

ANAL
PAPILLAE

FIG. 2.—Outline drawings of the anal papillae of "Oregon K" *Drosophila* larvae representing extreme variants in size, the larger from a selected strain grown on a medium with 7 per cent salt added, the smaller from an unselected strain grown on normal medium with no added salt.

of each generation on normal *Drosophila* medium to which various concentrations of sodium chloride had been added, the concentrations being adjusted so that only 20–30 per cent of the eggs laid on the medium survived to the adult condition. No artificial selection was made, the selection pressure being entirely the natural selection exerted by the stringent medium.

After 21 generations of selection in this way, the survival of the various strains on different concentrations of salt was tested and the mean size of the anal papillae estimated by measurements on 20 individuals from each culture at each concentration of salt (Fig. 3). The selected stocks became somewhat more tolerant of high salt concentration, though the difference was not very great. However, there is no doubt that some genetic variability exists in the capacity of the animals to adapt themselves to the environmental stress and that this genetic variability has been utilisable by the natural selection employed.

A number of further deductions can be made from Figure 3. In the first place, it is clear that the size of the anal papillae tends to increase with increasing concentration of salt in the medium, although the effect is rather slight until the concentration reaches a high level. For any one stock the curve relating size of papillae to the salt concentration gives a picture of a physiological function which we might call its "adaptability." By a comparison of the selected stocks with the corresponding unselected ones, it is clear that two things happen to these curves of adaptability. In the first place, their steepness increases and to some extent their general shape changes; that is to say, the se-

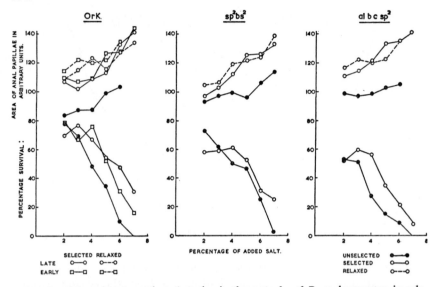

Fig. 3.—Selected and unselected strains in three stocks of *D. melanogaster*, in relation to the salt content of the larval medium. *Above*, the size of the anal papillae at various concentrations, in units derived from micrometer measurements. *Below*, the percentage of adults appearing from a given number of eggs. For the wild-type stock, two selected strains were prepared, one selected also for early emergence and the other for late. The papillae of the selected stocks were measured both in larvae derived from parents grown in the selection-medium (7 per cent added salt) and in "relaxed" lines in which there had been one generation on normal medium between the end of the selection and the setting-out of larvae on the various concentrations.

lection favours, as might be expected, those genotypes which endow the individual with a relatively high capacity to carry out an onto-genetic adaptation to the stress of high salt content. Second, the general level of the curves is raised. One might refer to this general level as the "level of adaptation to high salt content"; we can say, therefore, that the level of adaptation has been increased. A third, and perhaps most important point, is that the anal papillae in the selected races remain larger, even at low salt content, than the papillae of the unselected strains at the same concentration. The adaptation to high salt content which has been produced by 21 generations of selection is not immediately reversible by 1 or 2 generations in the normal medium. In the botanical terminology employed by Turesson (1930), the ecotype which has been produced in relation to high salt concentration is to some extent an ecogenotype. The character of the adapted strain depends, of course, on its genotype, as all characters of all strains do, but the point to notice is that the genetic difference between the selected and unselected strains is expressed also in the normal low salt medium. We have obtained a result which is effectively the same as would have resulted from the direct inheritance of acquired characters but which has been produced, not by the mechanisms which are usually thought of in connection with Lamarck's hypothesis, but by a population-genetical mechanism which involves selection.

The failure of the selected strains when grown in normal medium to revert completely to the condition of the unselected strains must depend on a certain inflexibility of their developmental processes. Although their adaptability becomes higher, as we have seen, it is not large enough to allow the anal organs to regress completely on the low salt medium. Such lack of flexibility in the developmental system has been referred to as "canalisation" (Waddington, 1940, 1942).

It is sometimes useful to discuss development in terms of a diagram in which the course of normal development is represented as the bottom of a valley, the sides of which symbolise the opposition that the system presents to any stresses which attempt to deflect development from its normal course. A cross-section of the valley represents, in fact, the curve that we have defined as the adaptability of the system, with the minor modification that the scale on which the stress is represented is reversed as between the two sides of the valley, so that it measures divergencies from the normal—below it on one side or above it on the other. The surface which in this way symbolises the developmental potentialities of the genotype has been called the "epigenetic landscape."

This diagrammatic form of representation is particularly appropriate for discussing certain points which emerge from some other *Drosophila* experiments. In these, quite abnormal environmental stresses were applied to the developing system, and artificial selection was made for certain categories of response. Although both the stresses and the selection were artificial, these experiments reveal a type of process which might well go on in natural populations under the influence of natural stresses and natural selection.

In the first experiment (Waddington, 1953; Bateman, 1956), heat shock was applied to pupae of an age which was known to be suitable for producing a number of phenocopies affecting the cross-veins. In point of fact, several different phenocopies appeared, involving absence of one or another of the cross-veins or in some cases increases in venation (Fig. 4). If selection was exercised for any specific one of these types of phenocopy, strains could be rapidly built up which responded to the standard stress by a high frequency of this particular developmental abnormality. Moreover, after fairly intensive selection it was possible to produce strains in which the particular modification

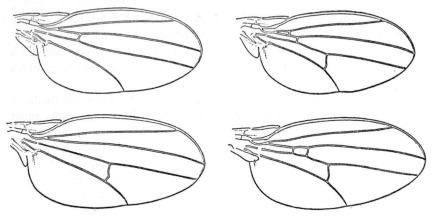

FIG. 4.—Some types of venation phenocopies induced by a heat shock to the 18-hr. pupa in *D. melanogaster* (Bateman, 1956).

which had been selected for appeared in high frequency even in the absence of the stress. We had again carried out the process, which I have called "genetic assimilation," by which selection produces genotypes which modify development in the same manner as did the original environmental stress.

An attempt was also made to produce the genetic assimilation of a very remarkable phenotypic modification which, if it appeared in nature, would probably be considered of macro-evolutionary importance (Waddington 1956, 1957a). If the eggs of a normal wild-type *Drosophila* stock are treated with ether vapour soon after laying, a certain proportion of them develop a bithorax phenotype (Fig. 5; cf. Gloor, 1947). If one exerts artificial selection for the capacity to respond to this peculiar environmental stress, one can increase the frequency of the response—or, by selecting against it, decrease it. Again, after something over 20 generations of selection, it was possible to produce an assimilated bithorax stock in which the phenotype is developed in high frequency even in the absence of any ether-vapour treatment (Fig. 6).

It seems profitable to discuss these last two experiments in terms of the canalisation model mentioned above (cf. Waddington 1957b). We can picture the development of the cross-vein region (or of the thorax) proceeding under normal circumstances along a certain valley leading to the normal adult condition (Fig. 7). The slope of the sides of the valley towards the bottom means that the system is to some extent resistant to stresses which might tend to produce an abnormal end result. The fact that the system responds by phenocopy formation to certain stresses applied at definite times can be represented by

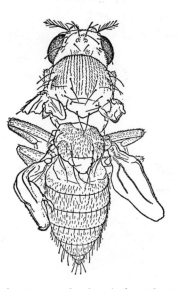

FIG. 5.—The bithorax phenotype as developed after ether treatment of the egg. The main wings have been removed to show more clearly the transformed metathorax. The individual depicted is actually from the "assimilated" stock and developed *without* ether treatment (Waddington, 1956).

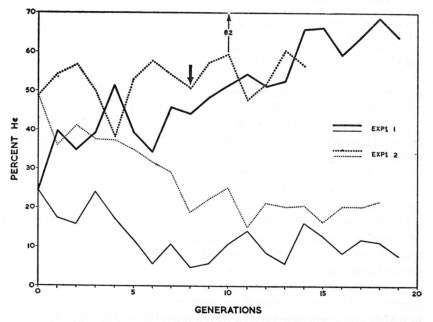

FIG. 6.—The progress of selection for or against bithorax-like response to ether treatment. Two experiments are shown, starting from two wild-type populations which reacted with rather different frequencies (Waddington, 1956).

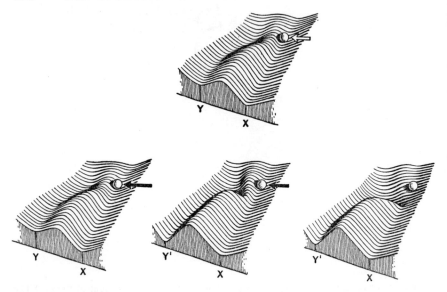

FIG. 7.—Modification of the epigenetic landscape by selection. The upper drawing shows the situation in the unselected foundation stock; a developmental modification Y will occur only if an environmental stress (*white arrow*) forces the developing system to cross a threshold or col. Of the lower figures, that on the left shows the Baldwin-Lloyd Morgan hypotheses—that a new gene mutation (*black arrow*) appears which substitutes for the environmental stress, everything else remaining unaltered. The two lower right figures show stages in the selection of genotypes in which threshold is lowered (requiring only a "small" gene mutation or, eventually, a single specifiable mutation) and the course of the developmental modification is made more definite and directed to the optimal end-result, Y (Waddington, 1957b).

drawing a side valley, reached over a col, at that time in development. The particular configuration of the surface drawn at the top of Figure 7 represents the developmental potentialities of one specific genotype. In any large population the genetic variation in the frequency with which the response occurs will correspond to variations in the height of the col above the main valley floor. Similarly, variation in the type of phenocopy produced (an absence of the posterior or the anterior cross-vein, etc.) will be represented by variations in the course of the side valley. Selection, we have seen, has been able to utilise both types of variation. In the assimilated stocks we have selected and combined low-col genes until we have reached a condition in which the col is non-existent and the floor of the upper part of the main valley leads off into what was originally the side branch. In the selection of one particular phenocopy rather than another, we have selected genotypes in which one particular type of developmental modification is particularly favoured; that is, we have made the course of the side valley more definite and have led it to our chosen end point.

We may ask ourselves where this genetic variability has come from. Was it perhaps created during the course of the experiment? There is rather good reason to believe that this was definitely not the case in the work involving the cross-veinless phenocopies. For instance, cross-veinless types occur spontaneously in some wild stocks; that is to say, genes which tend to lower the height of the col which defends the side valley are present in sufficiently high frequency for an occasional individual to contain sufficient of them to abolish the col even before selection starts, although the frequency of such combinations is so low that natural selection would scarcely be able to utilise them in the absence of the reinforcement produced by the environmental stress. Again, when selection for environmental response was made in highly inbred stocks, no effect was produced, indicating that new mutations were not occurring frequently enough to be effective (Fig. 8). This experiment also shows definitely that no direct

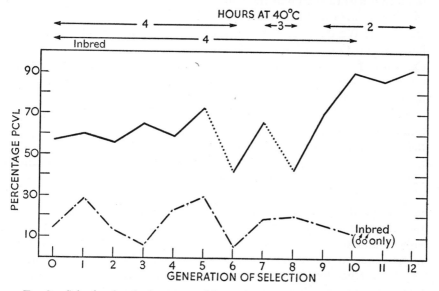

Fig. 8.—Selection for the frequency of formation of a broken posterior cross-vein in response to a temperature shock. *Above,* a wild-type stock, subjected for five generations to a 4-hour treatment, but later to treatments of only 3 and 2 hours; *below,* an inbred stock, subjected to 4-hour treatments throughout the experiment (Bateman, 1956).

Lamarckian inheritance of the acquired character is occurring in this system.

In the bithorax experiments, however, and also in another experiment involving the dumpy-wing phenotype (Bateman, 1956), there is a strong suggestion that genes acting in the direction of selection turned up during the course of the experiments. Since the experiments involved some hundreds of thousands of flies, the occurrence of such mutations is not so unexpected that we have to attribute it to the environmental stress itself. The mutations presumably occurred in the normal manner, that is, "at random." But although the change in the chromosomal nucleoprotein may well have been quite undirected, the phenotypic effects of the genes were certainly influenced by the selection which had been practiced on the stock. The new "bithorax-like" gene has a strong tendency to produce bithorax phenotypes (actually by a maternal effect, but that is irrelevant to the present discussion) when in the genetic background of the selected stock but only a very weak tendency to do so in a normal, unselected, wild-type background. A similar consideration applies to the "dumpy-like" gene. Selection, if you like, by reducing the height of the col and making the side valley more definite, has produced genotypes whose developmental potentialities are such that the course of development is easily diverted to the production of the particular adult condition that has been selected for. We have, as it were, set the developmental machine on a hair trigger. Quite a number of gene mutations, which are random at the level of nucleoprotein structure, are likely to produce this preset phenotype, and are therefore by no means random in their developmental effects.

The particular importance of this conclusion concerns the evolutionary origin of *co-ordinated* effects on the subunits of a structure, of the kind which were illustrated in the forelimbs of the gibbon and pangolin. The adult form of any animal is the result of the interaction between its genotype and the environmental stimuli and stresses to which the developing system has been subjected. If one thinks of the stresses produced by a life dependent on digging for food, it is clear that the stimuli may be very complex. When only a single stress is involved and the response of the developing system shows a certain approximation to an all- or none-character, as in the temperature-shock or ether-treatment experiments, one can represent the system by a diagram involving a single col or even a sharply defined threshold. When one considers the more complex stresses which arise in real life, such a representation becomes more difficult and also more artificial. But the essential point is that the complex stresses give rise to developmental responses which are co-ordinated. If in a wild population these responses are of adaptive value, natural selection will occur and will increase not only the intensity of the response but also its co-ordination. It will build up genotypes whose developmental potentialities include a high capacity for producing a well organised and harmonious adaptive phenotype. This capacity may then be released by quite a variety of random changes in the nucleoproteins of the chromosomes.

In this way, by taking into account the possibility of selection for both capacity to respond and type of response to environmental stresses, we can once again find justification for attributing the "appearance of design," or co-ordinated adaptations, to the epigenetic processes which we know to have co-ordinated effects; and we can reduce our dependence on the abstract principle that natural selection can engender states of high improbability. We have, in fact, found evidence for the existence of a "feedback" between the conditions of the environment and the phenotypic effects of gene mutations. The "feedback" circuit is the simple one, as follows: (1) environmental stresses produce developmental modifications; (2) the same stresses produce a natural selective pressure which tends to accumulate genotypes which respond to the stresses with co-ordinated adaptive modifications from the unstressed course of development; (3) genes newly arising by mutation will operate in an epigenetic system in which the production of such co-ordinated adaptive modifications has been made easy (Waddington 1957*b*).

Before concluding, I should like to return to the earlier point that the stresses to which an animal will be subjected depend at least in part on its own behaviour. Nearly all animals live in surroundings which offer them a much greater variety of habitats than they are willing to occupy. Naturalists, of course, are very familiar with the fact that closely related species often show markedly different preferences for particular types of habitat; even within species, different races may exhibit relatively specific patterns of behaviour. These obviously play a considerable evolutionary role in connection with reproductive isolation (e.g., on *Drosophila,* Knight, Robertson, and Waddington, 1956; Koref and Waddington, 1958; Spieth, 1957). They may also affect more general choice of living conditions (e.g., Waddington, Woolf, and Perry, 1956), but this field is still very incompletely explored. For instance, it is clear that cryptic coloration is of very little use to an animal unless its behaviour is such that it makes use of the possibilities of concealment which are offered to it, but we know little about the genetic correlations, if any, between the production of cryptic coloration and the appropriate types of behaviour, although Kettlewell (1956) has shown that melanic moths do in fact tend to settle on the darker areas of trees more frequently than would be expected by chance. It is clear, however, that here again selection will be operating not on the isolated components—behaviour on the one side and developmental and physiological response on the other—but on an interlocking system in which behaviour and other aspects of function mutually influence one another.

The result of this discussion is to suggest that we have perhaps been tempted to oversimplify our account of the mechanism by which evolution is brought about. This mechanism—the evolutionary system, as it may be called—has often been envisaged as consisting of no more than a set of genotypes which are influenced, on the one hand, by a completely independent and random process of mutation and, on the other, by processes of natural selection which again are in no way determined by the nature of the genotypes submitted to them. Perhaps such a simplification was justified when it was a question of establishing the relevance of Mendelian genetics to evolutionary theory, but it can only lead to an impoverishment of our ideas if we are not willing to go further, now that it has served its turn.

In point of fact, it would seem that we must consider the evolutionary system to involve at least four major subsystems (Fig. 9). One is the "genetic system," the whole chromosomal-genic mechanism of hereditary transmission; the second is natural selection; a third, which might be called the "exploitive system," comprises the set of processes by which animals choose and often modify one particular habitat out of the range of environmental possibilities open to them; and the fourth is the "epigenetic system"—that is, the sequence of causal processes which bring about the development of the fertilised zygote into the adult capable of reproduction. These four component systems are not isolated entities, each sufficient in its own right and merely colliding with one another when impinging on the evolving creature. It is inadequate to think of natural selection and variation as being no more essentially connected with one another than would be a heap of pebbles and the gravel-sorter onto which it is thrown. On the contrary, we have to think in terms of circular and not merely unidirectional causal sequences. At any particular moment in the evolutionary history of an organism, the state of each of the four main subsystems has been partially determined by the action of each of the other subsystems. The intensity of natural selective forces is dependent on the condition of the exploitive system, on the flexibilities and stabilities which have been built into the epigenetic system, and so on.

Very much remains to be done in working out the theory of evolution from this more inclusive point of view. But one general point is already clear. We can now see that the system by which evolution is brought about has itself some degree of organisation, in the sense that its subsystems are mutually interacting, and, in fact, mutually interdependent. In the recent past we have been working with a theory in which the obvious organisation of the living world had to be engendered *ab initio* out of non-organised basic components—"random" mutation, on the one hand, and an essentially unconnected natural

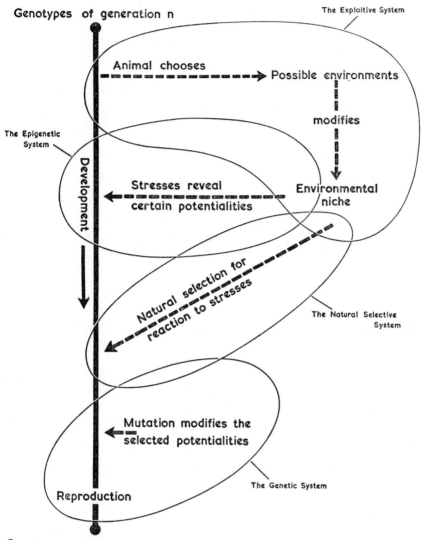

FIG. 9.—The logical structure of the evolutionary system. Changes in gene frequency between successive generations involve the operation of four subsystems: the exploitive, the epigenetic, the natural selective, and the genetic (Waddington, 1959).

selection on the other. We had to rely on a Maxwell demon, and persuade ourselves not merely that natural selection could show some of the properties of such a useful *deus ex machina* but that it had them so fully developed that we needed nothing further. This was a rather uncomfortable position, and we can now escape from it.

REFERENCES

BATEMAN, G. 1956. "Studies on Genetic Assimilation." Ph.D. thesis, Edinburgh University. *J. Genet.* (in press).

DURRANT, A. 1958. "Environmentally Induced Inherited Changes in Flax," *Proc. X^{th} International Congress in Genetics,* I, 71.

GLOOR, H. 1947. "Phaenokopic Versuche mit Aetter an Drosophila," *Rev. suisse zool.,* LIV, 637.

GLOOR, H. and CHEN, P. S. 1950. "Ueber ein Analorgan bei Drosophila Larven," *Rev. suisse zool.,* LVII, 570.

HESLOP-HARRISON, J. W. 1920. "Genetical Studies in Moths," *J. Genet.,* IX, 195.

HIGHKIN, H. R. 1958. "Transmission of Phenotypic Variability in a Pure Line," *Proc. X^{th} International Congress in Genetics,* II, 120.

KETTLEWELL, H. B. D. 1955. "Selection Experiments in Industrial Melanism in the Lepidoptera," *Heredity,* IX, 323.

―――. 1956. "Investigations on the Evolution of Melanism in Lepidoptera," *Proc. Roy. Soc. Lond. B.,* CXLV, 297.

KNIGHT, G. R., ROBERTSON, A. and WADDINGTON, C. H. 1956. "Selection for Sexual Isolation within a Species," *Evolution,* X, 14.

KOREF, S. S. and WADDINGTON, C. H. (in press, *Evolution*).

MAYR, E. 1958. "Behavior and Systematics," p. 341 in *Behaviour and Evolution,* eds. ROE and SIMPSON. New Haven: Yale University Press.

SPIETH, H. T. 1958. "Behaviour and Isolating Mechanisms," p. 363 in *Behavior and Evolution,* eds. ROE and SIMPSON. New Haven: Yale University Press.

TURESSON, G. 1930. "The Selective Effect of the Climate upon Plant Species," *Hereditas,* XIV, 99.

WADDINGTON, C. H. 1940. *Organisers and Genes.* London: Cambridge University Press.

―――. 1942. "The Canalisation of Development and the Inheritance of Acquired Characters. *Nature,* CL, 563.

―――. 1953. The Genetic Assimilation of an Acquired Character. *Evolution,* VII, 118.

―――. 1955. "On a Case of Quantitative Variation on Either Side of the Wild Type," *Zeits. ind Abst. u. Vererb. Lehre,* LXXXVII, 208.

―――. 1956. "Genetic Assimilation of the Bithorax Phenotype," *Evolution,* X, 1.

―――. 1957a. "The Genetic Basis of the Assimilated Bithorax Stock," *J. Genet.,* LV, 241.

―――. 1957b. *The Strategy of the Genes.* London: Allen and Unwin; New York: Macmillan Co.

―――. 1959. In *Nature,* CLXXXIII, 1654.

WADDINGTON, C. H., WOOLF, B. and PERRY, M. M. 1954. "Environment Selection by *Drosophila* Mutants," *Evolution,* VIII, 89.

TH. DOBZHANSKY

EVOLUTION AND ENVIRONMENT

Even before the days of the sputniks, it was quite usual for astronomers and biologists to be asked by laymen whether living, sentient, and rational beings are likely to exist on heavenly bodies other than the planet earth. Being neither an astronomer nor a chemical biologist, this writer is not competent to answer such inquiries. However, speculation about the possible inhabitants of other planets does impinge upon a fundamental problem pertinent to the understanding of the evolution of life here on earth: Is the course of evolution determined by the environment in which it occurs?

Almost without exception, the hypothetical Martians are imagined in the likeness of men. You have probably seen them pictured emerging from their flying saucers; they are vertebrate animals, presumably mammals walking erect, with heads rather larger in relation to the bodies than in terrestrial humans, and having something like a pair of radio antennae to suggest possession of highly refined sense organs. These fantasies do, however, have interesting implications. If life arose independently in various parts of the cosmos, its evolution is assumed to have taken courses everywhere not unlike that on our own planet. Starting with some kind of primordial virus, evolution is bound to produce something like man. This assumption is surely not confined to science fiction; it has been ably defended by authoritative biologists and must be accorded the status of a scientific hypothesis.

Hoyle (1955) believes that there may be some one hundred billion (10^{11}) planetary systems in the galaxy of the Milky Way not unlike the one in which we live. Between one hundred million and one billion galaxies can be seen with the aid of the strongest telescope now existing. Shapley (1958) gives one hundred million as a conservative estimate of the number of planets on which the environments are deemed propitious for the existence of life as we know it on earth.

THEODOSIUS DOBZHANSKY is Professor of Zoology at Columbia University. Most famous for his genetics research with *Drosophila,* Professor Dobzhansky was inspired to become a biologist upon reading *Origin of Species.* He came to America from his native Russia in 1927 to work with Thomas Hunt Morgan. He is a former president of the Genetics Society and of the Society for the Study of Evolution, and he has recently been awarded the Elliott Medal of the National Academy of Sciences.

403

Even if the origin of life is an improbable event, the number of places where life could have arisen in the cosmos and the length of time during which these events could have taken place is very large. The possibility that life has, in fact, arisen independently in many places is certainly to be reckoned with.

The question which interests us is whether similar evolutionary developments may have occurred, given more or less similar environments, on more than one planet.

Another way to ask the same question is whether repeated origins of life on earth would result in re-enactment of evolutionary histories similar to that which actually occurred in the past.

We have barely reached the point of asking such questions. The answers can at best be speculative, since the events with which they are concerned can be neither observed nor experimented with. Matters may, however, be helped by inverting the question thus: What agencies make the evolutionary changes in a group of organisms follow parallel paths, and which make them diverge? So stated, the problem is whittled down to a microevolutionary level and thus rendered accessible to experimental study.

EVOLUTION FROM WITHIN

Although they have rather few adherents at present, the theories of autogenesis, which regard evolution as a process completely determined from within the organism, must be considered in connection with the problem stated above. According to these theories, variously named "orthogenesis," "nomogenesis," "aristogenesis," etc., evolution comes from endogenous causes and is largely independent of the environment. The best statement of this view, free of overt mysticism, is that of Berg (1926). He hoped that biology would eventually find "intrinsic and constitutional agencies laid down in the structure of the protoplasm, which compel the organism to vary in a determined direction." And he thought that "evolution is to a considerable degree predetermined . . . an unfolding or manifestation of preexisting rudiments." It was, in short, preformation on the species and higher levels, as well as on the individual level. This would indeed be an easy solution of the problem of evolution if it were not a pseudo-solution. The theory of nomogenesis says in effect that life on earth developed as it did, not because it existed in a certain environment, but because it was made from the start to develop that way. If life were to arise repeatedly, on earth or elsewhere in the cosmos, it would develop again the same way because it contains certain pre-existing rudiments and no others. The assumption of autogenesis is really an implicit denial that evolution occurs at all; what happens is a gradual un-covering of things originally hidden under a series of wrappings; every-thing that will ever appear is there from the beginning.

Strictly speaking, theories of autogenesis cannot be disproved. It is impossible to disprove that, for example, man's ancestors were de-termined to develop into men. They did develop that way, and, since these ancestors no longer exist, one cannot prove that they could have, under other conditions, developed into something else. Autogenetic theories were rather popular for a time with comparative morpholo-gists and paleontologists, but it has been shown that assumptions of this kind are not necessitated by anything in the available evidence. This has been demonstrated particularly clearly in the works of Simp-son (1953) and of Rensch (1954). Nothing in the known history of life on earth compels one to believe that the evolution is predeter-mined or that organisms are able to change in just one direction.

The evidence from all fields of biology has converged to favor the biological, or synthetic, theory of evolution. Evolution is, in part, ectogenesis; it is brought about by causes outside the organism or, more precisely, through interactions between the organism and its environment. The evolutionary transformations which occur in a group of organisms depend on the environments in which these organisms are placed. Given similar environments, the evolutionary events will tend to be similar. However, different organisms in the same general en-vironment will undergo different changes. The environment determines the changes which occur not directly but only by way of natural selec-tion, a process first clearly expounded by Darwin. The biological theory of evolution is the heir and the direct descendant of Darwin's original theory of evolution by natural selection.

Evolution from Without

A century ago Darwin (1859) wrote:

It may be said that natural selection is daily and hourly scrutinizing, throughout the world, every variation, even the slightest; rejecting that which is bad, preserving and adding up all that is good; silently and in-sensibly working, whenever and wherever opportunity offers, at the im-provement of each organic being in relation to its organic and inorganic conditions of life.

Darwin's statement remains fully valid today. Natural selection acts generally to improve the adaptation of the organism to the "condi-tions of life" in a given environment. Interaction between the or-ganism and its environment in the process of natural selection is the principal driving force of evolution. With very few exceptions, the changes which occur in evolution have the immediate effect of promoting the harmony between the organism and the environment, regardless of whether these changes may, or may not, be useful in the long run.

This does not mean that every trait or character of every organism must be adaptive as such (for a discussion of the concept of adaptive trait see Dobzhansky, 1956). For example, some species of *Drosophila* have eyes of a brighter and others of a more subdued red color. There is no reason to think that the precise shade of the eye color is important to these flies, but Nolte (1958) has shown that the color depends upon the proportions and the distribution in the eye tissues of two different pigments. The shade of the eye color is an indicator of the pattern of physiological processes in the developing organism. An adaptive trait is merely an outward sign of an adaptive development pattern. It is not the "trait" but the path which the development takes in a given environment that helps or hinders the survival and reproduction of the organism in that environment.

The crucial problem is evidently just how the environment determines which changes and which adaptations do occur. Consider the evolutionary transformations which have led to the emergence of the human species from its prehuman ancestors. The development of, for example, the erect body posture or the expansion of the brain cortex has made man a biological species supremely successful in most diverse environments. Furthermore, these developments did not occur in anticipation of living, or "in order" to fit man to live in his present environments. Natural selection had no foresight; at every stage of the process the changes that took place must have been useful to their carriers in the environments in which they lived at the time when these changes took place. Even traits which are decidedly injurious when considered in isolation may really be adaptive, if they became established in evolution because they happened to be concomitants of useful traits. Thus difficult childbirth—an absurdly unadaptive trait—appears to be an adjunct of the erect body posture, which is clearly adaptive. The advantage gained by freeing the hands for useful work evidently outweighed the drawback of painful childbirth. And yet one may reasonably ask: Were the adaptations which occurred in our ancestors really inevitable in the environments in which they lived? Could our ancestors have coped with their environments also in some other manner, by developing some different adaptations?

The problem here under consideration must be stated carefully if it is not to become a pseudo-problem. The evolutionary history of man, like the evolutionary history of any species, is unique. Unless one is prepared to renounce the principle of causality, which I am not prepared to do, one is compelled to say that the evolutionary development of the hominid stock was ineluctably determined to go exactly as it did. But all that "determined" in the foregoing sentence means is that we assume that cause-and-effect relations, and not caprice, prevail in nature. Given exactly the environments which obtained, say two million years ago, and exactly the genetic materials which our ancestral species had at that time, the evolutionary changes which happened were bound to happen. This is, however, trite; environment is never exactly the same twice, and the genetic composition of a population does not remain exactly the same from one generation to the next.

The problem is really this: How great a diversity of evolutionary events may arise because of rather minor variations in the genetic composition of the populations of a living species and because of chance differences in the environments to which this species is exposed? This problem is not trivial; it is possible—and, indeed, it is often assumed implicitly—that minor variations in the environment and in the genetic materials on which the environment acts will produce only correspondingly minor heterogeneities in the resulting evolutionary processes. If so, the evolution may be said to be rigidly determined by the environment. Evolutionary changes would have to be regarded as imposed on the organism by the environment. The environment calls the tune; given a certain genetic constitution of a living species, the species can either change in a certain way or die out.

On the other hand, the occurrence of one evolutionary event may condition the subsequent events. Evolutionary histories could, then, take divergent courses because the antecedent events were different. What happens in evolution may be decided mainly by the nature of the organism roused to action by the environment. The environment might then play the role of a stimulating or conditioning, rather than of a determining, agent. This may sound like a relapse to a belief in autogenesis. However, autogenetic theories postulated that the evolutionary history was predetermined by the "intrinsic and constitutional agencies" in the organism itself, allowing the environment merely to decide whether the changing organism continued to live or died. By contrast, the modern biological theory of evolution assumes that natural selection is the chief propellant of evolutionary change.

Natural selection is a very interesting kind of response of the population to its environment, because it tends to increase the congruity between the two. However, the congruity may be attained in more than one way. Plants may become adapted to aridity by reduction of their evaporating surface or by transformation of leaves into spines. Some plants combat aridity by developing a waxy coating on their leaves. Still other plants become adapted by going through the active parts of their life-cycles during a short humid season and remaining quiescent at other seasons.

Even apparently similar adaptations may be built from genetically different components. Geneticists have shown that, at least in higher organisms, there are numerous genes that produce very similar effects on the development of the body. The difference between a large and a small variety of a species may be a result of summation of the effects of many genes, each changing the size by a tiny increment. Suppose that a certain body size is adaptive in a certain environment. A given body size may then be attained by selection of a number of genes which influence the body dimensions. Which ones of the many possible genes with such action become selected is immaterial, so long as the optimal body size is approached. The result is that in some organisms races similar in appearance are known to be genetically not identical (see, for example, the work of Ford [1955] on the moth, *Triphaena comes*).

Environment does not impose specific changes on the organism, either directly, as believed by old Lamarckians, or via natural selection, as assumed by classical Darwinists. Nor is the role of the environment reduced to an *ex post facto* judgement of what is fit or unfit to survive, as believed by adherents of autogenesis. The role of the environment in evolution is more subtle. I know of no better way to describe it than to borrow Toynbee's phrase—challenge and response.

To inhabit a cold country, a living creature must be able to resist low temperatures; to live in a tropical rain forest, it must withstand humid heat; to exist in a desert, it must be protected from desiccation; in some environments the amount of food is the limiting factor, in others, it is the presence of parasites or infectious diseases. A species may, or may not, respond to the challenge of environmental opportunity by adaptive changes of its genes (or, in the case of man, by adaptive changes in his tradition, i.e., in his culture). If the species does not respond, it may be deprived of certain resources and opportunities for living. It may become extinct. If it does respond, it improves or, at least, preserves its grasp and domination of the environment. Just how the response is given, what kind of genetic changes occur, which organs or functions become modified and to what extent, is immaterial, so long as the over-all fitness of the organism in its environment remains high enough for life to endure. The environment thus instigates, foments, conditions, and circumscribes evolutionary changes; but it does not decide exactly which changes, if any, will occur.

DETERMINISTIC FACTORS

MUTATION

Lack of understanding of the sources of heritable variation was the Achilles heel of Darwin's theory. Heritable variation is the fountainhead of evolution. Evolution is change in the genetic constitution of the succeeding generations of a species or a population. Natural selection would be futile if the progenies of the surviving fittest were no different, at least on the average, from what the progenies of the eliminated unfit would have been. Darwin was satisfied that heritable variance was present in the populations of all organisms for which there existed relevant evidence. But he did not know the source of this variance.

By a quirk of a kind which abounds in the history of ideas, De Vries thought that he was overthrowing Darwin's theory when, in reality, he started to discover the way out of Darwin's greatest predicament. De Vries held that the mutants which he found in the evening primrose were giving birth, without the benefit of natural selection, to full-fledged new species. It remained for Morgan and his school to show that mutations do nothing of this sort; most mutations alter only a single gene at a time. Still later, Chetverikov, Haldane, Wright, and Fisher put things in proper perspective. The process of mutation supplies the genetic raw materials from which evolutionary changes may be constructed by natural selection. Mutation is the source of heritable variation which Darwin vainly tried to uncover.

The proximate causes of mutation still remain unknown, even though many mutagens, i.e., factors speeding up the mutation process, have been discovered. The greatest apparent difficulty for any theory which considers mutation to be the source of raw materials of evolution is that a majority of mutations that arise are detrimental to their carriers, at least in the environment in which the species normally lives. The occurrence of mutations is responsible for populations carrying so-called genetic loads, i.e., accumulations of genetic variants which, under certain conditions, produce hereditary diseases, malformations, and constitutional weaknesses of various kinds.

These matters have been discussed repeatedly by many authors; the present writer recently had an opportunity to do so in another place (Dobzhansky, 1959). Very briefly, the detrimental effects of most mutations are a consequence of their being essentially errors in the process of self-reproduction of the genes; mutations arise regardless of whether they may, or may not, be useful at a given time and place, or ever, or anywhere; some mutations, nevertheless, do enhance the fitness of their carriers; useful mutations are particularly likely to be found if a population of a species is placed in an environment different from that in which it normally occurs; some of the mutations which are detrimental under normal environments are useful in new ones.

It is a different aspect of the phenomenon of mutation that concerns us here. Mutation is recurrent. Although careful study often shows that two similar, but independently arisen, mutants are not completely identical, there is, nevertheless, good reason to think that the same change in the gene does occur repeatedly. Every kind of mutation has a certain probability of occurrence. The origin in a population of a certain number of mutants is as inevitable as a certain number of automobile accidents in a country. This amounts to saying that if an evolutionary change requires merely the occurrence of a certain mutation, this change is bound to take place, given enough time and a population of sufficient size.

Experimental verification of the above deduction became possible with the development of the genetic study of microorganisms. Most mutations are, on the whole, rare; but, with some microorganisms, large enough numbers of individuals can be raised to estimate the frequencies of the mutants. The pioneering work of Luria and Delbruck (1943), Demerec and Fano (1945), and Luria (1946) showed that mutants conferring on the colon bacteria, *Escherichia coli*, a resistance to certain bacteriophages arise at rates of the orders of 10^{-7} to 3×10^{-9}. Suppose, then, that we start with a line of colon bacteria susceptible to the attack of a given strain of the bacteriophage, and we wish to obtain a resistant strain. Success or failure may depend on the number of the bacterial cells in a culture exposed to the bacteriophage. If this number is small—say 10^6 or smaller—the culture will only rarely contain mutant cells. But if many such cultures or a large culture with 10^9 or more cells is exposed, some mutants are almost certain to be available. The susceptible cells will be destroyed by the bacteriophage, and the resistant mutants will be the survivors. Resistant strains may easily be obtained from these survivors.

The bacterium-bacteriophage system is a good model of elementary evolutionary events in various organisms, including the higher ones. The environment offers a challenge (presence of the bacteriophage), to which the bacteria may respond by changing into a resistant variety. It may seem that the response depends upon an accident—mutation. But it depends also on the number of individuals exposed to the challenge. If this number is sufficiently large, the appropriate accident becomes probable or even certain. If the experiment is made properly, its success is assured; bacteriophage-resistant strains of colon bacteria will be obtained whenever desired.

A greater complexity can be introduced into the model without loss of its deterministic quality. Demerec (1945) and others have analyzed the resistance of the bacterium *Staphylococcus aureus* to penicillin. Complete resistance to massive doses of this drug depends on the possession not of one but of several genes, each conferring upon the bacteria only a small increment of resistance. Exposure of normal, non-resistant bacteria to high concentrations of penicillin yields no resistant strains. All the bacteria are killed. This is as expected if the mutations of the genes for resistance are rare and independent. Suppose that a complete resistance to penicillin is due to the summation of the effects of three genes, which mutate to resistance at rates as high as 10^{-6}. The probability of simultaneous mutation of all three genes is then 10^{-18}; 10^{18} individuals is a number far too great to be obtained in experiments even with bacteria.

The difficulty can, however, be obviated. Susceptible bacteria are exposed to concentrations of penicillin which enable individuals carrying a single mutant for resistance to survive. A weakly resistant strain is isolated and exposed to a higher concentration of penicillin, which kills the single mutants but lets double mutants survive. Repeated selection by progressively greater concentrations results, then, in obtaining highly resistant bacteria. This is an illustration of Fisher's dictum that selection is a method to secure realization of what would be in the highest degree improbable without it.

SELECTION IN SIMILAR ENVIRONMENTS

We have seen that the accidental and apparently capricious character of mutation does not preclude elementary, microevolutionary, changes from being predictable and reproducible. Provided that the probability of the occurrence of a certain kind of mutation in a given environment is known, the experiment may, at least in theory, be so arranged that the mutant is obtained. The experiments described above obviously involve not mutations alone but interaction of mutation with selection. A large culture of colon bacteria usually contains several cells resistant to bacteriophages, but these cells are so small a minority among susceptible ones that, to find them, a selecting agent is indispensable. Introduction into the bacterial culture of an inoculum of bacteriophage causes death of the susceptible cells and, consequently, isolation of the resistant cells.

Reproduction in experiments of historic evolutionary changes is usually impossible of attainment, for the simple reason that this would require time intervals far greater than the life-span of a human experimenter or even of several generations of experimenters. Resynthesis of some naturally existing allopolyploid species by hybridization of other species is the outstanding exception to this rule of non-reproducibility of evolutionary histories. Allopolyploidy is, however, a special type of evolutionary event, which we cannot discuss here, despite its interest. Many other situations have, however, been brought to light by zoological and botanical studies, from which the decisive role of the environment in the causation of evolutionary changes can safely be inferred.

Comparative studies on the racial variation in different species, often not even closely related ones, have disclosed remarkable parallelisms in the characteristics of races which inhabit similar environments. Some of these "rules of geographic variation" had been known for a long time, but they have recently been critically re-examined, chiefly by Rensch and his school (reviewed in Mayr, 1942; Dobzhansky, 1951; Rensch, 1954). For example, among warm-blooded vertebrates, the races which inhabit colder climates differ from the races of the same species living in warmer climates, as a general rule, in the following characters: larger body size; legs, tails, ears, and bills relatively shorter; coloration lighter; the fur warmer; in birds the wings more pointed; relatively larger hearts, pancreas, livers, kidneys, stomachs, and intestines; larger number of young per litter or of eggs per clutch. The present writer (Dobzhansky, 1933) observed that in species after species of lady beetles (Coccinellidae) the races of arid lands (the American Southwest, Central Asia) show a reduction in the dark pigmentation as compared with those in more humid climates. On a microgeographic scale, Cain and Sheppard (1954) found that English colonies of the snail *Cepaea nemoralis* show higher incidence of brown and unbanded shells if they inhabit beach or oak woods than if they live in hedgerows or on meadows. Interestingly enough, these rules do not apply to colonies of the same species in France (Lamotte, 1951).

The rules of geographic variation used to be a happy hunting ground for partisans of Lamarckism and selectionism, abounding in data interpretable as their predilections decreed. Nowadays these disputes may, I hope, be bypassed. The rules attest in any case that the environment is important as an instigator of evolutionary changes. At the same time, it must be emphasized that what has been observed are rules indeed, not laws. Exceptions to the rules do occur, as Rensch, who has contributed more than anyone else to their study, has duly stressed. And while these exceptions do not exactly prove the rules, they are in some ways as valuable as the rules themselves. The lesson to be derived from them is that, although the environment may guide the evolution of living things, it does not prescribe just what change must occur.

A similar conclusion follows from the study of evolutionary trends operative on scales far grander than the just considered trends or rules of geographic racial variation. This matter has been analyzed so thoroughly by Simpson (1953) and by Rensch (1954) that a mere mention will suffice here. One of the trends observed by paleontologists in numerous fossil lineages is progressive increase in body size; chronologically more recent forms are very often larger than their ancestors. This enlargement has been happening in all sorts of animals, vertebrates as well as invertebrates, marine as well as land forms, predators or herbivores. Yet even this is only a rule, not a law. In some phyletic lines evolutionary changes have been taking place for long geological periods without appreciable alteration in body size, and in some others the changes were even toward a smaller size.[1]

SOURCES OF RANDOMNESS

SEXUAL REPRODUCTION

Darwin's estimate of the role of sexual reproduction in evolution was, of necessity, ambivalent. On the one hand, he thought ". . . that it is a general law of nature (utterly ignorant though we be of the meaning of the law) that no organic being self-fertilizes itself for an eternity of generations; but that a cross with another individual is occasionally— perhaps at very long intervals—indispensable." He knew that the genetic variability needed for selection to be effective is particularly great in the progeny of hybrids and "mongrels." On the other hand, if the heredity of a child was, as Darwin thought, a result of a commingling of parental heredities, then sexual reproduction would turn out to be a leveler, rather than an enhancer, of genetic variability.

Mendel's discovery that genes do not blend but segregate in heterozygotes has changed the situation entirely. Hardy and Weinberg deduced from Mendel's law of segregation that unfixed genes present in a sexual (Mendelian) population will maintain constant relative frequencies in the gene pool unless mutation, selection, or genetic drift intervenes. The variety of genotypes which may arise in a Mendelian population owing to segregation and recombination of genes may be

---

[1] A note should be taken of an interesting attempt by Schmalhausen (1958) to describe the roles of the environment and of natural selection in terms of the information theory. The basic unit of evolution is a Mendelian population of a species, which represents the automaton in the sense of cybernetics. The environment, the "biogeocenosis," acts as a source of problems which the automaton is designed to solve.

immense. In a population with n unfixed genes, each represented by only two alleles, 3^n genotypes, 2^n of them homozygous, are potentially possible.

How large may n be in the populations of various species is a problem which unavoidably presents itself. The work in this field happens to be beset with many difficulties; it will suffice for our purpose simply to take note of the existence of two hypotheses the evidence for and against which remains as yet inconclusive (Dobzhansky, 1955). The classical hypothesis assumes that individuals of a species, such as *Homo sapiens* or *Drosophila melanogaster,* are homozygous for most of their genes. Unfixed genes, i.e., represented in the population by more than a single allele, are a minority, and even among them one allele is "normal" and widespread, and the others are more or less defective. The normal alleles yield normal individuals, while the defective ones contribute to the genetic load which the population carries.

Some facts do not readily fit in with the classical hypothesis. They are more easily encompassed by the balance hypothesis, which supposes that most individuals in a Mendelian population are heterozygous for many genes. Furthermore, each of many gene loci is represented in the gene pool by several or by many alleles, which have been selected in the process of evolution because they yielded highly fit heterozygotes with other alleles present in the gene pool of the same Mendelian population. The same alleles may, however, produce homozygotes which are poorly adapted and even inviable. Mutant alleles which are harmful to their possessors when homozygous and are harmful or at least useless when heterozygous constitute the mutational genetic load which natural selection tends to minimize.

I think that the evidence available for populations of several sexually reproducing organisms tallies better with the balance hypothesis than with the classical hypothesis of population structure. Suffice it to mention that Wallace (1958) has shown that, in *Drosophila,* the average effect of X-ray-induced polygenic mutations is, at least under certain conditions, heterotic, while the same mutants are deleterious to homozygotes. Therefore, natural selection has at its disposal ample materials from which to erect a balanced gene pool. This does not prove, of course, that the classical hypothesis is completely wrong. The truth lies probably somewhere in between, and different organisms may have different population structures. For our present purposes this is not very important, except insofar as the balance hypothesis would suggest that individual members of a Mendelian population are heterozygous for a greater average number of genes than is likely on the classical hypothesis.

Let us make the conservative assumptions that this number, n, lies between 50 and 100 genes and that each gene is represented in the gene pool of a population by only 2 alleles. Mendelian segregation and recombination of these genes could then engender between 3^{50} and 3^{100} genotypes, among which between 2^{50} and 2^{100} would be homozygous ones. Now mankind consists, at present, of between 2^{31} and 2^{32} persons. Even though man is certainly not the most numerous species living on earth, it is clear that the number of genotypes that are potentially possible far exceeds the numbers of individuals of any species in existence. The mechanisms of meiosis and sexual reproduction, of which Mendelian recombination is a consequence, are prodigiously efficient in producing variation.

Only a fraction—and, indeed, only a minute fraction—of the potentially possible genotypes can be realized. Furthermore, in outbreeding sexual species, most genotypes that arise occur in only one individual. There is not likely to be another person anywhere with a genotype exactly like mine; the same is true of other people, excepting those who have monozygotic twin brothers or sisters. No matter how large a progeny a person may have, his genotype is unlikely to be re-created precisely; his genes are assorted at meiosis, only half of them pass into every sex cell, and different sex cells receive different complements of genes. Excepting monozygotic twins, every human genotype is like a work of art. It is absolutely unique. But, unlike some works of art, no genotype is immortal—the angel of death will not tarry long.

Non-geneticists may remain unimpressed by the astronomic numbers of the potentially possible gene combinations. After all, gene combinations are merely outcomes of reshuffling a relatively much more modest number of gene variants. However, at least among higher organisms, the fitness of a genotype is determined by the configuration, the gestalt, of the component genes. It must be emphasized that the development of an organism cannot be adequately understood as the outcome of a gradual accretion of "characters," each produced by a separate gene. The genes function as members of an ensemble, like players in a symphony orchestra rather than like soloists. The uniqueness of a genotype in a sexual outbred species is, therefore, not a theoretical consideration but a very practical actuality. I am an individual not only because I differ from other persons in some "traits" and resemble them in others; my individuality is an outcome of my gene pattern and of my whole development pattern, which never occurred in the past and will probably not recur in the future.

Experiments on three species of *Drosophila* have shown how potent and prolific is the gene recombination fostering the production of new genotypes (see Dobzhansky, Levene, Spassky, and Spassky, 1959, and Spiess, 1959, for further references). In each of the three species we selected 20 chromosomes from the gene pools of two natural populations. As shown by a special test, these chromosomes yielded normal or only slightly subnormal viability in double dose (i.e., were normal to subvital in homozygotes). These chromosomes were, accordingly, similar in their action; they acted ostensibly alike. All possible intercrosses were then made; with 20 chromosomes, this means 190 intercrosses. Females having different combinations of the initial chromosomes were bred to males homozygous for recessive mutant genes with easily observable effects. These genes acted as genetic "markers." From each intercross 10 sons were chosen (a total of 1,900 males). Since crossing over takes place between chromosomes in *Drosophila* females, most of the chromosomes of their sons—the 1,900 males— were recombination products between the parental chromosomes. The 1,900 recombination chromosomes were then tested for their effects on the viability of homozygotes.

Although the 20 initial chromosomes of each species were chosen deliberately to be as alike as possible in their action, an astonishing variety appeared among the recombination products. In *D. pseudoobscura,* 77 recombination chromosomes, i.e., 4.1 per cent of the 1,900 chromosomes tested, were lethal when homozygous. About 1 in every 5 among the 190 chromosome combinations studied gave at least one "synthetic" lethal recombination product. In other words, recombination of the gene contents of "healthy" chromosomes not infrequently yields chromosomes which cause lethal hereditary diseases when homozygous! Numerous less spectacular recombination products deserve no less attention than the lethals. Although the original chromosomes gave normally viable or only slightly subnormal homozygotes, the entire spectrum of viabilities, from normal, through subvital, semilethal, and to lethal chromosomes, have been found among the recombination products.

An idea of the magnitude of this release of genetic variability by recombination may be given by the following figures. We compare the variances of the viabilities of the recombination products with the total variances observed among the chromosomes in the gene pool in the natural population tested. For the 3 species studied, we have obtained the following figures: *D. pseudoobscura,* 43 per cent; *D. persimilis,* 24 per cent; *D. prosaltans,* 25 per cent. In other words, although the original chromosomes were similar in their action, the recombination of their gene contents has re-created in the experiments from one-fourth to four-tenths of the total genetic variance present in the natural populations of the species examined.

The aspect of this story that is interesting to us here is that it is a matter of chance which of the many possible recombination products of the parental genotypes happen to be formed in a given sex cell. This degree of indeterminacy would be unimportant if there existed large enough numbers of individuals that any potentially possible gene combination would be certain to appear sooner or later. It becomes important because the populations of even the most abundant species are far smaller than the numbers required to accommodate the immense potentialities of the process of the gene assortment. A great majority of the possible gene combinations will certainly not arise at all.

RANDOM GENETIC DRIFT

Apart from the non-realization of a multitude of potentially possible genotypes, the finiteness of population sizes may have another important consequence. As pointed out particularly by Sewall Wright, accidents of sampling in the passage of genes from the gene pool of one generation to that of the succeeding one lead to random fluctuations of the gene frequencies in populations. Such fluctuations may cause genetic divergence in populations of limited genetically effective sizes. How important this random genetic drift in evolution is, is an open problem, which has unfortunately led to some unedifying polemics. I have no intention of entering this dispute here, except to point out that the random genetic drift by itself is not regarded by anyone as bringing about major evolutionary changes—least of all, changes in adaptive character. Evolution depends on a balance of several factors. Accidents of sampling in small populations may be instrumental in evolution only as components of evolutionary patterns involving both determinate and random changes in gene frequencies (Wright, 1955, and other works).

Interactions of natural selection with certain forms of random genetic drift are particularly interesting. Only a brief account of some experiments in which this is observed can be given here. Natural populations of many species of *Drosophila* are mixtures of two or several chromosomal types. Since flies with different chromosomes interbreed freely, individuals found in nature may have the two chromosomes of a pair of the same type (structural homozygotes) or of different types (structural heterozygotes). Each type of chromosome occurs in populations of a species in a certain geographic region; some chromosomal forms are widespread, and others are more limited in distribution. Experimental populations of *Drosophila* can be created in the laboratory, and they can be made to contain any desired proportions of two or more chromosomal types. The flies with different chromosomes are, however, unequally fit to live in the experimental populations. Natural selection acts accordingly; the incidence of some chromosomal types rises, and of others declines, from generation to generation.

The outcome of the experiments is simplest if the chromosomal types in an experimental population are of geographically uniform origin, i.e., derived from ancestors collected in the same geographic locality. In *D. pseudoobscura*, which is the species used most extensively in such experiments, the highest fitness is exhibited usually by heterozygotes with the two chromosomes of a pair of different type but of the same origin geographically. The homozygotes have a lower fitness. Because the heterozygotes are heterotic, natural selection establishes genetic equilibrium in the experimental populations. The two or more competing chromosomal types are preserved in the populations, each with an equilibrium frequency which usually remains constant for as long as the experiment lasts.

Figure 1 shows the outcome of four replicate experiments with populations containing two chromosomal types, both derived from the natural population of *D. pseudoobscura* of a certain locality in California (Dobzhansky and Pavlovsky, 1953). All the experimental populations at the start had 20 per cent of the chromosomal type ST

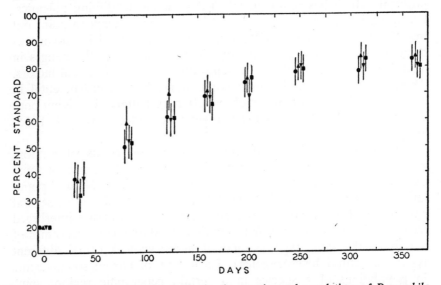

Fig. 1.—The action of natural selection in experimental populations of *Drosophila pseudoobscura*, the progenitors of which came from the same natural population. The four replicate experimental populations are shown by different symbols. The vertical lines indicate the range of two standard errors up and down from the observed frequencies. It may be seen that the changes in the frequencies of the chromosomal types which took place in the four populations were the same within the limits of the experimental errors.

and 80 per cent of the type CH. A year later (about 15 fly generations), the populations contained 80–84 per cent of ST and 16–20 per
cent of CH. The fact that deserves emphasis is that, with reasonable
precautions taken to control the experimental environments, the outcome of the experiments is reproducible. The vertical lines in Figure 1
indicate the limits of two standard errors up and down from the observed values. The four experimental populations have behaved alike.

Another group of four experimental populations was quite similar
to those shown in Figure 1, except that in the second group the ST
chromosomes came from a natural population in California, while the
CH chromosomes came from a population of a locality in Mexico.
The outcome of natural selection in the second group of four populations is shown in Figure 2. A year after the start, one of the popula-

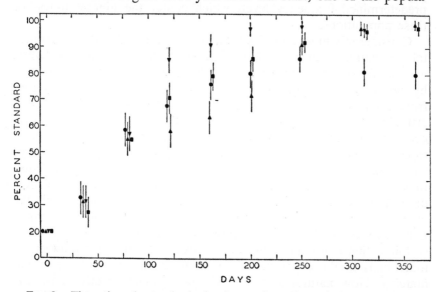

FIG. 2.—The action of natural selection in experimental populations of *Drosophila
pseudoobscura*, the progenitors of which came from different natural populations. It
can be seen that the four replicate populations diverged significantly in the course of
time.

tions had 80 per cent of ST chromosomes, while the three other populations had 97–99 per cent. Moreover, Figure 2 shows that the progress of the selection was more rapid in some populations than in
others. In short, the four replicate experiments with chromosomes of
different geographic origin failed to give reproducible results. Every
population behaved somewhat differently from the others (Dobzhansky and Pavlovsky, 1953).

When, a few years ago, I reported the results of the above experiment to a group of biologists, one of the colleagues present com-

mented that he is unable to find any virtue in experiments which are not reproducible. I could not gainsay the rule that any investigator who repeats a scientific experiment under similar conditions should obtain the same result which I claim to have obtained. And yet, is this so intractable a situation that it must remain outside the framework of our analysis? Replicate experimental populations do yield reproducible results if they contain *Drosophila* flies of uniform geographic origin (Fig. 1). The chromosomes in these experimental populations existed together in the same natural population; their gene contents were mutually adjusted, or coadapted, by natural selection to produce heterotic heterozygotes on the genetic background of the local population; the action of the natural selection observed in our experimental populations is, then, merely causing the chromosomal types to find the predetermined frequency levels which confer the highest fitness on these populations.

Considerably more complex processes are enacted in the experimental populations which contain mixtures of chromosomes of diverse geographic origins. The flies in these experimental populations are hybrid progenies from crossing different geographic races—a race from California and a race from Mexico. These hybrids are entirely artificial products, in the sense that such hybrids presumably never occurred in nature (the probability of a fly migrating from California to central Mexico, or vice-versa, is negligible). In any case, a large variety of genotypes must arise in the populations following the interracial hybridization. We do not know in how many genes the races differ and, as a consequence, cannot estimate even approximately the number of new gene combinations which may potentially be formed in the hybrid populations in the process of gene assortment. One thing certain is that that number must be vastly greater than the numbers of individuals in the experimental populations (1,000–4,000 approximately). Now natural selection will not remain inactive until the fittest of all the potentially possible genotypes is produced; it will augment the frequency of any relatively fit array of genotypes that happens to arise first in a given population. Different genotypes will probably arise in different populations. The divergent results in replicate experiments in apparently identical populations kept in ostensibly identical environments are a consequence. Such, at least, is the working hypothesis to be tested.

The following test was devised (Dobzhansky and Pavlovsky, 1957). The hypothesis postulates that the varying results of the selection process in the experimental populations arise from a disproportionality between the population size and the capacity of the sexual process to generate new gene combinations. If so, the outcomes of selection should be more variable in smaller populations and less so in larger ones. The operation of selection would presumably become wholly determinate in ideal infinite populations. We have, accordingly, made 20 experimental populations, all descended from F_2 generation hybrids between flies from California carrying a chromosome of the type denoted AR and flies from Texas with a chromosome called PP. However, 10 of these populations descended from groups of 20 flies taken at random from the F_2 hybrid progenies; each of the other 10 populations descended from 4,000 "founders" of the same origin.

Although some of the populations came from small and others from relatively large groups of founders, so great is the fecundity of the flies that all the experimental populations grew equally large one generation after the start. About 17 months (some 20–21 generations) later, the populations descended from small numbers of founders contained from 16 to 47 per cent PP chromosomes. Those descended from larger numbers of founders had from 20 to 35 per cent PP chromosomes. The "small" populations gave, indeed, more variable results than did the "large" ones. The variance of the observed frequencies in the former is about 27, and in the latter about 119, or 4.4 times larger. The difference is statistically significant.

The experiments now under way are giving a further verification of the hypothesis. We have set up ten new experimental populations with AR chromosomes from California and PP chromosomes from Texas. All the populations are descended from groups of 20 founders; the populations are permitted to expand, but, at intervals of about 4 months, each population is reduced to a sample of 20 founders and permitted to expand again. Moreover, in five of these populations the original foundation stock came from mixing together a dozen different California and a dozen Texas strains. In the remaining five populations the founders are hybrids of only a single California and a single Texas strain. Natural selection has acted in all these populations, and a significant heterogeneity of the outcomes has appeared in both series. The heterogeneity is, however, strikingly greater among the populations which had genetically more heterogeneous foundation stocks.

While the evolutionary changes of the kind observed in the laboratory experiments are suggestive, they cannot be said to have proved that phenomena of the same kind are also of importance in evolution in nature. Fortunately, even before these experiments were completed, Mayr (1954) summarized a great deal of evidence from zoological systematics which solidly substantiates the validity of the inference. In species after species and in different groups of animals, an interesting contrast is observed between the variability of continental and of island populations. The inhabitants of extensive, but more or less continuously inhabited, territories, such as continental masses, may show relatively little geographical differentiation. By contrast, populations isolated on islands or by some distributional barriers are often very appreciably different from each other and from the continental populations. Mayr has stressed the fact that environmental differences between parts of the continent may be much greater than those between the islands and the adjacent portion of the continent. The magnitudes of the racial differences are thus not proportional to the environmental differences in the territories which the races inhabit.

Mayr has pointed out that, despite environmental differences, genetic differentiation of continental populations may be impeded by migration and interchange of genes between the populations. However, populations isolated on islands or by other barriers to migration are not only more or less protected from the leveling effect of the interpopulational gene exchange. More important still, populations of islands and other distributional pockets may be descended from a single pair, or from small groups, of migrants from the continent. These migrants bring with them not the entire gene pool of the parental population but only a small segment thereof. The migrants are comparable to the small groups of the "founders" of our experimental *Drosophila* populations. Now, if the balance theory of the population structure is correct (see above), the gene pool of a Mendelian population is an internally balanced system. Natural selection will act in an island population to bring about a new balanced state, in place of the one disrupted by the sudden shrinkage of the gene pool in the founding population. This genetic reconstructon alone might be expected to cause the isolated population to become different from the continental one; any peculiarities of the island environments would certainly act as a further stimulus to differentiation.

EVOLUTIONARY RESPONSE TO THE ENVIRONMENT

The elementary evolutionary events are changes in the incidence of genes in populations. The allele or alleles of a gene which was present in the gene pool of an ancestral population may gradually be replaced by another allele or a group of alleles. The replacement occurs generally under the control of natural selection and, consequently, indirectly under the control of the environment. However, Wright (1955) pointed out:

Each gene replacement inevitably has extensively ramifying pleiotropic consequences. In this situation genes that have favorable effects at all will also, in general, have many, more or less, unfavorable effects, with the net effect dependent on the array of other genes. Evolution depends on the fitting together of favorable complexes from genes that cannot be described as in themselves either favorable or unfavorable. The consequence of this situation is that there is not one goal of selection, but a vast number of distinct possible goals.

Divergence of evolutionary paths within the same environment (or, rather, within the same array of environments) is made possible by the multiplicity of adaptive "goals" (adaptive peaks, to use the perhaps more felicitous metaphor devised also by Wright). Such a divergence may occur even with microevolutionary changes which involve merely single gene substitutions. For example, it has been shown by Demerec and others that the bacteriophage-resistant, as well as antibiotic-resistant, mutants which arise in a strain of bacteria are not always the same. The bacteria have evidently several gene loci, the mutation in any one of which confers resistance. Whichever of the possible mutants happens to be available in the culture exposed to the selecting agent becomes the progenitor of a resistant strain. This is one of the consequences of the opportunism of natural selection.

The possibility of becoming adapted to the same environment in a variety of ways opens access to a multiplicity of evolutionary paths. This is most evident with evolutionary changes which entail alterations in many genes, and especially in organized gene systems. The experimental populations of *Drosophila* described above are a case in point. In these experimental populations different genetic systems adapted to the environment have been shaped by natural selection. The environment was as uniform in all the populations as could easily be obtained with the technique used. That the control of the experimental environment was satisfactory has been shown by the reproducibility of the selectional changes observed in replicate experiments on populations of uniform geographic origin (see above). And yet the reproducibility vanishes in populations of geographically mixed origin. The genetic systems which arise from recombination of the genes contributed by the geographic races crossed are clearly not the same in different populations. The experimental populations diverge, despite the environmental uniformity.

The genetic systems which were formed by natural selection in our experimental populations are probably real novelties. As stated above, it is most unlikely that any of these systems merely re-created the genotypes of any natural population living somewhere between California and Mexico or between California and Texas or elsewhere. On the other hand, I am not suggesting that it is an inexorable law that all evolutionary events must be unique and non-recurrent. Indeed, elementary mutational-selectional events may be both repeatable and reversible (see above). As pointed out, among others, by Muller

(1939), it is all a matter of probability; the greater the number of the genes changed, the more advanced the integration of a genotypic system; or the longer the series of consecutive mutational changes in a locus, the more remote is the possibility that the changes which have occurred will be undone or that they will ever follow each other again in the same order. This is what the contrast between the outcomes of the experiments on populations of geographically uniform and of geographically mixed origins has taught us. An elementary evolutionary event is, but an evolutionary history is not, likely to be repeated.

The fact that genetically similar populations may respond differently to the challenge of the same environment does not invalidate the basic principle that evolutionary changes are evoked by the environment. However, the challenge presented by the environment may be answered in different ways or may not be answered at all. This is as true of the microevolutionary and mesoevolutionary changes that we have considered above as it is of macroevolutionary ones. Consider, for example, the adaptations to life in salt and fresh water and on land. All the 21 now living phyla of the animal kingdom (after Simpson, Pittendrigh, and Tiffany, 1957, but counting Protozoa as a phylum) are believed to have arisen in the sea. Ignoring the three phyla consisting exclusively of parasites (Mesozoa, Nematophora, and Acanthocephala), we find that every phylum still contains some marine forms. (However, only few trochelminthes are marine.) Most phyla have also evolved some representatives that live in fresh water, but six of them have not, including such ancient ones as Brachiopoda and Echinodermata that flowered in the past.

Adaptation to land life has been attained, and doubtless independently, by Arthropoda, Chordata, one class of Mollusca, some Annelida, Nematoda, a few Platyhelminthes, and Nemertea, but not by the others. Among the land-living groups of Arthropoda and Chordata, there have occurred several radiations back to life in fresh and salt waters. The class Insecta contains more species than the rest of the animal kingdom combined. Several insect orders include some freshwater dwellers, but insects appear to be remarkably unsuccessful in readaptation to marine life. The order of flies, Diptera, nevertheless did evolve a few truly marine forms, such as the fly *Pontomyia*, living in the plankton near the coral reefs (Mackerras, 1950).

Adaptive convergence of different organisms living in similar environments has rightly been emphasized as evidence of the effectiveness of natural selection. Thus some desert-dwelling cacti in the Americas look remarkably like desert euphorbias in South Africa, and yet they belong to different families and have evolved from presumably less similar ancestors. Wolflike, molelike, squirrel-like, and mouselike mammals exist both in Australia and in the rest of the world, but in Australia these mammals are marsupials, and elsewhere they are placentals. An even more spectacular adaptive radiation of marsupials, paralleling that of the placentals, occurred in South America during the Tertiary, when the continent had few placental mammals. Similar environments open similar opportunities, and similar opportunities sometimes evoke the evolutionary emergence of at least superficially similar organisms, even if these have to arise from dissimilar sources.

The phenomena of parallel and convergent evolution are so spectacular that it becomes advisable to stress that they do not invariably or necessarily occur. Many ecological types of animals and plants are absent in many geographic regions in which the environments seem to be perfectly suitable for them. This has been pointed out, among others, by Kusnezov (1956); several parallel types of ants adapted to desert biota have evolved on different continents from dissimilar ancestors, but there exist also very conspicuous absences of certain adaptive types in places where they would, to all appearances, find suitable living conditions. This last point obviously rests on an insecure inference; but one has to be even more uncritical to maintain the opposite, namely, that the absence of some form of life in a given region means that it could not live there.

Evolution is a creative response of living matter to environmental opportunity. I am aware that some biologists regard the word "creative," borrowed as it is from aesthetics and metaphysics, as inappropriate for the characterization of biological processes. I am unable, however, to find a more apt phrase. Creativity implies origination of novelties, of things or events or ideas which are not known to have occurred before, at least not in identical form. As shown above, there are good reasons to think that evolutionary histories are unique and non-recurrent, despite the fact that elementary evolutionary events are repeatable. Creativity implies, furthermore, production of something endowed with internal cohesion, congruity, unity, or harmony. The planning and construction of a building may be a creative act; its destruction is not, although invention of novel methods of wrecking may conceivably be. Evolution by natural selection generally tends to promote the adaptedness of species or populations, to increase the consonance between the organism and its environment—in short, to maximize the probability of the preservation and expansion of life. This is not contradicted by the shortsightedness and the opportunism of the evolutionary process; immediate gains may eventuate in future harm and ultimate extinction. The risk of failure or non-fulfilment is indeed a characteristic of creativity. Anything really new, being made or planned for the first time, faces the hazard of frustration. By a curious misunderstanding, some scholars have rejected the biological theory of evolution as being crassly mechanistic and relying too much on "blind" chance and have preferred various forms of autogenesis. And yet it is the former which visualizes a creative process resulting in the emergence of real novelties, while theories of autogenesis assume no creativity but merely unfolding of what was performed from the beginning.

In conclusion, we may return briefly to the speculations about the possible extra-terrestrial organic evolutions mentioned earlier in the present article. Assume for the sake of argument, as some biologists and astronomers have assumed, that the simplest life, more or less resembling the primeval life on earth, arose in several places in the cosmos. Assume, further, that the environments which this life faces on other planets are not too different from the terrestrial environments. And, finally, assume that the possible ways of executing certain biological functions are circumscribed by the nature of life's physical substratum and by its chemical potentialities. It still would not follow that the same drama of evolution of life is likely to have been enacted again and again in different places. The adaptive inventions which occurred in the historic development of life on earth were not guaranteed either by the structure of the living substance or by the environment. They were creative responses of life to the challenges of the environment. If life did arise in many places in the universe, it may have become extinct or may have produced organisms either less perfect or more perfect than did life on our little planet; it is not likely to have done the same thing more than once. However, we do not know for sure; we may leave the decision to him whose gaze will be the first to behold the life on other planets, if there be such.

The author is obligated to his colleague, Professor J. A. Moore, for many discussions of the topics dealt with in this article.

LITERATURE CITED

BERG, L. S. 1926. *Nomogenesis*. London: Constable.

CAIN, A. J., and SHEPPARD, P. M. 1954. "Natural Selection in Cepaea," *Genetics*, XXXIX 89–116.

DEMEREC, M. 1945. "Production of *Staphylococcus* Strains Resistant to Various Concentrations of Penicillin," *Proc. Nat. Acad. Sci.*, XXXI, 16–24.

DEMEREC, M., and FANO, U. 1945. "Bacteriophage Resistant Mutants of *Escherichia coli*," *Genetics*, XXX, 119–36.

DOBZHANSKY, TH. 1933. "Geographical Variation in Lady-Beetles," *Amer. Naturalist*, XVII, 97–126.

———. 1951. *Genetics and the Origin of Species.* 3d ed. New York: Columbia University Press.

———. 1955. "A Review of Some Fundamental Concepts and Problems of Population Genetics," *Sold Spring Harbor Symp. Quant. Biol.,* XX, 1–15.

———. 1956. "What Is an Adaptive Trait?" *Amer. Naturalist,* XC, 337–47.

———. 1958. "Variation and Evolution," *Trans. Amer. Phil. Soc.* (in press).

DOBZHANSKY, T., LEVENE, H., SPASSKY, B., and SPASSKY, N. 1959. "Release of Genetic Variability, through Recombination. I. *Drosophila prosaltans," Genetics* XXXXIV, 75–92.

DOBZHANSKY, T., and PAVLOVSKY, O. 1953. "Indeterminate Outcome of Certain Experiments on *Drosophila* Populations," *Evolution,* VII, 198–210.

———. 1957. "An Experimental Study of Interaction between Genetic Drift and Natural Selection," *ibid.,* XI, 311–19.

FORD, E. B. 1955. "Polymorphism and Taxonomy," *Heredity,* IX, 255–64.

KUSNEZOV, N. N. 1956. "A Comparative Study of Ants in Desert Regions of Central Asia and of South America," *Amer. Naturalist,* XC, 349–60.

LAMOTTE, M. 1951. "Recherches sur la structure génétique des populations naturelles de *Cepaea nemoralis," Bull. biol. France,* Suppl., XXXV, 1–239.

LURIA, S. E. 1946. "Spontaneous Bacterial Mutations to Resistance to Anti-bacterial Agents," *Cold Spring Harbor Symp. Quant. Biol.,* XI, 130–38.

LURIA, S. E., and DELBRUCK, M. 1943. "Mutations in Bacteria from Virus Sensitivity to Virus Resistance," *Genetics,* XXVIII, 491–511.

MACKERRAS, I. M. 1950. "Marine Insects," *Proc. Roy. Soc. Queensland,* LXI, 19–29.

MAYR, E. 1942. *Systematics and the Origin of Species.* New York: Columbia University Press.

———. 1954. "Change of Genetic Environment and Evolution." In *Evolution as a Process,* ed. HUXLEY, HARDY, and FORD, pp. 157–80. London: Allen & Unwin.

MULLER, H. J. 1939. "Reversibility of Evolution Considered from the Standpoint of Genetics," *Biol. Rev.,* XIV, 261–80.

NOLTE, D. J. 1958. "Eye Pigment Relationships in Three Species Groups of *Drosophila," Evolution,* XII, 519–31.

RENSCH, B. 1954. *Neuere Probleme der Abstammungslehre.* Stuttgart: Enke. English translation, *Evolution above the Species Level* (in press).

SCHMALHAUSEN, I. I. 1949. *Factors of Evolution.* New York: McGraw-Hill Book Co.

———. 1958. "Regulatory Mechanisms of Evolution," *Zool. Zhur.,* XXXVII, 1291–1306.

SHAPLEY, H. 1958. *Of Stars and Men.* Boston: Beacon Press.

SIMPSON, G. G. 1953. *The Major Features of Evolution.* New York: Columbia University Press.

SIMPSON, G. G., PITTENDRIGH, C. S., and TIFFANY, L. H. 1957. *Life: An Introduction to Biology.* New York: Harcourt, Brace and Co.

SPIESS, E. B. 1959. *Cold Spring Harbor Symp. Quant. Biol.* (in press).

WALLACE, B. 1958. "The Average Effect of Radiation-induced Mutations on Viability in *Drosophila melanogaster,*" *Evolution,* XII, 532–56.

WRIGHT, S. 1955. "Classification of Factors of Evolution," *Cold Spring Harbor Symp. Quant. Biol.,* XX, 16–24.

SEWALL WRIGHT

PHYSIOLOGICAL GENETICS
ECOLOGY OF POPULATIONS
AND NATURAL SELECTION

The purpose of the present paper is to consider the mathematical framework of the theory of evolution at a succession of levels of complexity. We shall begin with the very inadequate theory that can be based on properties assigned the separate genes. At the second level we take cognizance of the basic conclusion of physiological genetics that the effects of genes depend on those with which they are associated. It is still assumed that the selective values of total genotypes are constant within a population of given density in a given environment. At the third level we accept from ecology the fact that the members of a population may interact in such ways that the relative selective values of total genotypes may, after all, be functions of their relative frequencies. At the fourth level we return to physiological genetics to recognize that the deterministic processes considered at the first three levels can carry the population toward only one—and that not, in general, the highest—of a very large number of selective peaks. We are led to consider the possibilities of passage from peak to peak by the joint action of deterministic and random processes. At the fifth level we return to the ecology of populations to consider the consequences of subdivision of the species into partially isolated demes. The problems of species cleavage and the evolution of higher categories are excluded. Discussion will be restricted to populations of sexually reproducing diploids.

SEWALL WRIGHT has been in the department of genetics at the University of Wisconsin since 1955; prior to this he was associated with the University of Chicago for almost 30 years. He is especially well known for his theoretical considerations of the mechanics of evolution. His work and writings have covered such topics as the genetics of guinea pigs, population genetics, and the laws of heredity as applied to livestock breeding. The present paper was written for the Darwin Centennial Celebration and was preprinted in *Perspectives in Biology and Medicine* (Autumn, 1959).

Systems of Gene Frequencies

The theoretical genetics of populations may be considered to have begun with Pearson's (1) demonstration that the 1:2:1 Mendelian ratio tends to maintain itself indefinitely in a large random-breeding population derived from F_2 of a cross. A few years later Hardy (2) and Weinberg (3) independently pointed out that any array of gene frequencies at a locus ($\Sigma q_{Ii} A_{Ii}$, where A_{Ii} is a particular allele at locus A_I and q_{Ii} is its proportional frequency)[1] tends to remain unchanged in a large self-contained population in the absence of disturbing factors such as mutation and selection, and thus that the frequency of the zygotes resulting from random mating becomes stable immediately after attainment of equality of gene frequencies in the sexes in the array $(\Sigma q_{Ii} A_{Ii})^2$ for one locus.

If mating is not at random, the zygotic array, in the absence of other disturbing factors, is given by $(1 - F)[\Sigma q_{Ii} A_{Ii}]^2 + F\Sigma(q_{Ii} A_{Ii} A_{Ii})$, where F is the inbreeding coefficient, defined as the correlation between uniting gametes with respect to additive effects (4, 5, 6). Random mating will be assumed here unless otherwise stated.

It was noted by Weinberg (7) that two pairs of alleles approach randomness of combination gradually under random mating. Robbins (8) showed that the deviation from random combination falls off in each generation by the mean recombination percentage and thus by 50 per cent for loci in different chromosomes. A full demonstration of the behavior of any number of loci in the absence of disturbing factors was given by Geiringer (9). There is gradual approach to the array

$$\prod_I \left(\sum_i q_{Ii} A_{Ii} \right)^2.$$

It is often convenient to think of the field of gene frequencies in geometric terms. Any given array of gene frequencies may be represented as a point in a closed system located so that the length of perpendiculars to the boundaries (lines if two dimensions, areas if three dimensions, solids if four dimensions) represent the frequencies. There are two possible two-dimensional systems:

Figure 1—$(p_1 A_1 + p_2 A_2 + p_3 A_3)$, $\Sigma p = 1$, equilateral triangle of unit height;

Figure 2—$[(1 - p)a + pA][(1 - q)b + qB]$, square of unit height.

There are three possible three-dimensional systems:

[1] While it is customary to use superscripts to distinguish alleles, subscripts only for loci, it is more convenient in general formulas of population genetics to use double subscripts, as above, in the symbols for both the gene and its frequency to avoid confusion with exponents.

Figure 3—$(p_1A_1 + p_2A_2 + p_3A_3 + p_4A_4)$, $\Sigma p = 1$, regular tetrahedron of unit height;

Figure 4—$(p_1A_1 + p_2A_2 + p_3A_3)$ $[(1 - q)b + qB]$, $\Sigma p = 1$, triangular prism of unit height, with equilateral triangles of unit height at top and bottom;

Figure 5—$[(1 - p)a + pA]$ $[(1 - q)b + qB]$ $[(1 - r)c + rC]$, cube of unit height.

More extensive systems can be represented by networks that bring out the relations much less completely. There are five four-dimensional systems. The bounding solids (systems in which one gene is absent) can be

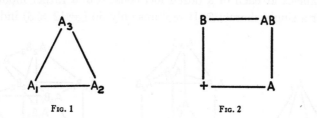

FIG. 1   FIG. 2

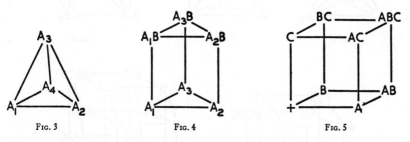

FIG. 3   FIG. 4   FIG. 5

FIGS. 1–5.—FIGS. 1, 2 (*top row*): gene frequency systems with two independent frequencies. FIGS. 3–5 (*bottom row*): systems with three independent frequencies.

recognized in Figures 6–10, but not all simultaneously. It cannot be brought out adequately that these have no internal points in common and that the locations of non-degenerate systems are not included in any of them. Lines representing the gene frequencies must be perpendicular to *all* lines in the solid boundary to which they are dropped:

Figure 6—$(p_1A_1 + p_2A_2 + p_3A_3 + p_4A_4 + p_5A_5)$, $\Sigma p = 1$. This four-dimensional system is bounded by five regular tetrahedra.

Figure 7—$(p_1A_1 + p_2A_2 + p_3A_3 + p_4A_4)[(1 - q)b + qB]$, $\Sigma p = 1$. This four-dimensional figure is bounded by two regular tetrahedra (top and bottom), and four triangular prisms. The p's are measured by perpendiculars to the latter, the q's to the former.

Figure 8—$(p_1A_1 + p_2A_2 + p_3A_3)(q_1B_1 + q_2B_2 + q_3B_3)$, $\Sigma p = 1$, $\Sigma q = 1$. This system is bounded by six triangular prisms. The p's are measured by perpendiculars to the three that lack A_1, A_2, and A_3, respectively, and the q's by ones to the three that lack B_1, B_2, and B_3, respectively.

Figure 9—$(p_1A_1 + p_2A_2 + p_3A_3)[(1 - q)b + qB][(1 - r)c + rC]$, $\Sigma p = 1$. This system is bounded by three cubes and four triangular prisms.

Figure 10—$[(1 - p)a + pA][(1 - q)b + qB][(1 - r)c + rC][(1 - s)d + sD]$. This is a four-dimensional rectangular co-ordinate system with sides of unit length. There are eight bounding cubes.

Four alleles at each of a dozen loci constitute a rather modest "gene pool" for a single character. It requires only 36 (= 12 × 3) independent

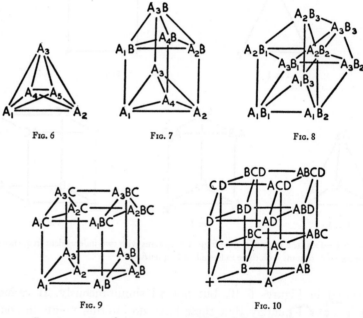

FIGS. 6-10.—Gene frequency systems with four independent frequencies

variables (q's) to describe the set of gene frequencies. The number of different potential genotypes is, however, a million million (10 combinations at each of the 12 loci). Systems involving four alleles at each of 100 loci involve 300 independent gene frequencies but imply the possibility of enormously more genotypes (10^{100}) than there are elementary particles in the visible universe. It seemed obvious, at first, that mathematical theory of population genetics had best be related to systems of gene frequencies rather than to zygotic frequencies. We shall consider the unfortunately very inadequate formulation that can be made at this level after some general considerations.

Some General Considerations

Let w_i be the reproductive value of a given gene, relative to some standard, over the period of a full generation, on the basis of the viability and productivity of the individuals that carry it (giving full weight to homozygotes and half-weight to heterozygotes). The difference in gene frequency between offspring and parent generation is obviously

$$\Delta q_i = q_i \frac{w_i}{\bar{w}} - q_i = q_i \frac{w_i - \bar{w}}{\bar{w}}, \tag{1}$$

where $\bar{w}$ $(= \Sigma q_i w_i)$ is the average of the reproductive values for all alleles. If this is expressed in terms of reproductive differences by writing $(1 + s_i)$ in place of w_i, we have $\Delta q_i = q_i(s_i - \bar{s})/(1 + \bar{s})$. In many cases the mean difference, $\bar{s}$, is so small, on taking the most appropriate standard, that the denominator may be treated as unity in the above expression without serious error.

In some connections it is desirable to deal with absolute rates of increase (or decrease) and absolute reproductive values. These will be represented by capital letters. The formulas are the same after substituting W and S for w and s, but the denominators cannot be dropped if the whole population is increasing or decreasing rapidly, even though the differences among alleles are small.

We have used here a model that applies exactly only to populations with discrete generations. A model designed for populations that are changing continuously is more appropriate in many cases and leads to some mathematical simplification, although to somewhat less transparency of meaning. Haldane (10) showed that the effect of overlapping of generations is usually small. Fisher (11) based a formulation for a continuous population on an equation given by Lotka (12),

$$\int_0^\infty e^{-mx} l_x b_x dx = 1,$$

in which l_x is the proportion of survival to age x, b_x is the birth rate at age x, and m, which Fisher called the "Malthusian parameter," measures the momentary growth rate of the population to which it pertains. It can be applied to a particular gene by proper averaging of the individuals that carry it.

If the absolute reproductive value of a gene for a small fraction (Δt)

of a generation is $(1 + m\Delta t)$ in a continuous population, that for a period equal to an average generation is $(1 + m\Delta t)^{1/\Delta t}$, which becomes e^m with infinitesimal Δt. Thus e^m corresponds to W, and m to log W, if this period is treated as if it were a discrete generation. The change of gene frequency in this interval Δt may be written

$$\Delta q = q \left(\frac{1 + m\Delta t}{1 + \bar{m}\Delta t} \right) - q = q \left(\frac{m - \bar{m}}{1 + \bar{m}\Delta t} \right) \Delta t, \text{ leading to } \frac{dq}{dt} = q\,(m - \bar{m}).$$

This is similar in form to the discrete formula $\Delta q = q(S - \bar{S})/(1 + \bar{S})$ except for the denominator (13). Thus we can pass from the discrete formula to the corresponding continuous one merely by dropping the denominator $\bar{W}(= 1 + \bar{S})$ in the former and replacing S by m with a change in meaning that is often slight.

Absolute reproductive values may increase with increasing density of population up to a certain point but must always fall off as density becomes excessive. Relative reproductive values are probably also often functions of density. The effects of changes in population size on its composition can be dealt with in ways similar to those used by Lotka (12) and Volterra (14) or by Nicholson and Bailey (15) in their theories of the growth curves of interacting species. The first two formulations were in terms of differential equations, the last in difference equations.

As the simplest case, assume that the reproductive values vary linearly with the size of the whole population $(W_i = 1 + a_i - b_i N_T)$, where N_T is the total number of individuals. Let N_i be the number of representatives of a given gene such that $\Sigma N_i = 2N_T$. Then

$$\Delta N_i = N_i\,(W_i - 1) = N_i\,(a_i - b_i N_T) \tag{2}$$

$$\Delta q_i = q_i\,\frac{W_i - \bar{W}}{\bar{W}} = q_i\,\frac{[\,(a_i - \bar{a}) - (b_i - \bar{b})\,N_T]}{1 + \bar{a} - \bar{b}N_T}. \tag{3}$$

Thus genes may increase in proportional frequency up to a certain density of population, $N_T = (a_i - \bar{a})/(b_i - \bar{b})$ and then decrease, or vice versa.

In the later sections we shall deal largely with the discrete model for change of gene frequency but will shift to the continuous model where more convenient. We shall not go further into density effects.

In concluding this section, it may be noted that the general formula for change of gene frequency from recurrent mutation is $\Delta q_i = (\Sigma q_j u_{ji}) - q_i(\Sigma u_{ij})$, where u_{ji} is the rate of mutation from A_j to A_i and u_{ij} is the converse.

FIVE LEVELS OF THEORY

1. THEORY IN TERMS OF GENE FREQUENCIES AND CONSTANT GENE EFFECTS

Consider the familiar case of a single sort of recurrent mutation (frequency q) that arises from its type allele at the rate v per generation, while reverse mutation can occur at the rate u per generation. The rate of change in the frequency of the mutant gene from these causes is thus $v(1 - q) - uq$, in which the latter term is usually negligible as long as the mutation is rare. Let $w(= 1 - s)$ be the reproductive value of this mutation relative to type. Then $\bar{s} = sq$, and the change in gene frequency due to this cause is $q(w - \bar{w})/\bar{w} = -sq(1 - q)/(1 - sq)$ or $-sq(1 - q)$ to a close approximation if sq is small. Thus the total rate of change of the frequencies of the deleterious mutation may be written as follows, ignoring second-order terms:

$$\Delta q = v(1 - q) - sq(1 - q) = -s(1 - q)\left(q - \frac{v}{s}\right). \qquad (4)$$

Gene frequency rises to a stable equilibrium at the value $\hat{q} = v/s$, since $\Delta q = 0$ at this point and at other values is opposite in sign to $(q - \hat{q})$. This value is generally small because of the usual smallness of the mutation rate in comparison with selective differences.

In the case of a favorable mutation, $\Delta q = -uq + sq(1 - q)$, there is gradual displacement of the old-type gene until the mutation reaches near-fixation at the frequency $\hat{q} = 1 - (u/s)$.

In a system in which each gene replacement always makes the same contribution to the reproductive value under given conditions of density and environment, there is just one best genotype, under given conditions, and the system moves steadily toward fixation of this from any initial composition, until this progress is balanced by recurrent mutation.

We refer to the point in the set of gene frequencies toward which selection tends to drive the species as the "selective peak." In this case it may also be called the "reproductive peak," since it is the system in which the mean reproductive rate ($\bar{W}$) is highest. At the first level of theory, this peak system is one in which all individuals are homozygous in all favored genes, making it possible to speak of a "peak genotype." This does not hold, in general, at the next level. At the third level, the selective and reproductive peaks may be different.

The point in the set of gene frequencies toward which the population moves under the influence of all factors (including, for example, mutation as well as selection) is the "deterministic peak." In the case of the single favorable mutations discussed above, this is at $q = 1 - (u/s)$ instead of at $q = 1$, the selective and reproductive peak.

The theory at this first level leads to the conception of a long-established species as one in which all individuals are homozygous for the "type" allele at most loci and heterozygous for deleterious mutations at a few and in which only occasional individuals are homozygous for any deleterious mutation.

The only possibility for further evolution under the constant conditions is by the occurrence of *novel* (in contrast with recurrent) mutations that are favorable from the first. This must be a very rare occurrence. If one occurs, the chance that it will be lost by accidents of sampling while it is still rare are so great that its chance of becoming established is only $2s$ (16). After it has reached a secure frequency, the process of displacement of the type gene is steady but very slow,

$$\frac{dq}{dt} = sq\,(1-q)\,, \qquad t = \frac{1}{s}\log\left[\frac{q}{1-q}\,\frac{1-q_0}{q_0}\right],$$

the number of generations required to increase the ratio of its frequency to type from q_0 to q (17). A mutation that increases reproductive value by 1 per cent in a long-established species must be considered to be unusually favorable. Once safely established, with a frequency of perhaps 10^{-5} in a species with several million individuals, it would require 230 generations to reach a frequency of 10^{-4} and another such period to reach 10^{-3}. It would pass from 9 per cent to 50 per cent, and from this to 91 per cent in two similar periods and would then slowly eliminate the remaining type genes. While many such mutations could theoretically be moving toward fixation simultaneously, the likelihood that this would happen is extremely small, for reasons indicated above.

Enormously more evolutionary change is to be expected from changing conditions. Any change is almost certain to be unfavorable and to lower the reproductive rate. Some of the recurrent mutations carried by the species may be better adapted than their established type alleles and may now work their way toward new equilibria if the new conditions persist, according to the above formulas. The process may be a relatively rapid one if the new conditions are almost lethal to the previous type. The evolution of resistance of scale insects to cyanide and of house flies to DDT (18) and of melanic mutations in moths in industrial regions in which a light color has ceased to be protective (19) are familiar examples.

With sufficiently frequent changes in conditions, stability may never be reached, and evolution may be a continuous process. It is, however, somewhat of the nature of a treadmill. This is especially the case if conditions return to a previous state, since then the goal of evolution becomes just what it had been before, under the assumptions of this section.

2. ALLOWANCE FOR DOMINANCE AND FACTOR INTERACTION

The preceding theory is highly inadequate in its premises from the standpoint of physiological genetics. It is obvious that selective processes actually operate on genotypes as wholes. The assignment of constant selective values to individual genes completely bypasses the complicated relations of the genes to the characters with which individuals confront their environments, internal as well as external.

Dominance in varying degrees is a very common complication among alleles. Chains of dependence of detectable effects of genes on the presence of particular genes at other loci, reciprocal dependence, thresholds, and ceilings in the effects of multiple factors that contribute to quantitative variability are all common phenomena at the level of ordinary characters. Different characters, moreover, are associated in their genetic physiology by the phenomenon of pleiotropy, which is expected to be an almost universal consequence of the ramifying physiological effects of any primary gene action and which seems always to be found when looked for sufficiently diligently.

The relations of genes to selective value as a character are still more complex. The net selective value of a gene tends to depend mainly on the most important pleiotropic effect. Thus very minute theoretical selection pressures on a character are likely to be overruled by more important pressures due to pleiotropic effects on other characters (20–22). Again the optimal grade of a quantitatively varying character is more likely to be near the mean in a long-established species than near either extreme. This introduces a type of complication which becomes of special importance at our fourth level of theory.

We assume here that a constant selective value (w_T), relative to some standard, can be assigned to each total genotype that is possible from the array of genes under consideration under any given conditions of environment and population density (or persisting set of such conditions).

The general formula for change in a gene frequency under selection can still be written $\Delta q_i = q_i(w_i - \bar{w})/\bar{w}$, but w_i here is not a constant. It is a function of the frequencies of all interacting genes. We may deal with absolute reproductive values as before by replacing w's by W's and may shift to the continuous model by dropping $\overline{W}$ in the denominator and modifying (slightly in most cases) the interpretation of the W's. The effect of changes in density may be investigated as before, but this leads to greatly increased complexity because of increase in the number of parameters describing the interaction of loci.

In studying the effects of reaction systems, it now becomes convenient to express the formula in terms of genotypic selective values instead of net genic ones (23–26). The most general demonstration is given in the last reference:

$$\Delta q_{Ii} = \frac{q_{Ii}\,(1 - q_{Ii})\,\partial \overline{w}_I / \partial q_{Ii}}{2\overline{w}_T}. \tag{5}$$

If there are multiple alleles at any locus, it is assumed that, in the equation for given q_i at locus A_I, the frequencies of its alleles are expressed as

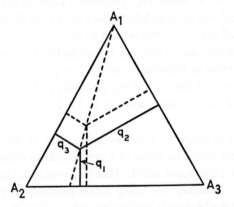

Fig. 11.—System of three alleles. In the partial derivatives $\partial q_2/\partial q_1$ and $\partial q_3/\partial q_1$, q_2 and q_3 are treated as constant fractions of their sum $(1 = q)$, so that their values are $-q_2/(1 - q_1)$ and $-q_3/(1 - q_2)$, respectively. They measure the changes in the gene frequencies q_2 and q_3 relative to an elementary change in q_1 as the locus of the population moves along the line connecting it with the locus of fixed A_1 (upper corner).

fractions of their total frequency $[q_i = R_{ji}(1 - q_i), \; \partial q_j/\partial q_i = -R_{ji} = -q_j/(1 - q_i)]$. It may be noted that $\partial \overline{w}_T/\partial q_{Ii}$ is the slope of the multidimensional surface $\overline{w}$ along the line leading to homallelic A_{Ii} at the same locus (and for the given set of gene frequencies at other loci [Fig. 11]).

A formula that is often more convenient in determining the actual rates of change of gene frequencies may be obtained by expressing the frequencies of genotypes at a locus in the usual form: q_i^2 for any homozygote A_iA_i and $2q_iq_j$ for any heterozygote A_iA_j and taking partial derivatives according. We shall indicate such derivatives by primes to distinguish them from the preceding:

$$\Delta q_i = q_i \frac{\left(\dfrac{\partial \bar{w}}{\partial q_i}\right)' - \sum_j q_j \left(\dfrac{\partial \bar{w}}{\partial q_j}\right)}{2\bar{w}}, \qquad j \text{ includes } i. \quad (6)$$

A partial derivative in this case does not give the slope of surface $\bar{w}$ in any direction, if there are multiple alleles, but merely the contributions of an elementary change in the specified gene frequency to change in $\bar{w}$.

The formulas took rather simple, but, as one can take cognizance of all possibile interactions among genes at any number of loci and among any number of alleles, subject only to constancy of the relative selective values of the total genotypes, they are necessarily far from simple in application. Thus $\bar{w}_T (= \Sigma f_T w_T)$ is the average of values assigned all possible genotypes (10^{12} in number in the system of four alleles at each of a dozen loci referred to earlier). Each genotypic frequency, f_T, is the product of as many quadratic terms as there are loci (appropriate frequency terms in the expansion of

$$\prod_I (\Sigma q_{Ii} A_{Ii})^2.$$

As many equations are required as there are independent gene frequencies (thirty-six in the above case) to describe a single step in the trajectory of the population in the system of gene frequencies. It is obvious that actual application is practicable only for simple models, ones that involve very few genes, or, if many, relations of dominance and interaction that can be generalized simply.

The formula is only an approximate one, even under completely random mating, if there are interactions among the loci. Selection itself brings about deviations from random association, which, as noted, are obliterated only gradually even in the case of loci in different chromosomes. The equilibrium deviations are, however, small if the recombination rate is much greater than the selective deviation (27, 28) and can be ignored for most purposes unless there is strong selection or close linkage.

Otherwise it is possible to treat recombination as a special sort of mutation. Thus the combinations of two alleles at two loci (AB) (ab), (Ab), (aB) may be treated as if four alleles, with mutations occurring only in the two heterozygotes $(AB)/(ab)$ and $(Ab)/(aB)$ (29).

The simplest application of equation (5) is to a pair of alleles.

Genotype	f	w	
A_1A_1........	q_1^2	$1 + s_1 + s_2$	$\bar{w} = 1 + 2s_1q_1 - (s_1 - s_2)q_1^2$,
A_1A_2........	$2q_1q_2$	$1 + s_1$	$d\bar{w}/dq_1 = 2s_1 - 2(s_1 - s_2)q_1$,
A_2A_2........	q_2^2	1	$\Delta q_1 = -q_1(1 - q_1)$

$$\Delta q_1 = -q_1(1 - q_1)[(s_1 - s_2)q_1 - s_1]/\bar{w}. \qquad (7)$$

The complete formula for Δq_1 should also include the mutation terms $u_{21}(1 - q_1) - u_{12}q_1$. The selection term is now a cubic. Equilibrium ($\Delta q_1 = 0$) is possible not only in the neighborhood of $q_1 = 0$ and $q_1 = 1$ but from selection by itself if s_2 is opposite in sign to s_1:

$$\hat{q} = \frac{s_1}{s_1 + (-s_2)}.$$

This is obviously unstable if the homozygotes are superior to both heterozygotes and thus at separate selective peaks of $\bar{w}$, but stable in the opposite case (11), of which the first recognized and most extreme examples were the balanced lethals of *Oenothera* species and certain laboratory strains of *Drosophila melanogaster*. It may be noted that the "peak" in the surface $\bar{w}$ in cases in which there is superiority of the heterozygote is at a mathematical maximum [$(d\bar{w}/dq_1) = 0$], which is not true of the two peaks in the opposite case.

Many cases of polymorphism probably due in many cases to superiority of heterozygotes have come to light in natural populations in such conspicuous characters as color and such easily tested ones as blood group specificities. The occurrence of more than 160 alleles at the B locus in cattle with no such obvious reason (30) as for the hundreds of alleles estimated in self-incompatibility loci of certain plants raises the question whether most supposedly single genes would not turn out to consist of numerous slightly different isoalleles if there were as delicate tests for difference as for antigenic specificities. Dobzhansky and his associates have obtained evidence for a great deal more heterozygosis in wild populations of *Drosophila* species than had previously been considered likely (31). The importance of overdominance with respect to productivity in cultivated plants and domestic animals is at present one of the most controversial issues in population genetics (32–36).

The most plausible physiological explanation for overdominance as a possibly very common phenomenon seems to be that of East (37), who pointed out that it would occur if both of two alleles have qualitatively different positive effects that tend to be manifested irrespective of the second allele in the zygote if the conditions for manifestation are provided and otherwise do not interfere much with manifestation of other reaction systems for which the conditions are provided. Consider the average effects in a random-breeding population, subject to different environmental conditions in different parts of its range, one of which (frequency p) provides the condition for functioning of gene A_1, the other for its allele A_2. We suppose that s and t are considerably larger than x and y:

Genotype	w_1 (A_1 Functions) Frequency p	w_2 (A_2 Functions) Frequency $(1-p)$	$\bar{w}$ $[= pw_1 + (1-p)w_2]$
A_1A_1........	$1+x$	$1-t$	$1 - (1-p)t + px$
A_1A_2........	1	1	1
A_2A_2........	$1-s$	$1+y$	$1 - ps + (1-p)y$

There is strong overdominance if each allele is completely dominant in the suitable environment ($x = y = 0$) and some overdominance if $(1-p)t > px$ and $ps > (1-p)y$. This can easily be generalized. Equilibrium from local differences in selection has been discussed from somewhat different viewpoints by Levene (38) and Li (39).

The same principle applies to successive environments in a seasonal or other cycle except that here the net selective value is the product and the weights appear as exponents. Again x and y are supposed to be small compared with s and t:

Genotype	w_1 (Weight p)	w_2 Weight $(1-p)$]	$\bar{w}$
A_1A_1........	$1+x$	$1-t$	$(1-t)^{1-p}(1+x)^p$
A_1A_2........	1	1	1
A_2A_2........	$1-s$	$1+y$	$(1-s)^p(1+y)^{1-p}$

Dempster (40) may be consulted for a general discussion of equilibrium from overdominance.

The possibility of this sort of equilibrium greatly extends the conception of the genetic composition of a species from that reached at the first level. Many or all loci may be strongly heterallelic.[2]

[2] The term "heterallelic" has been applied to loci in populations in which at least two alleles are present, in contrast with the term "homallelic" for loci in populations in which one allele is fixed (41). An isogenic population is homallelic in all loci. It is convenient to use "nearly homallelic" (or "weakly heterallelic") where nearly all individuals are homozygous in the same sense, as expected of most loci at the first level of theory, and "strongly heterallelic," as above, where at least two alleles are both fairly common.

Following is the general two-factor case with dominance at both loci. Only the selection terms are given for Δp and Δq:

Genotype	f	w	
A-B-........	$(1-p^2)(1-q^2)$	1	$\bar{w} = 1 - rq^2 - sp^2$
			$\qquad + (r + s - t)p^2q^2$
A-bb........	$(1 - p^2)q^2$	$1 - r$	$\Delta p = p^2(1 - p)$
			$\qquad [(r + s - t)q^2 - s]/\bar{w}$
aaB-........	$p^2(1 - q^2)$	$1 - s$	$\Delta q = q^2(1 - q)$
			$\qquad [(r + s - t)p^2 - t]/\bar{w}$
aabb........	p^2q^2	$1 - t$	

$$(8)$$

The frequencies at the two loci change wholly independently only if $(1 - t) = (1 - r)(1 - s)$, but if the selective differences are so small that $\bar{w}$ may be dropped from the denominators of Δp and Δq, the condition for independence becomes additivity of the selection effects $(t = r + s)$.

There is a possibility here that there may be two selective peaks $(1 - r$ and $1 - s$, both higher or both lower than 1 and $1 - t)$. In these cases, the frequency system tends to move toward one of the peaks, not necessarily the higher, according to the initial gene frequencies.

The evolution of populations at this level of theory has been treated from another viewpoint by Fisher (11, 42). Assuming that "fitness" (essentially, mean reproductive value $\bar{W}$) has been analyzed into additive contributions from the component genes plus non-additive components due to dominance, interaction, and non-random mating of a certain type, he arrived at "the fundamental theorem of natural selection": "The rate of increase in fitness of any organism at any time is equal to its genetic variance in fitness at that time." Genetic variance was here defined as merely the additive component, rather than the total variance due to heredity. The continuous model was used with the Malthusian parameter as the measure of fitness under postulated given conditions of population density and environment. In terms of the discrete model and letting a's represent the additive contributions of genes to selective value W(26):

$$\frac{\Delta \bar{W}}{\bar{W}} = \sigma^2_{\Sigma a/\bar{W}}.$$

$$(9)$$

As noted above, the theory at this level permits much more persistent variability than is probable at the first level. It also permits multiple peak genotypes instead of only one. But as the processes considered here can move the system only toward one peak in reproductive value and thereafter hold it there, there is no possibility of attaining a possibly higher peak, apart from changes in conditions that alter the system of peaks.

This obstacle to evolutionary progress was not present at the first level of theory.

The limitation on amount of evolution, in the rare event of a novel favorable mutation is not, however, as severe as at the first level of theory. Such a mutation may have interaction effects which reverse the direction of selective advantage of other pairs of genes. The changes in the frequencies at these loci may in turn unsettle other loci and so on. The establishment of a single favorable novel mutation may thus be followed by considerable readjustment within the previously established system.

Again, however, secular change in the prevailing environmental conditions seems much more likely to produce extensive evolutionary change than novel mutations. Change in conditions depresses the mean reproductive value but, by reversing some of the relative selective values of alleles, creates a new store of additive variance. The adaptability of the species in this respect may also be much greater than under the first form of theory because of the possibly much greater store of heterozygosis due to overdominance. The species exhausts the store of additive variance in moving toward the new equilibrium, but not necessarily that which had been due to overdominance.

3. COMPLICATIONS FROM DEPENDENCE OF SELECTIVE VALUE OF TOTAL GENOTYPES ON GENE FREQUENCIES

The assumption made in the preceding section that the relative selective values of total genotypes are constant under given conditions may well hold approximately for competition in coping with the environment. From ecology studies it is clear, however, that there are often interactions among individuals of the population that are favorable for some genotypes and unfavorable for others. Thus the relative selective values of total genotypes are necessarily functions of the frequencies of some or all of the genotypes. It becomes desirable to consider how the theory must be modified on dropping the above assumption.

The consequences in a number of important special cases have been presented by Haldane (43). More generally, it has been shown that the formula for the change in frequency of the genes can be expressed approximately as follows (25, 26, 44): It is assumed that

$$\frac{\partial q_j}{\partial q_i} = -\frac{q_j}{1 - q_i}, \text{ etc.,}$$

$$\Delta q_{Ii} = \frac{q_{Ii}(1 - q_{Ii})\left[\Sigma w_T\left(\partial f_T/\partial q_{Ii}\right)\right]}{2\bar{w}_T},$$

(10)

in which

$$\left[\Sigma w_T \frac{\partial f_T}{\partial q_{Ii}} \right]$$

can also be written

$$\left[\frac{\partial \bar{w}_T}{\partial q_{Ii}} - \left(\overline{\frac{\partial w_T}{\partial q_{Ii}}} \right) \right].$$

If the selective values of total genotypes are constant (all $\partial w_T/\partial q_{Ii} = 0$), the formula reduces to that previously given as equation (5). Absolute reproductive values (W) can be substituted for the relative ones in these formulas.

The mutation terms are not included above and can be added. Lewontin (45) has recently suggested that everything affecting gene frequency (mutation, non-random mating, etc.) may be incorporated into coefficients of the frequencies of the genotypes and has applied this method to pairs of alleles. This could be done in principle for multiple alleles and multiple loci, giving coefficients more complicated than the coefficients called W here but occupying the same place in the equations. Points of equilibrium (deterministic peaks) can be found in any case from the set of equations, $\Delta q_{Ii} = 0$.

Returning to evolutionary theory, the most important difference from that at the second level is that selection does not, in general, tend to move the system toward a peak value in reproductive capacity, $\overline{W}$, but toward some other point, which we must now distinguish as a selective peak.

From a mathematical standpoint, it is convenient to distinguish cases in which it is or is not possible to obtain a quantity

$$V = \int \frac{\Sigma w_T \, (\partial f_T/\partial q_{Ii})}{\bar{w}_T} \, dq_{Ii},$$

which is the same for all q_{Ii}'s. If it is obtainable, it behaves as a sort of (negative) potential which determines by its gradient—in conjunction with the term $(\frac{1}{2})q(1 - q)$—the trajectory of the gene frequency system toward a selective peak. This quantity was called the "internal selective value of the population (V_I)" in a preceding paper (26). The symbol V will be used here without subscript.

In the continuous model (in which $\bar{w}_T$ is dropped from the denominator) we have

$$\frac{\partial q_{Ii}}{\partial t} = \tfrac{1}{2} q_{Ii} \, (1 - q_{Ii}) \frac{\partial V}{\partial q_{Ii}}$$

where V is obtainable.

The quantity V can be obtained in any case in which only one pair of alleles is under consideration. Several examples were given in the reference above (26). It can, of course, be obtained in any case in which the reproductive values of total genotypes can be treated as constant, since it is then identical with $\overline{W}$.

There are two important categories in which V can be obtained even though there are two or more independent gene frequencies and the reproductive values of total genotypes are functions of the gene frequencies.

1. The absolute reproductive values of total genotypes all involve the same function (ψ) of some or all of the gene frequencies and no other function of these frequencies. Here $W = w\psi$, $\overline{W} = \overline{w}\psi$, and

$$V = \int \left[\frac{1}{\overline{w}\psi} \Sigma (w\psi) \frac{\partial f}{\partial q} \right] dq = \int \left(\frac{1}{\overline{w}} \frac{\partial \overline{w}}{\partial q} \right) dq = \log \overline{w}. \tag{11}$$

The peak values of V are not, in general, the same as those of $\overline{W}$.

An example is that in which the presence of certain genotypes has either a beneficial or an injurious effect on the population as a whole. Because of this, there will be one or more high points in reproductive value $\overline{W}$, but if there are no differences in selective value, the surface V is level. It is likely, however, that genotypes that damage the population as a whole benefit themselves as social parasites. It is also likely that genotypes that benefit the population as a whole by self-sacrifice may suffer relatively in their own reproductive rates. The social parasites will increase in frequency, and the social benefactors tend to be eliminated, though the population tends to suffer in both cases (25, 27, 43).

Another special case is that in which there are differences among relative selective values (w), but the sort of competition on which this depends has no effect on the size of population. In this case $W = w/\overline{w}$, $\overline{W} = 1$, $V = \log \overline{w}$. This is the opposite of the first case above, in that the surface $\overline{W}$ is level, while there are one or more peaks in selective value (17, 25, 26). On the other hand, the characters that make for success in competition may be responsible for a lowering of mean reproductive rate so that there are peaks in both $\overline{W}$ and V but at different places.

2. The other category referred to above is that in which the selective value of each genotype is a function of only its own frequency. Assume here that $\overline{w}$ differs so little from 1 that it can be ignored in the denominator in (V). Let

$$w_i = \chi(f_i), \qquad \overline{w} = \sum_i [f_i \chi(f_i)]. \tag{12}$$

Assume that $\chi(f_i)$ can be expanded in powers of f_i. If a term in $\chi(f_i)$

is $s_{i(n)}f_i^n$, the corresponding terms in $\bar{w}$ and V are $\Sigma s_{i(n)}f_i^{n+1}$ and $\Sigma s_{i(n)}f_i^{n+1}/(n+1)$, respectively.

The effects of a given power term on V is parallel to that on $\bar{w}$, so that the selective and reproductive peaks coincide if there is only one such term. This does not hold for a series of such terms, however. It also does not hold in the special case in which a term in $\chi(f_i)$ is s_i/f_i. The corresponding terms in $\bar{w}$ and V are Σs_i and $\Sigma(s_i \log f_i)$, respectively.

In this category selective value is a more or less complicated function of abundance. If the selective value increases with abundance, there tends to be a runaway process toward fixation of one or another type according to the initial conditions. If, on the other hand, a relatively high selective value tends to decrease with increasing abundance, a stable equilibrium tends to be reached, thus causing the system to be strongly heterallelic. The former condition might, however, be reversed by sufficient overdominance and the latter by sufficient superiority of the homozygotes. The nature of the equilibrium can be determined only from consideration of all factors. Following is a simple example:

Genotype		w
A_1A_1........	q_1^2	$1 + s_1 + t_1q_1$
A_1A_2........	$2q_1(1 - q_1)$	1
A_2A_2........	$(1 - q_1)^2$	$1 + s_2 + t_2(1 - q_1)$

$$\bar{w} = 1 + s_1q_1^2 + s_2(1 - q_1)^2 + t_1q_1^3 + t_2(1 - q_1)^3$$
$$\Delta q_1 = q_1(1 - q_1)[q_1^2(t_1 - t_2) + q_1(s_1 + s_2 + 2t_2) - (s_2 + t_2)]/\bar{w}. \tag{13}$$

Assume, for simplicity, that $t_2 = t_1 = t$, $\hat{q} = (s_2 + t)/(s_1 + s_2 + 2t)$. There is stable equilibrium if $(s_2 + t)$ and $(s_1 + t)$ are both negative; unstable equilibrium if both are positive. A special case $(s_1 = a, s_2 = b - a, t = -b, b > a)$ was discussed by Wright and Dobzhansky (45). In this case the heterozygote is always exactly intermediate, yet there is stable equilibrium at $\hat{q} = a/b$. It is evident that in other cases there may be stable equilibrium even though the heterozygote is inferior to both homozygotes, and there may be unstable equilibrium even though there is overdominance. Lewontin (46) has given more complicated examples that illustrate these last two points. Conversely, it is evident that a tendency to a runaway process because of a selective advantage of abundance may be overbalanced by sufficient overdominance and that a tendency to stable equilibrium because of a selective advantage of rarity may be over-balanced by sufficient inferiority of the heterozygote.

In general, there is no quantity V. Nevertheless, the possible trajectories of systems converge toward one or more selective peaks, although in most cases in somewhat spiral paths. In limiting cases there may be cyclic movement (13, 25, 26).

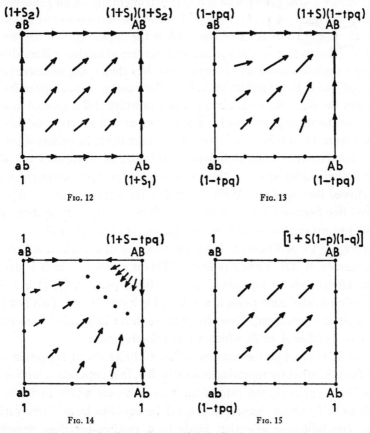

FIGS. 12–15.—Direction and relative magnitudes of change of gene frequencies in four two-factor cases (no dominance) in which the relative selective values are as given in the corners. Dots indicate no change.

Figures 12–15 indicate the trajectories in a number of simple two-factor systems. It is assumed in all of them that the heterozygotes are always at the geometric mean of the homozygotes so that the analysis can be based on gametes instead of zygotes. In this case the factor 2 does not appear in the denominator of the expressions for change of gene frequency.

In Figure 12, genotypic relative reproductive values are constant, and there is no interaction. The trajectories converge toward selective peak values in the upper-right corner. If the absolute reproductive values are also constant, the peak reproductive value coincides with the selective peak, but if the absolute reproductive values are of the form $W = w/\bar{w}$, the surface $\overline{W}$ is level.

In Figure 13 the presence of AB acts detrimentally on all genotypes, including AB itself—term $(1 - tpq)$—but AB also has a selective advantage over all others. There is a selective peak in the upper-right corner (fixation of AB). The nature of the surface of mean reproductive values depends on the values of s and t. If s is equal to or less than t, the selective peak is at a low point in reproductive value—the case of a social parasite. Reversal of the signs of s and t gives the case in which AB is a social asset but at a disadvantage individually. The arrows are all reversed in this case.

In Figure 14, AB has a selective advantage over the others when rare, but a disadvantage when abundant. In this case the surfaces V and $\overline{W}$ are essentially parallel. If $t > s$, there is a selective peak or better ridge along the curved line $pq = s/t$. With reversal of the signs of t and s, this same curved line becomes a trough from which gene frequency systems move either toward fixation of AB or toward loss of either A or B.

In Figure 15, AB benefits from the presence of ab, which suffers from the presence of AB (s and t positive). This is a case in which V does not exist. The surface of reproductive value has a peak at $(\frac{1}{2}, \frac{1}{2})$ if $s > t$, a depression at the same point if $s < t$, and is level if $s = t$. This last is the case that is represented. Gene frequencies move in parallel lines toward fixation of either A or B, which are at selective ridges.

Since it is possible for mass selection to bring about reduction in fitness (as measured by reproductive value $\overline{W}$), in a population with a store of additive variance, the rate of increase in fitness which such selection tends to bring about cannot, in general, be equal to its additive variance (25). The following equation holds in a random-breeding population 26). The corresponding continuous case was derived independently by Crow and Kimura (47):

$$\frac{\Delta\overline{W} - \overline{\Delta W}}{\overline{W}} = \sigma^2_{\Sigma w/\bar{w}} \left(= \frac{\Delta V)}{\overline{W}} \text{ if } V \text{ exists} \right). \tag{14}$$

It may be noted that if there is not random mating, the formula is, in general, more complicated in terms of reproductive values even under constancy of the total genotypes:

$$\frac{\Delta \bar{W} - 2\overline{\Delta a}}{\bar{W}} = \frac{\Delta \bar{W} - \overline{\Delta W} + \overline{\Delta R}}{\bar{W}} = \sigma^2_{\Sigma a/\bar{W}}. \tag{15}$$

In these formulas the a's, are the additive effects of genes, and R is the additive effect of dominance and interaction. The most complete analysis is that of Kimura (13), using the continuous model. Essentially, he has analyzed the term $\overline{\Delta R}$ above into separate components for dominance deviations and Kempthorne's (48) components of the interaction effect.

The terms $\overline{\Delta W}$ and $2\overline{\Delta a}$, or its components, affect the rate of increase of fitness in somewhat the same way as do changes of environment or of population density. The frequencies of other genotypes are, indeed, part of the environment of each individual. The entity under consideration, however, is the system of gene frequencies, and it is decidedly awkward to treat the selective effect of changes in this itself as if it were a part of its own environment.

The conclusions at this third level enrich the theory to some extent but, on the whole, raise more difficulties in evolutionary theory than they solve. It is true that the equilibrium that may be established by a shift from selective advantage to disadvantage beyond a certain frequency may give rise to a heterogeneity that is adaptive in using the resources available to the species and also gives increased adaptability to changing conditions and that the opposite process may be an advantage in special cases, such as establishment of one or another character that is neutral except as an arbitrary signal. On the other hand, the tendency toward fixation of characters that are advantageous to their possessors but harmful to the species raises a difficult problem.

4. MULTIPLE SELECTIVE PEAKS AND RANDOM PROCESSES

We have referred several times to the possibility that there may be more than one selective peak and that deterministic processes can move a gene frequency system only toward one of these, not necessarily the highest. It is desirable to consider how serious an obstacle this is to progress under natural selection.

As already noted, two selective peaks may readily occur with only one pair of alleles. The case of reciprocal translocations in plants, associated with semisterility of the heterozygotes, is formally of this sort. The case of reciprocal translocations in animals is somewhat similar but bifactorial. Cases can be cited in which there are two peaks among genotypes in grade of development of a character that is affected by two or more loci, but these do not seem to be sufficiently common to constitute an important obstacle to progress by mass selection.

More important is the class of cases in which two characters are physiologically incompatible. The difficulties in combining the highest grades of beef and milk production in the same breed of cattle or in combining the best mutton type with heavy fleece in sheep are illustrations from artificial selection. Simpson's alternative adaptive zones in phylogenies are probably often in this category (49). In cases in which a peak system of such a sort is well established, there is probably little or no possibility of passage to an alternative well-defined peak system by any process except radically redirected selection. In the incipient stages, passage to one or another may, however, occur by processes to be discussed here.

The question that we wish to consider here is whether physiological and ecologic situations occur at all frequently which lead to a great multiplicity of peaks separated by shallow saddles.

It is fairly obvious that one sort of case is extremely common. This is the case in which the optimum of a quantitatively varying character is at an intermediate grade. It is indeed probably rather unusual for the momentary optimum of any such character to differ much from the mean, even though in the course of geologic time it may come to be outside its former range. Such characters usually behave genetically as if determined more or less additively, on an appropriate scale, by multiple factors of which no single ones are of importance. There are inevitably several selective peaks, and there may be a great many (23).

These peaks may not differ very much as far as the character in question is concerned. If, however, we take account of the practical universality of pleiotropic effects, the differences become of primary importance. These pleiotropic effects contribute, of course, to selective value. Gene frequency systems with peak values with respect to the character in question may not be peak values after all effects are considered. While many reaction systems doubtless evolve relatively independently of one another, there are probably always some genes in common. Each of the vast number of selective peaks, when all characters are considered, thus probably marks a step in a somewhat different direction from its neighbors, which may be of evolutionary significance if there is some way by which the system may take it.

Before going further, we may note that there may also be a multiplicity of peaks relative to a character of which the extreme grade is optimal. There may be a physiological limit. Some gene complexes may give this limiting value or a close approach to it with a minimum of unfavorable pleiotropic effects while others have such effects. The former are at selective peaks, the latter in selective valleys in spite of their high selective value for the character in question. A tendency toward homeostatic protection against a slight deleterious tendency which breaks down with accumulation of multiple factors that contribute to this would usually mean that gene systems that put the character in question slightly but safely above the desirable physiological limit would be more likely to be at selective peaks than ones which include more plus factors than are necessary (50).

A genetic system can take the step from one selective peak to a higher one only by some non-selective process. A novel mutation may do this by creating a new peak, but this must be an excessively rare event. The alternative is a random departure from the strictly deterministic effects of the various processes. This may itself be due to some unique event in the history of the population, or it may be a cumulative consequence of many small accidental deviations.

A single extreme reduction in numbers such as occurs in the origin of a colony may result by accident in such an extreme deviation from the previous array of gene frequencies that selection of the same sort as before carries the system to a different selective peak. A succession of such bottlenecks in size of population increases the likelihood that this will occur (51, 52). At the other extreme, the accumulation of the small deviations in gene frequency that occur in each generation by mere accidents of sampling may conceivably have the same effect even in a population of constant size. This is much more likely, however, if the population goes through a marked cycle in its size. The sampling variance is $\sigma^2_{\Delta q} = q(1 - q)/2N$ in one generation in a population of effective size N, nearly twice this in two generations, and so on. With a population cycle so short that there is little selective adjustment, the effective population number is approximately the harmonic mean for the separate generations. This is governed predominantly by the smaller numbers (51, 53).

`Similarly, a single extreme environmental deviation and the ensuing drastic selection may upset gene frequencies so much that thereafter the same sort of selection as before may drive the system to a new selective peak. The cumulative effect of fluctuations may also take the system across a selective valley (23, 54). In the simplest case—directed effect $\Delta q = \bar{s}q(1 - q)$, fluctuation $\delta q = (s - \bar{s}) q(1 - q)$—the variance of gene frequencies is $\sigma_{\Delta q}^2 = \sigma_s^2 q^2 (1 - q)^2$ each generation. Here, as in the case of accidents of sampling, the cumulative effect of the (squared) deviations results is a random drift, in contrast with the steady drift due to the average selective difference between alleles. It is assumed here that there is an equilibrium point from opposition between selection and other directed pressures.

A random drift can have only a deleterious effect by itself just because it is random. On the other hand, the joint operation of directed and random processes tends to result in greater progress than the directed process by itself. We shall consider two models.

Suppose that a person sets out in a dense fog to walk always up the steepest slope in a hilly country. He is almost certain to find himself soon at the top of a rather low knoll with nowhere to go without violating his resolve to go always uphill. If, instead, he had walked wholly at random, he would almost certainly have remained most of the time on somewhat low ground, since the hilltops are relatively few. If, however, he tends in the main to walk uphill but also takes many steps in random directions, he may not reach the actual summit of any hill but will not be brought to a stop on the top of a lower one. Ultimately he will find himself on much higher ground than if rigorously adhering to the steepest slopes.

A mechanical model can be made by comparing the behavior of Mexican jumping beans with perfect spheres of the same size. Since gravity is to take the place of selection, we must invert our scale and replace peaks by hollows of various depths. On a level surface the spheres would be stationary. The beans would hop about but not get very far, even in a long period of time. On an irregular surface, a sphere started from a particular point would always end in a certain hollow, not likely to be one of the deeper ones. A jumping bean, started at the same point, would move deviously to one or another hollow, escape from this if shallow, and move on to another—and so on until it had found its way to one of the deeper ones. The sphere represents a gene frequency system under strictly deterministic control by the gradient, and the jumping bean represents one in which control by the gradient is qualified both by purely random movements (corresponding to accidents of sampling) and others (due to asymmetrical shape) that correspond to selective fluctuations.

Returning to the case of gene frequency systems, the resultant of the mean of the directed processes ($\overline{\Delta q}$) that tend to establish a certain equilibrium frequency at a deterministic peak, and random processes (measured by $\sigma_{\Delta q}^2$) that tend to bring about deviations from this, is a probability curve within which the frequency system keeps wandering. The formula can be derived from the condition that all moments of the curve be the same as before, after allowing for the occurrence of directed and random deviations in each generation (41, 55, 56):

$$\phi(q) = \frac{C}{\sigma^2_{\Delta q}} \exp\left[2\int\left(\frac{\overline{\Delta q}}{\sigma^2_{\Delta q}}\right) dq\right], \qquad \int_0^1 \phi(q)\,dq = 1. \qquad (16)$$

This formula does not give the total probability distribution for the gene in question but merely a cross-section of the multidimensional probability distribution of the entire reaction system, defined by a particular set of relative frequencies among its alleles and a particular set of gene frequencies at other loci. There is greatly increased complexity with non-random mating even for single pairs of alleles (57).

No equally general formula has been arrived at for this multidimensional distribution as a whole. In the case of internal selective value V for a gene frequency system, mutation rates v and u to and from a specified allele (frequency q) in each of multiple pairs and random drift due only to accidents of sampling in a population of effective size N, the formula is as follows (26):

$$\phi(q_1, q_2 \ldots) = C\,e^{2NV} \prod_i \left[q_i^{4Nv-1}(1-q_i)^{4Nu-1}\right]. \qquad (17)$$

This formula was given earlier (24) for the case of constant selective values of total genotypes ($\overline{W}^{2N}$ in place of e^{2NV}). It should be noted that these formulas assume the absence of fluctuations in selection (58).

The multidimensional probability distribution, whatever the nature of the random processes, is, in general, one with a vast number of maxima corresponding roughly to the selective peaks in the surface V but shifted from these by mutation pressures. If a gene frequency system, confined for a time to the neighborhood of one of these peaks, is to pass under control of another peak after a reasonable interval, the population must be subject to random processes $\sigma^2_{\Delta q}$ of the same order as the directed change per generation ($\overline{\Delta q}$) or greater. It is, moreover, not likely to occur unless the population is strongly heterallelic ($\hat{q}$ not too close to either 0 or 1). If the random deviations are too small, the population is held firmly to an intermediate equilibrium point—i.e., the standard deviation of the probability distribution, σ_q, is too small—cf. A, Fig. 16. If random drift goes to the extent of fixation of one allele or the other (cf. E, Fig. 16), or if the system is carried to a homallelic peak, at either of which $\sigma^2_{\Delta q}$ becomes 0, the process comes to an end. A continuing process thus requires both a relatively large σ_q in order that gene frequency may drift a long way from a previous value and also a large average value of $\sigma_{\Delta q}^2$. The product $\sigma_q \sigma_{\Delta q}^2$ may serve as a rough index of the degree to which a given probability distribution is favorable for passage from peak to peak.

The mathematically simplest example is that in which the only directed processes are those of reversible mutation—$\Delta q = v(1 - q) - uq$—and the

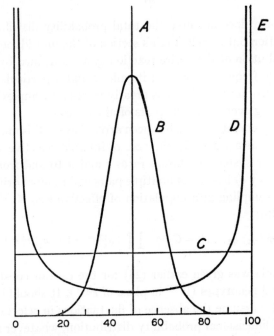

Fig. 16.—Probability distributions assuming $\Delta q - v(1 - q) - vq$, $\sigma_{\Delta q}^2 = q(1 - q)/2N$. In A, N is indefinitely great and $\sigma_{\Delta q}^2 = 0$. In C, the product $\sigma_q \sigma_{\Delta q}^2$ is maximum. In B and D, this product is half as great as in C. In E, $\sigma_{\Delta q}^2 = 0$ because $q(1 - q) = 0$.

only random process is that due to sampling. In this case $V = 1$ in the formula above and

$$\sigma_q^2 = \int_0^1 (q - \bar{q})^2 \phi(q) \, dq = \frac{\bar{q}(1 - \bar{q})}{[4N(u + v) + 1]},$$

and the average value of $\sigma_{\Delta q}^2$ is

$$\frac{1}{2N} \int_0^1 q(1 - q) \phi(q) \, dq = \frac{1}{2N} [\bar{q}(1 - \bar{q}) - \sigma_q^2].$$

The product $\sigma_q \sigma_{\Delta q}^2$ is maximum for varying $(u + v)$ if $4N(u + v) = 2$. In the symmetrical case, $u = v = 1/(4N)$, $\bar{q} = \frac{1}{2}$, $\phi(q) = 1$. The optimal distribution is thus flat-topped by this criterion (cf. C, Fig. 16). The index is about half its optimal value if $4N(u + v) = 24$, $\phi(q) = Cq^{11}(1 - q)^{11}$ in the symmetrical case, a rather narrow distribution (cf. B, Fig. 16), or if $4N(u + v) = 0.28$, $\phi(q) = Cq^{-0.86}(1 - q)^{-0.86}$ a rather extreme U-shaped distribution (cf. D, Fig. 16). Conditions are thus fairly favorable by this criterion over a wide range. To be directly pertinent, the situation would, of course, have to be modified slightly by introduction of low selective peaks in conjunction with other loci.

The case above was chosen only for mathematical convenience. In other cases, the expressions for σ_q and $\sigma_{\Delta q}^2$ can be integrated only empirically. The situation is, however, essentially similar for all probability distributions of similar spread. For a given σ_q it seems, indeed, to be somewhat more favorable in the case of random drift due to fluctuations in selection than to accidents of sampling, because the distribution $\phi(q)$ becomes bimodal if σ_q is large (54) and can never lead to complete fixation by itself (59). We have dealt here with the distribution for a single gene. A full analysis would obviously require consideration of the multidimensional case with multiple peak values of V.

A primary condition for a continuing process is, as noted, that the population continue to be strongly heterallelic on passing from control of one peak to control of another. It is not likely that equilibrium is often due to opposed mutation pressures, since this implies almost complete absence of selective differences. Equilibrium due to opposition between recurrent mutation and selection is usually at such a low gene frequency that no sort of random drift is likely to be effective. The only sort of equilibrium yet considered that seems likely to be important in this connection is one due to opposing selection pressures, whether from overdominance, selective advantage of alleles when rare, or a compromise.

There may be two doubly heterallelic selective peaks due wholly to opposed selection pressures even with only two pairs of alleles. Consider a character with intermediate optimum such that genotypes $A_1A_1B_3B_3$ and $A_3A_3B_1B_1$ are, on the average, superior to the extreme genotypes $A_1A_1B_1B_1$ and $A_3A_3B_3B_3$. Assume, however, that the single heterozygotes are slightly superior to either of the intermediate homozygotes in selective values, on the average, perhaps because of superiority of the extreme types under special conditions and shifting dominance of the sort expected under East's hypothesis. The balanced double heterozygotes may be expected to have the highest average selective values of all. Assume the array $[(1 - p)A_1 + pA_3][(1 - q)B_1 + qB_3]$.

SELECTIVE VALUES (w)

	A_1A_1	A_2A_1	A_2A_2
B_2B_2....	$1-t$	1	$1-r$
B_2B_1....	1	$1+x$	1
B_1B_1....	$1-r$	1	$1-s$

Assume relative selective values as indicated in the table. Those for the extreme types are assumed equal for the sake of symmetry about the line $p = (1 - q)$. Then

$$\bar{w} = 1 - r\,[\,(1-p)^2(1-q)^2 + p^2q^2\,] - s\,[\,p^2(1-q)^2\,] - t\,[\,(1-p)^2q^2\,]$$
$$+ 4xp\,(1-p)\,q\,(1-q)\,.$$

The rates of change of p and q may readily be found from the formula $\Delta p = (\tfrac{1}{2})p(1-p)\partial\bar{w}/\partial p$ and $\Delta q = (\tfrac{1}{2})q(1-q)\partial\bar{w}/\partial q$. If x is not too large in relation to s and t, there are two selective peaks separated by a saddle point, the positions of all of which are readily found by putting $\Delta p = 0$, $\Delta q = 0$. The probability distribution of values of p and q in a population of effective size N is given by the formula

$$\phi\,(p,\ q) = \frac{C\bar{w}^{2N}}{p\,(1-p)\,q\,(1-q)}\,. \tag{18}$$

Table 1 shows the array of genotypic selective values in a case in which s and t are equal. The corresponding mean selective values, $\bar{w}$, of possible populations are given in Table 2 at intervals of 0.25 of p and q. There are peak values at $\bar{w}$ at 0.25, 0.75 and 0.75, 0.25 along the line $p = (1 - q)$ separated by a shallow saddle point at 0.50, 0.50. The relative frequencies in the cross-section of $\phi(p, q)$ along the high ridge, $p = 1 - q$, are shown in Figure 17 for a population of effective size $N = 1,000$.

TABLE 1

RELATIVE SELECTIVE VALUES (w) OF GENOTYPES
USED FOR TABLE 2 AND FIGURE 17

	A_1A_1	A_2A_1	A_2A_2
B_2B_2.........	0.97	1.00	0.81
B_2B_1.........	1.00	1.03	1.00
B_1B_1.........	0.81	1.00	0.97

It may be seen that a population under control of the peak at 0.25, 0.75 would drift at random about this for a long time (long because random drift with $2N = 2,000$ is a very slow process). Ultimately, however, it may be expected to drift across the low point at 0.50, 0.50 and come under control of the other selective peak. In this symmetrical case, it would have as good a chance of ultimately returning to control of the first peak, and so on indefinitely, if these two peaks are all that are accessible and other evolutionary processes have not altered the systems.

The situation is very different with even a slight selective difference between the two balanced homozygotes. Table 3 shows a set of genotypic

TABLE 2*

MEAN SELECTIVE VALUES (w) AT INDICATED GENE FREQUENCIES AND GENOTYPIC SELECTIVE VALUES OF TABLE 1

q	p				
	0	0.25	0.50	0.75	1.00
1.00........	0.970	0.971	0.945	0.891	0.810
0.75........	0.971	0.981	0.971	0.941	0.891
0.50........	0.945	0.971	0.980	0.971	0.945
0.25........	0.891	0.941	0.971	0.981	0.971
0..........	0.810	0.891	0.945	0.971	0.970

* There are peak values $\bar{w} = 0.981$ at both 0.25, 0.75 and 0.75, 0.25, with intervening saddle point $\bar{w} = 0.980$ at 0.50, 0.50. The corresponding distribution of gene frequencies along the diagonal $p = 1 - q$ is given in Fig. 17 for populations of size 1,000.

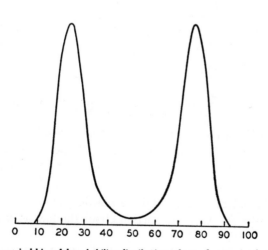

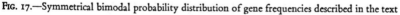

FIG. 17.—Symmetrical bimodal probability distribution of gene frequencies described in the text

selective values in which these are at disadvantages of 4 and 6 per cent, respectively, in relation to the single heterozygotes. Some values of $\bar{w}$ are shown in Table 4. Again there are two peaks, one at 0.254, 0.746 and one at 0.842, 0.158, separated by a low point on the ridge $p = (1 - q)$, at 0.452, 0.548. A population of effective size 500 that happened for historical reasons to be under control of the lower peak would drift at ran-

TABLE 3

RELATIVE SELECTIVE VALUES (w) OF GENOTYPES
USED FOR TABLE 4 AND FIGURE 18

	A_1A_1	A_2A_1	A_2A_2
B_3B_3.........	0.94	1.00	0.64
B_3B_1.........	1.00	1.05	1.00
B_1B_1.........	0.64	1.00	0.96

TABLE 4*

MEAN SELECTIVE VALUES (w) AT INDICATED GENE FREQUENCIES AND
GENOTYPIC SELECTIVE VALUES OF TABLE 3

q	p				
	0	0.25	0.50	0.75	1.00
1.00........	0.940	0.944	0.895	0.794	0.640
0.75........	0.944	0.963	0.944	0.888	0.795
0.50........	0.895	0.944	0.961	0.947	0.900
0.25........	0.794	0.888	0.947	0.969	0.955
0..........	0.640	0.795	0.900	0.955	0.960

* There are peak values $\bar{w} = 0.963$ at 0.254, 0.746 and $\bar{w} = 0.971$ at 0.842, 0.156, with intervening saddle point $\bar{w} = 0.961$ at 0.452, 0.548. The corresponding distribution of gene frequencies along the diagonal $p = 1 - q$ is given in Fig. 18 for populations of size 500.

dom about this for a long time before drifting across the low point. Once well across, however, it would come practically permanently under control of the high peak. The probability curve at the left in Figure 18 is incomplete. That at the right is on a scale reduced about 6,000-fold and may be considered to be the total distribution curve—along the cross-section $p = (1 - q)$—since the portion about the low peak is too low to be visible.

A system with only two selective peaks is of only minor evolutionary interest. There can be only a single non-degenerate selective peak within a set of multiple alleles as a result of overdominance (60). There may be others in the degenerate systems represented by the boundary lines or corners. These become non-degenerate deterministic peaks as a result of recurrent mutation, which has increasing importance from the standpoint of passage between peaks as the number of alleles increases.

Theoretically, there may be any number of selective peaks with only one pair of alleles if selective advantage is a function of gene frequency,

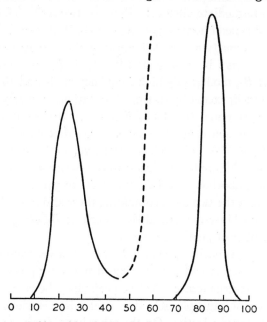

Fig. 18.—Asymmetrical bimodal probability distribution of gene frequencies described in the text. The curve at the left is on a scale about 6,000-fold that on the right.

but this requires very implausible types of functional relationship. Practically, the situation seems to be similar to that of overdominance.

The possible number of non-degenerate peaks mounts rapidly with the number of loci in a reaction system. With n pairs of alleles, 2^{n-1}, such peaks are possible, the number of corners separated by at least two gene replacements. The probable number is, of course, smaller. Consider a quantitatively varying character in which the grades are determined additively by four pairs of alleles of about equal importance and little or no dominance (cf. Fig. 10). Assume that the optimum is intermediate, so that there are six relatively superior homozygotes (those in $A_1B_1C_3D_3$, $A_1B_3C_1D_3$, $A_1B_3C_3D_1$, $A_3B_1C_1D_3$, $A_3B_1C_3D_1$, and $A_3B_3C_1D_1$). Assume, however, that there are places or times in which any of the homo-zygotes except the most extreme may be at an advantage and that there is enough shifting dominance with respect to selective advantage that the single heterozygotes have a slight over-all superiority. There may be selective peaks in the neighborhood of all six superior homo-zygotes that are strongly heterallelic in all respects.

Multiple alleles at multiple loci increase somewhat the possible number of selective peaks. Returning to the two-factor case considered earlier, the occurrence of intermediate alleles A_2, B_2 in the two series (cf. Fig. 8) gives a third balanced type of homozygote $A_2A_2B_2B_2$. With overdominance and not too much superiority of double heterozygotes, one may expect to find three peaks. One may be represented by $A_1(A_2)B_3(B_2)$ to indicate pre-dominance of A_1B_3, moderately high frequency of A_2 and B_2, and virtual absence of A_3 and B_1 except by recurrent mutation. Similarly, there is one that may be represented by $A_3(A_2)B_1(B_2)$ for analogous reasons. The only fully non-degenerate selective peak is one that may be represented by $A_2(A_3, A_1)B_2(B_1, B_3)$. This peak is located well in the interior of the sys-tem represented in Figure 8, but closest to the corner A_2B_2, while the other two are in the neighborhoods of A_1B_3 and A_3B_1, respectively, only slightly in the interior from the two faces containing these and A_2B_2. In the case of the four loci, a third intermediate allele at each $(A_2B_2C_2D_2)$ would increase the possible number of peaks considerably.

A reaction system consisting of only four loci is a very simple one. With more extensive systems and interlocking of many by pleiotropic effects, the number of non-degenerate selective peaks may be enormous.

The existence of multiple selective peaks is a serious obstacle to progress by pure mass selection. On the other hand, it gives an enormous-ly richer field of potential modes of adaptation to a particular environ-ment than that given by a single peak, provided that passage from peak to peak is possible. The joint action of directed and random processes seems to open up such a possibility. The question must be considered whether the process can occur rapidly enough to be significant.

It is easy to show that, on starting from a single gene frequency, q, pure random drift from accidents of sampling gives a variance of $\sigma_q^2 = q(1 - q)[1 - (1 - 1/2N)^n]$ in n generations (44) or approximately $\sigma_\infty^2(1 - e^{-n/2N})$, where the limiting value at complete fixation is $\sigma_\infty^2 = q(1 - q)$. It is evident that n must be of the order of N for this sort of random drift to be likely to bring about passage from one selective peak to another. A more complete demonstration of this point has been made by Kimura, who has found the successive forms taken by the probability distribution on starting from a single gene frequency, not only in this case (61) but also in the presence of selection (58, 59, 62).

Thus random drift from accidents of sampling is of very little importance in any reasonably large random-breeding population, as has often been noted (51, 53). It is a significant factor within an isolated population only if its numbers pass through small bottlenecks, either at its foundation or intermittently thereafter. Spurway (63) has accounted for the establishment of reciprocal translocations in subspecies of the newt, *Triturus cristatus*, by the hypothesis that during the expansion of the range of the species after the glacial period new advance colonies were often established by single sperm-bearing females. Mayr has stressed the importance of a small number of founders in the differentiation of island populations (63*a*).

There may be much more random drift from fluctuations in the selection coefficients. The case of fluctuations in the case of equilibrium maintained by overdominance is of especial interest. Letting $\bar{s}$ and $\bar{t}$ be mean selective disadvantages of the two homozygotes relative to the heterozygotes, we have

$$\overline{\Delta q} = -q(1-q)[\bar{s}q - \bar{t}(1-q)] = -(\bar{s}+\bar{t})q(1-q)(q-\hat{q}), \ \hat{q} = \frac{\bar{t}}{\bar{s}+\bar{t}},$$

$$\delta q = q(1-q)[(s-\bar{s})q - (t-\bar{t})(1-q)],$$

$$\sigma^2_{\Delta q} = q^2(1-q)^2[\sigma^2_s q^2 + \sigma^2_t (1-q)^2 - 2\sigma_s\sigma_t r_{st} q(1-q)].$$

Consider, first, the case in which there is fluctuation merely in intensity ($r_{st} = 1$, $\hat{q}$ constant):

$$\sigma^2_{\Delta q} = \sigma^2_{s+t} q^2(1-q)^2(q-\hat{q})^2.$$

Substitution in the formula for $\phi(q)$ gives an expression in which the ordinate at $q = \hat{q}$ is always infinitely greater than at any other value of q, indicating that the distribution is confined to the equilibrium point, as it obviously must be, since $\sigma_{\Delta q}$ is merely a multiple of Δq in this case.

If, however, s and t vary equally and in perfect negative correlation,

$$(\sigma^2_s = \sigma^2_t, \quad r_{st} = -1, \quad s+t \text{ constant}),$$

$$\sigma^2_{\Delta q} = \sigma^2_t q^2(1-q)^2,$$

$$\phi(q) = \frac{\Gamma(a-2)}{\Gamma(a\hat{q}-1)\Gamma[a(1-\hat{q})-1]} q^{a\hat{q}-2}(1-q)^{a(1-\hat{q})-2}, \quad a = \frac{2(\bar{s}+\bar{t})}{\sigma^2_t},$$

$$\bar{q} = \frac{a\hat{q}-1}{a-2},$$

$$\sigma^2_q = \frac{\bar{q}(1-\bar{q})}{a-1}. \tag{19}$$

Both $\bar{s}$ and t must be positive if there is to be overdominance on the average. Both must be small and q_i^2 large if the amount of random drift is to be large enough to be important. The process can be a rather rapid one under these conditions.

In the case of equilibrium between mutation pressure and selection, with or without dominance, Kimura has found the formula for the probability distribution at any stage from a single initial gene frequency to approach to the stable state, under fluctuation of the selection coefficient (58, 59). In the case of no dominance, he found that the variance increases at about the rate $\sigma_s^2/8$ per generation, which may be rapid enough to be important.

The physiological complications introduced at the fourth level of theory seem, on the whole, to raise more difficulties than are solved by the introduction of the effects of random processes into the theory. At the first and second levels, we noted that environmental change could bring about extensive evolutionary change, but return to the original conditions redirects the process toward the same goal as before. The principal addition at the fourth level is the recognition that mere fluctuations in conditions and hence in the selection coefficients may overcome to some extent the obstacles from a multiplicity of selective peaks by means of joint action of these random processes with the directed ones.

5. PARTIAL ISOLATION AND INTERDEMIC SELECTION

At the fifth level of theory, we return to population ecology to take cognizance of the fact that species are not usually even roughly panmictic. There is often division into subspecies, of these into local races, and these ultimately into small random-breeding demes.

There are many patterns of population structure. A number of different mathematical models have been considered, all necessarily much simpler than situations in nature. In a two-dimensional continuum of uniform density, accidents of sampling can produce very little differentiation unless the effective sizes of the neighborhoods (populations within which the parents of an individual may be considered to be drawn at random) are decidedly small. Random differentiation (both local and regional) is great if this size is of the order of 20, not negligible if 200, but there is almost the equivalent of universal panmixia over an indefinitely larger area if it is as large as 1,000 (64, 65). Malecot (66) has investigated this situation from the standpoint of the falling-off of the correlation between individuals with distance.

The situation is much more favorable for random differentiation if there are scattered centers of high density so that the increment to ancestral generations is small compared with the moderately large populations at the centers (6). Random drift is enormously greater within a linear range.

The simplest model mathematically is the rather unrealistic one of a collection of "island" populations, each absorbing a certain percentage of immigrants drawn at random from the whole.

No satisfactory mathematical treatment of selection including local differences in direction or degree, jointly with random processes, throughout a species has been arrived at.

For our purpose, however, attention need be focused on only a single deme without any assumptions about the structure of the species as a whole. We assume that this deme includes an effective proportion, m, drawn from outside in each generation and that these immigrants have the frequency Q of the gene that is under consideration:

$$\Delta q = - m (q - Q).$$

The differentiation of demes, whatever the reason, implies intermediate gene frequencies in the species as a whole at all loci that are involved. It also tends to imply that each deme is heterallelic in these loci. The approximate equilibrium values arising jointly from crossbreeding and genic selection are as follows (53):

$$\Delta q = s q (1 - q) - m (q - Q)$$

	$\hat{q}$ if $s > 0$	$\hat{q}$ if $s < 0$
$\lvert s \rvert \gg m,$	$1 - (m/s)(1 - Q),$	$mQ/(-s),$
$\lvert s \rvert = m,$	$\sqrt{Q},$	$1 - \sqrt{1 - Q},$
$\lvert s \rvert \ll m,$	$Q\left[1 + \dfrac{s}{m}(1 - Q)\right],$	$Q\left[1 - \dfrac{(-s)}{m}(1 - Q)\right].$ (20)

These equilibria provide a broader basis of heterozygosis for the joint action of directed and random processes than in a panmictic population. Random drift from accidents of sampling, moreover, occurs separately in each deme on the basis of its own population size and thus much more extensively than in an undivided species of the same size as the whole. If random drift is occurring independently in 1,000 demes, each of effective size 1,000, the chance of passage from one selective peak to another, somewhere, is a million times as great as in a panmictic population of the same total size. Moreover, the demes may differ greatly in size. Some may be so small that random drift from sampling is very rapid indeed. Thus there may be portions of the range in which colonies are continually being established, persisting a few generations, and then becoming extinct. The line of ancestry of a colony, or large group of colonies, may pass through many bottlenecks consisting of only one or a few pairs. The effective size of such demes is exceedingly small (51, 52).

The probability distribution for gene frequencies q (more fully, q_{Ii}) for any number of alleles at any number of loci, assuming that the absorption of immigrants with gene frequencies Q (more fully, Q_{Ii}) to the extent m in each generation is as follows. The expression Πq^{4NmQ-1} involves terms for every allele at every locus (25, 26, 58):

$$\phi\,(q_{Ii},\ q_{Ij}\ \ldots\ q_{Ji},\ q_{Jj}\ \ldots) = C\,e^{2NV}\Pi\,q^{4Nm\,Q-1}\,. \tag{21}$$

Random drift from fluctuations in selection is also more important within demes insofar as these are independent than in a panmictic population as large as all demes combined.

Two sorts of random drift that do not occur at the preceding levels of theory must be recognized: that due to fluctuations in the amount of immigration (measured by σ_m^2) and that due to fluctuations in the gene frequency of immigrants (measured by σ_Q^2). With respect to the former, in association with the simplest model of selection (54):

$$\overline{\Delta q} = \bar{s}\,q\,(1-q) - \bar{m}\,(q-Q)\,,$$

$$\delta q = (m-\bar{m})\,(q-Q)\,$$

$$\sigma_{\Delta q}^2 = \sigma_m^2\,(q-Q)^2$$

$$\phi\,(q) = C\,(q-Q)^{2a}\,e^{-2b}\,, \tag{22}$$

where

$$a = \frac{s\,(1-2Q) - \sigma_m^2 - \bar{m}}{\sigma_m^2}\,, \qquad b = \frac{s}{\sigma_m^2}\,\frac{(q-Q)^2 + Q\,(1-Q)}{q-Q}\,.$$

There can be no random drift below Q if $\hat{q} > Q$ or above Q if $\hat{q} < Q$. If $\bar{s} = 0$ and $\hat{q} = Q$, there can be no random drift at all; and $\phi(q)$ is infinitely greater at $q = Q$ than at any other value of q (67). If, however, $\hat{q}$ and Q are well separated, there can be considerable random drift.

With respect to fluctuations in the gene frequency of immigrants, again assuming the simplest model of selection (54):

$$\overline{\Delta q} = \bar{s}\, q\, (1 - q) - \bar{m}\, (q - Q) ,$$

$$\delta q = \bar{m}\, (Q - \bar{Q})$$

$$\sigma^2_{\Delta q} = \bar{m}^2 \sigma^2_Q ,$$

$$\phi\,(q) = C \exp \left\{ \frac{1}{\bar{m}^2 \sigma^2_Q} [\, - \bar{m}\, (q - \bar{Q})^2 - \bar{s}\, q^2\, (\tfrac{2}{3} q - 1)\,] \right\}. \quad (23)$$

If there is no selection ($\bar{s} = 0$),

$$\phi\,(q) = C \exp \left[- \frac{(q - Q)^2}{\bar{m}\, \sigma^2_Q} \right].$$

This is a normal probability curve with variance $(\tfrac{1}{2})\bar{m}\sigma^2_Q$. Random drift is negligible unless m is so large that the conditions on which the equation for $\phi(q)$ was based hold only very roughly.

The conception of the genetic composition of a species that is divided into numerous partially isolated demes is as far as possible from that indicated at the first level of theory. We expect a large number of alleles at each locus that is not in some way protected from mutation and thus a great deal of heterozygosis. We expect the demes to drift widely apart, under the same environmental conditions, from the joint action of directed and random processes, and even more, of course, where environmental conditions are different.

There is necessarily interaction between adjacent demes. Those in which population size is growing more rapidly than in their neighbors because of superior environment tend to modify the compositions of the latter unless these have acquired superior adaptations. Of more interest here are differences in composition than have arisen under similar environments by the processes considered above. A deme that has come under the influence of a selective peak that has a higher reproductive value $\overline{W}$ than its neighbors will tend, other things being equal, to contribute more immigrants than it receives and grade up these neighbors until they come under the control either of the same selective peak or of a higher one based on combination of gene frequencies in the donor and recipient demes.

Demes with low reproductive value, because of social parasitism, tend to be displaced by neighboring demes in which social parasitism has not become established and which hence are high in $\overline{W}$. Conversely, traits that benefit the population but that are neutral or worse to the possessors in intrademic selection are favored in interdemic selection. Thus the latter is decidedly more favorable to the evolution of co-operation stressed by many authors (68–70) than is intrademic selection. What happens when there is a conflict between intrademic selection governed by V and interdemic selection governed primarily by $\overline{W}$ and dispersiveness depends on whether or not the pressure from immigration overbalances the local trend.

There may be conditions in which a lower reproductive value is more adaptive than a higher one. A form that reproduces so rapidly in an island environment that it destroys itself by destroying its food supply, except in the rare cases in which it manages to get to an unoccupied island in time, might be displaced by a variant that reproduced no more rapidly than its food supply, provided that the latter could get started somewhere.

Adaptive value is more difficult to define sufficiently precisely for mathematical use than the other sorts of values which we have used (39, 71). It may perhaps be used roughly for whatever it is that determines success in interdemic selection. The term "external selective value" (V_E) was used for this property in a preceding paper (26), in contrast with the internal selection of the population (V_I in that paper, V in this).

The question may be raised whether the large amount of heterozygosis and consequent large amount of segregation of suboptimal types are compatible with persistence of the species. Haldane (72) pointed out that the depreciation from maximum productivity due to a deleterious mutation ($\hat{q} = v/s$) is equal to twice the mutation rate, irrespective of the degree of selection—($\overline{w} = 1 - 2s\hat{q} = 1 - 2v$). The fraction of maximum productivity left by n deleterious mutations is thus $(1 - 2v)^n$ or approximately e^{-2nv}. With mutation rates of the order of 10^{-5} to 10^{-6}, thousands of mutations may be carried, taking into account that the species may be adjusted to a productivity far below the maximum.

In the case in which all heterozygotes at a locus are assumed to have the standard productivity but homozygotes are at various degrees of disadvantage (s), $\overline{w} = 1 - \Sigma s\hat{q}^2$, $\hat{q} = (1/s)/\Sigma(1/s)$. If all homozygotes are at the same disadvantage, $\overline{w}$ becomes $1 - (s/n)$. This may seem to limit rather severely the number of loci in which such alleles may be carried. On the other hand, the kinds of cases to which we have given most weight, such as multifactorial with intermediate optimum, are ones in which the value of s tends to be exceedingly small (28).

A balance between immigration and selection with $m < s$ ($\overline{w} = 1 - 2s\hat{q} \approx 1 - 2mQ$) or with $m > s$ ($\overline{w} \approx 1 - 2sQ$) implies severe depreciation in productivity unless m or s is very small.

It is clear that subdivision into demes is of most direct significance for the evolution of the species in the case of alleles with very small selective differences (modifiers, polygenes, isoalleles) and among demes that are rather strongly isolated. The importance for major mutations is not in any joint effect of directed and random processes on them directly but is in the bringing-about by these means of a background of modifiers at some time and place that makes possible the establishment of major mutations with useful properties that are almost certainly overbalanced in most genetic backgrounds by unfavorable effects (6, 50). We conclude that the joint action of natural selection and random processes, even though largely restricted to isoalleles, may produce shifting patterns in a species with a favorable population structure that are directly or indirectly of first importance in evolution.

A population structure that is favorable to rapid evolutionary change by no means insures that such change will take place in the absence of an adequate ecologic opportunity. If the ecologic pressure of other species is such as to restrict the one in question to a narrow niche in which the only opportunity is for a gradual perfection of the adaptations that it has already developed, evolution can be very slow under the most favorable genetic conditions and population structure.

If, however, the species is presented with a major ecologic opportunity such as may arise if a slowly perfected minor adaptation turns out at a certain stage to open up an extensive new way of life or if the species is the first of its general kind to reach unoccupied territory or is among the few survivors of a devastating change of conditions, the achievement of a favorable population structure may permit an exploitation of this opportunity that is very rapid in terms of geologic time (27, 44, 73, 74).

Experimental and Observational Evidence

The present paper has been concerned with the mathematical framework of evolutionary theory and has touched only slightly on experimental and observational data. There has been a large amount of experimental work on selection that abundantly attests to the effectiveness of this factor.

We are coming to have some knowledge of the actual population structure and genetics of certain wild species by such studies as those of Goldschmidt with *Lymantria;* Sumner, Dice, Blair, and others with *Peromyscus;* Patterson, Dobzhansky, and their many associates with *Drosophila* species; Ford and his associates with species of Lepidoptera;

Clausen and others with many plant species. Not least in importance in this connection are studies of the population genetics of man.

There has been relatively little study of the actual joint effects of selection and random sampling. Kerr and Wright (75) and Buri (76) have studied this matter in populations of *Drosophila melanogaster* of controlled very small size. Dobzhansky and Pavlovsky (77) have found a remarkable diversification of the goals reached by selection if carried out on populations started from different small samples (using chromosome rearrangements of *D. pseudoobscura*).

Dobzhansky and Wright (78) and Wright, Dobzhansky, and Hovanitz (79) have made an analysis of the distribution of lethals in wild populations of *D. pseudoobscura* from the standpoint of joint action of mutation, selection, dispersion, and accidents of sampling. One of the most comprehensive studies from this joint standpoint is that of Lamotte (80) on the frequencies of genes that affect the banding pattern in the colonies of the snail *Cepaea nemoralis* in a large part of France. Epling and Dobzhansky (81) and Wright (82) have studied and analyzed the distribution of blue and white flowers of *Linanthus parryae* in the Mohave Desert, a distribution that is remarkably spotty both among and within areas of all sizes. As in most cases, no final conclusions could be reached. This, it seems to me, is still the case with respect to rather large annual changes in frequency of a color gene in a small population of the moth *Panaxia dominula* studied by Fisher and Ford (83) and Sheppard (84) (cf. Wright [54]). The difficulty is that it is not a matter of deciding between mutually exclusive alternatives but of reaching conclusions on the relative importance of factors which are acting simultaneously.

The very extensive studies of the distribution of human blood group genes throughout the world are obviously very important material in the relation of population structure to genetics. It is still not clear how far the differences among populations are due to random drift that occurred at a time when numbers were small (53) and how far to selective differences among localities. The persistent polymorphism itself presumably depends on selection (and perhaps also recurrent mutation), but this does not necessarily imply selective differences among localities. Glass (85) has made an instructive study of the amount of random drift in a small religious community. Brues (86) has worked out a theory of the world distribution from the standpoint of joint occurrence of selection and random drift.

SUMMARY

The mathematical framework of the theory of evolution has been considered at a succession of levels of complexity with respect to physiological genetics and the ecology of populations.

At the first level, the theory takes account only of mutations and selection coefficients that may be treated as constant for each gene under given conditions. This leads to the conception of the species as homallelic at each locus except for deleterious mutations, maintained at very low frequencies, and for very rare favorable mutations on the way to displacement of the previous type allele. Evolution is largely restricted to readjustment to secular changes in the environment but may occasionally involve fixation of a novel mutation that happens to be favorable from the first.

At the second level, cognizance is taken of the indirectness of the physiological relation between primary gene action and ultimate characters, thus including dominance and interaction in the formulation but with the assumption that the selective value of the total genotype is constant under given conditions of environment and population density. Overdominance provides a means by which loci may remain strongly heterallelic. This indirectness provides something of an obstacle to evolutionary progress, but reproductive value (under given conditions) still increases at a rate equal to its additive variance.

The complication from dependence of relative selective values of total genotypes on gene frequencies is considered at the third level. The selective value of the population (where definable) tends to increase according to the additive variance of the selective values of individuals, but this is not true of the mean reproductive value of the population. This may decrease as selection carries the gene frequencies toward a selective peak. One important case is that in which the selective value of each genotype is a function of its own frequency. Selective values that rise with abundance tend to cause a runaway process toward homogeneity in some respect or other, according to the initial frequencies, while selective values that decrease with rising gene frequency provide a means which, similarly to overdominance, may determine persistent heterozygosis. Another important case is that in which all selective values involve a common function of the gene frequencies. Modes of selection in which the success of certain types of individuals is associated with lowering of the growth rate of the population come here. At this level it is not clear how natural selection avoids the blind alley of social parasitism.

At the fourth level, it is recognized not only that interaction may lead occasionally to situations in which there is more than one selective peak in the system of gene frequencies but that there are certain widespread phenomena that insure the existence of a vast number of such peaks. These include intermediacy of the optimum in quantitative variability and pleiotropy. These constitute serious obstacles to evolutionary progress by mass selection, if not capable of being overcome, but greatly enhance the evolutionary potentialities of the array of genes on hand, if they can. The possibilities are explored of passage from one peak to another by means of the joint action of selection and random processes. Random processes are effective in proportion to the amount of heterozygosis. It is brought out that there may be many peaks that are heterallelic in multiple respects among which evolutionary progress may occur. Random sampling, however, is not effective in an isolated random-breeding population unless the latter is decidedly small. Long-period fluctuations in the environment constitute a more generally effective process.

Account is taken at the fifth level of the effects of subdivision of the species into a large number of partially isolated demes. Such a situation insures genetic heterogeneity of the species as a whole and, through occasional crossbreeding, adds to the ways in which a considerable degree of heterozygosis may be maintained in the local populations and thus additional random processes (fluctuations in amount of crossbreeding and in the gene frequencies of the immigrants). The importance of random sampling is enormously greater than in an undivided population of the same total size. The effects of all random processes are amplified by occurrence, more or less independently, in the separate demes and by interdeme selection which extends throughout the species the influence of demes that have attained a high reproductive peak. Interdeme selection based on degree of adaptation among the demes also tends to overcome the tendency for isolated populations to succumb to social parasitism.

.The theory is deterministic only in an exceedingly limited sense. It is essentially a theory of the conditions that are favorable for an ever continuing process that is essentially unpredictable in its details. There can be no formula for serendipity. It is concluded that the most favorable conditions are those of balance: a balance among the directed processes that insures the maintenance of a high degree of heterozygosis in minor factors and a balance between the directed processes as a group and various sorts of random ones that insures extensive random drift about the equilibrium positions of the gene frequencies. All these conditions are met in the highest degree where there is a certain balance between isolation and crossbreeding within each of a large number of local populations of the species.

From a more general standpoint, all of this is merely an elaboration in terms of modern genetics of the conception of evolution by natural selection advanced by Darwin in the *Origin of Species* a hundred years ago.

REFERENCES

1. PEARSON, K. 1904. "On a Generalized Theory of Alternative Inheritance with Special Reference to Mendel's Laws," *Phil. Tr. Roy. Soc. London*, A, CCIII, 53–86.
2. HARDY, G. H. 1908. "Mendelian Properties in a Mixed Population," *Science*, XXVIII, 49–50.
3. WEINBERG, W. 1908. "Über den Nachweis der Vererbung beim Menschen," *Jahresb. Verein f. vaterl. Naturk. in Württemberg*, LXIV, 368–82.
4. WRIGHT, S. 1922. "Coefficients of Inbreeding and Relationship," *Am. Naturalist*, LVI, 330–38.
5. ———. 1922. *The Effects of Inbreeding and Crossbreeding on Guinea Pigs. III. Crosses between Highly Inbred Families.* (United States Department of Agriculture, Bulletin No. 1121.)
6. ———. 1951. "The Genetical Structure of Populations," *Ann. Eugenics*, XV, 323–54.
7. WEINBERG, W. 1909. "Über Vererbungsgesetz beim Menschen," *Ztschr. f. ind. Abst. u. Vererb*, I, 277–330.
8. ROBBINS, R. B. 1918. "Some Applications of Mathematics to Breeding Problems. III," *Genetics*, III, 375–89.
9. GEIRINGER, H. 1948. "On the Mathematics of Random Mating in a Case of Different Recombination Values for Males and Females," *Genetics*, XXXIII, 548–64.
10. HALDANE, J. B. S. 1927. "A Mathematical Theory of Natural and Artificial Selection. IV," *Proc. Cambridge Phil. Soc.*, XXIII, 607–15.
11. FISHER, R. A. 1930. *The Genetical Theory of Natural Selection.* London: Clarendon Press.
12. LOTKA, A. J. 1925. *Elements of Physical Biology.* Baltimore: Williams & Wilkins.
13. KIMURA, M. 1958. "On the Change of Population Fitness by Natural Selection," *Heredity*, XII, 145–67.
14. VOLTERRA, V. 1931. *Leçons sur la théorie Mathématique de la Lutte pour la Vie.* Paris: Gauthier-Villars.
15. NICHOLSON, A. J., and BAILEY, V. A. 1935. "The Balance of Animal Populations," *Proc. Zoöl. Soc. London*, pp. 551–98.
16. HALDANE, J. B. S. 1927. "A Mathematical Theory of Natural and Arti-

ficial Selection. V. Selection and Mutation," *Proc. Cambridge Phil. Soc.*, XXIII, 838–44.

17. ———. 1924. "A Mathematical Theory of Natural and Artificial Selection," *Tr. Cambridge Phil. Soc.*, XXIII, 19–41.

18. CROW, J. F. 1957. "Genetics of Insect Resistance to Chemicals," *Ann. Rev. Entomol.*, II, 227–46.

19. FORD, E. B. 1956. "Rapid Evolution and the Conditions Which Make It Possible." *Cold Spring Harbor Symp. Quant. Biol.*, XX, 230–38.

20. WRIGHT, S. 1929. "Fisher's Theory of Dominance," *Am. Naturalist*, LXIII, 224.

21. ———. 1929. "The Evolution of Dominance," *Am. Naturalist*, LXIII, 556–61.

22. ———. 1934. "Physiological and Evolutionary Theories of Dominance," *Am. Naturalist*, LXVIII, 25–53.

23. ———. 1935. "Evolution in Populations in Approximate Equilibrium," *J. Genetics*, XXX, 257–66.

24. ———. 1937. "The Distribution of Gene Frequencies in Populations," *Proc. Nat. Acad. Sc.*, XXIII, 307–20.

25. ———. 1949. "Adaptation and Selection," chap. 20 in *Genetics, Paleontology and Evolution*, ed. G. L. JEPSON, G. G. SIMPSON, and E. MAYR. Princeton: Princeton University Press.

26. ———. 1956. "Classification of the Factors of Evolution," *Cold Spring Harbor Symp. Quant. Biol.*, XX, 16–24.

27. ———. 1945. "Tempo and Mode in Evolution: A Critical Review," *Ecology*, XXVI, 415–19.

28. ———. 1952. "The Genetics of Quantitative Variability," in *Quantitative Inheritance*. ("Ag. Res. Council Publication.") H.M. Stationery Office.

29. KIMURA, M. 1956. "A Model of a Genetic System Which Leads to Closer Linkage by Natural Selection," *Evolution*, X, 278–87.

30. WRIGHT, S. 1939. "The Distribution of Self-sterility Alleles in Populations," *Genetics*, XXIV, 538–52.

31. DOBZHANSKY, TH. 1950. "Genetics of Natural Populations. XIX. Origin of Heterosis through Natural Selection in Populations of *Drosophila pseudoobscura*," *Genetics*, XXXV, 288–302.

32. HULL, F. H. 1952. "Recurrent Selection and Overdominance," chap. 28 in *Heterosis*, ed. J. W. GOWEN. Ames, Iowa: Iowa State College Press.

33. CROW, J. F. 1948. "Alternative Hypotheses of Hybrid Vigor," *Genetics*, XXX, 477–87.

34. ———. 1952. "Dominance and Overdominance," chap. 18 in *Heterosis*, ed. J. W. GOWEN. Ames Iowa: Iowa State College Press.

35. LERNER, I. M. 1954. *Genetic Homeostasis.* New York: John Wiley & Sons.

36. ROBINSON, H. E., and COMSTOCK, R. E. 1956. "Analysis of Genetic Variability in Corn with Reference to Probable Effects of Selection," *Cold Spring Harbor Symp. Quant. Biol.*, XX, 127–35.
37. EAST, E. M. 1936. "Heterosis," *Genetics*, XXI, 375–97.
38. LEVENE, H. 1953. "Genetic Equilibrium When More than One Ecological Niche Is Available," *Am. Naturalist*, LXXXVII, 331–33.
39. LI, C. C. 1955. "The Stability of an Equilibrium and the Average Fitness of a Population," *Am. Naturalist*, LXXXIX, 281–96.
40. DEMPSTER, E. R. 1956. "Maintenance of Genetic Heterogeneity," *Cold Spring Harbor Symp. Quant. Biol.*, XX, 25–32.
41. WRIGHT, S. 1938. "The Distribution of Gene Frequencies under Irreversible Mutation," *Proc. Nat. Acad. Sc.*, XXIV, 253–59.
42. FISHER, R. A. 1941. "Average Excess and Average Defect of a Gene Substitution," *Ann. Eugenics*, IX, 53–63.
43. HALDANE, J. B. S. 1932. *The Causes of Evolution.* New York: Harper & Bros.
44. WRIGHT, S. 1942. "Statistical Genetics and Evolution," *Bull. Am. Math. Soc.*, XLVIII, 223–46.
45. WRIGHT, S., and DOBZHANSKY, TH. 1946. "Genetics of Natural Populations. XII. Experimental Reproduction of Some of the Changes Caused by Natural Selection in Certain Populations of *Drosophila pseudoobscura*, *Genetics*, XXXI, 125–56.
46. LEWONTIN, R. C. 1958. "A General Method for Investigating the Equilibrium of Gene Frequency in a Population," *Genetics*, XLIII, 419–34.
47. CROW, J. F., and KIMURA, M. 1956. "General Theory of Population Genetics: Synthesis," *Cold Spring Harbor Symp. Quant. Biol.*, XX, 54–59.
48. KEMPTHORNE, O. 1954. "The Correlation between Relatives in a Random Breeding Population," *Proc. Roy. Soc. London*, B, CXLIII, 103–13.
49. SIMPSON, G. G. 1944. *Tempo and Mode in Evolution.* New York: Columbia University Press.
50. WRIGHT, S. 1956. "Modes of Selection," *Am. Naturalist*, XC, 5–24.
51. ———. 1940. "Breeding Structure of Populations in Relation to Speciation," *Am. Naturalist*, LXXIX, 232–48.
52. ———. 1941. "On the Probability of Fixation of Reciprocal Translocations," *Am. Naturalist*, LXXV, 513–22.
53. ———. 1931. "Evolution in Mendelian Populations," *Genetics*, XVI, 97–159.
54. ———. 1948. "On the Roles of Directed and Random Changes in Gene Frequency in the Genetics of Populations," *Evolution*, II, 279–94.
55. ———. 1952. "The Theoretical Variance within and among Subdivisions of a Population That Is in a Steady State," *Genetics*, XXVII, 312–21.
56. ———. 1945. "The Differential Equation of the Distribution of Gene Frequencies," *Proc. Nat. Acad. Sc.*, XXXI, 383–89.

57. MORAN, P. A. P. 1958. "A General Theory of the Distribution of Gene Frequencies. I. Overlapping Generations," *Proc. Roy. Soc.*, B, CXLIX, 102–12. "II. Nonoverlapping Generations," *Ibid.*, 113–16.

58. KIMURA, M. 1956. "Stochastic Processes and Distribution of Gene Frequencies under Natural Selection." *Cold Spring Harbor Symp. Quant. Biol.*, XX, 33–51.

59. ———. 1954. "Process Leading to Quasifixation of Genes in Natural Populations Due to Random Fluctuations of Selection Intensities," *Genetics*, XXXIX, 280–95.

60. ———. 1956. "Rules for Testing Stability of a Selective Polymorphism," *Proc. Nat. Acad. Sc.*, XLII, 336–40.

61. ———. 1955. "Solution of a Process of Random Genetic Drift with a Continuous Model," *Proc. Nat. Acad. Sc.*, XLI, 144–50.

62. ———. 1957. "Some Problems of Stochastic Processes in Genetics," *Ann. Math. Stat.*, XXVIII, 882–90.

63. SPURWAY, H. 1953. "Genetics of Specific and Subspecific Differences in European Newts," *Symp. Soc. Exper. Biol.*, VII, 200–237.

63a. MAYR, E. 1954. In *Evolution as a Process*, ed. J. HUXLEY, A. C. HARDY, and E. B. FORD. New York: Macmillan Co.

64. WRIGHT, S. 1943. "Isolation by Distance," *Genetics*, XXVIII, 114–38.

65. ———. 1946. "Isolation by Distance under Diverse Systems of Mating," *Genetics*, XXXI, 39–59.

66. MALÉCOT, G. 1948. *Les mathématiques de l'hérédité*. Paris: Masson and Cie.

67. CROW, J. F., and KIMURA, M. 1955. "Some Genetic Problems in Natural Populations," *Proc. 3rd Berkeley Symp. on Math. Statistics and Probability*, pp. 1–22. Berkeley: University of California Press.

68. WHEELER, W. M. 1923. *Social Life among the Insects*. New York: Harcourt, Brace & Co.

69. ALLEE, W. C. 1931. *Animal Aggregations: A Study in General Sociology*. Chicago: University of Chicago Press.

70. EMERSON, A. E. 1958. "The Evolution of Behavior among Social Insects," chap. 15 in *Behavior and Evolution*, ed. ANNE ROE and G. G. SIMPSON. New Haven: Yale University Press.

71. CAIN, A. J., and SHEPPARD, P. M. 1954. "The Theory of Adaptive Polymorphism," *Am. Naturalist*, LXXXVII, 321–26.

72. HALDANE, J. B. S. 1937. "The Effect of Variation on Fitness." *Am. Naturalist*, LXXI, 337–49.

73. WRIGHT, S. 1941. "The 'Age and Area' Concept Extended," *Ecology*, XXII, 345–47.

74. ———. 1941. "*The Material Basis of Evolution* by R. Goldschmidt," *The Scientific Monthly*, LIII, 165–71.

75. KERR, W. E., and WRIGHT, S. 1954. "Experimental Studies of the Distribution of Gene Frequencies in Very Small Populations of *Drosophila melanogaster*. III. Aristapedia and Spineless," *Evolution*, VIII, 293–302.
76. BURI, PETER. 1956. "Gene Frequency in Small Populations of Mutant Drosophila," *Evolution*, X, 367–402.
77. DOBZHANSKY, TH., and PAVLOVSKY, OLGA. 1957. "An Experimental Study of Interaction between Genetic Drift and Natural Selection," *Evolution*, XI, 311–19.
78. DOBZHANSKY, TH., and WRIGHT, S. 1941. "Genetics of Natural Populations. V. Relations between Mutation Rate and Accumulation of Lethals in Populations of *Drosophila pseudoobscura*," *Genetics*, XXVI, 23–51.
79. WRIGHT, S., DOBZHANSKY, TH., and HOVANITZ, W. 1942. "Genetics of Natural Populations. VII. The Allelism of Lethals in the Third Chromosome of *Drosophila pseudoobscura*," *Genetics*, XXVII, 363–94.
80. LAMOTTE, M. 1951. "Recherches sur la structure genetique des populations naturelles de *Cepaea nemoralis*," *Bull. Biol., Suppl.*, XXXV, 1–238.
81. EPLING, C., and DOBZHANSKY, TH. 1942. "Genetics of Natural Populations. VI. Microgeographical Races in *Linanthus Parryae*," *Genetics*, XXVII, 317–32.
82. WRIGHT, S. 1943. "An Analysis of Local Variability of Flower Color in *Linanthus Parryae*," *Genetics*, XXV, 139–56.
83. FISHER, R. A., and FORD, E. B. 1947. "The Spread of a Gene in Natural Conditions in a Colony of the Moth, *Panaxia dominula* L.," *Heredity*, I, 143–74.
84. SHEPPARD, P. M. 1951. "A Quantitative Study of Two Populations of the Moth, *Panaxia dominula* L.," *Heredity*, V, 349–78.
85. GLASS, BENTLEY. 1954. "Genetic Changes in Human Populations, Especially Those Due to Gene Flow and Genetic Drift," *Advances in Genetics*, VI, 95–139.
86. BRUES, ALICE M. 1954. "Selection and Polymorphism in the A-B-O Blood Groups," *Am. J. Phys. Anthrop.*, XII, 559–98.

A. J. NICHOLSON

THE ROLE OF POPULATION DYNAMICS
IN NATURAL SELECTION

By the middle of the last century the unfolding of the fossil record of life on this earth had already provided strong evidence for the truth of the theory of evolution. This new evidence presented Darwin with an intellectual challenge to account for evolution by finding its mechanism. His remarkable ability to recognise essentials enabled him to select, from the fragmentary information about living things available to him, the four essential factors which, by their interaction, can cause and preserve progressive changes in organisms. These are (1) the occurrence of variations in characters among the individuals of any given species; (2) the "strong principle of inheritance," by which term he apparently referred simply to the known fact that individuals strongly tend to resemble their parents and often distant ancestors also; (3) the multiplication of organisms under favourable conditions; and (4) the evident limitation of numbers in all species.

Darwin's Theory of Selection by Competition

Although Darwin knew little of the mechanisms underlying these four factors, his knowledge of their general characteristics was sufficient to enable him to develop his primary hypothesis, which he presented in the following two passages in his *Origin of Species*.

As many more individuals of each species are born than can possibly survive; and as, consequently, there is a frequently recurring struggle for existence, it follows that any being, if it vary however slightly in any manner profitable to itself, under the complex and sometimes varying conditions of life, will have a better chance of surviving, and thus be *naturally selected*. From the strong principle of inheritance, any selected variety will tend to propagate its new and modified form [Darwin, 6th ed. (1888), p. 5].

Natural selection acts solely through the preservation of variations in

ALEXANDER J. NICHOLSON is Chief of the Division of Entomology, Commonwealth Scientific and Industrial Research Organization, Canberra, Australia. He has worked and written extensively on various entomological topics and on the balance of animal populations.

some way advantageous, which consequently endure. Owing to the high geometrical rate of increase of all organic beings, each area is already fully stocked with inhabitants; and it follows from this, that as the favoured forms increase in number, so, generally, will the less favoured decrease and become rare [*ibid.*, p. 133].

Note that Darwin's primary hypothesis is readily divisible into two parts: (1) the production of variations and the preservation of those which are advantageous (genetics) and (2) the multiplication of organisms living in favourable environments when they do not fill them, which sooner or later is checked when a population reaches the capacity of its environment (population dynamics), thus indirectly causing the displacement of the less fit by the fitter forms.

Since the *Origin of Species* biologists have devoted a great deal of their attention to the study and elaboration of his theory of natural selection. It is notable that they have paid by far the greatest attention to the genetical aspects of his theory, particularly in recent years. Unquestionably the greatest advance in this field was made by Mendel, although he was unaware of the bearing of his discoveries upon evolutionary theory. His investigations were also made about a century ago. He showed that some varieties of plants are able to pass on their characteristic properties unchanged to many, or to all, of their offspring, even when interbreeding with other varieties. Geneticists have greatly improved our understanding of natural selection by following Mendel's lead in making experimental studies of inheritance. This work has led to a far more detailed understanding of the nature of variations and the different ways in which they may be inherited.

On the other hand, remarkably little attention has been paid to the population dynamics content of Darwin's theory. This is surprising, for numerical considerations occupy a particularly prominent place in Darwin's primary hypothesis. It seems generally to be assumed that, as animal numbers are necessarily finite, the less fit must be eliminated automatically by the preferential preservation of fitter individuals and that more detailed knowledge of the mechanism of replacement is unnecessary. Darwin was very conscious of the need for more knowledge, for he said: "We know not exactly what the checks are even in a single instance. . . . This subject of the checks to increase has been ably treated by several authors, and I hope in a future work to discuss it at considerable length, more especially in regard to the feral animals of South America" (*ibid.*, p. 83). What a boon to biology it would have been, had Darwin realised this hope!

Darwin considered the apparently contradictory facts (1) that animals living under favourable conditions produce sufficient offspring to cause multiplication and (2) that each species is observed to maintain a recognisable degree of abundance in each area it occupies, although its numbers may vary, even greatly, from year to year and from place to place. Thus, in spite of their strong innate tendency to multiply, organisms do not do so, except temporarily, in nature. Instead, the number of reproducing offspring produced over any long period can differ little from the number of parents. Consequently, the preferential preservation of individuals with advantageous properties necessarily leads to the progressive displacement of individuals not possessing this advantage. It is this which makes selection an effective mechanism in evolutionary progress. Were it not for the displacement of old forms by newer and more potent forms, the organic world would be in a state of chaos. As Darwin says, "Each new variety or species, when formed, will generally take the place of, and thus exterminate its less well fitted parent" (1859, p. 53). The parent form is displaced while still well fitted to flourish in the species habitat. It is unfit only in the sense that it cannot compete successfully with the new variety.

Note that, as the following discussion is mainly concerned with population problems, the word "environment," unless otherwise specified, is used to refer to the conditions to which the species population is subject. Because the presence of other individuals of the same species plays a unique part in the regulation of populations and in natural selection, this outstandingly important factor is detached from the other factors in the individual's environment, so that it may be considered separately.

The principle of natural selection is often referred to as "the survival of the fittest." This phrase has been severely criticised on the ground that it immediately poses the question "Fittest for what?" As the quotations at the beginning of this chapter make clear, Darwin simply meant the fittest to survive. Using the word in this sense, it is tautological to speak of "the survival of the fittest." However, this is a convenient and appropriate phrase which reminds the reader that, according to Darwin's concept, the primary and active influence of natural selection is the preferential preservation of individuals possessing advantage over those of the previously normal form, whereas the elimination of this less fit form is a secondary effect due to the disadvantage suffered by individuals of this form.

The statement Darwin made, when defining his primary hypothesis, that "each area is already fully stocked with inhabitants" is not strictly true, but it is sufficiently true to be valid in his argument. As Darwin mentioned several times, favourable changes in the environment, such as some seasonal variations, cause populations temporarily to be less than sufficient to fill their environments. This permits multiplication, which is checked when the environments are once again filled. With animals, the environment often appears to be far less than completely filled by the resident populations. There are several reasons for this, apart from the one just given. Important among these are the action of natural enemies, which can hold their phytophagous prey far below the level permitted by the availability of food plants; some behavioural characteristics, such as the claiming of territories, intolerance of even slight degrees of crowding, and intraspecific strife, which automatically limit the population of a species at a density far below that which the species environment would permit; and the fact that often only a fraction of the food apparently available is actually accessible or suitable for use. Thus the impression that animals are commonly far less numerous than their environments would permit is, in general, illusory.

OCCURRENCE OF SELECTION IN LABORATORY CULTURES

Many experiments have been carried out with laboratory populations of the Australian sheep blowfly, *Lucilia cuprina* Wied., in order to determine how they react to important changes in the different environmental influences. In most of the experiments the limiting factor was the quantity of food supplied daily to each experimental culture. Generally the adults were denied access to the larval food by placing a plastic lid on the pot containing it, the flies laying their eggs through narrow slots in the lid. This made it possible to study separately adult and larval competition for food. According to the experiment, either the adult food or that of the larvae was supplied in limited quantity, the food of the other stage being provided in excess of the amount which could be consumed, although sometimes the food for both stages was limited. The experimental populations were maintained in large cages specially designed to permit the introduction of food and the counting of the various developmental stages with a minimum disturbance to the populations.

Each experimental population was subjected to conditions somewhat different from any of the others. These conditions were maintained constant for periods of many months in each experiment, although subsequently they were often deliberately changed, in order to determine the effect of such change. In the various experiments, for example, different percentages of some particular developmental stage were destroyed, different quantities of food or of water were supplied, or favourability for oviposition was varied by providing different kinds of egg-laying sites.

It was found that, even when conditions were relatively very adverse, each population succeeded in maintaining itself in a state of stability, in the sense that it did not tend to increase or to decrease progressively with time. In most situations, however, there was a marked periodic fluctuation in density. The data obtained showed that the stabilising mechanism was competition for food. Increased destruction or reduced oviposition caused by some relatively adverse factor automatically led to a reduction in the intensity of competition for food. This exactly compensated for the effects of the adverse influence, for the number of births was found to equal the number of deaths and the mean population levels during successive moderately long periods remained approximately constant throughout each experiment. This stabilising influence of competition upon populations is referred to as "density-governing reaction," for it holds populations at, or fluctuating about, densities related to the prevailing environmental conditions and it automatically holds populations in a state of stability under widely differing and often relatively very adverse conditions (see Nicholson, 1954, 1957).

It can logically be argued that if, say, the destruction suffered by a species from the action of a particular adverse factor decreases because the species has developed improved defenses against this factor, the effects upon the population should be the same as those produced by a reduction in the severity of this factor. This is because the intensity of competition automatically increases as a population grows, whatever may be the cause of this. However, apart from this indirect evidence that density-governing reaction can automatically hold a species in a state of stability in spite of even great changes in its properties, some of the experiments provided direct evidence for this.

Thus in eight out of ten concurrent experimental cultures of *L. cuprina* the fairly regular population oscillations which took place over a period of about eighteen months began to change in period and in amplitude, and the population levels began to rise appreciably (see Nicholson, 1957, Fig. 8). This strongly suggested that considerable changes in the properties of the flies had taken place. All these cultures were governed by adult competition for small quantities of ground liver, the larvae being given more food than they could consume. Flies taken from the four cultures in which changes in the general population levels and in the character of the fluctuations were most marked were compared with flies of the original stock strain. Dissection showed that flies of the strains taken from these four cages could develop far more eggs than stock-strain flies when provided with the same minute amount of ground liver. With the recognition that this new characteristic had been developed in the populations, it was easy to account for the observed changes in the patterns of population maintenance and for the general rise in population levels.

After subcultures from these four cultures had been maintained for about a year, during which the adults continued to compete for minute amounts of ground liver, it was found that they could all produce far more than the replacement number of eggs, even when the adults were given water and sugar only.

More detailed studies indicated that selection first produced strains of flies which could develop and lay eggs when their meals of ground liver were smaller than the minimum required by their predecessors. By a series of similar small steps, selection improved these strains to the point of being able to produce vastly more than the replacement number of offspring, even when denied a meat meal. This radical change in properties occurred under conditions which, apart from the induced changes in population densities, remained constant throughout each experiment. The new properties selected were quite unnecessary for the maintenance of the populations; for flies of the stock strain, from which the selected strains were developed, were able to lay far more eggs than were necessary for maintenance under the conditions imposed upon the populations.

Selection of another kind also took place in these experiments. Flies from the stock culture, attracted to liver in a covered pot, scarcely ever laid eggs through the slots in the plastic lid, unless stimulated by contact with ground liver placed near the slots. By contrast, flies of the selected strains laid eggs readily through holes in plastic lids upon which there was not even a trace of ground liver. The ability to do so was a necessary concomitant of their special ability to develop eggs without first having a meat meal; for, without it, scarcely any of the eggs developed could have been laid when the adult food became greatly depleted or had been removed by the competing flies. As it is extremely unlikely that this ability to lay eggs, even when not stimulated by the taste of meat, could be another phenotypic manifestation of the gene complex underlying the improved ability to develop eggs, it was almost certainly due to independent selection. With the progressive depletion of ground liver by increasing competition, flies requiring relatively little stimulation by contact with ground liver to induce them to lay eggs were inevitably more successful than their fellows in leaving offspring.

LABORATORY DEMONSTRATIONS OF COMPETITIVE SELECTION

About three years after the beginning of the experiments just discussed, two other experimental populations were set up with flies from the same stock culture. That selection of the same kind as occurred in the earlier cultures was operating in these cultures became evident within a few months, and the ability of some individuals to develop eggs without first having a meat meal developed rapidly. One cannot ignore the possibility that one or more flies from an already selected strain may have gained access to the stock culture, although great care had been taken to avoid this. However, tests indicated that the properties of the stock strain had remained unaltered; for numerous individuals of this strain which were allowed ample time for egg development but were not given a meat meal showed no greater oöcyte development than did wild flies similarly treated, when examined by dissection both before and after the new experiments were set up.

In one of these experiments the population was governed by competition for a daily supply of 0.1 gm. of ground bullock's liver for the whole population, the larvae being provided with ample food. Some of the results of this experiment are presented graphically in Figure 1. The fluctuating line records the number of flies in the cage at intervals of two days. Each vertical line represents the number of flies which subsequently emerged from eggs laid on the day of record. Because larval competition had been eliminated, almost all eggs gave rise to full-sized adult flies, and so the number of eggs laid is approximately represented by the vertical lines. The horizontal broken lines record the mean density of the flies over the period spanned by each line and correspond to the categories in the first column of Table 1.

TABLE 1

EFFECTS OF PROGRESSIVE SELECTION OF INCREASING ABILITY OF ADULTS OF *L. cuprina* TO UTILIZE GROUND LIVER FOR EGG PRODUCTION

(Analysis of Data upon Which Fig. 1 Is Based)

Period (Days)	Mean Population of Flies	Offspring Produced per Day at 5,000 Level	Ratio of Offspring to Parents	Ratio of Emergences to Deaths	Mean Life of Flies (Days)
0–88	628	0	1.12	1.03	6.9
47–146 ...	1,161	100	1.27	1.08	7.7
89–202 ...	2,488	450	1.16	1.04	6.0
147–242 ...	3,207	1,350	1.32	1.01	5.7
203–98	4,281	1,600	1.10	1.01	4.9
243–341 ...	6,032	2,100	1.03	1.03	4.9
299–380 ...	8,051	2,800	1.04	1.03	4.9
342–434 ...	9,348	3,500	1.00	1.01	4.9

Inspection of Figure 1 shows that the number of offspring collectively produced by the flies increased progressively with time; and Table 1 shows that, at a density of 5,000, the number of offspring

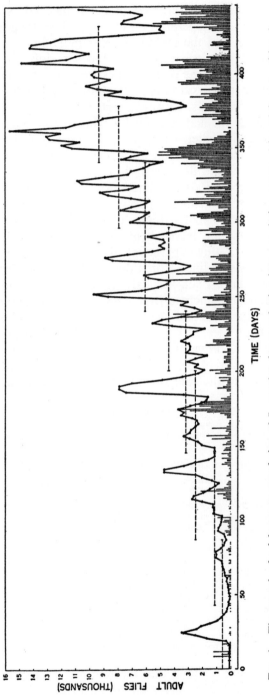
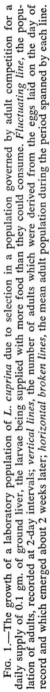

Fig. 1.—The growth of a laboratory population of *L. cuprina* due to selection in a population governed by adult competition for a daily supply of 0.1 gm. of ground liver, the larvae being supplied with more food than they could consume. *Fluctuating line,* the population of adults, recorded at 2-day intervals; *vertical lines,* the number of adults which were derived from the eggs laid on the day of record and which emerged about 2 weeks later; *horizontal broken lines,* the mean adult population during the period spanned by each line.

collectively produced per day increased progressively from zero to an estimated 3,500. This shows that the flies continued throughout the experiment to develop greater efficiency in utilising the daily supply of ground liver for the production of offspring. This increase in efficiency was confirmed by direct tests in which flies of similar selected strains competed for a minute amount of ground liver with flies from the parent stock: flies of the selected strains collectively developed many times as many eggs as did their competitors.

It should be noted that all the oöcytes in each individual are in the same stage of development at any given moment, so that a fly which develops from a fully fed larva produces either a batch of over 200 eggs (Webber, 1955, Fig. 4) or no eggs at all. Consequently, each fly which succeeded in laying eggs when the population did not depart far from the equilibrium density made a relatively very large contribution to the gene pool of the next generation, whereas approximately 99 per cent of the flies did not contribute to it. The speed of selection in these experiments was doubtless partly due to this property.

Density-governing reaction in this experiment compensated for the disturbing influence of biological improvement by controlling the population at general levels, which induced an intensity of competition just sufficient to cause the number of offspring to be only slightly greater than the number of parents (Table 1, first and fourth cols.). Also, the ratio of emergences to deaths departed little from unity, in spite of the great increase in the mean population from 628 to 9,348. The ratio of offspring to parents throughout the whole period of the experiment was only 1.045; so, in spite of the rapid increase in population density, on the average 20 parents collectively produced rather less than 21 offspring.

Such automatic adjustment of density-governing reaction at an intensity which compensates for the disturbing influence of changes in the properties of organisms, or in those of their environments, and so maintains populations in a condition of stability is referred to as "compensatory reaction."

Thus, by preventing indefinite increase, compensatory reaction held the population in a state of stability, in spite of great changes in the properties of the flies. An important part of the mechanism was the density-related depletion of food. As selection progressively reduced the minimal amount of food required by a fly for full egg development, more eggs were collectively produced, and the population grew. The resultant increased intensity of competition reduced the amount of food obtained by an average individual, and so population growth was arrested when density-induced difficulty in finding adequate food prevented the flies from producing more than sufficient offspring to replace the parent generation. The value of this equilibrium density necessarily rose with the continued selection of improved properties.

When the density of the flies was above or below the equilibrium density related to prevailing conditions and properties, the severity of competition caused the production of less or of more than the replacement number of offspring—reactions appropriate to cause an approach toward equilibrium. However, because of the time-lag between this initiation of corrective reaction, in the form of egg-laying, and its operation some two weeks later, when adults derived from these eggs first appeared, there was an alternate over- and undershooting of the progressively rising equilibrium density. In spite of the consequent and apparently erratic fluctuations, the general level of the population during all periods was clearly related to the prevailing equilibrium level (Table 1, first and fifth cols.).

Food depletion was not the only density-governing factor operative. As is shown by the last column in Table 1, the mean life of the flies fell as the density of the flies increased; and other data showed that in the region of peak densities the lives of the flies were exceptionally short. As the flies take three to seven days to develop eggs after they have fed, it is clear that at the higher densities many of the flies which had obtained sufficient food to develop eggs must have died before they could lay them. In addition, other experiments have shown that the egg production of even fully fed flies falls steeply with increasing crowding. These two factors and probably others as well opposed multiplication by reacting with increasing severity as the population grew, thus adjusting the population to fluctuate about lower equilibrium levels than those determined by food depletion alone. Thus compensatory reactions of several kinds co-operated in countering the tendency of the increasingly efficient flies to multiply rapidly.

The recording of quantitative data in this experiment unfortunately had to be discontinued at the last point shown in Figure 1; but the culture was continued under the same conditions for more than a year. The general level of the population was seen to rise continually, but the population became so large that it was difficult to handle. In an attempt to reduce oviposition, the supply of ground liver for the adults was discontinued. Surprisingly, the flies continued to develop eggs at far more than the replacement rate. Thus, without any change in the conditions to which the population was subject, selection had produced a strain of flies which could develop eggs without eating any meaty food—an essential need for blowflies of the stock strain and of all wild blowflies examined. The conclusion seems inescapable that the flies had developed the ability to develop eggs at the expense of food originally obtained by the larvae.

MECHANISM AND EFFECTS OF COMPETITIVE SELECTION

In the examples of selection so far discussed, the daily supply of ground liver was only a small fraction of that required collectively by the flies for egg production, and it was all consumed in a short time. Thus, by their own activities, the flies produced each day a gradation of conditions from complete favourability to definite unfavourability. This simulated, in turn, all conditions of plenty and of restriction of the food supply that could exist anywhere in nature. Any fly that visited the daily quota of food immediately after it had been placed in the cage obtained sufficient food to enable it to develop eggs or to stimulate it to lay eggs already developed. A little later in the day, only those flies which were exceptionally efficient in utilising minute quantities of food can have been successful in fully developing eggs. Thus flies needing relatively small amounts of ground liver for complete egg development collectively laid disproportionately large numbers of eggs. The consequent displacement of the less efficient genotypes caused the population as a whole to produce more offspring than previously, for more eggs resulted from the consumption of a given quantity of food. The severity of competition for food intensified as the population grew until it prevented the flies from producing more than the replacement number of mature offspring. That this actually happened is shown by the fourth and fifth columns of Table 1. The slight surplus of offspring produced permitted increase in the mean population level in relation to the improving properties of the flies.

Such stabilisation of the degree of competition at a severity which prevented the production or survival of more than a replacement number of mature offspring was necessarily adjusted to the average properties of the individuals. Consequently, competition was too severe for the less fit flies, which therefore failed to leave a replacement number of offspring, whereas it was not sufficiently intense to prevent the fitter flies from multiplying, until the improved properties of the population as a whole induced a sufficient intensity of competition to arrest this.

Such selection, without the aid of changing environmental conditions, progressively fits organisms to live in less and still less favourable environments, so long as genetic variability continues to produce forms which are more potent than the forms already selected. Note that the standard of efficiency necessary for the production and survival of offspring to maturity progressively increases and that compensatory reaction at all times holds the population in a state of stability. This is the mechanism of "hyperadaptation," "the production of qualities which not merely make the species suitable to live in its existing environment, but fit it successfully to oppose hazards beyond those to which it is exposed during selection" (Nicholson, 1955, p. 291). In the example discussed, the potency, which greatly exceeded the minimal needs of the species initially, was increased to a remarkable extent under constant environmental conditions, and it enabled the flies to do without a requisite that had previously been absolutely essential. This is a surprisingly radical change in properties to be produced under constant conditions—and in so short a time.

Selection was due to the fact that favoured individuals could lay eggs when the population density was too high to permit their fellows to do so. It might be thought that this ability to exist at higher numbers was advantageous to the species; but this is not true. The only effects of increasing density upon the flies were shortened lives, greater difficulty in obtaining food and in developing eggs, and ultimately a condition of gross overcrowding that appeared to cause distress.

However, the advantageous qualities selected could increase the chances that the species would maintain itself in previously unfavourable environments; for it would enable the flies to live and to reproduce where little or no adult food was available. This was not a need of the species under the conditions to which the flies were subjected and so could not have influenced selection. The selection was not purposive but resulted automatically from the fact that some individuals possessed an advantage over their fellows.

In all the experiments so far discussed, selective and density-governing influences operated upon the same developmental stage (the adult) in the production of strains of flies which not only could develop mature eggs but could also lay these through slots when no meaty food was provided for the adults. Compensatory reaction to the improved ability to produce mature offspring permitted the population to rise to higher equilibrium densities, related at all times to the degree of such biological improvement. When selection and density-governing reaction act upon different age groups, selected improvement in properties does not necessarily increase population density, which may be decreased or even left unchanged.

For example, Figure 2 graphically presents the results obtained with an experimental culture governed initially by larval competition for food and later by adult competition as well. When the adults were supplied with an unlimited supply of ground liver, the mean adult

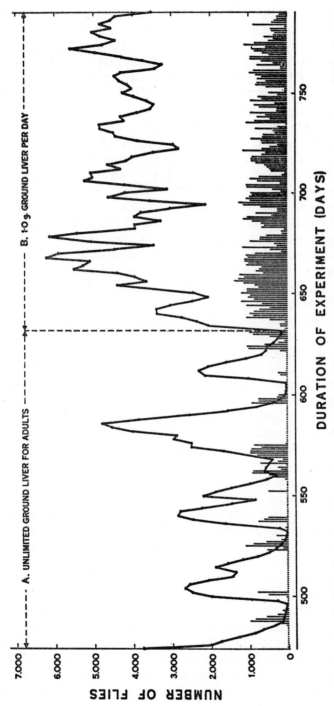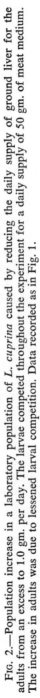

FIG. 2.—Population increase in a laboratory population of *L. cuprina* caused by reducing the daily supply of ground liver for the adults from an excess to 1.0 gm. per day. The larvae competed throughout the experiment for a daily supply of 50 gm. of meat medium. The increase in adults was due to lessened larval competition. Data recorded as in Fig. 1.

density was 1,252; but later, when the supply of ground liver was limited to 1 gm. per day, the adult population increased to a mean of 4,042 (see Nicholson, 1954a, Table 2). This inverse relation between adult food intake and fly numbers was due to the fact that the mean number of larvae which competed each day was reduced from 8,794 to 981 when the adult food was restricted, so greatly reducing the intensity of larval competition.

It is evident that similar results (but in reverse order) would have been produced, had the adults been provided daily with the same small quantity of food throughout the experiment and if selection had reduced the food requirements of the flies for egg development, as in the experiments already discussed. An increased ability to utilise the food for egg production, being equivalent to an increase in the amount of food supplied, would increase the intensity of larval competition and so cause a decrease in the mean adult population.

It might be thought that a reduction in population numbers is disadvantageous to the species and that therefore selection could not produce it. There is, however, no justification for the belief that possible benefit to the species ever influences the direction of selection. In the example under discussion, individuals with improved ability to produce eggs necessarily leave more offspring than the others. So, as larval competition does not discriminate between the progeny of the fit and less fit adults, the less fit adult forms are inevitably displaced. Compensatory reaction to this improvement in egg-laying, by intensifying larval competition, decreases the population density of the adults. Such population decrease has already become evident in two current experiments with *L. cuprina,* in which both adult and larval competition operate and selection has favoured improvement in adult properties.

Natural selection is a ratchet-like process which continually preserves preferentially each more potent form as it appears. It is purely incidental that species commonly benefit by such selection, in the sense that their ability to cope with subsequent environmental change is improved. This is simply an automatic resultant of selection which plays no part in its causation.

The outstanding feature of competitive selection is that, through the medium of density-induced compensatory reaction, it always adjusts the standard of potency necessary for survival at a level that causes the elimination of an existing form whenever a new and more potent form appears. As the examples given have shown, such automatic raising of the standards necessary for preferential preservation can lead to the progressive development and preservation of greatly improved properties, without the aid of any changes in the environment and so in the needs of the species. However, environmental changes may increase the material available for further competitive selection by inducing selection in various directions, so changing the genotype. New recombinations may thus appear, and mutations and recombinations which were previously not significant, or were disadvantageous, may acquire selective advantage with the new genetic background.

WALLACE'S THEORY OF SELECTION BY ADVERSE ENVIRONMENTAL INFLUENCES

Although Darwin and Wallace regarded their theories as being essentially the same, they emphasised different parts of its mechanism. Darwin's arguments were concerned dominantly with competitive selection, which causes the less fit forms to be displaced as a secondary effect of the preservation of fitter forms, whereas Wallace, when illustrating the operation of natural selection, referred almost exclusively to what may be called "environmental selection," the active principle of which is the direct elimination of the unfit.

Thus Wallace said:

Let some alteration of physical conditions occur in the district . . . any change in fact tending to render existence more difficult to the species in question, and tasking its utmost powers to avoid complete extermination; it is evident that, of all the individuals composing the species, those forming the least numerous and most feebly organised variety would suffer first, and, were the pressure severe, must soon become extinct. The same causes continuing in action, the parent species would next suffer, would gradually diminish in numbers, and with a recurrence of similar unfavourable conditions might also become extinct. The superior variety would then alone remain, and on a return to favourable circumstances would rapidly increase in numbers and occupy the place of the extinct species and variety [1858, p. 58].

Apparently he did not clearly realise that competition plays an important part in selection, in addition to being the mechanism causing the numerical limitation of populations in their environments.

It should be noted that the process described by Wallace does not lead to precise qualitative adjustment of the properties of organisms to their environments. He considers that properties superior to those absolutely necessary for existence under normal conditions are selected under the stress of unusually adverse conditions and that the consequent tendency to multiply indefinitely when conditions again become favourable is checked when the population reaches a new and higher level of environmental limitation. This, in an elementary form, is the concept of density-induced compensatory reaction to changes in properties, which adjusts the density of a population at a level that is always related to the properties of the species and to those of its environment.

With competitive selection, the standard necessary for preferential preservation is determined by the properties of the more potent individuals, which induce a sufficient intensity of competition to displace their less fit fellows. Hence the standard of selection automatically rises as a result of the biological improvement already selected, thus causing evolutionary advancement to continue, even in a constant environment, just so long as superior genotypes continue to appear.

By contrast, with environmental selection the standard required for preservation is determined by the innate intensity of the adverse influence of environmental factors, which is uninfluenced by the selection of improved properties in the organisms. Consequently, the maximum degree of evolutionary advancement that can be produced by environmental selection is that at which all individuals have a barely sufficient defense to enable them to survive under the prevailing intensity of the selective factor. It does not necessarily produce this degree of advancement, for appropriate genetical material may not be available. This does not threaten the existence of the species unless the collective adverse effects of all non-reactive factors prevent the production and survival to maturity of the replacement number of offspring, even in the absence of competition. The nature of the selected biological improvement is not wholly determined by the nature and intensities of the adverse factors; for the direction of evolutionary change must often be biased by the chance occurrence of gene changes appropriate for selection by only one of the potentially selective adverse influences.

ROLE OF COMPETITION IN ENVIRONMENTAL SELECTION

Suppose animals of a certain species produce only slightly more than the replacement number of offspring, even when they are free from crowding. In the absence of any inimical environmental influence, the population would grow until it induced the slight intensity of density-governing reaction necessary to destroy the small surplus or to prevent its production. If some non-reactive environmental factor should destroy a portion of this surplus fraction, compensatory reaction would cause the population to fall to a new and still lower equilibrium level. The population would remain in existence, and the selection of defensive properties could proceed; but this would have little effect upon the average properties of the individuals, for, by hypothesis, at least the replacement fraction of individuals (i.e., the great majority) already had defensive properties sufficient for survival. Here the standard of selection would necessarily be very close to the existing properties of the animals: if it were a little lower, there would be no selection, and if a little higher, more than the surplus fraction would be destroyed, thus exterminating the animals. A close approach to qualitative balance between the animals and their environment would exist, but the existence of the species would be most precarious. Even slight deterioration in the environment would cause extinction.

In nature this perilous situation can seldom exist, for all organisms living under favourable conditions produce a considerable surplus of offspring over replacement requirements. The part of this surplus that is not destroyed or prevented by non-reactive adverse environmental factors is removed by density-induced adverse influences, such as competition, which automatically cause the population to be maintained in a state of stability at, or fluctuating about, an equilibrium level determined by the interaction between the organisms and their environments.

The way in which variations in the severity of non-reactive destructive factors are automatically compensated for by appropriate changes in the intensity of competition is illustrated by the results obtained in four experimental cultures of *L. cuprina* which were governed by competition for adult food. In three of the cultures 90, 75, and 50 per cent of all emerging flies were respectively destroyed, whereas in the fourth there was no such destruction. Each population oscillated about a different equilibrium density, and all maintained a condition of stability in spite of the widely differing conditions to which they were subjected. The results of the density-induced compensatory reaction to changes in the degree of destruction are illustrated by Figure 3, each point shown being the mean of daily observations taken over periods of more than seven months. Note that decreasing destruction induced a compensatory decrease in fertility and in the number of emerging flies. The surplus fraction of the offspring produced was caused to equal the fraction eliminated by the prevailing intensity of destruction. The number of flies surviving, represented by the interval between the two solid lines, increased, thus raising the adult population density and increasing the severity of competition. It was this which caused the flies to lay fewer eggs and so compensated for the lessened destruction to which they were subjected.

Let us consider a population in which some adults possess properties which make them less vulnerable than their fellows. These necessarily would be selected, progressively leading to a population less subject to destruction. The consequent growth of the population would

LIMITATION BY ADULT FOOD

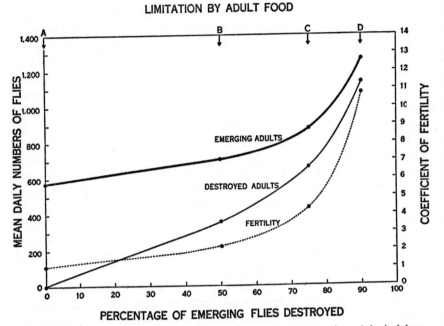

FIG. 3.—The effects of destroying different percentages of emerging adults in laboratory cultures of *L. cuprina* governed by adult competition for a daily supply of 0.5 gm. of ground liver, the larvae being supplied with more food than they could consume. Each of the points in the experiments—*A, B, C,* and *D*—represents the mean of daily observations made over periods exceeding 7 months. The coefficient of fertility is the mean number of offspring produced per individual, whether male or female.

increase the severity of competition, which in turn would reduce the number of offspring produced, thus compensating for the decreased incidence of destruction, just as happened when the externally determined degree of destruction was reduced (Fig. 3). An analysis of this series of experiments has been given elsewhere (Nicholson, 1954*a,* Table 1). Many other experiments with *L. cuprina* in which the favourability of the environment was greatly changed in other ways also showed how compensatory reaction automatically holds populations in a state of stability in spite of even intensely adverse influences (Nicholson, 1955).

The ability of organisms to produce a considerable surplus of offspring confers upon them the property of resilience. Their populations are maintained in a state of stability in spite of great variations in the intensity of adverse environmental influences and also in spite of even great changes in their own properties caused by natural selection. The buffering agency making this possible is compensatory reaction, the mechanism of which is usually some form of competition.

Density-governing reaction is the mechanism which makes environmental selection possible, for it maintains populations in a state of stability even when inimical environmental factors intensify considerably. Therefore, when there is an adverse change in the environment, there is no need for selection to evolve new properties in order to permit the continued existence of the species. The species may maintain its original properties until such time as appropriate genetical material for selection happens to occur. However, the intensification of an adverse factor raises its standard of selection, and so some phenotypes which were previously sufficiently potent for survival are no longer viable. This causes an adaptive change in the species, in the sense that the improved properties selected are related to the intensified factor. This is not an obligatory fitting of the species to its changed environment, but simply an increase in fitness to cope more effectively with a particular environmental hazard.

Years ago I considered the situation in which adult insects are subject to attack by birds, which remain constant in number because of their territorial behaviour, the population being governed by the induced severity of attack by larval parasites. The birds become less successful in attacking the insects as the resemblance of these to their backgrounds or to distasteful insects increases. It was concluded that

an insect exhibiting mimetic resemblance is slightly less liable to attack than a closely related non-mimetic insect, but this is only a protection from the particular enemy which acts as a selective agent; and the very fact of this special protection, tending as it does to cause an increase in numbers, in turn causes an increase in the severity of the attack delivered by those enemies which control the numbers of the species. Therefore neither the species nor the individual, on the average, enjoys any protection due to the possession of mimetic resemblance [Nicholson, 1927, p. 90].

The last sentence refers to the argument that any relaxation in the attack by birds is compensated for by an increased severity of attack by the larval parasites and that the chance of an individual's being destroyed remains the same, whether the species has developed mimetic resemblance or not—the whole surplus, and no more, necessarily being destroyed. However, improved resemblance may permit the species to spread into environments which were previously denied to it because of the intensity of attack by birds, and the standard of selection in these new environments would necessarily be higher. This may have helped considerably in perfecting the mimetic resemblance which is so striking in some animals; but it is not essential to assume any such raising of selection standards to account for the selective development of resemblance.

These conclusions are in striking contrast to a statement made by

Cott that "we have given grounds in the foregoing pages for the belief that the biological needs of security, subsistence and reproduction have exerted, through the operation of natural selection, striking modifications in the appearance of animals—modifications which involve form, coloration and behaviour" (1954, p. 65). Possibly he was speaking metaphorically, but many other authors have made similar statements implying that natural selection can act in this purposive way to maintain a species in existence. How it could do so is never stated.

A species is threatened with extinction only when non-reactive adverse environmental influences collectively destroy almost the whole surplus of offspring or prevent its production. The population is then reduced to a sufficiently low density to make competition negligible. The chance that a favourable gene change will occur is also reduced to a minimum, this being positively related to population size. Resilience being reduced to negligible proportions, the need of the species is great, but the chance of selection satisfying this need is remote. However, long before deterioration of the environment reduces a species to this perilous position, the individuals are seriously affected by the same adverse influences, those unable to cope with them being eliminated. This leads to selection in the direction of satisfying the later needs of the species for preservation and its needs in other places where conditions were previously somewhat unfavourable. The chance that favourable genotypes will appear is relatively great, for resilience can maintain the stability of the species for a very long time while awaiting their occurrence, even in a deteriorating environment. Therefore, environmental selection, under the protective cloak of compensatory reaction, leads to hyperadaptation and so tends to make provision for the later vital needs of the species.

INTERACTION OF COMPETITIVE AND ENVIRONMENTAL SELECTION

There can be little doubt that environmental factors cause mortality or interfere with the reproduction of all species under most, if not all, of the conditions to which they are subject in nature; and some degree of competition is inevitable, for otherwise there would be no resilience and so the species could not exist. Consequently, species must often be subject to selection of both kinds.

The two mechanisms commonly do not act independently but supplement each other. Thus

The action of climate seems at first sight to be quite independent of the struggle for existence; but in so far as climate chiefly acts in reducing food, it brings on the most severe struggle between the individuals, whether of the same or of distinct species, which subsist on the same kind of food. Even when climate, for instance extreme cold, acts directly, it will be the least vigorous individuals, or those which have got least food through the advancing winter, which will suffer most [Darwin, 6th ed. (1888), p. 84].

The implication is that many of the individuals killed by extreme cold would have survived, had there been no deficiency of food or no weakening due to the intensity of competition. Thus, as is probably true in all situations, environmental and competitive selection each plays its part in the elimination of the less fit individuals.

Because of the great variety of situations within the range of most species, adverse weather conditions, such as severe heat, cold, dryness or wetness, do not affect all individuals of a population equally. Some individuals may happen to be in situations which provide protection from the inimical influence, whereas others are fully exposed to it, purely by chance. The consequent mortality would not lead to any selection unless some of the exposed individuals happened to possess properties that enabled them to survive exposure to the inimical influence. Pure environmental selection would then lead to an improvement in, say, the cold-hardiness of the species.

Commonly, however, exposure to such adverse influences is not simply a matter of chance. Most species subject to such hazards have evolved behaviour patterns which cause them to favour protective situations. Those individuals in which such behaviour is relatively poorly developed are more likely to be exposed to the adverse weather conditions and so are most likely to die. Selection for cold-hardiness would continue, but, in addition, there would be selection for improvement in adaptive structures and behaviour, such as appropriate development of sense organs and of behaviour, which would cause the possessors to seek favoured situations and to remain in them. This, also, would be due to environmental selection.

As the number and the capacities of protective situations are necessarily limited, there may not be room for all individuals when a population is large. Therefore, even though all seek such situations with efficiency, some individuals must be unsuccessful in occupying one and so are exposed and likely to die. Here competition plays its part. The successful are the first comers or those which are sufficiently strong and aggressive to force out the weaker. Competitive selection therefore supplements environmental selection by favouring those individuals best equipped to find protective situations quickly; but, in addition, it may select quite different kinds of properties which give the possessors an advantage over their fellows in successfully occupying favourable situations. Although the immediate and evident cause of the elimination of the less fit is destruction by adverse weather, in this situation it is not the selective factor. The less fit are selectively exposed to destruction because they are denied occupation of protective situations by their more potent fellows. The properties selected may have no direct adaptive relation to the operative destructive factor. For example, there may be modifications in size, structure, or behaviour which give advantage in competition. So, in spite of appearances, selection of such properties is exercised by competition and not by the environmental influences which destroy the displaced individuals.

A similar situation exists when animals are subject to attack by predators. Any improvement in protective properties, such as fleetness or resemblance to their backgrounds, is likely to be selected. However, as with adverse weather conditions, which individuals are destroyed may not be determined wholly by their inferior properties of defense or of avoidance. The environmental selection of such properties is likely to be supplemented by competition for and within refuges, thus leading to the evolution of characters which simply give competitive advantage not directly related to the activities of the predators. The more potent individuals force their less fit fellows into places where they are more subject to attack. The fraction of population that is so displaced is that which exceeds the capacity of the refuges at the time, and so the development of such competitive behaviour strongly tends to maintain a population at a fairly constant level.

This mechanism has doubtless led to the development of territorial behaviour in many animals, notably birds. Individuals which successfully lay claim to a territory make provision for their future needs and often for those of their offspring. Those which cannot do so because all favourable places are already occupied are forced into unfavorable environments, where they cannot successfully rear offspring and where they are likely to be ineffective and weakened and therefore more subject to destruction by predators, disease, or exposure to adverse physical conditions. Thus the advantage most likely to be selected is the ability to dominate their fellows rather than a higher degree of direct protection against inimical environmental factors. The proximate causes of mortality may be predators, diseases, and adverse weather conditions; but the primary cause is that an insufficient number of potential territories exists to meet the needs of all and that the more potent individuals drive away the weaker.

SELECTION DUE TO INTERSPECIFIC COMPETITION

Competition between different species for the same requisites gives rise to the interaction of competitive and environmental selection of a particularly important kind. It has been concluded that, "for the steady state to exist, each species must possess some advantage over all other species with respect to some one, or group, of the control factors to which it is subject" (Nicholson, 1933, p. 147). In nature different species competing for the same requisite are seldom, if ever, completely coextensive both spatially and ecologically. Each of several competing species with overlapping distributions can maintain itself in those places where it possesses an advantage over all the others; and it can also spread into neighbouring habitats of the others and remain there indefinitely—the tendency for the locally inferior species to be displaced being offset by continued invasion from the areas in which it enjoys advantage. A similar situation exists when the species have overlapping, but somewhat different, niches, provided that the differences are sufficiently great to give each an adequate advantage over all the others with respect to at least one of the governing factors.

The underlying mechanism is that induced density changes in each species adjust the reaction of its special governing factor at an intensity which, when added to the adverse influences of all other factors, including those of competitors, is just sufficient to permit the production of a replacement number of surviving offspring. That is to say, competitors act like any other inimical environmental factor, and their effects upon the mortality or natality of the species concerned are automatically compensated for by density-governing reaction.

In the regions of overlap, those individuals of the locally inferior species which most successfully resist displacement by the superior species are most likely to survive and reproduce. Such selection tends to cause an approach toward the potency of the locally superior species. This is presumably what Darwin had in mind when he said: "Natural selection tends only to make each organic being as perfect as, or slightly more perfect than, the other inhabitants of the same country with which it comes into competition. And we see that this is the standard of perfection attained under nature" (1888, p. 255). Note that the selection of such improvement in the properties of an inferior species toward the standard of a superior competitor is completely dependent upon the inferior species possessing advantage in some situations; for otherwise the intensity of the governing reaction induced by the superior species would be too great for the inferior one to withstand, and so it would be exterminated.

Selection of approximation in the potencies of competing species is likely to be submerged or countered by selection of another kind. Those individuals which inhabit competitor-free environments are likely to be the most successful in leaving viable offspring. Consequently, selection must favour individuals which choose and make the best use of such environments. This means that the species will evolve distinctive properties which will tend to cause each to retreat from the areas of overlap, thus reducing interspecific competition. Each species tends to improve those properties that give is special advantage, and the consequent divergence of properties causes the species to occupy distinctive niches. Natural selection, therefore, does tend to make each organic being as perfect as the other inhabitants of the same country with which it comes into competition, in the sense that it enables them to withstand such competition. It does so, however, by causing them to withdraw from competition rather than by increasing the competitive efficiency of the weaker species.

Competitive and environmental selection combine in the production of divergence in properties. Those individuals that stray into competitor-dominated environments fail to leave a replacement number of offspring, and so the properties which underlie such straying tend to be eliminated directly by an inimical environmental factor—the competitors. On the other hand, properties which favour success within the predator-free environments are preserved by competitive selection there. These special adaptations would tend to make the individuals favour such environments, and so they would reduce straying. The circumstance leading to such special adaptations is the confinement of the species to a particular habitat by the action of competitors. Such selection is therefore intraspecific, although induced by interspecific competition.

Great divergence of properties between species where they compete, as compared with the properties of the same species when not subject to interspecific competition, has been described by Lack (1947, chap. VII) and is probably due to the mechanism just outlined. For example, the mean beak depth of *Geospiza fortis* was observed to be only slightly greater than that of *G. fuliginosa*, and the range of beak depths differed little between the species when each was isolated on a separate island. On three other islands of the Galapagos group these finches occurred together and competed for seeds. It was observed that the beak depth of *G. fortis* was much greater, and that of *G. fuliginosa* much smaller, than in the same species when isolated and also that the range of beak depths of the two species taken together was much greater where these finches competed than where they did not. It is considered probable that the development of a powerful beak by *G. fortis* and of a more slender beak by *G. fuliginosa* adapted these species to deal effectively with the larger- and the smaller-sized seeds, respectively. Where there is no interspecific competition, a beak of intermediate size is probably advantageous, as it enables the birds to deal effectively with seeds of a wide range of sizes, although the largest and smallest seeds may present difficulties.

When competitors restrict the distribution of a species to a fraction of the environment that would otherwise be favourable to it, adaptation to this particular fraction is produced by the change in the relative intensities of the various selective influences to which the species is subjected. Biological improvement is thus due to intraspecific selection, although the conditions which lead to selection are in part determined by interspecific competition.

When an invading superior species comes into competition with the whole population of a resident species, it exterminates this species; for it induces and maintains a greater intensity of adverse action by the common governing factors than the inferior species can tolerate. Whereas with intraspecific selection the displacement of an inferior form improves the properties of the successful form by removing inferior genetic material from the gene pool, with interspecific selection there is no such benefit, as victor and vanquished do not share a gene pool. The resultant of true interspecific selection (selection between species) is thus confined to the extermination of inferior competitors. Although such extermination is associated in our minds with the normal course of evolution, interspecific selection is not truly a factor in evolution, in the sense of descent with modification.

Concept of Qualitative Balance between Organisms and Their Environments

Some animals, notably insects, so closely resemble their backgrounds that they are virtually invisible. This is due to the possession of forms and colour patterns, often very complex, that conceal the normal features of their external anatomy. The resemblance is accentuated by behavioural characteristics, such as immobility, orientation in relation to the features of their backgrounds, the choice of appropriate resting places, and the assumption of attitudes which increase their resemblance. So many different characters are combined in the production of such near-perfect resemblance that it could scarcely have been produced by chance. The only tenable explanation is that it has been perfected by some selective factor which was influenced by appearance (Nicholson, 1927; Cott, 1954). That this resemblance often confers a high degree of protection upon the possessors has been demonstrated by numerous experiments (Cott, 1940, chap. 10).

Here natural selection has caused a very precise fitting of many of the characters of the animals to those of their environments. Other examples of environmental fitting are the possession of precisely adjusted photoperiod responses in plants, which insure the subsequent development of flowers and of fruits at exactly the right season, and the breaking of diapause in many insects, by response to a particular temperature change, which causes development to be resumed at the right time to permit the active stages to be reached just when seasonal conditions become favourable to them. Such examples are commonly used when illustrating the nature of adaptation—but this is misleading, for only occasionally does natural selection direct change toward the precise fitting of a character to some environmental influence.

One or more of the properties of the animals and plants just mentioned are closely adjusted to some particular environmental factor, but their other properties are not so adjusted. For example, all must be capable of producing more than the replacement number of mature offspring in the absence of crowding; for otherwise the species could not persist. This ability is the resultant of the selective mechanisms already discussed, and it causes the species to be qualitatively out of balance with their environments. They tend to multiply indefinitely, but this is checked by density-induced governing reaction. This reaction is an efficient mechanism which can truly be said to adapt species populations to fit their changing environments; but established usage in evolutionary contexts precludes the use of the word "adaptation" to refer to such quantitative adjustment.

In the examples just given, the advantage which leads to selection is a closer approach of one or more properties toward precise correspondence with some important environmental influence. Those individuals possessing properties more in harmony with such environmental influences than those of their fellows leave greater numbers of mature offspring, and so they displace the others. It is unusual, however, for advantage to be related to such limited objectives. Any improvement in properties leading to the production or survival of larger numbers of offspring is inevitably selected. Even when such increased success in leaving offspring is due to a closer fitting of some property to a particular environmental influence, selection leads to a further overbalancing of environmental properties by those of the species, which has to be rectified by compensatory reaction. Selection therefore does not operate to meet the existing needs of a species, by creating and maintaining qualitative adjustment to environmental influences, but it does provide improved protection against subsequent environmental deterioration, although uninfluenced by this need.

Throughout the writings of Darwin's followers, numerous arguments occur which imply that natural selection does adjust the properties of organisms closely to those of their environments. Many biologists imply that such qualitative adjustment is the necessary product of natural selection and the essential characteristic of adaptation, as the following quotations indicate:

The precision with which living forms have grown through evolution to fit their various environments is described as *adaptation* [Srb and Owen, 1953, p. 452].

Adaptation is an extremely complex two-way fit between population and environment; . . . the environment is extremely complex and any sort of change in it may require changed adaptation which in turn may lead to extinction if organisms fail in adaptive change [Simpson, pp. 293 and 299].

An organism is regarded as adapted to a particular situation . . . only in so far as we can imagine an assemblage of slightly different situations, or environments, to which the animal would on the whole be less well adapted [Fisher, 1930, p. 38].

In a constant environment the great majority of the individuals of a species are very precisely fitted to their habitat, and almost any change from the typical will be a disadvantage [Barnett, 1958, p. 13].

If adaptation were, in fact, a precise complementary relation between the properties of organisms and those of their environments and if this qualitative fitting were necessary for the continued existence of species, it would greatly interfere with the process of natural selection. Thus it has been argued:

Random mutations present the possibility of developing new characters for which a use may or may not be found; if they occur at a time when all the circumstances are propitious they may prove to be highly advantageous and lead to profound modifications of structure, physiology, habit or geographical distribution. The essence of the process is the timing of the appearance of the new factor [Matthews, 1958, p. 98].

Such chance coincidence in the occurrence of an appropriate mutation exactly when and where a need for it arises is so remote that, if it were necessary, selection would be completely ineffective as an evolutionary force.

To account for the fact that most species successfully maintain themselves in environments which vary considerably from place to place and change with the seasons and from year to year, certain explanations have been developed that appear to stem from a belief in the necessity for qualitative balance between organisms and their environments. Thus Thoday (1958) considers that a population can maintain itself in a slowly changing environment only by variability among its individuals and that this variability consists of either genetic or phenotypic versatility. Mather, considering populations subject to cyclic environmental changes, suggests that "sometimes an intermediate phenotype, adjusted to the average needs of the different generations could suffice, or a continuously varying plasticity of development in response to external circumstances could meet the changing conditions" (1955, p. 56). Similar stress upon the vital need for organisms to adjust their properties in relation to change in their environments have been expressed by many authors.

The implication of these views is that, "faced by a given degree of environmental change, groups with lower phenotypic variation, lower genetic variability, lower mutation rates, or any combination of these are more likely to become extinct" (Simpson, 1953, p. 297). Extinction would result from the lack of such qualities only when the degree of environmental change was very great or when the innate resilience of a population was exceptionally low; for compensatory reaction can commonly adjust populations to cope with considerable changes by modifying their densities. The existence of this mechanism has generally been overlooked. The mechanisms of qualitative response just mentioned undoubtedly play an important part in producing the changes in characters which are often observed associated with environmental change—but the new characters are probably unnecessary.

Even if environmental fit existed, natural selection could not maintain it, for selection would be required to eliminate all variants, irrespective of whether their survival value were lower or higher than normal. When, for example, some individuals produced more eggs than those of the successful normal form, natural selection would be required to remove these more prolific individuals; otherwise the population would more than counterbalance the inherent resistance of its environment and so would multiply without check. To account for the observed fact that populations do not continue to multiply indefinitely, the conclusion is inescapable that some density-related check must operate.

Although some biologists appear to believe that adaptation necessarily consists of a close qualitative adjustment of the properties of a species to those of its environment, probably all recognise Darwin's principle that individuals with advantageous properties are preserved at the expense of other individuals. Thus Thoday says: "In any particular set of environmental conditions some of the kinds of individual will succeed in producing more offspring than others. Their kinds will therefore multiply more than the others and, since the numbers that can survive are limited, will gradually replace the others. This is the basis of evolution by natural selection" (1958, p. 316). Similarly, Waddington asserts that, "given that more offspring are conceived than are necessary to preserve the numbers of the population, and that there are inherited variations between individuals, natural selection *must* occur" (1958, p. 5).

Biologists who believe that the product of natural selection is a close qualitative adjustment of organisms to their environment presumably assume that the advantageous qualities selected are necessarily closer approaches to such adjustment. Consequently, they see no inconsistency between the preferential survival of the fitter individuals and the concept of qualitative fitting. As has been shown, these concepts are completely incompatible. Even when some character or group of characters, such as those which constitute mimetic resemblance, exhibit close fitting to some environmental influence, it is these characters alone, and not the species itself, that are fitted to the environment. Whatever may be the nature of an improved property, it confers selective advantage only if it permits the possessors to produce more mature offspring than their fellows. This always tends to cause further overbalancing of the environment, which has to be compensated for by density-induced governing reaction.

NATURE OF ADAPTATION

Darwin made frequent reference to the fact that few, if any, species are perfectly adjusted to their environments; but he appeared to consider that natural selection does not lead to the preservation of qualities appreciably better than are necessary for existence. Thus he said:

In each well-stocked country natural selection acts through the competition of the inhabitants, and consequently leads to success in the battle for life, only in accordance with the standard of that particular country. . . . Natural selection will not necessarily lead to absolute perfection; nor, as far as we can judge by our limited faculties, can absolute perfection be everywhere predicted [Darwin, 1888, p. 260].

This and many other statements by Darwin make it evident that he did not regard the precise qualitative fitting of an organism to its environment as essential, in spite of the fact that he said: "Lighten any check, mitigate the destruction ever so little, and the number of the species will almost instantaneously increase to any amount" (1888, p. 82). This could be interpreted as meaning that species are qualitatively adjusted so closely to their environments that a slight relaxation of a check would lead to indefinite increase. This is inconsistent with the views expressed throughout the *Origin of Species* and also with his earlier statement: "Lighten any check in the least degree, and the geometrical forces of increase in every organism will almost instantly increase the average numbers of the favoured species" (Darwin, 1858, p. 48).

He evidently appreciated the principle of compensatory reaction of density to changed conditions, for he said: "If not one head of game were shot during the next twenty years in England, and, at the same time, if no vermin were destroyed, there would, in all probability, be less game than at present, although hundreds of thousands of game animals are now annually shot" (Darwin, 6th ed. [1888], p. 96).

Darwin did not define what he meant by the word "adaptation"; but the way he used it shows that he simply meant suitability or the process of creating it. For example, he said:

The advantage of plumed seeds no doubt stands in the closest relation to the land being already thickly clothed with other plants; so that the seeds may be widely distributed and fall on unoccupied ground. In the water-beetle, the structure of its legs, so well adapted for diving, allows it to compete with other aquatic insects, to hunt for its own prey, and to escape serving as prey to other animals [1888, p. 94].

Such adaptations make the possessors more effective in utilising environmental resources and in successfully coping with competitors, enemies, and other unfavourable influences. They are analogous to the "fitness" of winning athletes rather than to the "fit" of a key to a lock.

Using the term in this broader sense of "suitability" and "effectiveness," we can truly say that adaptation is the characteristic resultant of natural selection. Adaptation, in this broader sense, is not limited to precise conformity with the environment but may be improved to any extent above the minimum degree of suitability necessary to enable organisms to exist.

It is almost inconceivable that natural selection could take place in a species which is not already sufficiently well adapted to its existing environment to produce at least a replacement number of mature offspring when uncrowded. If less than this number of offspring were produced, the dwindling of the population would progressively reduce the chance that an advantageous gene change would occur, and the time during which natural selection could operate to prevent extinction would be short. As has been shown, the selection of improved properties does not have to await the occurrence of a need for them.

Properties of any kind which make the possessors relatively more successful in leaving mature offspring are necessarily selected. This, incidentally, is the only attribute of an advantageous property that directly determines its preferential preservation by selection. So long as suitable genetical material becomes available, selection continues to preserve properties which are advantageous to the possessors in this sense, even though these may be quite unnecessary for the immediate welfare of the species. Although the preservation of such advantage to individuals benefits the species by improving resilience, thus enabling it to cope better with subsequent changes in the environment, this is purely a fortuitous result. It in no way influences the course of selection.

Natural selection always leads to the evolution of biological improvement beyond that necessary for the maintenance of the stability of a species in its existing environment. I have used the word "hyperadaptation" to refer to such improvement, in order to avoid the sense of qualitative fitting which is often associated with the word "adaptation"; but the new term is not really necessary, except for special emphasis, provided that it is understood that all adaptations preserved and evolved by selection characteristically exceed the minimum requirements of a species to maintain itself under prevailing conditions. In spite of the similar implications of the words, "hyperadaptation," being the direct product of selection in relation to existing influences, differs fundamentally from "prospective adaptation" and "preadaptation." These terms refer to properties which by chance enable a species to cope effectively with a new influence differing in kind from those which selected these properties or which enable a structure or a physiological process evolved to perform a particular function to serve a new purpose.

Although selection is limited to preserving and developing advantageous phenotypic properties, by doing so it also preserves and tends to create physiological harmony between the underlying developmental processes. When a gene change occurs, not only must it initiate changes in developmental processes appropriate to produce an advantageous character in the phenotype, but, to confer selective advantage, these changes must also be compatible with all the other developmental processes which underlie the essential properties of the phenotype. Particularly in the early stages of embryonic development, the developmental mechanisms which ultimately produce the numerous structures and properties of the mature organism must all cooperate in great harmony, often within the same cell. Any important modification of one of these mechanisms, resulting from gene change, is likely to interfere in some degree with closely associated developmental mechanisms, thus disturbing the pre-existing harmony and interfering with the development of the whole organism. Even if the organism is not prevented from reaching maturity, it seems highly probable that one or more of the phenotypic characters would be adversely affected by such interference. This effect is illustrated by tests made with selected strains of *L. cuprina*.

One would expect the ability to develop eggs without first having a meat meal to be advantageous to wild blowflies. It was therefore considered probable that selection of some other kind interfered with the development of this adaptation in nature. As it seemed possible that this could be due to larval competition, larvae of each of the five selected strains already mentioned were caused to compete with larvae of the original stock strain. Twenty-four larvae from a selected strain were made to compete for 1 gm. of larval food with twenty-four larvae from the original stock strain, there being four replicates of such competition tests with each of the strains. The results have been combined in Figure 4. It will be noted that, whereas most larvae of the original strain gave rise to adults, few did so in the selected strains and that the larval weights of the selected strains were, in general, markedly lower than those of the original strain. These relations were

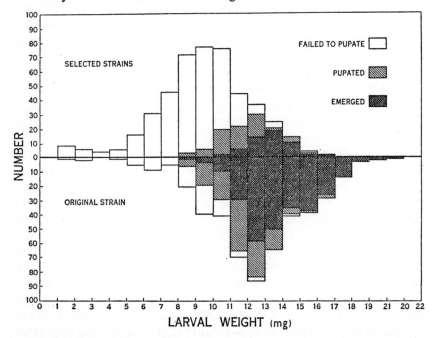

FIG. 4.—The combined results of tests in which larvae of five selected strains of *L. cuprina* competed with equal numbers of larvae of the original stock strain, at a total density of 48 per gram of larval medium.

found to obtain in each of the replicates of the competition tests with each of the five selected strains.

This deterioration in larval potency in the selected strains was clearly related to the selection of greater adult potency, and not simply to the absence of larval competition, for it did not take place in the stock cultures which had been free from larval competition for years.

Current experiments indicate, however, that such induced larval deterioration cannot be wholly responsible for the failure of selection to confer upon natural populations of *L. cuprina* the improved adult adaptation which was developed in the experimental cultures. For example, in a current experiment an originally weakly selected strain is subjected to intense larval and adult competition for food. Initially only about 4 per cent of the flies could develop eggs without a meat meal, but, after about a year, 18 per cent could do so. Such progressive improvement in adult potency, in spite of severe larval competition, indicates either that the adult potency confers a higher survival value than larval potency or that some internal adjustment has been selected which makes the development and maintenance of both larval and adult potency compatible.

Recently, larvae obtained from this experimental culture were caused to compete for food with larvae from the original stock culture, using tests of the kind upon which Figure 4 is based. There was no significant difference between the competing strains in larval weights or in the number of adults produced. This indicates that selection had at least greatly reduced disharmony between the development of larval and adult adaptation.

These examples merely supplement existing evidence that the selection of a favourable property sometimes leads to the deterioration of properties of other kinds and that modifying factors may be selected to produce developmental harmony, as well as harmony between phenotypic properties. The fact that the occurrence of any significantly important gene change is likely to create some developmental disharmony puts, as it were, a brake upon the operation of natural selection. Every population is subject to numerous influences, each of which can affect mortality or natality. Each of these operates with a different intensity. Adaptation tends to be forced predominantly in the direction favoured by the most intense factors, but these factors do not alone determine the compromise between the various potential adaptations which is achieved by a species in a particular environment. There may be conflict between the potential adaptations themselves. Thus improved modifications of limbs for the purpose of climbing may be incompatible with fleetness. Which of these alternatives prevails depends largely upon the initial chance occurrence of a gene change that happens to favour one of them. This accident tends to determine in which direction further evolutionary change must proceed. In addition to this discriminative factor, there is developmental interference, which is likely to check the development of adaptation in certain directions more than in others.

When considering the process of adaptation in general terms, these brakes upon progress in selection can be regarded as operating randomly in intensity and in direction. Consequently, when a species is split into a number of local populations, one must expect selection to bias adaptation in the direction determined by the locally most powerful influences. The existence of ecotypes showing special adaptation to local conditions is well known. Mayr says:

> Whenever and whatever tested, it has been shown that every population of a species is adapted to the conditions of the respective local environment. Furthermore, it has been shown that this adaptation is due to a balance of genetic factors which is often so delicate that it may respond to the seasonal and annual changes of the environment [1949, p. 517].

Such balance is the resultant of the combined influences of different kinds and intensities of selective factors upon genetic structure. Each tends to cause further adaptive change in a particular direction; but conflicting requirements for appropriate genetic changes must lead in time to a balance between the forces which respectively favour and oppose selection along each of the potential lines of adaptation. The intensification or relaxation of one or more of these selective influences disturbs this balance and tends to cause improved adaptation in relation to those influences which are relatively more potent than before.

Thus the relation often observed between the properties of ecotypes and those of their local environments can readily be accounted for as the resultant of automatic response to differences in local selection pressures. There is no evidence whatever that this relation produced by selection is necessary for the preservation of each local population. Because of the great resilience of populations, which results from compensatory reaction to environmental change, it is highly probable that any one of the ecotypes could successfully maintain itself in all the other local environments if it were protected from competition with the locally selected ecotype.

Adaptation is therefore not a qualitative balance between organisms and their environments; nor is it a phenotypic optimum, for each of the selective influences operating could produce further improvement in adaptation related to it if it were not hampered by the effects of selection in other directions. The adaptation of an organism as a whole should rather be regarded as an obligatory compromise resulting from the various selection pressures to which it is subject and from the varying degrees of resistance to adaptation in different directions.

INTENSITY AND STANDARDS OF SELECTION

Let us consider a population exposed to the influence of some adverse environmental factor, the intensity of which is uninfluenced by changes in population density, the population being maintained stable by some non-selective governing factor. If the properties of all individuals were equal, environmental diversity would determine the fraction destroyed under given intensity of the environmental factor; only those individuals which happened to live in protective situations would survive. Should gene change lead to the appearance of a form that was inherently slightly less liable to destruction than the normal form, some individuals of this form would survive because the place they happened to occupy was slightly protective, but insufficiently so to permit the survival of an individual of the normal form. Inevitably, relatively more individuals of the new form would survive. When the fraction destroyed is very small, the advantage is slight, and selection is inevitably slow; but it is evident that this advantage must increase if the destructive influence of the environmental factor is intensified.

Haldane has examined this situation mathematically. Considering two competing types, *A* and *B,* of individuals of the same species, he says:

If in one generation the ratio of *A* to *B* changes from *r* to *r* $(1 + k)$ we shall call *k* the coefficient of selection. . . . The value of *k* will increase with the proportion of individuals killed off by selection, but after selection has become intense enough to kill off about 80% of the population it increases rather slowly, roughly as the logarithm of the number killed off per survivor—sometimes even as the square root of the logarithm [1932, p. 97].

The underlying reason appears to be that as higher percentages of individuals are destroyed, good fortune plays an increasingly important part as a cause of survival. It is therefore evident that the efficiency of selection is only slightly greater when a species is threatened with extinction by the prevailing intensity of the selective factor than it is when a species is not so threatened.

When individuals with a superior survival value appear in a population that is initially subject to a high degree of destruction by a non-reactive environmental factor, the preferential preservation of the superior type reduces the degree of destruction by it. Governing factors automatically compensate for this by increasing destruction due, say, to competition. Biological improvements which appear subsequently are selected in the same way, leading to a progressive improvement in adaptation without any change in the characteristics of the selective agency. The consequent reduction in the percentage destroyed by the selective factor decreases the efficiency of environmental selection; but, as has already been shown, this decrease may not be as great as might be expected. Thus, because of the resilience conferred upon a species by the production of a considerable excess of offspring, environmental selection is not limited to the production of a particular degree of adaptation but may progressively develop great improvement in adaptation related to it, even when the selective agency itself remains unchanged. Such selection does not necessarily lead to an increase in the population; for, as has already been shown in the discussion related to Figure 3, such reduction in the percentage destroyed by the selective factor may lead to an actual reduction in the number of individuals reaching the stage upon which the selective factor operates.

Environmental factors can be directly selective only if they are adverse. Consequently, the adaptations they select are necessarily defensive, including avoidance. Competitive selection may also lead to the development of defensive properties, but it is not limited to doing so. Any inheritable property which gives an advantage to the individual possessors is selected, whether this be related to adverse or to favourable factors in the species environment or to the influence of other individuals of the same species. Destruction and failure to produce offspring caused by competition is far less due to chance than when these adverse affects are produced by an environmental factor. An increase in the intensity of competition increases the selective advantage of the superior individuals over their fellows, even though their intrinsic properties remain unchanged. For example, if the number of birds is only slightly greater than can be accommodated in the potential territories, many individuals with comparatively poor qualities are successful. If, however, the number of birds is greatly increased, only the more potent birds occupy the territories, and they drive away all the others. Thus the standard of potency necessary for survival increases as the population increases.

Such increase in selective efficiency with increase in the intensity of competition has been demonstrated by laboratory experiments with *L. cuprina*. Two groups of larvae were caused to compete with each other for the same limited supply of food. One of these groups had the advantage that it was derived from eggs which hatched six hours before those of the other group. In one series of experiments, competition was only moderately severe, six larvae of each group being placed together in 1 gm. of medium. In the other, competition was somewhat greater, twenty-four larvae of each group competing together for the same food. Figure 5 combines the results of these replicated experiments. It records the weight groups of the larvae after all the food had been consumed, the number of larvae which gave rise to adults being shown by the crosshatched columns. The group given a competitive advantage was little more successful in producing adults than the other group at the lower population density, but intensification of competition caused by quadrupling the density gave it exclusive success.

Thus density-induced compensatory reactions to changes in the properties of organisms hold populations in a state of stability that permits the progressive improvement of adaptation by both environmental and competitive selection, even when there is no environmental change. Competitive selection is far more versatile than environmental selection, for the adaptations developed are not limited to defensive properties. There is an upper limit to the perfection of adaptation that environmental selection can produce, this being reached when none of the individuals exposed to the selective factor is adversely affected by it. By contrast, there is no upper limit to the biological improvement that may be produced by competitive selection, for this can proceed just so long as advantageous gene changes occur.

As has been shown, the efficiency of environmental selection tends to fall progressively as adaptation improves. On the other hand, the efficiency of competitive selection improves progressively as adaptation progresses. This is because density-governing reaction always adjusts competition at the intensity necessary to destroy the surplus of individuals produced or to prevent its production, irrespective of whether adaptation is poorly or highly developed. That is to say, the standard necessary for survival in the face of competition automatically rises as adaptation improves.

CREATIVE INFLUENCE OF NATURAL SELECTION

It sometimes happens that environmental conditions determine with some precision the nature of a particular property that an organism must possess in order to survive. For example, in regions where weather conditions vary greatly from season to season, it may be essential that seeds of a particular kind of plant should germinate within a week or two of a particular date or that animals should enter into an inactive resting state at a particular time in order to enable them to survive during adverse periods of the year. In general, however, environmental conditions do not determine the necessary properties of

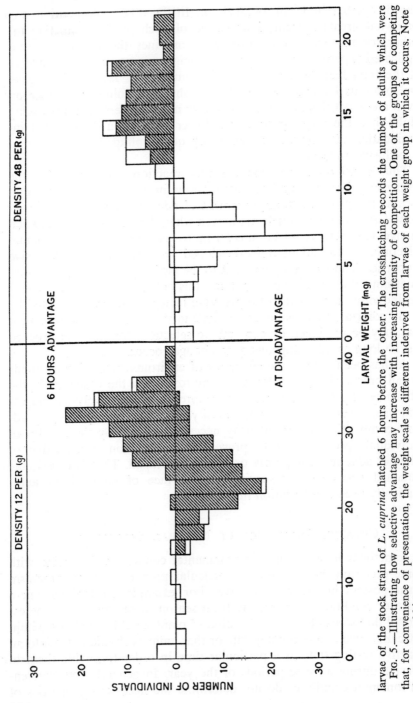

larvae of the stock strain of *L. cuprina* hatched 6 hours before the other. The crosshatching records the number of adults which were

FIG. 5.—Illustrating how selective advantage may increase with increasing intensity of competition. One of the groups of competing that, for convenience of presentation, the weight scale is different inderived from larvae of each weight group in which it occurs. Note the two sets of histograms.

organisms so precisely. There are commonly many different possible lines of adaptation to a particular influence, all of which could be effective. Natural selection plays an important part in determining which line of adaptation is followed, and it may be said to choose from the heterogeneous mass of available genetic material only that which will lead to biological improvement. As Huxley has said, natural selection is "a positive factor in evolution, guiding and determining the types of change produced" (1947, p. 28). It is a creative process and not merely a sieve.

For example, consider a species of animal which is subject to serious attack by predators. Any individuals which have properties making them less liable to attack than their fellows are more likely to produce offspring, and so their properties tend to replace those of their more vulnerable fellows within the species. There are, however, many kinds of advantageous properties which could produce this effect, such as fleetness, a covering of armour, resemblance to backgrounds, distastefulness advertised by some easily recognisable feature, the habit of hiding in protective situations, and the choice of predator-free habitats. It seems almost inevitable that chance must initially determine which kind of adaptation is selected. The kind of gene change which happens to occur is completely independent of selective influences. By chance, such a change may cause a slight degree of adaptation in a particular direction. Further improvement in the same direction is then favoured, for most of the potential kinds of adaptation are in some degree incompatible with one another. This tendency toward unidirectional adaptation is intensified as the adaptation improves. This is an important factor in the production of divergence between sibling species.

It cannot be argued that such evolutionary improvement is due to the chance occurrence of a succession of appropriate gene changes, for many other kinds of gene changes occur that are not preserved. Just as an artist is creative when he produces a masterpiece by selecting and appropriately placing the pigments available to him, so natural selection creates and develops adaptation by using only those gene changes that are appropriate at any given stage in the development of adaptation.

The improvement of adaptation in a particular direction is often dependent upon the selection of auxiliary adaptations. Operating alone, such adaptations may be of no importance to the possessors, but, by augmenting the effects of some other adaptation, they achieve selective value when this adaptation appears and while it is being developed. A good example has already been given. The selection in *L. cuprina* of the ability to develop eggs fully, even when the adults do not obtain a meat meal, was largely dependent upon the concurrent selection of the ability to lay eggs without the stimulus of tasting meat.

The selection of auxiliary adaptation is a notable feature of the creativeness of natural selection. The evolution of such beautiful and complex structures as eyes is presumably the resultant of such interdependent selection. Incidentally, the fundamental differences in the structure of the eyes of vertebrates, molluscs, and insects provides a good example of the opportunist way in which natural selection makes use of the material that happens to be available to it. Each evidently had an independent origin, each has evolved upon quite different lines, and, in each, many different structures have been evolved to work together in harmony in order to produce effective vision. Such complex structures as eyes are almost certainly the product of competitive selection, for they are not primarily defensive mechanisms. Their importance is mainly that they enable their possessors to exploit their environments more effectively.

Competitive selection may lead to the production of structures and properties of quite different kinds from those possessed by their predecessors. Such novelties appear to be generally concerned with the way of life of the animals rather than with new needs created by environmental change. For example, the novelties may be sense organs or organs of locomotion, such as legs, wings, or fins. These almost inevitably must have appeared initially by chance as barely functional precursors. The development and perfection of such structures give the possessors an advantage over their fellows in finding requisites and in enabling them to move into environments which are only temporarily favourable or are inaccessible to their fellows. The ability of certain selected strains of *L. cuprina* to develop eggs when the adults are deprived of suitable food is another example of a novelty. In this example the steps which led to its production and perfection have been observed and described.

When we examine the fossil record of life, it is the frequent appearance of novelties that particularly excites our admiration. It is the outstanding feature of evolutionary change. Evolution presents the appearance of being inventive in the creation in organisms of novel features which improve potency in exploiting environmental resources and in coping with hazards. Such adaptations, far from causing the organisms to be merely sufficiently fit to cope with their environments, consist of properties and structures which enable them to free themselves to a large extent from environmental trammels by countering inimical influences and by enabling them to exploit their environments more effectively. Many animals have gone a step further by developing structures and behavioural characteristics which enable them to modify their environments to their own advantage.

The evolution of novelties would have been impossible, were it not for the fact that compensatory reaction always maintains the standard of selection at the level necessary for the preferential preservation of any improvement at any time during the evolution of adaptation.

SPECIATION

Darwin placed great stress upon the importance of divergence of character in evolution. He argued that extreme variants may often have the great advantage of being able to use environmental resources unavailable to the rest of the species and that selection of such variants would in time lead to the splitting of the original species into several species with distinctive characters. He did not say how these extreme variants could maintain their identity in spite of the swamping effects of interbreeding with other variants.

To prevent this effect, it seems essential that some physical barrier should exist between two or more of the variants in order to prevent interbreeding, at least during the earlier stages of divergence. This would permit selection to operate independently in different portions of the species population. The accumulation of independent changes in the genotypes, whether due to chance or to selection by differing environmental influences, would often lead in time to intergroup sterility, because of the probable developmental disharmony when the groups crossed. If the physical barriers between these groups subsequently disappeared, further divergence would be favoured by interspecific competition in the way already described, which was illustrated by reference to divergence between sympatric species of *Geospiza*. Such accentuated divergence is possible because the breeding groups into which the original species has become divided no longer share a common gene pool. Each is free to improve adaptation to those habitats in which it enjoys advantage, and intraspecific selection tends to cause a withdrawal from the habitats initially shared with other daughter species. Such divergence in properties enables the daughter species collectively to exploit far more environmental resources than the parent species could have done, had the same selective influences acted upon it. This is because gene flow within the species would strongly tend to interfere with the full development of the different adaptations which local influences in different parts of the species range most strongly tend to produce.

It probably often happens that when two populations of a species, which were previously isolated geographically, come together, genetic divergence has not proceeded far enough to make interbreeding impossible. However, if the divergence is appreciable, it commonly happens that the offspring from intergroup matings are relatively less viable or less fecund. If so, intragroup selection will eliminate individuals which mate most readily with other groups, so raising the status of the groups to the rank of species.

These considerations indicate that speciation must be regarded as a by-product of the biological improvement caused by intragroup selection. The essential features of such selection are the preferential preservation of the fitter individuals and the displacement of the genes of the less fit individuals from the gene pool of the group. The splitting of organisms into the genetically isolated groups we call "species" has played a very important part in evolution, for it has permitted selection to proceed untrammeled within each group, so permitting adaptations of innumerable kinds in the different groups. Had organisms not divided into genetically isolated groups, the numerous and beautiful adaptations so characteristic of living things could not have evolved, nor could organisms have used the resources of the world in the efficient way they do.

General Application of the Conclusions Reached

The main factual evidence used in reaching the conclusions presented concerning the influence of population dynamics upon natural selection is that provided by laboratory experiments with the blowfly *L. cuprina*. In such a general discussion a full account of these experiments would have been inappropriate. This will be published as soon as possible in other articles. However, in these experiments the governing mechanism was competition for food. As such governing mechanisms are outstandingly important in relation to natural selection and as the populations of various organisms are governed by mechanisms other than competition for food, the question arises as to whether the broad conclusions reached are valid for other organisms living under very different conditions.

Let us consider the general situation. If the properties of an organism fit it to live in a given environment, the organism will tend to multiply, for this is an outstanding characteristic of all living things. No matter what kind of factors are operative, it is inevitable that sooner or later the increase in numbers will induce sufficient opposition to further multiplication to prevent the production and survival of more than the replacement number of offspring. It is immaterial whether this is due to the depletion of some requisite or to the intensification of attack by enemies or to any other governing factor. Although only density-governing factors can adjust populations to prevailing conditions, the level at which population growth is arrested is strongly influenced by factors which are not themselves influenced by the population density. Whatever other effects they may produce, they can influence populations only by affecting reproduction or survival. When more than the replacement number of offspring survive, the populations inevitably grow; and when less than this number survive, owing to induced unfavourable reactions in the environment, the populations are forced to decrease. Only in this way can populations living in favourable environments be prevented from multiplying indefinitely; and it is axiomatic that, in any population which does not increase or decrease progressively, the number of offspring which reach reproductive maturity must equal the number of parents, on the average. We can safely conclude, therefore, that any species which succeeds in maintaining itself over long periods is held in a state of stability by density-governing reaction. A fuller discussion leading to these general conclusions has been given elsewhere (Nicholson, 1954b, pp. 58–61).

Density-governing reaction automatically compensates for any increase in the efficiency of the organisms or change in the favourability of their environments, by an appropriate adjustment of density. Such compensatory reaction always holds populations at densities which permit the fitter individuals to survive and cause the elimination of the less fit. This leads to hyperadaptation—the production of properties which often greatly exceed those necessary for the survival of the species. If the appropriate genetical material for such improvement does not occur, the population can maintain its stability even when the environment changes greatly, for hyperadaptation already evolved provides species with a high degree of resilience. Natural selection is left completely free to preserve any new advantageous property, however greatly this may exceed the efficiency necessary to balance the properties of the environment.

Conclusion

As the foregoing considerations are concerned primarily with the influence of population dynamics upon natural selection, genetical influences have been referred to only incidentally, in spite of their importance in this process. They confirm the essential features of the theories of natural selection put forward by Darwin and Wallace. It will be evident that many of the conclusions reached conform closely to those reached by other investigators who did not specifically take population dynamics into account; but it is believed that they make clearer the mechanisms which underlie observed evolutionary phenomena. So much has been written about natural selection that it is impossible to be sure that any apparently new idea has not previously been presented. However, whether new or not, some of the more important conclusions reached are evidently not at present fully appreciated by biologists. It is hoped that this re-examination of the theory of natural selection in relation to population dynamics will clarify some rather confused aspects of this theory and that it may influence biologists to pay greater attention to the natural regulation of populations when considering the causes of evolution.

Bibliography

Barnett, S. A. (ed.). 1958. Preface to *A Century of Darwin*. London: William Heinemann, Ltd.

Cott, H. B. 1940. *Adaptive Coloration in Animals*. London: Methuen & Co., Ltd.

———. 1954. "Allaesthetic Selection and Its Evolutionary Aspects," in *Evolution as a Process*, ed. J. Huxley, A. C. Hardy, and E. B. Ford. London: George Allen & Unwin, Ltd.

Darwin, C. 1858. Abstract of a letter from C. Darwin, Esq., to Professor Asa Gray, Boston, U.S., dated Down, September 5, 1857, *Jour. Linn. Soc. London,* III, 50–53.

———. 1888. *Origin of Species*. 6th ed. London: John Murray.

Fisher, R. A. 1930. *The Genetical Theory of Natural Selection*. Oxford: Clarendon Press.

Haldane, J. B. S. 1932. *The Causes of Evolution*. London, New York, and Toronto: Longmans, Green & Co.

Huxley, T. H., and Huxley, J. 1947. *Evolution and Ethics*. London: Pilot Press, Ltd.

Mather, K. 1955. "Polymorphism as an Outcome of Disruptive Selection," *Evolution,* IX, 52–61.

Matthews, L. H. 1958. "Darwin, Wallace, and 'Pre-Adaptation,' " *Jour. Linn. Soc. (Bot.) London,* LVI, 93–98.

Mayr, E. 1949. "Speciation and Selection," *Proc. Amer. Phil. Soc.,* XVIII, 514–19.

Nicholson, A. J. 1927. "A New Theory of Mimicry in Insects," *Australian Jour. Zool.,* V, 10–104.

———. 1933. "The Balance of Animal Populations," *Jour. Anim. Ecol.,* II, 132–78.

———. 1954a. "Compensatory Reactions of Populations to Stresses, and Their Evolutionary Significance," *Australian Jour. Zool.,* II, 1–8.

———. 1954b. "An Outline of the Dynamics of Animal Populations," *ibid.,* pp. 9–65.

————. 1955. "Density Governed Reaction, the Counterpart of Selection in Evolution," *Cold Spring Harbor Symp. Quant. Biol.,* Vol. XX.

————. 1957. "The Self-Adjustment of Populations to Change," *ibid.,* Vol. XXII.

SIMPSON, G. G. 1953. *The Major Features of Evolution.* New York: Columbia University Press.

SRB, A. M., and OWEN, R. D. 1953. *General Genetics.* San Francisco, Calif.: W. H. Freeman & Co.

THODAY, J. M. 1958. "Natural Selection and Biological Progress," in *A Century of Darwin,* ed. S. A. BARNETT. London: William Heinemann, Ltd.

WADDINGTON, C. H. 1953. "Epigenetics and Evolution," in *S. E. B. Symposia,* Vol. VII: *Evolution.* Cambridge: Cambridge University Press.

————. 1958. "Theories of Evolution," in *A Century of Darwin,* ed. S. A. BARNETT. London: William Heinemann, Ltd.

WALLACE, A. R. 1859. "On the Tendency of Varieties To Depart from the Original Type," *Jour. Linn. Soc. London,* III, 53–62.

WEBBER, L. G. 1955. "The Relationship between Larval and Adult Size of the Australian Sheep Blowfly *Lucilia cuprina* (Wied.)," *Australian Jour. Zool.,* III, 346–53.

EVERETT C. OLSON

MORPHOLOGY, PALEONTOLOGY, AND EVOLUTION

During the years of 1958 and 1959 the work of Charles Darwin has been reviewed and analyzed in great detail; the progress of thought about evolution has been summarized, collated, and related to disciplines far afield from biology; and the future has been explored. In general, it would seem, we feel that the charge implicit in the *Origin of Species* has been well carried out and that much that is to be known about evolution is, at least in broad outlines, now known. There are, of course, degrees of difference in evaluation of successes, from healthy skepticism to confidence, that the final word has been said, and there are still some among the biologists who feel that much of the fabric of theory accepted by the majority today is actually false and who say so. For the most part, the opinions of the dissenters have been given little credence. This group has formed a vocal, but little heard, minority.

There exists, as well, a generally silent group of students engaged in biological pursuits who tend to disagree with much of the current thought but say and write little because they are not particularly interested, do not see that controversy over evolution is of any particular importance, or are so strongly in disagreement that it seems futile to undertake the monumental task of controverting the immense body of information and theory that exists in the formulation of modern thinking. It is, of course, difficult to judge the size and composition of this silent segment, but there is no doubt that the numbers are not inconsiderable. Wrong or right as such opinion may be, its existence is important and cannot be ignored or eliminated as a force in the study of evolution.

Pertinent to the present paper is the fact that many who are not satisfied with current theory, the "synthetic theory," or simply "selection theory," are to be found in the ranks of the paleontologists and

EVERETT C. OLSON is Professor of Geology at the University of Chicago. He is a past president of the Society of Vertebrate Paleontology and editor of the journal, *Evolution*. He is the author (with Robert L. Miller) of *Morphological Integration* (University of Chicago Press, 1958).

morphologists. This is true in spite of the fact that the role of the structural areas of biology, anatomy, and morphology have figured prominently in the development of Darwinian evolution, as recently reviewed by Simpson (1959) and earlier with different emphases by Cole (1944), Zimmerman (1953), and others. In view of these excellent sources, no further historical review is needed but it is of some importance, perhaps, to re-emphasize that morphological information has provided the greatest single source of data in the formulation and development of the theory of evolution and that even now, when the preponderance of work is experimental, the basis for interpretation in many areas of study remains the form and relationships of structures.

One of the most significant events in development of recent evolutionary theory has been the synthesis of information and concepts from several contributing disciplines which reached fruition in the late 1940's and the 1950's and continues to play an important role today. This produced what has come to be known as the "synthetic theory of evolution" but has also been variously termed "selection theory," "neo-Mendelian theory," and "neo-Darwinian theory." It is unfortunate that occasionally it is called *"the* theory of evolution," as if no other could exist. Contributions to this formulation have come from many sources. Such names as Julian Huxley, J. B. S. Haldane, R. A. Fisher, Ernst Mayr, G. Ledyard Stebbins, Sewall Wright, and G. G. Simpson come immediately to mind, but there are many others. Somewhere on the fringes are such paleontologists as A. S. Romer, T. S. Westoll, Glen Jepsen, Bryan Patterson, Norman Newell, and even your writer, and various anatomists, in particular Dwight Davis. Synthesis is by no means complete, but that which has taken place has been extremely important. It is only necessary to refer to the pages of the thirteen volumes of *Evolution,* which draws material from many fields, to see the impact which it has had. This organ is, perhaps, somewhat biased, since its birth was not unrelated to the synthetic movement, but the relatively strong adherence to the synthetic theory and interpretation of data within its framework is notable not only in this publication but in others such as *Genetics, Ecology,* and so forth.

The true significance of the current evolutionary formulation is that it has provided an integrating framework for a highly diverse array of disciplines within biology and has even brought some ordered relationships between and within fields of social and humanistic thought. Like any great formulation, whether correct or not, it has played an extremely important role in human thought. Whatever the merit, however, there can be no excuse for failure to scrutinize and examine the structure for flaws, both minor and major, and to continue to study strengths and weaknesses in relationship to the increasing body of knowledge. No one person is competent to cover all aspects of such a study, so that the responsibility for continuing review must rest upon the shoulders of many. This does, however, seem to be an appropriate time to raise some questions as to the adequacy of the synthetic theory, particularly from the viewpoints of morphology and paleontology as I see them. First, some aspects of current thought on evolution will be considered. Then the roles of inheritance and selection as related to morphology and evolution will be studied. Finally, the problems of paleontological evidence and evolution will be reviewed.

CONCEPTS OF ORGANIC EVOLUTION TODAY

It is certain that few negative responses would result from the simple question "Is the general concept of organic evolution valid?" were it to be submitted to the biologists working in the various disciplines today. If, however, a second question were asked, one requiring a definition of organic evolution, it is equally likely that a varied suite of answers would result, and, if the answers were honest, there would be a fair sprinkling to the effect "I don't know." As shown by various studies directed to "comparative evolution"—for example, Stebbins (1950), White (1954), Boyden (1953), and Dougherty (1955)—and the wide variety of phenomena with evolutionary implications, evolutionary theory cannot be a simple construct that patterns and explains integrated systems of "laws." On the contrary, it is a very complex structure, composed of many ideas and concepts, variously arrayed into lesser structures, and more or less equal as contributors to the broad, over-all concept. In fact, there are very few, if any "laws" specifically peculiar to the theory of evolution, in the same way that there are laws in physics and chemistry. The discussions of Beckner (1959, pp. 157–58) are pertinent to this matter.

In this sort of circumstance, where the total theory consists of parts, none of which is in itself completely verifiable but gains strength from the others, lies a basis for very different points of view among those who, in general, ascribe to the central theme. This is a healthy situation, since dominance by any one area which overrides the possible conceptual contributions from others, as genetics has tended to do in evolution, is likely to reduce the effectiveness of the advantage inherent in it. On the other hand, there are some possible dangers in the diversity. Emphasis in a particular subdiscipline may give special importance to the particular data of the area and form a basis for unwarranted attack upon, or dismissal of, data and conclusions from another area based upon misunderstanding or ignorance. The whole structure, however, does not necessarily fall or even become seriously damaged, as one or another of its parts is modified or even drastically altered. Thus, in spite of the continuing attacks, modifications, and new data, there exists today a general concept of evolution, whose meaning is somewhat different to various students of organic evolution, but whose basic correctness is rarely challenged.

The statement is frequently made that organic evolution is no longer to be regarded as a theory, but is a fact. This, it seems to me, reveals a curious situation that causes considerable difficulty in understanding evolution both among laymen and among biologists who are not intimately concerned with its study. If organic evolution can be defined simply and loosely as the changes of organisms through successive generations in time, then it can hardly be questioned that, within our understanding of the earth and its life, evolution has occurred. In this sense it must be considered a reality. As opposed to the ideas of fixed species and constancy of life-form, a theory of evolution has been in the thoughts of various men since well before the birth of Christ. Documentation of changes of organisms with time, from the paleontological record, often views evolution as a matter of change of form, something which is specific and which is considered factual. In contrast with this are other meanings, contained, for example, in the statement by Mayr (1959): "At present it may be helpful to delimit the concept of 'organic evolution' more precisely. It refers to a change in genetic properties from generation to generation owing to reproduction." Wright (1959) speaks of "the mathematical exposition of the theory of evolution." Simpson (1953), on the other hand, defines "natural selection as differential reproduction," which, applied to the genotype, is essentially the delimitation of Mayr quoted above.

The last three statements and definitions express a basic concept of the "synthetic theory" of evolution and, by the use of the definite article, imply that this is *the*—presumably *the only*—theory of evolution. The fact is, of course, as any of these writers would, I am sure, acknowledge immediately, that there are other possible statements of the theory of evolution. If, however, the passage from Mayr is taken in context with other statements in the cited paper, it is difficult to escape the impression that most ideas not encompassed by this statement are excluded from a proper concept of evolution. The statement is made, in effect, that those who do *not* agree with the synthetic theory do *not* understand evolution and are incapable of so doing, in most cases because they think typologically.

The existence of a variety of interpretations has led to misunderstandings among biologists, and even to conclusions by non-biologists that there are many students of organisms who seriously question the theory of evolution. Somehow mechanism and process seem to have become confused. Organic evolution—the process of orderly change of successive generations through time—does occur and apparently has occurred for the total period of of life on the earth. There can be many theories of *how* it occurred, each of which may explain part or all of what has been observed, and these theories may be in complete conflict without invalidating the basic fact of evolution. By definition, if a definition is made exclusive, however, we may arrive at a denial of evolution by a denial of all or part of the possible processes. Denial of natural selection, if validated, would be fatal to the synthetic theory, but not a denial of evolution unless it were conceived only from this point of view. However, some avid proponents of the synthetic theory would appear to operate within this general framework; they eliminate as competent students of evolution, because of their inability to under- stand *the* theory, those who may disagree. Regardless of the apparent merit and strength of the synthetic theory, it seems to me that the more cautious and thoughtful attitudes, as expressed by Stebbins (1959) or particularly by Lerner in *The Genetic Basis for Selection* (1958), are more appropriate. Lerner, considering the general suc- cess and future role of present theory, writes as follows: "It is, there- fore, not to be expected that the keys which we can forge now will un- lock anything but another door in a probably infinite series."

Four more or less discrete concepts of organic evolution are found in the literature of the past fifty years. There are many minor variations and different shades, but, in general, most thoughts seem to center in one of the following areas of explanation:

1. *Synthetic theory,* basically involving Mendelian inheritance, selection, and change through gradual accumulation of small characters.
2. *Saltation theories,* involving major, abrupt reorganizations, by muta- tion or some other type of germ-cell reorganization.
3. *Metaphysical theories,* calling upon outside motivations or non- physical internal directive forces.
4. *Lamarckian* or *neo-Lamarckian theories,* involving inheritance in one way or another of acquired characteristics.

Except for the relatively widespread following of Michurinist doc- trines in the Soviet Union in recent years, the great majority of stu- dents have been, and still are, proponents of the basic ideas of the synthetic theory. Of somewhat dubious position, and perhaps forming a fifth category, are the ideas of cytoplasmic inheritance and the re- sults of studies of mechanisms of inheritance in microorganisms in general, as well as in some macroorganisms which may not fit the concepts of the synthetic theory precisely but probably can be inte- grated into a broader framework without serious disruption of this theory. Proponents of theories other than the first listed have met very strong and generally well-reasoned opposition during the last quarter-century. There have been some highly vocal proponents of other concepts, for example, the geneticist Goldschmidt (1940) arguing for "saltation" as a dominant factor, Schindewolf (1954) among the paleontologists, and V. Bertalanffy (1952), to mention but a few. All students who work with the fossil record and are interested in evolution must be concerned with apparent abruptness of change, rapid initiation of new groups, and discontinuities. There is a great difference, however, among paleontologists in the value given to the factor of the incompleteness of the record and the bias of samples. Simpson, elsewhere in this volume, gives an excellent review of the whole problem, with the selectionist point of view in mind but with clear statements as to the problems which some of the findings raise. Efremov (1950) presents a somewhat different point of view, with emphasis in particular upon the evolution of environmental types. Both conclude that the apparent breaks are due in large part to natural sampling, not to actual jumps in evolution. Saltations are not needed to explain the record, as Simpson notes. Of course, as he makes clear, this in itself is no proof that they did not in fact take place.

It is this last sort of situation that throughout plagues rational discussion of the basic ideas of evolution. The difficulties of the logic of inductive reasoning have been argued for all science, but, while they are applicable to evolution and somewhat relevant to this point, they are not specifically what is in mind. Rather, the problem of proof or refutation of any particular postulate in evolution, no matter how appealing or absurd it may be, is difficult because of the very nature of the biological world to which organic evolution pertains. Generalizations are difficult because of the extreme complexity of the primary components of organisms—organic molecules—the complexity and heterogeneity of the organization of organic systems, organisms, and populations, and the highly ramified and complex processes characteristic of living entities. A series of statements taken from a consideration of selection theory by Beckner (1959) seem to me to express the nature and structure of the theory of evolution and are pertinent to the problems raised by its complexities. The following short passages summarize his general concept:

> The scientific interest of modern evolutionary theory derives from its success in integration into a single body of theory the results and data from the most diverse branches of biology; paleontology, genetics, ethology, systematics, biogeography, ecology, etc. . . .
> It is of philosophical interest to see how this [i.e., integration from

preceding sentence] is accomplished, for these sciences show a staggering diversity of context and principles . . . [p. 159].

Evolutionary theory is of philosophical interest because of the way it integrates principles of the most diverse sorts, but in addition, it is of interest because we find the most diverse patterns of concept formation and explanation unified into a single theory [p. 160].

My own view is that evolution theory consists of a family of related models; that most evolutionary explanations are based upon assumptions that, in individual cases, are not highly confirmed, but that the various models in the theory provide evidential support for their neighbors.

If this series is acceptable as a rational statement of the structure of evolutionary theory—and it appears to me that this is the case—it provides a logical framework within which the many aspects of evolution can be studied and evaluated, in which the constructions from many fields can take a proper place, and under which structure can be molded and modified in terms of its constituents, with understanding of the function of each and the interrelated and interdependent natures of all.

The structure of the concept of organic evolution does not, from this point of view, rest firmly upon one or another proposition, except, of course, the propositions common to all science; and it is the excessive value given to one or another by overemphasis of one area within the total array of disciplines that appears to have caused a large part of the controversy and misunderstanding so often encountered and so rarely reconciled. It must be recognized that considerable extrapolation may be necessary to relate various models and that many, widely separated in concept or in discipline, may have essentially no common elements in their structures. Those more closely related usually have the intersupporting characters noted by Beckner, and, in many instances, serial passage through models of adjacent disciplines to those rather remote will reveal an otherwise unrecognized community or clarify the basic differences.

It may be well, for clarity, to note some of the sorts of models that enter into the theory. The most extensive and fully developed are *theoretical* models from the field of genetics, the mathematical models of such men as Wright and Fisher. Recently Lewontin and Kimura, in particular, have developed some phases of this area. The mathematics of genetic theory have been systematized and summarized by Kempthorne (1957). Somewhat different are *experimental* models developed and used extensively in studies of genetics and ecology, both in the laboratory and in field studies of populations. A third type may be called the *taxon* model, the model of systematic structure of a group. Models of mating patterns, for analysis of morphological cor-relation, for relative growth, and models at more complex levels, of ecological systems and systems evolving through time, of community interactions, and relationships of physical and cultural patterns are others that may be cited. The real function of evolution theory, as Beckner has stated, is the co-ordination of this vast hierarchy of individual models and their implications.

Selection theory, to date, has been the most successful integrating concept that has been advanced. That no organic event has been dis-covered that cannot be explained by the "synthetic theory," or selec-tion theory, as is often stated, is in a sense true. On the other hand, the feeling of a slight sense of frustration in the elasticity involved in de-veloping a universal explanation is hard to avoid, a feeling somewhat in sympathy with V. Bertalanffy (1952) when he noted "a lover of paradox could say that the main objection to selection theory is that it cannot be disproved." Morphologists and paleontologists feel this, perhaps, more strongly than many other students of biology, since they, in particular, are concerned with structure, or the static com-ponents of the organic world. The origins of these structures are often "explained" by abstract models that derive their principal data from "laws" of genetics, "laws" which may be under dispute by the geneticists themselves. The extent of assumption, interactions of as-sumptions, and the degrees of extrapolation give a sense of uneasiness when the animals and their structures are foremost in mind. Essen-tially, the student is faced with the following proposition: Given that certain "laws" of genetics are correct, a particular event or series of events must have taken place to produce a structure, if it be assumed that some particular set of conditions held during the course of pro-duction. Many genetic models, however, as Lerner (1958) has noted, go well beyond the evidence. They may not be trustworthy bases for the proposition. In the most given situations, however, some of the conditions that held during development can be deduced, even in paleontological studies, and there is good evidence that many of the genetic "laws" hold, at least over a small part of the organic world. But, in most cases, detailed steps of development and details of the environ-ment in which they took place are largely unknown. Thus, in ex-planation, it is usually true that we end up with several possible courses to the same end and that it is virtually impossible to choose between the several intelligently. In this sense, there is little or nothing that cannot be explained under the selection theory, and, at present, this theory appears to be unique in this respect.

The majority of evolutionists today appear to feel that the knowl-edge and "laws" of genetics, in a very broad sense, and the body of biological information now at hand provide a sufficient basis for understanding all major facets of organic evolution. Refutation or modification can be made only by demonstration of the falseness or inadequacy of genetic principles or by experimental observation of some type of evolutionary change not explicable under genetic-selection theory. Selection does occur; in fact, as generally defined, it is inevitable, granted that genetics plays a role in inheritance. It is only possible to question its importance to the whole evolutionary scheme. It is not sufficient to show that something could have happened otherwise, but rather that it could not have happened under the formulation that is the synthetic theory. This is indeed difficult, and, for all the suspicions that some paleontologists and morphologists may have about the adequacy of the theory, there is very little that they can do to confirm these feelings on the basis of the types of analysis that their materials allow. This may be further generalized, to the effect that there is no known way of attacking experimentally some of the areas in which doubts of the sufficiency of the synthetic theory arise—areas, for example, not subject to analysis because of the time factor.

This situation poses a frustrating dilemma for the sincere student who feels from his observations that there is more to evolution than can be studied, tested, and integrated under the synthetic theory, who is confident that real problems exist but also sees no way of making progress toward an understanding by means of the materials that raise the questions in his mind. Few feel that the genetic-selection theory is invalid, but rather consider that there is much evidence that it is not adequate. The hope of eventual study in this difficult area seems to be arising in some studies of microorganisms and some small problems that arise in genetics of macroorganisms (see, for example, Lerner, 1958). As yet these have produced little that has real meaning with respect to the queries that arise from fossil materials.

Morphology, Paleontology, Inheritance, and Selection

Although it is difficult to find many specific points in the fields of heredity and evolution, beyond the most self-evident mechanisms of biological continuity, upon which there is full agreement, the success of the synthetic theory in unification of highly diverse areas has gained for it remarkably wide acceptance. Such success and agreement, while natural, pose certain dangers—danger that matters pertinent to the area of study may be missed, obscured, or deemed unimportant if they are peripheral to the central construction; danger that actually relevant facts and inferences that cannot be incorporated in the theory will be summarily dismissed as inapplicable; and danger of expenditures of vast amounts of time and energy in much too limited contexts.

It is difficult, as a contemporary, to judge whether or not the current formulation of evolutionary theory has fallen prey to any of these dangers as yet, but it is surely not impossible that this has been happening or will happen. The general history of major formulations of the past argue for caution in making evaluations.

Current theory basically involves two concepts—Mendelian inheritance and selection. Each was born a rather simple, straightforward principle, and each has undergone enormous ramification and modification without, however, loss of the basic idea. Selection has changed considerably in its meaning from the original Darwinian sense, and this change has been a source of misunderstanding about the role of selection in evolution. The two concepts have been woven into a truly remarkable fabric and have produced an extremely versatile and flexible structure, which is subject to almost limitless variation and manipulation.

The immense development of Mendelian genetics, the concept of Mendelian populations (Dobzhansky, 1950), and ramifications by means of biometrical and mathematical genetics through successive levels of complexity and highly varied objectives make a fascinating story, recently summarized by Lerner (1958, chap. i). Organic evolution as currently conceived cannot be fully understood without knowledge of such genetics, from the fundamental concept of unit transmission of heritable characters to the sophisticated doctrines of modern theory in which the basic unit concept has become masked. Sometime in the future a different basis for understanding of the natural and experimental observations of population changes with time may be developed, but for the present, at least, none that is generally applicable seems evident.

Only a small and strongly biased sample of the total organic world has been studied with respect to the operation of the processes of inheritance, and the part of all life that can ever be available is infinitesimally small. Extrapolation, however, is a necessary and accepted method in all science and of great value under judicious use. In extrapolations there are two levels of danger. One involves extrapolation to unstudied circumstances in which the materials or processes appear to be more or less commensurate with those from which extension is made. Additional supplemental, or even dominant, factors that might be operating in the case to which extrapolation is made may be insufficiently emphasized or missed completely. Some recent studies point to the dangers of extrapolation from a few well-studied types of organisms, both macro- and microorganisms, to other, reasonably similar, groups. Some recent studies on microorganisms suggest possible patterns of inheritance that do not fit the usual Mendelian model (Benzer, 1955, Fraenkel-Conrat, 1959, Lederberg, 1957). The work reported by Ephrussi (1953) is an interesting development of possibly challenging circumstances that might be missed in lieu of direct study, as he notes in his Introduction:

I have tried to show that the model of Mendelian analysis applied to classical materials of genetics, while it achieved amazing progress contained in the theory of the gene, and thus supplied a basis for understanding of at least one aspect of evolution, has at the same time confined our attention to the nuclear genes and thus driven us into an impasse with respect to understanding of development.

The whole area of cytoplasmic inheritance is, of course, one which is generally recognized but which is not considered basically important in the formulation of the majority of models in present evolutionary theory, existing, at most, under some concept of generalized non-random effect. Its relative significance in studies basic to the models has probably been properly assessed, but this is not the point. Extrapolation of these models into unstudied areas may overlook this, or some other factor, that is critical and yet not evident in results of non-experimental observations. There is certain to exist, along with acceptance of a broad generalization, a strong tendency to consider new observations under the existing pattern rather than to weigh the evidence with respect to how it might bear upon the generalization itself. Cytoplasmic inheritance has been used merely as a possible example of the difficulties that may arise, since it is a known phenomenon of at least some significance. As other items are emerging from studies of inheritance, factors of which we now have no knowledge will probably become discernible. They must be viewed objectively, not from a too limited perspective, or their significance may be lost even if their existence is noted.

A second level of possible difficulty in extrapolation lies in the extension of observations to levels that are incommensurate, in the case of evolution theory, to levels beyond those to which we can apply direct observation. This is common practice at the present time. We are unable to make observations through lengths of time that even remotely approach those apparently necessary to accomplish the sorts of changes seen in the fossil record. Modern theory projects its generalizations from observations of very small changes over short periods of time, both in kind and in quantity, to account for all evolutionary change. Thereby it is possible to point to Mendelian inheritance and derived concepts of inheritance, as basic to all evolutionary change.

Now this may be correct, but it is done today with such confidence, even where great elasticity is necessary, that it seems very important to note once again that this may not be at all correct, that there may exist factors of which we have no knowledge and which we most certainly never will recognize unless the possibility of their existence remains an important part of our thinking.

Selection in evolution—here natural selection—is the other basic aspect of the synthetic theory, the aspect that complements Mendelian inheritance in the process of change. Elaboration has affected the concept of selection no less than that of Mendelian inheritance, but, in addition, selection is subject to a second difficulty that adds considerably to the confusion concerning it. Selection has had very different meanings to different evolutionists, and to some extent these different meanings are specific to particular areas of biology. Even within a single discipline—genetics, for example—there is a spectrum of meaning attached to the term. In clarification of this problem, especially the confusion between artificial and natural selection, Lerner (1958, pp. 5–15) has devoted some 10 pages to the consideration of types of selection and the consequences of evolution in terms of them as developed upon Mendelian inheritance patterns. Lerner defines selection as follows: "Selection can be defined in terms of its observable consequences as the *non-random differential reproduction of genotypes.*" Later (p. 15) he states: "Natural selection is a term serving to say that some genotypes leave more offspring than others. It can be deduced to have existed and its intensity can be measured only *ex post facto.*" Within the five levels of complexity considered by Wright (1959) there is an extremely interesting series of modifications of the role and meaning of selection as conditioned by the theory and constitution of the particular model under which selection is envisaged. In an earlier statement Wright (1955) presents a more general view of selection as "a wastebasket category that includes all causes of directed change in gene frequencies that do not involve mutation or introduction from without." Simpson (1953) defines natural selection as "differential reproduction." Mayr's "delimitation" of *organic evolution* is essentially equivalent to the definition of *natural selection* of Simpson and Lerner. A large vocabulary has evolved to express the various aspects of selection: natural selection and artificial selection, phenotypic selection (Haldane, 1954), disruptive selection (Mather, 1955), canalizing selection (Waddington, 1942), stabilizing selection (Schmalhausen, 1949), and so forth at considerable length.

All the terms and concepts noted to this point have come in large part from genetics, with paleontological contributions largely those of Simpson, and those of Waddington and Schmalhausen coming in part from developmental biology. Many morphologists and paleontologists use the term "natural selection" freely but generally in a way that is somewhat at odds with the various meanings cited above. Superficially, differences may appear to be slight, but basically they are important. First, the attention of the morphologist tends to be centered upon form and involves to some extent a typological aspect—typological in that there is some rather concrete, visual image involved. Students with this point of view are not quite the unreconstructed villains of the field of evolution as those described by Mayr (1959). But there is the strong tendency to think in terms of morphology as characteristic of an animal, that there is a *form* representative of a species and *metric characters* characteristic of a genus. What often may appear to be a purely typological view is not, in fact, based on a disregard or ignorance of population concepts and variability but upon initial concern with stages in evolution *represented* by some genus or species, or even a representative of some higher category. Beyond this, and a shorthand method of speaking appropriate to phylogeny, paleontologists and morphologists do, I believe, tend to view selection in a way that differs importantly from the view implicit in the various definitions cited above. There is a strong tendency to include within the concept of selection the sense of adaptation, or, more generally, cause is a usual companion of thoughts on selection. There is, at the phenotypic level, something of an approach to Wright's concept of the "wastebasket of causes," with, however, particular concern for those aspects directly related to corporeal survivorship. The relationship of genotypic and phenotypic selection seems to be commonly considered as a very direct one (see, for example, Kurtén, 1955). Adaptation is sensed as a basic aspect of evolution, not thought of so much as "after the fact" but as something positive and directive. Thus, when he reads that evolution is "change of genetic properties from generation to generation owing to differential reproduction" (Mayr, 1959), he is somewhat taken aback; and when he reads further a point we have noted before that "no phenomenon has ever been found in organic nature that cannot be interpreted within the framework of the modern, synthetic theory of evolution" (Mayr, 1959), he may feel a bit indignant or else that what he is doing must be considered outside evolutionary thinking or at least related to it only remotely.

It is undoubtedly in part misunderstanding that has promoted conflicting views and some studies, particularly those of Simpson, have aided in reducing differences. The differences between phenomena observed in various disciplines, however, have a basic importance and should broaden outlooks by providing multiple testing grounds for all ideas. The paleontologist tends to see organisms distributed through vast spans of time, but in small fragments at many stations. He deals with morphology and sees order in its change. He witnesses major trends and catches glimpses of motivations in physical events. He sees what appear to be highly adaptive types of organisms side by side with what appear to be adaptive "monstrosities." He sees groups of organisms, apparently in their prime, fade and disappear through "short" periods. And he may ask: "All this through shift in gene frequencies, in genetic shift through differential reproduction and slow change through successive populations?" Even though he may answer Yes, there still exists for many a feeling of remoteness between the concepts of evolution seen in the elegant genetic constructions of such students as Wright or Fisher and the equally penetrating considerations of morphology and evolution as displayed by paleontologists such as Romer, Watson, or Westoll. The efforts to bridge the gap leave a real feeling of remoteness at the operational level and in many cases a feeling that the explanations of genetics and selection are not significantly applicable to some of the types of phenomena observed in much of the fossil record.

Specific categories of problems are considered in the last section of this paper. In the present section an effort has been made to consider some basic concepts of the current theory of evolution, some of the consequences of the concepts, and the various interpretations and misunderstandings that appear to exist. That differences do exist and are somewhat area-specific may be merely a function of the materials and the result of misunderstanding. The point has been made that the very conciseness, consistency, and tightness of the synthetic theory, combined with almost limitless flexibility due to the nature of the definition of selection, can lead to acceptance of generalizations not applicable over the whole range of evolution. This possible danger is amply revealed in some studies of the last decade which seem more concerned with fitting results into the current theory than with evaluation of results in terms of a broader outlook. Further, of course, much research is conceived and carried out within the framework of the theory, and, no matter what its excellence, it is not likely to break out of this framework. It seems clear that the synthetic theory is applicable to a wide area of evolution, and it may be applicable to most or to all. Its potential should be pushed to the extreme limits, but not to the extent that we are blinded to other possibilities and that contrary suggestions are summarily dismissed sometimes in reluctance to abandon or modify the elegance of the model that has been constructed with such devoted labor.

PALEONTOLOGY AND EVOLUTION

Paleontological studies, by virtue of the perspective of long periods of time, should be the source of some of the most important data and concepts of evolutionary theory. They have provided the indispensable description of history of life and have revealed a vast amount of evidence concerning general phenomena of change that have aided in molding evolutionary thought. Yet, *in toto,* the contributions to the current theory, in my opinion, are much less than those from neontology, particularly from genetics. Perhaps this is inevitable, since the important element of testing by experimentation is not possible with fossil materials. The fossil record, on the other hand, has been a source of data that have been considered by various students as somewhat contrary to the concepts developed in genetics and related fields and this in itself can be an important contribution. This evidence has been "explained" to the satisfaction of many, although not all. Simpson has penetrating analyses and has given serious, mature consideration to many of the problems. Although he has drawn most of his examples from fossil mammals, he has by no means neglected other groups. Various other paleontologists—Patterson (1949), Westoll (1944, 1949), and Schaeffer (1952) to cite a few—have treated fossil materials extensively within the general framework of the synthetic theory. All such studies have shown that the concepts of genetics and selection can be applied advantageously to a wide range of phenomena displayed in the fossil record. They start with acceptance of the general concepts and, proceeding from this base, make interesting applications and extensions. They have not revealed inconsistencies, but there is, of course, some question as to whether this is a likely outcome in view of the methodology.

Such critical studies are important and valid. The question that must be raised, however, is whether, in view of the breadth of interpretation, the interpolations, and the extrapolations, there really remains an impelling consistency, sufficient to invoke the principle of parsimony in favor of the application of a single hypothesis. Perhaps there is. Even these carefully conceived studies, however, to a degree fail to come to grips with some of the more complex and challenging questions of paleontology. Also it seems that there is a strong tendency to operate from a somewhat too limited model in terms of the actual variety of structures indicated by the life of today (see point 5 below). A general theory must relate the vast diversities of both modern and past patterns of life and change. It must be satisfactory at the very lowest and smallest levels observed under natural and laboratory conditions today and equally effective as applied to the grand scale of patterns revealed in the fossil record. The synthetic theory has proved extremely effective, although perhaps not infallible, at the low level but may leave much to be desired at grosser levels. Some questions of its efficacy in modern circumstances have been treated briefly by Lerner (1959, pp. 264–73). Problems that seem to be posed by the fossil record, in part and in kind, may be summarized under the following categories:

1. Problems posed by what may be called "adaptive monstrosities" in the fossil record. Under this category may be grouped organisms representing populations that appear to have carried their evolutionary development to lengths or in directions that are difficult to conceive as the result of adaptation working by means of selection. This category, of course, is highly subjective and open to criticism. Yet it is difficult to see how anyone who has pondered over the exhibits of fossils displayed in some of the great museums of the world can have failed to ask himself the questions that it poses. Among such types can be noted the massive glyptodonts, extremely heavily boned pareiasaurs, armoured dinosaurs and some therapsids with bony skull roofs several inches thick, giant pterodactyls, haphazardly coiled ammonites, giant sauropod dinosaurs, and stegosaurian dinosaurs. In these museums also are housed such apparently remarkably well adapted forms as ichthyosaurs and seals, fast-running coelosaurs and running birds, and many other animals whose structural design attests to a remarkable suitability of form to environment, which we assume to be the result of adaptive evolution.

2. Parallelism in major structures, and particularly in suites of major structures, in evolving lines of populations related only at rather high categorical levels and with remote common ancestors in which the common structures did not exist. Well known cases are found (1) in amphibians, between the major groups apsidospondyls and lepospondyls and within the many groups of apsidospondyls; (2) immense parallelism in the development of multiple similarities in evolution of the holosteans from the paleoniscoid ancestor; (3) development of suites of mammalian characters in different lines of therapsid reptiles; (4) development of parallel structural features in different lines of ammonites. This seems to be a very prevalent pattern of evolution. It can be explained under selective theory in some cases (for example, Olson, 1959), but it does not seem that its prevalence is something that would be anticipated under the theory in terms of the usual models that are basic to it.

3. Extinctions of many types, but in particular those that involve the more or less concurrent demise of many different groups of organisms whose life-habits were very different and whose habitats ranged

over a wide series of major environmental types. The best-known example is the Late Cretaceous case in which some of the prominent types that died out are large terrestrial dinosaurs (ceratopsians, carnosaurs); semiaquatic dinosaurs (sauropods, hadrosaurs); small, swift, terrestrial bipedal dinosaurs, ichthyosaurs, plesiosaurs, mosausaurs (marine reptiles of varied habits and habitats), and ammonite cephalopods, among prominent invertebrates. There are many others, but these are enough to indicate the scope. Persistent floras pass through this time of change with only slight modifications, and various animals on land, in the sea, and in the air showed no major changes. Sedimentation, in places, continued without a break across the Cretaceous-Tertiary boundary. There is thus no evidence of major physical changes or of any factors totally disruptive to life.

4. Small features that show patterns of origin, persistence, and trends, often directional for some span of time, in spite of the fact that there is no apparent way of relating them to specific adaptations. The best examples are found in the teeth of mammals, perhaps because they are readily seen in these structures. Minor dental features, cusps, lophs, and cinguli in their presence, positions, and interrelationships, tend to be highly characteristic of species. It is difficult to consider that these small features are in themselves adaptive or even that their dispersal in similar fashion along part of the tooth row is adaptive. Various explanations are possible, and several have been proposed. Maybe one or more are correct. Some concrete evidence is needed. The appearance of the "crochet" sporadically in the molars of *Miohippus,* the consistency of this structure in descended species populations, and its eventual incorporation into the tooth pattern as an essential structural item are representative of another type of case. In two developing lines of reptiles—caseids (among synapsids) and pareiasaurs (among anapsids)—a simple tooth crown is supplanted in successive species by a minute tricupsed crown, hard to see with the naked eye in teeth over a centimeter long, and then by a serrated crown with five or more rather well-developed cuspules. Adaptive significance is difficult to understand.

5. This final point deals with modern species populations, partly to point up some of the problems that they themselves pose in terms of current evolution theory and also to emphasize that these various types, as well as others, must be considered when interpretations of fossil populations are made. In addition to "normal" population patterns, large interbreeding populations with continuous distribution, populations separated into smaller partially isolated segments, and small interbreeding populations—the type generally considered in evolutionary models—we may note some other patterns: (*a*) clines

with special examples, such as that of *Ensatina* (Stebbins, 1949), in which there is a series of marginally interbreeding subspecies which, by virtue of their geographic position, includes end members that are sympatric and do not interbreed; (*b*) discontinuous and non-interbreeding segments of species that maintain morphological similarity over considerable periods of time under somewhat diverse conditions. An excellent example is *Priapulus caudatus* (Hyman, 1951), which apparently lives in all colder seas, Arctic and Antarctic, in soft mud to depths of 500 meters. These mud beds are discontinuous. The sexes are separate, and there are no pelagic larvae, for the larvae live in the mud along with the adults. Other cases, in general, of so-called bipolar species are well known (see, for example, Ekman, 1953, pp. 250–63): (*c*) the nereid worm, *Nereis limnicola* (Smith, 1958) presents a very unusual situation, but must be considered. This worm is hermaphroditic, self-fertilizing, and viviparous. It lives in estuaries and fresh water along the Pacific Coast from California to Washington. There are strong morphological similarities between the discontinuous segments of this species over its range and no apparent trends from north to south. The problem of the nature of a species arises, but the question of selection and inheritance is of primary concern to us. These cases merely show the spread of types that must be considered and are not by any means a representative sample of the varieties.

The various situations pointed out from the fossil record are sufficient in themselves to be provocative without comment. Various of them have been explored by paleontologists and biologists, and it has been shown in most instances that explanation is possible under the current hypothesis. Yet it is not difficult for any objectively minded student to see that these cases, and many others like them, are likely to raise questions among the paleontologists who see them in their full array and complexity and then see them "explained," often piece by piece rather than in the full pattern, by the relatively simple means of selection theory. Somehow a theory in which each case seems to be a special case fails to convey a sense of adequacy.

Natural selection operating in terms of the raw materials supplied by genetic processes, which are conceived to be not qualitatively different throughout the organic world, must, if modern theory is accepted, be able to produce much that has been observed. In short, this single, unified system must produce the many types of opposites that exist and that appear to have developed under reasonably similar conditions of physical and biological environment. This is to some, at least, rather staggering to contemplate. Under current theory, the base may be broadened somewhat by bringing in the concept of random drift and calling upon unique "accidents." Further, of course, the selection theory depends upon probabilities in which "superiority" only increases probabilities of success. These items cannot greatly alter the situation for most cases, although Simpson (1944) has placed considerable confidence in the matter of drift in small populations in its relationship to the origin of higher categories.

If we return once again to the problem of what is meant by selection, especially in the meanings that it has to many paleontologists, the source of some of the difficulties becomes apparent. In one sense, as noted, selection is considered only as an after-the-fact description of genotypic differences between successive populations. Other concepts, however, such as Wright's (elsewhere in the present volume), include the idea of "causes of directed change." If some such inclusion as this is not made, then there is a gap in the path of evolutionary significance which must be closed by the use of the idea of pressures upon selection, a slight shift, but technically an important one. The use of terms such as "adaptive peak," "adaptive values," "selection advantage," all point out ways that this aspect is introduced. The principal basis of Wright's evolutionary concept, for example, rests on the idea of the balance in populations as dependent upon various disturbing factors or opposing forces, selective forces and mutations. The concept of "adaptive peak" is very important, expressing essentially the resultant of various forces. Thus, when the idea of selection is being questioned in terms of effects, it is essential that it be understood in what context it is being questioned. Is it with respect to changes in genotypic frequencies, in terms of the effects of frequencies, or in relationship to causes of directed changes of the genotype structure? Is concern with a few specified loci, or is the total structure of the genotype involved? Or, from a rather different point of view, is selective advantage in terms of phenotypic expression of the genotype involved, and is it the total phenotype or only some limited aspect of it that is being considered?

In the present discussion we will accept, for the time being, the effectiveness of the concept of the Mendelian inheritance, so that questions can be confined to the matter of selection. We raise the question whether this process, broadly conceived to involve genotypic shifts, the forces that effect shifts, and the resultant phenotypic changes, can be considered effective as the major process in the production of the many results of evolution that have been discovered. This breadth is necessary to bring the concept to operational level for the paleontologist. But when the concept of selective advantage is brought, through this expansion, to essential equivalency with adaptive advantage, which seems to be the usual course of events, we run into the heart of problems that appear troublesome. Unless some meaning other than the usual one is given to the word "adaptive," such as reduction to the same level as the descriptive usage of "selective," adaptive advantage must in some sense refer to an improvement in terms of realized reproductive capacity. As the paleontologist or morphologist tends to think of adaptation, it is the expression of perfection of adjustment to environment. This is the mechanism that is thought of as providing for reproductive superiority in successive generations. This is the point of view under which the types of cases listed under points 1–5 above cause problems.

If an equation of selective advantage and adaptive advantage is made and selection is considered only as the observed consequences of non-random differential reproduction of genotypes—that is, as purely descriptive—then, of course, much that has occurred must be considered as adaptive, with random drift and unique events covering the rest. But this use seems to have little but a descriptive meaning. As soon as it is required that cause of changes in frequencies be explained and the idea of adaptation enters in a causal sense, things are less clear and problems in interpretation of observed events arise. The variety of phenomena and the opposing features of many of them appear to require manipulations of the available mechanisms to degrees that seem almost incredible.

Perhaps this is illusion and there are, in fact, no problems. Possibly this is the case, but it seems no more subject to demonstration than does the contrary proposition. If problems do exist, it is difficult to devise methods of approaching solutions. We are then in the position of believing, without definitive proof, that factors beyond those recognized at present are of major importance in some areas of evolution, but of not knowing just what they are or how they may be discovered. This is an unfortunate, negative situation.

There are, however, possible avenues of eventual attack. One area of approach involves research along fairly orthodox lines, research that might in effect strongly modify current concepts but would not be so radical that there would be no area of contact. A gradual shift of positions might be expected. Some studies noted earlier in this paper are now going on and may progress in this direction. With reference to studies of mechanisms of inheritance, new ideas are coming from studies of microorganisms. Some new discoveries may require reexamination of the ideas current today. It seems quite clear that the basically simple Mendelian inheritance system, even with its many modifications, is far from adequate for a full and final formulation. It is not quite clear as yet, I believe, from what direction a basis for significant modification may come.

Within the area of conservative approach, there may be new, or highly modified, ways of looking at the forces acting upon populations and the bases for shift in genotypic structures. Here, as in other areas, the whole matter of interrelationships or co-adaptation needs more consideration. It might be interesting, for example, to study the varying roles of directed, random, and so-called unique processes as they apply and are different, not only with respect to population size and structure, but also in terms of many factors critical to the survivorship of members at their various stages of development in different types of populations. Under some circumstances, it is quite possible that all viable members of a population are affected in their path to maturity and reproduction almost entirely by processes that are entirely random with respect to differences in genotypic structure within the population. Selection in the sense of adaptation would be operative only to the minimal level of survival. More generally, investigation of all aspects of integration from the genetic level to within and between populations, from both theoretical and experimental points of view, might do much to broaden the outlook and perhaps open the way for the understanding of things which are obscure at present.

Radical lines of investigation may open up new possibilities of approaching some of the problems that now seem untouchable, such as the problems of major steps in evolution. Just what directions these might take is uncertain, but it will require persons able to think in radical terms, outside the current framework, to undertake the early steps. If the doors to unorthodox thinking are left open and a place for the "sport" is held in the society of biologists, undoubtedly persons with at least the will to try will appear.

The paleontologist, as such, probably cannot occupy such a role, but if he has insight into his materials and knowledge of related fields, he can serve an important role by raising queries and doubts and by suggested alternatives that are less likely to come to the minds of persons intimately involved with studies close to the vital structures of current theory. It is in this spirit that this essay has been written and, I trust, will be received.

REFERENCES

BECKNER, M. 1959. *The Biological Way of Thought*. New York: Columbia University Press.

BENZER, S. 1955. "Fine Structure of a Genetic Region in Bacteriophage," *Proc. Nat. Acad. Sci.*, XLI, 344–54.

BERTALANFFY, L. VON. 1952. *Problems of Life*. New York: John Wiley & Sons.

BOYDEN, A. A. 1953. "Comparative Evolution with Special Reference to Primitive Mechanisms," *Evolution*, VII, 21–30.

COLE, F. J. 1944. *A History of Comparative Anatomy from Aristotle to the Eighteenth Century*. London: Macmillan & Co., Ltd.

DOBZHANSKY, T. 1950. "Mendelian Populations and Their Evolutions," *Amer. Naturalist*, LXXXIV, 401–8.

DOUGHERTY, E. C. 1955. "Comparative Evolution and the Origin of Sexuality," *Systematic Zool.*, IV, 145–69.

EFREMOV, I. A. 1950. "Taphonomy and the Geologic Record," Tr. Paleont. Inst. Acad. Sci. U.S.S.R., Vol. XXIV (in Russian).

EKMAN, S. 1953. *Zoogeography of the Sea*. London: Sidgwick & Jackson.

EPHRUSSI, B. 1953. *Nucleo-cytoplasmic Relations in Micro-Organisms*. Oxford: Clarendon Press.

FRAENKEL-CONRAT, H. 1959. "The Infective RNA of Tobacco Mosaic Virus," *Proc. 10th Internat. Cong. Genetics* (in press).

GOLDSCHMIDT, R. 1940. *The Material Basis of Evolution*. New Haven: Yale University Press.

HALDANE, J. B. S. 1954. *"The Origins of Life," New Biol.*, XVI 12–27.

HYMAN, L. H. 1951. *The Invertebrates*, III, 183–97. New York: McGraw-Hill Book Co., Inc.

KEMPTHORNE, O. 1957. *An Introduction to Genetic Statistics*. New York: John Wiley & Sons.

KURTÉN, B. 1955. "Contribution to the History of a Mutation during 1,000,000 Years," *Evolution*, IX, 107–18.

LEDERBERG, J. 1957. "Viruses, Genes, and Cells," *Bacteriol. Rev.*, XXI, 133–39.

LERNER, I. M. 1958. *The Genetic Basis of Selection*. New York: John Wiley & Sons.

MATHER, K. 1955. "Polymorphism as an Outcome of Disruptive Selection," *Evolution*, IX, 52–61.

MAYR, E. 1959. "Darwin and Evolutionary Thought." In *Evolution and Anthropology: A Centennial Appraisal*, pp. 1–10. Brooklyn: Theo. Gaus' Sons.

OLSON, E. C. 1959. "The Evolution of Mammalian Characters," *Evolution*, XIII, 344–53.

PATTERSON, B. 1949. "Rates of Evolution in Taeniodonts." In *Genetics, Paleontology and Evolution*, pp. 243–78. Princeton: Princeton University Press.

SCHAEFFER, B. 1952. "Rates of Evolution in the Coelacanth and Dipnoan Fishes," *Evolution*, VI, 101–11.

SCHINDEWOLF, O. H. 1955. "Evolution im Lichte der Paläontologie," *Compt. rend.* Cong. Géol. Internat. dix-neuvième Sess., XIX, 93–107.

SCHMALHAUSEN, I. 1949. *Factors of Evolution: The Theory of Stabilizing Selection*. New York: McGraw-Hill Book Co., Inc.

SIMPSON, G. G. 1944. *Tempo and Mode in Evolution*. New York: Columbia University Press.

————. 1953. *Major Features of Evolution.* New York: Columbia University Press.

————. 1959. "Anatomy and Morphology: Classification and Evolution, 1859 and 1959," *Proc. Amer. Phil. Soc.,* CIII, 287–306.

SMITH, R. I. 1958. "On Reproductive Pattern as a Specific Characteristic among Nereid Polychaetes," *Systematic Zool.,* VII, 60–73.

STEBBINS, G. L. 1950. *Variation and Evolution in Plants.* New York: Columbia University Press.

————. 1959. "The Comparative Evolution of Genetic Systems," in *Evolution after Darwin.* Vol. I *The Evolution of Life,* ed. SOL TAX. Chicago: University of Chicago Press.

STEBBINS, R. C. 1949. "Speciation in Salamanders of the Plethodontid Genus *Ensatina,*" *Pub. Zool., Univ. California,* XLVIII, 377–526.

WADDINGTON, C. H. 1942. "Canalization of Development and the Inheritance of Acquired Characters," *Nature,* CL, 563–65.

WESTOLL, T. S. 1944. "The Haplolepidae, a New Family of Late Carboniferous Fishes: A Study in Taxonomy and Evolution," *Bull. Amer. Mus. Nat. Hist.,* LXXXIII, 1–122.

————. 1949. "On the Evolution of the Dipnoi." In *Genetics, Paleontology, and Evolution,* pp. 121–84. Princeton: Princeton University Press.

WHITE, M. S. D. 1954. *Animal Cytology and Evolution.* Cambridge: Cambridge University Press.

WRIGHT, S. 1955. *Cold Spring Harbor Symp. Quant. Biol.,* XX, 16–24.

————. 1959. *Physiological Genetics, Ecology of Populations, and Natural Selection.* Paper 737, Dept. Genetics. Madison: University of Wisconsin. Also in *Perspectives in Biology and Medicine,* III, 107–51. Reprinted in the present volume.

MARSTON BATES

ECOLOGY AND EVOLUTION

Ecology is conventionally defined as the study of the environmental relations of organisms. It is considered by many (including me) to be a rather new word for an old subject—natural history. Others consider it a relatively new subject and explain its deficiencies as compared, say, with physiology, in terms of this newness. Points of view, vocabulary, and emphasis may certainly differ between people who call themselves "ecologists" and those who call themselves "naturalists"—though I am not sure that the ecologists have gained in the difference.

The study of the environmental relations of organisms and of their evolution would seem to be intimately and inextricably related. It is curious, then, to survey a collection of books labeled "evolution" and another labeled "ecology" and find very little connection between the two subjects, as formally presented. Students of evolution, certainly, are always preoccupied with the nature of the environment, with its changes, and with environmental adaptations. Yet they do tend to devote a great deal more attention to mechanisms within the organism, to the whole complex study that has come to be called "genetics," than they do to external, ecological considerations. Sometimes I suspect that this is from a lingering fear of falling into what might be called the "Lamarckian heresy" (though I hate to see Lamarck's name used as a dirty word). After all, natural selection—a strictly ecological process —began to regain respectability only with the publication of R. A. Fisher's book in 1930; and a sort of heretical aura lingers about the whole idea of "environment." I have just finished reading a new book which, after pious general statements that every organism is the consequence of hereditary potentials finding expression in particular environmental contexts, goes on to damn a wide variety of studies because they are "environmentalist."

MARSTON BATES is Professor of Zoology at the University of Michigan. In addition to his own extensive entomological research, he is well known for expediting research through his work with granting organizations. He has also been prominent in the cause for better scientific writing and has himself written countless papers and articles.

I am greatly oversimplifying, of course. But I find support in a remark of Charles Elton that "the discoveries of Darwin, himself a magnificent field naturalist, had the remarkable effect of sending the whole zoological world flocking indoors, where they remained hard at work for fifty years or more, and whence they are now beginning to put forth cautious heads again into the open air." The prestigious element in the biological world is much more interested in field problems in 1959 than it was in 1927, when Elton wrote. But microscopes remain more respectable than field glasses as biological instruments, and Lamarck remains some kind of horrible example of wrong thinking in the introductory textbooks. It is curious that De Vries and the others who thought they had banished the environment in the early years of this century get much more respectful treatment.

But the relative neglect of ecological study by evolutionists is much less striking and much more easily understood than the neglect of evolutionary study by ecologists. The ecologists, I suppose, have been very busy with the enormous task of analyzing things-as-they-are, so that they have little time or energy left to worry about how they got that way. The increasing recognition of paleoecology as a specific subject matter may help to change this.

However, I cannot really generalize about ecologists. That extremely useful book by Allee and his colleagues, *Principles of Animal Ecology,* includes a long final section on "Ecology and Evolution" which surveys the interrelations of the two subject matters very well. There seems, then, no point in trying to make another balanced survey here—even if I could. Perhaps most usefully, I can try to look at some general ecological ideas in evolutionary terms. I run the risk of merely restating the obvious; but sometimes, in restating the obvious, one gets slightly differing insights or hints of new relationships.

Ecology is organism and environment. It seems logical, then, to look first at organism, at the units of life used in ecological study, and then at environment and some of the different sorts of concepts of environment. Much of ecology, however, is concerned with the various kinds of relationships among organisms, with the study of community structure; and I should like to try to look at this from the evolutionary point of view.

Ecological Units

Organisms, from the point of view of ecological study, are dealt with in terms of three kinds of units: individuals, populations, and communities. These form a hierarchy, in that populations are made up of individuals, and communities made up of populations. Yet each kind of unit has its own special difficulties and conveniences; and the study of each requires rather special points of view and methods, turning on special objectives. In fact, the study of the ecology of individual organisms is sometimes separated off as "autecology" and that of communities as "synecology," leaving a not closely related intermediate field of "population ecology."

The concept of the individual organism extends through all of biology, and one can argue about whether individuals or cells are the most "basic," the most "objective," of biological categories. I would argue for the individual rather than the cell, not only because of the existence of acellular organisms, but also because it seems to me that a fundamental division in biological thinking exists between people who are primarily interested in events inside the organism and those interested in events outside. This is the division that Haeckel had in mind when he proposed the word "ecology" for the study of "outer-physiology," restricting physiology itself to the study of systems inside the individual.

The concept of the individual may be relatively objective, but it still carries all sorts of difficulties. There is occasionally the somewhat trivial difficulty of distinguishing between an individual and the colony or clone—sometimes decided rather arbitrarily, as when *Volvox* is called a "colony." There is the more interesting difficulty of separating individuals in time, of deciding when a new individual starts and when it stops, since we are dealing with a continuum—a difficulty that has different aspects with different kinds of reproductive mechanisms. And then one can question the usefulness of the idea of the individual—or of the cell, either—in relation to entities like virus particles.

The attempt to separate ecology and physiology, to separate what I like to call "skin-out biology" from "skin-in biology," creates serious difficulties—but so does any attempt to categorize approaches to knowledge. We have to remember that events inside the individual and outside form connected systems and that our separation is purely a matter of convenience. The study of digestion requires rather different methods from the study of food-getting behavior: and thus it is at times profitable to pursue them separately. But at other times we have to relate external and internal events, and we need to be careful that our system of organizing knowledge does not interfere with this.

The basic unit of life in ecology, then, is the individual organism. But individuals never occur in isolation in nature, and they can be kept in isolation in the laboratory only temporarily and with difficulty. Much of ecology consists of the study of the multitudinous relations that occur among individuals. These relationships fall into two broad classes: those among individuals of the same kind, or, in other words, within populations, and those among individuals of different kinds, or community relationships.

"Population" has become one of the most commonly used words in contemporary biology, and the history—the evolution—of this usage would make an interesting inquiry. It is an old word, of course, stemming from *populus* and meaning the peopling of an area or the number of people living there. The extension of the word to organisms other than man, then, is a metaphor—though one that has been dead for quite a long time. In Malthus, population seems always to mean numbers of people; and, while I have not made a special check, I do not recall that Darwin ever used the word "population" in its present general sense; he used the concept often enough, but usually under some such word as "numbers" or "inhabitants." Wallace, on the other hand, explicitly referred to *animal populations* in his 1858 essay. The shift from specific to general meaning in "population" has interesting parallels with the shift in "statistics" from its first usage in tabulating the affairs of state.

In one sense the point is trivial, but it might be thought about by the purists who object to the discussion of the epidemiology of hoof and mouth disease or potato blight and want to use words like "epizoology" and "epiphytology." There is, of course, a difference in the communication effect in the series from dead to dying to live metaphors; but I doubt whether purists are sensitive to such things.

In another way the point is important. The explicit labeling, recognition, and wide usage of the population concept has been one of the great gains of twentieth-century biology. Species as population, for instance, is the basis of contemporary taxonomy; and the idea of population permeates all recent discussions of evolution. I have the impression that the explicit recognition that a species name is always a label for a population of organisms first became firmly established around 1900 by people working on such diverse groups as birds, mammals, fish, molluscs, and butterflies. The consequences of this were clearly worked out in Karl Jordan's 1905 paper on geographical variation. Robson (1928) has reviewed much of this early work.

Many papers in this series deal with various aspects of population study, and we have all come to recognize that the problem of the origin of species is the problem of the origin of discontinuities in populations, that the evolution of species is the transformation of populations. It seems to me, however, that our studies at the next level, that of communities, have lagged, probably for the simple reason that they are immensely more difficult and complicated.

We are dealing with a series of increasingly abstract concepts. The individual idea is fairly concrete—examples of the individual can be seen, handled, preserved. Natural populations can only be inferred, though their characteristics can sometimes be studied quite precisely through appropriate sampling methods. Model populations can be set up in the laboratory and a great deal learned from their behavior. Populations can normally be defined without great difficulty. At the community level we have difficulty even in definition, both in defining the general concept and in defining particular communities. Yet natural communities are "real" enough; a particular population lives, not in isolation, but in a network of relationships with other populations. The biosphere is not a random aggregation of individuals and populations but a series of distinct and differing patterns—forests, lakes, seas, grasslands, deserts—a series of differing communities.

The community, in theory, is the smallest self-sustaining unit within the biosphere—a grouping of organisms in which energy transfer can be described primarily in terms of relations within the grouping. I visualize this most easily by thinking about a pond in a forest; if life in the pond can be described and understood with only occasional or casual reference to the surrounding forest, the pond and the forest are two communities. But in many cases the life of the pond is clearly a part of the life of the forest; the major animal life may be insects with adult stages in the forest, so that the populations present are determined as much by the character of the forest as by the character of the pond; detritus from the forest may be the primary source of organic matter; and so on. Similarly, the inhabitants of a rotting log or of the forest soil could not be considered to form a primary community. The community is the forest because it is only in terms of the plants, animals, and microbes of the forest as a whole that energy transfer and chemical cycles can be described. The migrating birds and big cats that wander in and out of the forest and cross community lines hardly blur this concept.

Some aggregations of organisms, like those of the ocean depths or of caves, are most conveniently treated as communities, even though they do not fit the criterion of independence from outside living influences. Allee *et al.* (1949, p. 437) avoid this difficulty by considering the community to be the smallest unit "that is or can be self-sustaining, or is continuously sustained by inflow of food materials."

Natural communities are rarely sharply bounded: the forest gives way gradually to scrub and grassland; and there is a beach between the forest and the lake or the sea. A forest dominated by oak may shift gradually to one dominated by pine. The communities are thus in a way modal points in the continuous biosphere; the transition zones between these definable modes are called *ecotones* by the ecologists.

On land, communities can be grouped into a series of major zones or landscape types, the *biomes,* corresponding with major climatic zones. The communities of inland waters and of the seas are less easily grouped into major categories, and quite different criteria must be used. Still and running water provide the basic division for inland waters. For the seas, the major grouping is in relation to shores or depth—pelagic, benthic, littoral, and the like. But boundaries are always fuzzy, and the definitions of both communities and groupings of communities tend to be somewhat arbitrary ways of dealing with the total interrelated system of the biosphere.

THE ENVIRONMENT

The idea of environment seems obvious and easy: it covers the surroundings, the setting, of an organism; it is the sum of the forces acting on the organism from the outside, in contrast with the forces that arise from the inside, from the nature of the organism itself. But when we start to work with this contrast between inside and outside, we soon get into difficulties.

The old "nature versus nurture" controversy is an example of one kind of difficulty. We now realize that the organism—the phenotype—is the end product of a particular genotype, a particular set of potentialities, developing in a particular context or environment. We cannot sort traits into two separate pigeonholes, one labeled "hereditary" and the other "environmental." Everything about the organism is a consequence of the interaction of both. The way in which the potentialities are expressed may be more or less rigidly determined, and we can investigate the degree of rigidity—or plasticity—but, in becoming involved with degrees, we have lost our absolutes.

Another kind of difficulty with the organism-environment contrast is illustrated in an extreme form by the human animal. When we investigate the environmental relations of the human species, what do we do about culture? Is culture an attribute of the man or of the environment? If I may oversimplify, it seems to me that, quite generally, psychologists treat culture as a part of the environment. Cultural pressures of one sort or another are universal for human individuals, and the psychologists are interested in the effects of this—in how individuals cope with their culture, how they rebel against it or conform to it, and in the stresses consequent on this adaptation.

The anthropologists, on the other hand, tend to regard culture as an essential attribute of the human animal, the attribute that enables him to adapt to deserts, tropical forests, arctic tundras, seacoasts, and mountains. The biologist, I think, has to take an ambivalent attitude, sometimes regarding culture as a part of the organism, sometimes as a part of the environment. Since human adaptations to climate and to other animals and plants are so largely cultural, the ecologist, like the anthropologist, frequently must regard culture as an attribute of the man. But the physiologist, studying the reactions of the organism to heat stress or its metabolism of nutritional requirements, must, like the psychologist, regard culture as one of the attributes of the environment. But in any case the contrasts, the either-or alternatives, have been lost.

Always, organism and environment are interacting systems, not contrasts. We now realize that the composition of the atmosphere and of the hydrosphere is not only a determinent of the conditions of life but a consequence of the activities of living organisms as well. Soil type governs vegetation—and vegetation determines soil type. Ecologists have attempted to cover these interrelations with the concept of the "ecosystem": the interdependence of living processes and physicochemical processes in any particular community situation.

The environment concept is thus a constant source of trouble, but I know of no way of getting along without it. One must go ahead and use it confidently—but also somewhat warily, keeping alert to the dangers. If we tried to avoid fuzzy and misleading words, I suspect that all verbal discourse would stop. This might make mathematicians and some kinds of logicians happy, but it would be hard on the rest of us.

We can look at the environment of a given individual, of a given population, or of a given community; and in each such case we are dealing with a different kind of concept. If we concentrate on the environment of a given individual, we still find that there are a number of different possible concepts, and I think it is useful to try to distinguish among these.

In the first place, we have environment as setting: the forces and materials among which the individuals live. This idea of the setting corresponds to the idea of the real world that the philosophers worry with. As scientists, we assume the reality of this external world and the possibility of analyzing and studying it. But, as biologists, we are concerned for the most part only with parts of the total reality—quite rightly, if we are to make any progress at all in our analysis. But I think it useful to stop, from time to time, and realize that we are acting selectively. The total environment, the setting, of a bird perched on a tree in a forest, of any organism anywhere, includes many factors that we know about and ignore and probably many others that we do not even know about. We deal, for instance, quite selectively with the spectrum of electromagnetic radiation. If we take a radio into the forest, we can detect noises that are translations of radiation (man-made or otherwise) that are part of the total reality surrounding our bird. But, as far as we know, this part of the electromagnetic spectrum has no effect on the bird or on any other organism (except instrument-making man), so we rightly ignore it in ecological analysis. Our concern is with the parts of this "total reality" that have some effect on the bird. As biologists, we are concerned, not with the total environment, but with the effective environment, or operational environment, of the organism.

The concept of operational environment has been discussed by Mason and Langenheim (1957). The definition of "environment" they arrive at, after a careful logical analysis of the problems presented by the concept, is interesting. They say:

> The environment of any organism is the class composed of the sum of those phenomena that enter a reaction system of the organism or otherwise directly impinge upon it to affect its mode of life at any time throughout its life cycle as ordered by the demands of the ontogeny of the organism or as ordered by any other condition of the organism that alters its environmental demands.

If the *operational environment* is the sum of the phenomena that directly impinge on the organism in some way, at some time, we might call "total reality" the sum of the phenomena that might conceivably impinge on the organism, the *potential environment*. In working with animals, at least, I think it useful to distinguish a third category, the *perceptual environment*. If we distinguish between ecologists and ethologists, between students working on the structure of interorganism relations and those interested in the behavior of organisms (a deplorable but, in fact, common distinction), we might say that the ecologists are concerned primarily with the operational environment, the ethologists with the perceptual environment. The student of evolution must necessarily be concerned with both.

If man had evolved in an environment in which wires carrying high-voltage electric currents were common, he would presumably have developed either sense organs enabling him to perceive electric charge at a distance or an immunity to electric shock. Both lions and pathogenic microbes were part of the environment in which man evolved, and the lion hazard was met by mechanisms of perception, the microbe hazard by mechanisms of resistance.

In some ways this is quibbling, but in other ways I think it is important. Its chief importance, perhaps, is that it helps us meet the constant danger of confusing the human perceptual environment with the operational environment of other organisms. We make much of the sin of anthropomorphism, but the sin of mistaking our perceptual world for total reality seems to me more heinous because it is more subtle, more difficult to recognize and avoid. The history of the study of echo-location in bats from the time of Spallanzini to the present (discussed by Griffin, 1959) illustrates the problem nicely.

Man has been able to extend his perceptual world greatly through the development of instruments—instruments that extend his senses, like microscopes, or that translate unsensed phenomena into terms that can be perceived, like Geiger counters. Our accomplishment with instrumentation is impressive, but mostly I am overwhelmed with the feeling of how ignorant we are, how much we have to learn. The problems are underlined by the simple act of taking a walk with a dog. Man's world is primarily visual; the dog's apparently olfactory. My forest is primarily a thing of color and form; the dog's forest seems to be made of smells. I know about mimicry and protective coloration; but I presume that there is another whole world of signal smells, warning smells, concealing smells, that I can only dimly glimpse. We have made very little progress in extending our chemical senses or in translating chemical phenomena into perceptible terms. Yet, looking at the animal kingdom as a whole, chemical stimuli seem to be at least as important as visual stimuli in governing the interrelations of organisms.

Psychologists have long delighted in showing us the extent to which our perceptual environment is the consequence, not of the nature of "outer reality," but of the nature of our sensory system and of the co-ordinating and interpreting nerve system. This is another example of the fallacy of either-or in the instance of organism and environment. In the case of man the perceptual environment is, in part at least, a creation of the organism. The sense-reality system works well enough under ordinary circumstances—otherwise we would have become extinct long ago—but it is easily broken down in experimental situations. If this applies to man, may it not also apply to other animals? This makes one more hazard in the way of study and interpretation.

The distinction between operational and perceptual environment applies primarily to animals. One can certainly discuss the behavior of plants and can find many different ways in which behavioral problems have been met, but it is pretty far-fetched to extend the idea of perception to plants, even though stimulus-response situations are common enough. But with plants, with microbes, and with some animal groups, the concept of operational environment may be adequate for all analytical purposes.

Problems of perception enter into evolution in many ways. I first started worrying about it in trying to compare the coral-reef environment with the rain-forest environment. Why is the reef such a gaudy place, the forest (even at its surface) relatively monotonous? This boils down, I suppose, to the question of why land plants are (with trivial exceptions) green, while corals, coralline algae, and other sessile reef organisms show a wide range of colors. Green is the color of chlorophyl, a consequence of its chemical structure, which, they tell me, makes it particularly efficient in absorbing energy for the photosynthetic process. The green of the land plants, then, is a chemical effect—or perhaps we could better say a physiological effect. The green of grasshoppers, tree snakes, caterpillars, and the like, on the other hand, is ecological, a consequence of natural selection, an adaptation to the biological environment rather than to the physical environment.

We can in general, it seems to me, distinguish between ecological adaptation and physiological adaptation. The difference, for us, is particularly striking in the visual world, in color, pattern, and form; but there are similar differences in smell, taste, sound, and the like. Visual ecological adaptations have been beautifully reviewed by Cott (1940) in his book on *Adaptive Coloration in Animals*. Mimicry, protective coloration, and the like have, from Darwin's day, played a very important part in the development of evolutionary theory; but there is, I think, still much room for study.

To get back to my forest and reef: I do not understand why land plants are green, while coralline algae come in many colors. Sunlight changes rapidly in passage through water; but it changes uniformly, and, if underwater coloration is a response to light wave length, the coloration ought to show a regular change with depth. Yet all sorts of colors occur at the same depth level—looking, of course, only at conditions near the surface. To what extent, on the reef (or in the forest), are we dealing with physiological phenomena and to what extent with ecological? We rapidly get into questions posed long ago by Henderson in his book on *The Fitness of the Environment* (1913); but I think it would help our understanding of the evolutionary processes to worry about these questions. And it would be helpful in this to distinguish among potential environmental factors, operational factors, and perceptual factors.

We get into all sorts of special difficulties when we try to deal with the environments of populations and communities, because we are compounding abstractions. We can simplify by a shift in vocabulary, regarding the environment of the population as the habitat of the species. In relation to communities, the environmental concept is most useful in dealing with physicochemical factors, with climate (and can we talk about climate with marine communities?) and the physicochemical nature of the substrate. But it is perhaps most useful to try to deal with community-environment relations as inseparable systems, as in the ecological term *ecosystems*.

COMMUNITY STRUCTURE

Much of evolutionary study is necessarily concerned with phenomena at the level of the individual. It is from the study of individuals that we can learn how the genotype finds expression in the phenotype, how characteristics are transmitted from generation to generation, how innovation occurs. Clearly, however, the significant unit in any general look at evolutionary processes is not the transient individual but the continuing population, and population studies have come more and more to dominate evolutionary thought. The study of the evolution at both the individual and the population level necessarily involves many sorts of ecological considerations, and these have been dealt with in various papers of the present symposium.

Work at the third level, on the evolution of communities, has received less attention, partly because of the difficulties and partly because it must depend in large part on prior understanding of individual and population behavior. Interpopulation relations have, to be sure, always preoccupied students of evolution—they are implicit in terms like "natural selection," "competition," "balance of nature." But our progress in understanding these relations—their origin, maintenance, and transformation—seems to me to have been relatively small in these last hundred years. We know a great deal more about individual behavior, about heredity and development, and a great deal more about population dynamics, than Darwin did. But we have not made comparable progress in our analysis of community behavior.

I suspect that we are at the point where a rapid development of both ideas and information is possible and probable. In this development, ecology and evolution will have to blend completely, ecology describing the relations that exist and evolution explaining how they got that way. One of the prime requisites for this sort of work is an appropriate conceptual frame for the organization of information. We need a usable system for the description of the anatomy of communities, and we need a "natural" system for community classification. Ecologists have been working on these problems diligently for quite a while now, and what appears to be a reasonable system is gradually emerging.

A basic issue, I think, is whether to look at the biological community as competitive or co-operative. Everyone is familiar with the post-Darwinian history of this controversy, and there is no point in reviewing it here. It has served chiefly to confuse the issues. The study of individual anatomy fortunately escaped this sort of obfuscation, since no one has worried about whether nerves, muscles, and connective tissue were competing for food, though, if we were intelligent leucocytes in a cosmic corpse, we might well see the internal distribution of food materials as a competitive struggle. I am a little afraid of Alfred Emerson's superorganism analogy, but certainly it is often illuminating.

The biological community is much more diffuse, much more abstract and difficult to define, than the individual organism. But, like the individual, it works as a system for dispersing and transforming energy; and its parts, whatever the mechanism, are normally nicely adapted and adjusted for the perpetuation of the system as a whole. The community, it seems to me, has to be viewed as an ongoing mechanism normally tending toward continuing stability. This does not mean that love and kindness are necessarily the cohesive principle that makes the thing work; co-operation and equilibrium may be achieved through a system of checks and balances, regulatory mechanisms which, in their immediate operation, are antagonistic and competitive. Competition or co-operation is another of those misleading either-ors. Rabbit and fox populations are, in the long run, just as interdependent as the algae and fungi that go to make up lichens. From the point of view of community functioning, I think it is a mistake to call one "antagonistic" and the other "mutualistic." The two pairings certainly represent quite different kinds of population relationships; but both are mutually adaptive, and I wish we could distinguish between them with words that were less loaded.

To get back to the problem of community anatomy: there is quite general agreement among ecologists that we can distinguish three primary components—producers, consumers, and decomposers. One of the interesting consequences of recent speculation about the origin of life is the realization that this need not always have been so, that the first "production" of organic materials may have been through non-living processes, and that life, then, may have started at the consuming level. This merely postpones a little the problem of the origin and evolution of the photosynthetic process.

Whatever the origin of these three categories of organisms, they have been with us for a long time. They do not, however, form a tight system, and the evolutionary pressures on them are somewhat different. A large proportion of the organic material built up by the producers never goes through the consumer part of the system at all; and some of it is not decomposed. It is particularly striking on land to notice the large volume of vegetative material that is not utilized by animals. A similar relation probably holds in the sea, but it is less obvious, especially in the plankton system, since the bulk of phytoplankton is vastly larger than the bulk of zooplankton and much of it never enters the consumer chain. (Precise data are hard to come by, but there is some discussion in the books by Sverdrup, Johnson, and Fleming, 1942, chaps. 18 and 19; and Hardy, 1956.) The organic materials built up by the producers and not utilized by the consumers are mostly decomposed; but here, too, there is an unused, though trivial, residue, accumulating as coal, oil, and other organic deposits.

This means that, for consumers as a group, the Malthusian propositions do not hold—they do not live up to the limit of the food supply; other kinds of limiting factors must be operating. For producers as a group, the limitations may be Malthusian—often the availability of some particular mineral like phosphorus—or the limit may be set by available space or water. The limitations on decomposers as a group may be Malthusian. In a tropical rain forest, for instance, there is no appreciable accumulation of organic materials; but in other situations, such as peat bogs, there may be a considerable accumulation unused by the decomposers.

About the possible evolutionary history of the decomposers, we know very little; they are not the sort of organisms that leave an abundant fossil record. It looks, however, as though they had been conservative, not changing much in basic form or function over a long period of geological time. On the other hand, both the bacteria and the fungi show an amazing diversity of species, with all sorts of very special adaptations, which surely reflect considerable plasticity at the population level.

One gets the impression that the chief producers of marine communities—the phytoplankton—have also been conservative over geological time, at least as far as basic types are concerned. On land we can see more clearly a succession of types, culminating in the flowering plants, which now and for some time past have been the dominant terrestrial producers. Their evolutionary history has been reviewed by Axelrod in a paper in the present symposium.

The consumers, from the point of view of energy and material transfer, are a sort of heavy frosting on the cake; but, like frosting, they present all sorts of attractions and have received a great deal of evolutionary attention. They consume the producers and each other in endlessly diverse ways, making a highly complicated and decorative sort of frosting pattern.

Here we get the concepts of the food chain and the pyramid of numbers. The food-chain idea is very neat, but unfortunately the actual analysis of food relations in a community usually shows all sorts of branchings and short cuts hard to fit into general sequences. Clearest are the first-order consumers, Elton's "key industry animals," the herbivores. These, in the marine environment, primarily make up the zooplankton. On land, as Ramsay (1952, p. 7) has pointed out, if one regards as first-order consumers the animals that are able to deal directly with green plant tissue (excluding eaters of seeds and fruits), they turn out to be curiously limited—including the gastropod molluscs, certain orders of insects, and certain orders of mammals. Only these have acquired the ability to break down the cellulose walls of plant cells, either mechanically or chemically, directly, or through symbiotic relations with microorganisms.

Once the plant material has been converted into animal flesh, other animals can deal with it easily, and we get a profusion of food relationships. There is a great loss of energy with each transfer, however, so that there can never be very many links in the food sequence. Slobodkin (1959) has calculated a peak possible efficiency in a first-order consumer (*Daphnia*) as 12 per cent, with 6 per cent a more likely average. Hutchison (1959), on this basis, has shown that five food "links" are about the maximum possible. The diversity comes not so much from the number of possible direct sequences as from the variety of ways in which sequences can occur.

We really do not have an adequate vocabulary for dealing with the different ways in which animals consume one another, which, I suppose, means that we do not have a logical classification of types of consumer feeding behavior. We ordinarily fall back on the old words "parasitism" and "predation," which work well enough in certain classical situations. "Predation" is a very useful word in discussing vertebrate behavior; and there is no trouble with the idea of parasitism in the context of microbes or helminths in relation to disease. But it takes a Procrustean process to fit the whole range of consumer behavior into *either* parasitism *or* predation. We are dealing with a whole spectrum of ways in which animals live off one another. From the point of view of mortality of the consumed animal, it might be more useful to recognize five modal points:

I. Death immediate and certain. The classical predation of carnivorous vertebrates, spiders, predatory insects, and the like.

II. Death postponed but certain. Here would come the whole range of "parasitoid" behavior in insects, also some infection phenomena, like rabies virus, once it has invaded nerve tissue.

III. Death probable but not inevitable.

IV. Death unusual. These last two doubtfully distinct categories would include most of the pathogenic phenomena shown by microorganisms and helminths. They would also catch a miscellaneous collection of other things, like the feeding behavior of lampreys.

V. Death never a consequence. Vampire bats would probably go here—though it is probably illogical to have a category system that separates lampreys and vampire bats! Here also would come the whole catalogue of arthropod ectoparasites and animals like mosquitoes that we do not ordinarily think of as parasitic. A great many microbial and helminth parasites would also fit here. This category would probably grade into a category of mutual immediate benefit in interindividual relations. Though when one stops to think about the typical cases of mutualism or commensalism—like the flagellates in termite guts—it is interesting how often the reciprocal relationship is not purely over food but involves food versus protection, or support, or dispersal, or something of that sort.

The inadequacy and artificiality of a classification like this is, in itself, interesting. It clearly does not represent any general evolutionary sequence, though various sorts of sequences can be imagined and (sometimes) described. In any system like this, we are looking at interindividual relationships and interindividual adaptations. If the two populations involved achieve a satisfactory fit, allowing for the continuity of both, it does not matter whether individuals are killed, harmed, or unharmed in the relationship.

When we think of parasitism, we are apt to think of the individual parasite-host adaptations and to assume that there must be a sequence from my Type II or III to Type V, a sequence of decreasing pathogenicity or virulence. This almost certainly has sometimes occurred, but I cannot believe that it has any force as a generalization; the development of host resistance is one way of achieving population balance, like the development of alertness or speed or concealment in the prey of predators. But I do not believe that the fact that malarial plasmodia belong to Type V in relation to mosquitoes and to Type IV in relation to man is an indication that plasmodia have a longer evolutionary history in mosquitoes than in man. In the short term open to observation, we can find cases in which the parasite shows a decrease in virulence with continuing association with a given host and cases in which virulence increases; probably both have happened also in long-term evolutionary trends.

In addition to the food relations among individuals and populations in communities, we have a wide variety of other sorts of interdependence. We might classify these as structural, reproductive, and dispersing.

"Structural relations" is perhaps a sort of wastebasket category. It includes at least three different sorts of things: protection from climate, shelter from enemies, and physical support. On land, not only do higher plants provide the productive energy base of the community, but they also provide it with physical structure. Trees in a forest serve a function analogous to that of the density of water in the sea: they allow the community to develop vertical differentiation. Scrub and grass communities show the same thing in a less spectacular fashion. Climbing and epiphytic forms in plants and climbing and perching adaptations in animals are all forms of interpopulation relationships. Bark, rot holes, branches, roots, fallen trunks and leaves, all contribute to the diversified physical structure of the community, all play their roles in community evolution. Plants sometimes act similarly in bottom communities in seas and inland waters; and in coral reefs we find the physical structure made up of a variety of types of organisms.

There is a long catalogue of kinds of organisms that depend on other kinds of organisms for physical support; and support grades into shelter and protection. Here, with protection, would come the whole series of phenomena classed as mimicry and protective coloration, of such importance in evolutionary theory.

Reproductive and dispersing interrelations are closely related categories. Insects and flowering plants provide the major case of reproductive relationships, and flowering plants also depend on animals in a wide variety of ways for the dispersal of seed.

The biological community can thus be looked at as a complex network of interrelations among the component populations. The system is in balance—it works, it persists through time as a system. It is axiomatic in evolutionary theory that a population cannot develop characteristics that are exclusively advantageous for another population; yet the populations of an undisturbed ("climax") community show all sorts of mutually adaptive traits. The study of the origins and development of this system, of its evolution, can well be called *paleoecology*.

Paleoecology: the Evolution of Communities

Paleontology has always in a sense involved ecology, since it is impossible to interpret a fossil without giving some attention to the environment in which it might have occurred. The emphasis in much of paleontology, however, has understandably been on morphology, on structural changes and phylogenies. It may be useful, then, to have a special word like "paleoecology" which forces attention on environmental changes and on population and community relationships in past times.

The term *paleoecology* (or *palecology*) was first proposed by Clements (1916, p. 279). He used it in a very broad sense to cover (in the words of Cain, 1944) "the whole study of the interactions of geosphere, atmosphere and biosphere in the past." One could thus say that paleoecology is primarily concerned with the evolution of eco-systems. The word was little used for many years—it is interesting to note that it does not occur in Carpenter's apparently exhaustive *Ecological Glossary* (1938). In a random check of contemporary ecological textbooks I find that "paleoecology" is either not mentioned or gets only casual treatment—a reflection of the ecological preoccupation with the present. Books on evolution are also apt to omit formal or organized treatment of the subject—one of the exceptions being Simpson (1953), who devotes chapter 5 to "Animal Communities." Botanists have tended to be more concerned with community evolution than have zoologists, perhaps because plant fossils tend more to occur as floral assemblages. The development of pollen analysis, for instance, has given considerable impetus to paleoecological study.

One gets the impression, however, that interest in and knowledge of paleoecology is growing very fast at the present time. This is partly a reflection of the development of new techniques for measuring past conditions, like the $O^{16}:O^{18}$ method of determining past temperature conditions. People have also been stimulated to think about past environmental conditions by the current studies on the origin of life, which underline the extent to which environmental conditions have been modified by living processes. And perhaps we have only recently reached the point in accumulating factual information at which paleoecological study and speculation become profitable. There must be a tremendous amount of pertinent information in the stratigraphic literature that is only slowly becoming easily available to biologists. The thick volume on marine paleoecology edited by H. S. Ladd (1957) is the sort of thing that makes background material available for the development of generalizations. The development of geochemistry (friends tell me that the best recent general review is Mason, 1958) is also closely related to the development of paleoecology. Currently, also, many studies of past climates are being carried out, though I have not noticed a general review since Brooks (1949).

A number of paleontologists have become interested in the specific problem of reconstructing past animal communities (e.g., Shotwell, 1958). We have the nice word "thanatocenosis" to distinguish a graveyard accumulation from a "biocenosis," or living community. The distinction is useful to remind us that we have to take special precautions if we are to reconstruct the living community from the evidence of the graveyard, where materials from diverse associations may be gathered together and where important community elements may not be represented. Newell (1959) has recently given a general discussion of "the nature of the fossil record" written largely from this ecological point of view.

Paleoecology might well be considered to cover "autecological" studies of the habits and environmental relations of particular kinds of organisms, as well as studies of community interest. The possibilities of this sort of study, I think, are most clearly demonstrated by the work on fossil hominids. The literature on this is large and scattered, but Bartholomew and Birdsell (1953) have written a summary from the ecological point of view. Recent detailed studies of the australopithecines of South Africa show nicely the possibilities of this sort of paleoecological work. Raymond Dart (with Dennis Craig, 1959) has recently written a non-technical account of this work. And I greatly admire the study by Clark (1952) of prehistoric Europe, which is largely ecological.

When we think in ecological terms, however, our primary focus is apt not to be on individuals or populations but on communities or ecosystems. The basic structure of the community—producers, decomposers, first- and higher-order consumers—was already established at the time the fossil record begins. Perhaps the development of the structure led to the beginning of the fossil record. Hutchinson (1959) remarks that "it is reasonable to suppose that strong predation among macroscopic metazoa did not begin until the late Precambrian, and that the appearance of powerful predators led to the appearance of fossilizable skeletons." Our first records are of marine forms, but through the Paleozoic we can see the extension of this system to the land and inland waters. The evolutionary history of communities since then has involved not so much the development of new kinds of relationships, or new community types, as the elaboration of niches and roles and the replacement of one kind of organism by another or others in particular roles (Simpson's "relay effect").

The over-all impression one gets on looking back over much of the geological record is of the stability of the system, even though the parts of the system are frequently changed. It is impossible to be sure, because of the nature of the fossil record, but it looks as though the total biomass and the total number of kinds of organisms have remained about the same for a very long time, possibly from the beginning of the Mesozoic and quite probably through the Cenozoic. If there is a major increase in the number of kinds of organisms in the Cenozoic as compared with the Mesozoic, it is because of the tendency toward multitudinous speciation among insects and seed plants. Beetles alone constitute a respectable proportion of the known kinds of organisms living today, and it is unlikely that any other group speciated quite so prolifically in pre-beetle times; but this does not really interfere with the generalization on stability of total biomass and continuity in range of diversity.

A general principle is beginning to emerge from a variety of different sorts of ecological investigation to the effect that the more diverse the composition of a community, in number of types and number of species, the more stable is the community as a whole and also the more stable are the various particular included populations (in terms of periodic or irregular fluctuations in numbers). Elton has discussed this at some length in the concluding chapters of his latest book (1958), and theoretical aspects of the principle have been explored by MacArthur (1955), Slobodkin (1958), and Margalef (1958).

Presumably, there is some "optimum" state of diversity beyond which unfavorable effects begin to appear. The limits, one would suppose, are set by the nature of the food-chain system, which, as Hutchinson has shown, cannot be extended indefinitely, and by availability of space and by limitations in general on niche subdivision. A relatively large variety of kinds of populations means, in sheer terms of utilization of space and energy, a relatively small number of individuals per population and a relatively low density for many populations, and there is a lower limit to the density of any population below which trends toward extinction start.

Our understanding of these relations would be greatly helped by studies of communities of very great diversity, like rain forests and coral reefs; but these are the kinds of communities about which we have least information. This, I think, is a reflection not so much of the difficulties of the study as of the fact that ecologists mostly live in mid-latitudes and in regions where the landscapes have been greatly disturbed by the actions of man.

If there is any basis for the principle that the evolution of communities tends toward an optimal diversity, one wonders why high-latitude communities are relatively undiversified and why, in general, the higher the latitude, the simpler the community structure. I suspect it has something to do with Pleistocene conditions, which, in the perspective of the geological record as a whole, are very peculiar. Living in Michigan, it seems to me clear that I am still living in the Pleistocene, even though at the moment there are no glaciers nearby. The environment of high-latitude communities, then, may be so new that there has not been time for the evolution of diversity. Certainly, the present tundra and the present taiga are new in their present locations. But, on the other hand, one can imagine that the communities as such simply moved back and forth with the shifting glaciations of the

Pleistocene, so that, even though they did not stay in one place, their evolution in time would not be discontinuous. But what were the pre-Pleistocene opportunities for the evolution of tundra and taiga?

One can notice the same process of reduction of diversity as one moves, in terrestrial communities, from the wet tropics toward regions of lower water availability. With the water gradient, there is a lessening not only of the number of kinds of things but also of the total biomass. This is not so clear with the temperature gradient until one approaches tundra conditions. But the answer to lessened diversity may, in both cases, be simply a matter of the frequency with which adaptations to the unfavorable climatic conditions can arise. But the phenomenon remains striking and curious. Why, in the taiga, is a forest community built around one species of tree; in the deciduous forests of mid-latitudes, around a few species of trees; and in the equatorial rain forest, around hundreds of species of trees? And what does this do to the "principle of competitive exclusion"?

Ecologists have devoted a great deal of effort to the study of community succession. The relevance of this to the study of community evolution is somewhat indirect. This emphasis again, it seems to me, is a function not so much of the cosmic significance of the process as of the fact that ecologists tend to live in mid-latitudes greatly disturbed by man. The subject, so vastly important for terrestrial ecologists, seems to be quite trivial in the minds of marine ecologists, who work with less drastically altered environments. Succession, I think, is analogous with wound-healing in an organism, not with evolution. "Natural succession," like the slow metamorphosis of a pond, might be compared with the ontogeny of an organism. A tremendous lot can be learned about physiology through the study of healing and developmental processes and about communities through succession. But I think it is important to keep the studies in proper perspective.

Ecology and evolution are interrelated in all sorts of ways. I have not touched on some of the most important relations. The whole process of natural selection is basically an ecological process—the problems of adaptation in structure and behavior are ecological problems. We can look at the evolution of major phyletic groups as turning on the occupation of new and different niches—I have not mentioned the niche concept directly. Ecological factors are clearly of basic importance in speciation, even when the primary isolation of populations is purely geographic. And we have the whole fascinating and unresolved question of ecological differentiation as a primary isolating mechanism in speciation.

We have learned a great deal in the century since 1859, and we can put together a plausible and in many ways satisfying theory of evolution, which we call the "synthetic theory" because it is a synthesis, among other things, of our knowledge of genetic mechanisms and our knowledge of ecology (natural selection). But I have an uneasy feeling that some important pieces are still missing from the structure of our theory. I do not know what these pieces are; but I think they have something to do with the fit of what we know about ecology with what we know about genetics and evolution. We have achieved a synthesis of sorts—but I think that, in the long run, we shall manage to make a much better one. And this better fit is going to be a consequence, in part at least, of a better understanding of ecology.

BIBLIOGRAPHY

ALLEE, W. C., EMERSON, A. E., PARK, O., PARK, T., and SCHMIDT, K. P. 1949. *Principles of Animal Ecology.* Philadelphia: W. B. Saunders Co.

BARTHOLOMEW, G. A. and BIRDSELL, J. B. 1953. "Ecology and the Protohominids," *Amer. Anthropologist,* LV, 481–98.

BROOKS, C. E. P. 1949. *Climate through the Ages: A Study of Climatic Factors and Their Variations.* New York: McGraw-Hill Book Co.

CAIN, STANLEY A. 1944. *Foundations of Plant Geography.* New York: Harper & Bros.

CARPENTER, J. R. 1938. *An Ecological Glossary.* Norman: University of Oklahoma Press.

CLARK, J. G. D. 1952. *Prehistoric Europe: The Economic Base.* New York: Philosophical Library.

CLEMENTS, F. E. 1916. *Plant Succession: An Analysis of the Development of Vegetation.* ("Publications of the Carnegie Institution of Washington," No. 242.)

COTT, H. B. 1940. *Adaptive Coloration in Animals.* London: Methuen & Co.

DART, RAYMOND, with CRAIG, DENNIS. 1959. *Adventures with the Missing Link.* New York: Harper & Bros.

ELTON, CHARLES. 1927. *Animal Ecology.* New York: Macmillan & Co.

———. 1958. *The Ecology of Invasions by Animals & Plants.* New York: John Wiley & Sons.

FISHER, R. A. 1930. *The Genetical Theory of Natural Selection.* Oxford: Clarendon Press.

GRIFFIN, DONALD R. 1958. *Listening in the Dark: The Acoustic Orientation of Bats and Men.* New Haven: Yale University Press.

HARDY, A. C. 1956. *The Open Sea; Its Natural History: The World of Plankton.* London: Collins.

HENDERSON, L. J. 1913. *The Fitness of the Environment.* New York: Macmillan Co. Reprinted, Boston: Beacon Press, 1958.

HUTCHINSON, G. E. 1959. "Homage to Santa Rosalia or Why Are There So Many Kinds of Animals?" *Amer. Naturalist,* XCIII, 145–59.

JORDAN, KARL. 1905. "Der Gegensatz zwischen geographischer und nicht-geographischer Variation," *Zeitschr. wiss. Zool.,* LXXXIII, 151–210.

LADD, HARRY S. (ed.). 1957. *Treatise on Marine Ecology and Paleo-ecology.* Vol. II: *Paleoecology.* (Geol. Soc. America Mem. 67.)

MACARTHUR, ROBERT. 1955. "Fluctuations of Animal Populations, and a Measure of Community Stability," *Ecology,* XXXVI, 533–36.

MARGALEF, D. R. 1958. "Information Theory in Ecology," *Yearbook of the Society for General Systems Theory,* III, 36–71.

MASON, BRIAN. 1958. *Principles of Geochemistry.* 2d ed. New York: John Wiley & Sons.

MASON, H. L., and LANGENHEIM, J. H. 1957. "Language Analysis and the Concept of Environment," *Ecology,* XXXVIII, 325–40.

NEWELL, NORMAN D. 1959. "The Nature of the Fossil Record," *Proc. Amer. Phil. Soc.,* CIII, 264–85.

RAMSAY, J. A. 1952. *A Physiological Approach to the Lower Animals.* Cambridge: Cambridge University Press.

ROBSON, G. C. 1928. *The Species Problem.* Edinburgh: Oliver & Boyd.

SHOTWELL, J. A. 1958. "Inter-Community Relationships in Hemphillian (Mid-Pliocene) Mammals," *Ecology,* XXXIX, 271–82.

SIMPSON, G. G. 1953. *Life of the Past: An Introduction to Paleontology.* New Haven: Yale University Press.

SLOBODKIN, L. B. 1958. "Formal Properties of Animal Communities," *Yearbook of the Society for General Systems Theory,* III, 73–100.

———. 1959. "Energetics in *Daphnia pulex* Populations," *Ecology,* XL, 232–43.

SVERDRUP, H. U., JOHNSON, M. W., and FLEMING, R. H. 1942. *The Oceans: Their Physics, Chemistry, and General Biology.* New York: Prentice-Hall.

C. LADD PROSSER

COMPARATIVE PHYSIOLOGY
IN RELATION TO EVOLUTIONARY THEORY

To describe the processes which go on today in living organisms is the task of physiology and biochemistry; the question of how organisms came to be as they now are has been of less concern to physiologists and biochemists than to morphologists. This is largely because experimental work can be done on relatively few kinds of animals and plants and not at all on fossils. Further, structural characters normally form the basis for criteria of taxonomy. Physiological characters are more labile than morphological ones and more subject to quantitative variation with environmental change. Most physiological characters have a multiple genetic basis, and many safety factors and alternate pathways for solving a given functional problem usually exist.

However, the measure of adaptedness to a given environment must depend on functional capacity, and it is of great interest to know the relative validity of using functional characters to describe species and the extent to which such characters are genetically or environmentally determined. Natural selection must be analyzed in functional terms whether by physiology or morphology. It is important to understand also the cellular mechanisms by which the same genotype can be made to produce varied phenotypes in different environments. A goal for physiologists is to understand the molecular basis for evolution.

UNIVERSALITY OF CELLULAR PHYSIOLOGY

Evolutionary theory was presented by Darwin and his followers largely in terms of morphological differences between organisms. Phylogenetic trees were constructed and pictures of "missing links" were drawn. Perhaps evolution would have been more quickly accepted if the emphasis had been less on morphological differences and more on functional similarities. The real marvel of living things is that they are

C. LADD PROSSER is Professor of Physiology at the University of Illinois. Among his many writings on the present topic, Professor Prosser is senior author of *Comparative Animal Physiology* (Philadelphia: W. B. Saunders Co., 1950) and editor of *Physiological Adaptation* (1958), published by the American Physiological Society.

basically so similar. Biochemically, far more evolution took place before there were living organisms as we know them than since.

It is estimated that the beginning of the chemical evolution which eventuated in organic evolution coincided with a transition from a reducing to an oxidizing atmosphere at not less than two billion years ago; the earliest fossils of the Cambrian are approximately 510 million years old. There is some evidence for earlier change to a stable oxidizing hydrosphere and of older algal fossils (1.5 billion years). In any case the period between the beginning of chemical evolution and the appearance of organisms that we would recognize as such was probably as long as the period since organisms appeared. Oparin has given a reasonably acceptable theory of the origin of life, and now experimental tests of this theory are in progress (Miller, 1955). For some two billion years, organic compounds were being formed in the seas under the influence of radiation impinging on the earth. Enzymatic reactions were developing, and molecular aggregates were being selected. The whole of life hinges on the properties of carbon compounds, and these must have evolved in great complexity and quantity before organic evolution could begin. Now we find that virtually every living plant, animal, and microorganism uses such common essentials as the following: high-energy phosphate bonds for transferring energy in biological work, stepwise electron transfer in intermediary metabolism, metalloproteins in oxidation, selective permeability to organic molecules and the active transport of ions by cell surfaces, control of protein synthesis by nucleic acids, and many similar functions. L-amino acids are universal in native proteins and D-ribosides in nucleic acids. Nearly as universal are desoxyribonucleo-protein (DNA-protein) as genetic material, potassium as the principal intracellular cation, and the presence of glycolytic-fermentative enzymes, together with or without aerobic oxidative enzymes. Protoplasm uses for key functions certain elements which are not the most abundant elements in the earth's crust. The principal types of organic molecules used in life processes were settled upon during the period of chemical evolution. Relatively few new biochemicals have appeared during organic evolution; rather, old classes of compound have been diverted to new uses, perhaps with minor alteration. Also, as organisms have become more specialized they have often lost the capacity for certain syntheses. It is no wonder that the most important physiological characters had evolved before organic evolution as visualized by Darwin began.

Phylogeny of Physiological Characters

The classification of animals and plants at the higher taxonomic levels aims to reflect phylogenetic relationships. Physiological and biochemical characters have been used to support relations established by anatomical and embryological evidence, but functional characters have not appreciably altered accepted schemes of phyletic relations. Conversely, phylogenetic order has been one source of unification for the diverse facts of comparative physiology. Examples of many of the classical concepts of evolution have been found for a variety of functional characters. For example, the use by unrelated animals of similar means of solving a functional problem—evolutionary convergence— is recognized in many areas of physiology. A number of examples of the phylogeny of physiological characters will be given, without citing the extensive references for each (see Prosser *et al.*, 1950; Baldwin, 1939; Wald, 1952).

OXYGEN TRANSPORT

Only in the most sluggish or smallest animals is sufficient oxygen carried in solution in body fluids. Therefore, many active animals have a metalloprotein which loads and unloads with oxygen up to saturation in proportion to the partial pressure of oxygen in the environment of the pigment molecules. Iron-containing porphyrins, coupled to a protein, are widespread as cytochromes in all aerobic cells. It is a relatively short step to hemoglobins; these pigments, different in protein but similar in heme, have evolved independently many times—in chordates, a few molluscs, some entomostracans, certain annelids, numerous holothurians, a few dipteran insects, even in some nitrogen-fixing bacteria, and elsewhere. In general, the hemoglobins of invertebrates are larger molecules than those of vertebrates. In the same vertebrate individual, embryonic and adult hemoglobins may be different, and within one species (e.g., man or sheep) several hereditary forms of hemoglobin are recognized, some of them controlled by a single gene. In an environment low in oxygen the amount of hemoglobin synthesized may increase but the kind remain unchanged. The sabellid and serpulid annelids use, in addition to hemoglobin, a closely related iron porphyrin protein, chlorocruorin, for oxygen transport. In other animals parallel transport pigments evolved —hemocyanin in molluscs and crustaceans; hemerythrin in sipunculids.

MUSCLE PHOSPHAGENS

A similar example of convergence and parallelism is in the energy-yielding phosphorylated compounds of muscle, the phosphagens. Phosphorylcreatine (PC) is the phosphagen of chordates as well as of ascidians and balanoglossids. Phorphorylarginine (PA) is the corresponding substance in most invertebrates—arthropods, molluscs, flatworms, roundworms, and coelenterates. In the echinoderms, PA is found in muscles of crinoids, asteroids, and holothurians, PC in ophiuroids; while most echinoids have PA, a few species have both PA and PC as adults, PA as larvae. The annelids, however, are diversified: many errant polychaetes have PC, some (e.g., *Nereis diversicolor*) have phosphorylglycocyamine, others (e.g., *Arenicola*), phosphoryltaurocyamine, and the oligochaete *Lumbricus* has phosphoryllombricine. Evidently phosphorylcreatine has evolved several times, and the annelids have experimented with various phosphagens much as they have with chlorocruorin and hemoglobin.

NITROGENOUS WASTES

A character with some phyletic correlation but influenced by the environment more than either of the preceding characters is the form of nitrogenous waste from protein catabolism. Most aquatic animals—protozoans, marine and fresh-water invertebrates, fresh-water and some marine fish—excrete most of their protein nitrogen as ammonia which diffuses freely away in water. A very few aquatic animals, *e.g.*, some parasitic helminths, have the wasteful practice of excreting undegraded amino acids. When water is slightly limited, many vertebrates—amphibians, mammals, some amphibious reptiles—excrete urea as the principal product of protein degradation. Where water is severely restricted, uric acid is the common product, as in terrestrial insects and most land reptiles and birds. Lungfish excrete ammonia when actively swimming, but they store urea when in estivation. Tadpoles excrete ammonia, but when they metamorphose into frogs or toads they shift to mainly urea. Embryos of snakes and birds put out ammonia and some urea before they shift to uric acid as their product —a sort of embryonic retention of a pattern. Terrestrial isopods continue to excrete mainly ammonia like their aquatic ancestors; this is perhaps one reason why they have not been more successful. Snails lack appropriate enzymes for making urea, although some terrestrial ones do excrete quantities of uric acid; aquatic snails excrete ammonia.

No animal excretes all its nitrogen in one single form, yet striking patterns of predominance exist. The form of waste is a somewhat labile character and can change in some animals according to water supply; in others it changes with embryonic development. Convergence on uric acid has occurred several times—insects, snails, reptiles and birds; urea has become the predominant waste in amphibians and mammals, in some turtles and earthworms. Several one-trial inventions have occurred, for example, guanine in spiders.

The products of purine degradation tend to be the same as those of protein breakdown although many exceptions to this rule occur. Animals which excrete ammonia have a long chain of enzymes for degrading purines to ammonia, while those with urea or uric acid excretion have lost some of the enzymatic steps for purines. Most mammals degrade their purines to allantoin (not all the way to urea), but higher primates stop at uric acid. The Dalmatian is unique among dogs in putting out uric acid; it does so not because of loss of the ability to make allantoin but because of its inability to reabsorb uric acid in the kidney. Nitrogen excretion provides many examples of characters which are genetically determined and phyletically correlated, yet sensitive to the environment and labile within limits.

PROTEOLYTIC ENZYMES

A less well-studied example is found in proteolytic enzymes. Trypsins are universal wherever animals digest proteins. Pepsin, with its acid optimum, appears to be confined to the vertebrates. Cathepsins act extracellularly in many invertebrates, intracellularly in vertebrates. There are many cathepsins, some activated by reducing compounds, some with more acid requirement than others. Evidently the alkaline proteases (trypsins) have remained more uniform during animal evolution, while the acid-requiring ones have been altered many times.

CHEMICAL MEDIATORS OF NERVE ACTION

Still less understood is the systematic variation in chemical transmitters acting at nerve endings. Acetylcholine is widely distributed throughout the animal kingdom, in some non-nervous tissues as well as in nervous systems. The hydrolyzing enzyme, acetylcholine esterase, is likewise widely distributed, from protozoans to the mammalian brain; it is found in ciliates but not in sporozoans, and it occurs in many non-nervous cells. The synthesizing enzyme, choline acetylase, is also widely found but it has not been studied so extensively as has the esterase. There is evidence for acetylcholine transmission as an excitor at neuromuscular junctions in sipunculids, annelids, echinoderms, and extensively in vertebrates, and in some central synapses of mammals; it acts as an inhibitor at cardioregulatory junctions in a few molluscs and in all vertebrates (except certain cyclostomes). Some closely related but different transmitter is indicated in insect nervous systems. Adrenaline and nor-adrenaline are clearly transmitters in the vertebrate autonomic system, e.g., as cardio-accelerators. These or similar catechol amines are present in many invertebrates but apparently not as active transmitters. However, 5-hydroxytryptamine (5HT), while present in vertebrates, seems usually not to be a nervous transmitter there; in molluscs it is a transmitter, e.g., in cardioacceleration in some clams. A variety of compounds related to adrenaline and 5HT have appeared in different animals as poisons—tyramine (coelenterates), octamine (cephalopods), and bufotenine (toads). Apparently, therefore, acetylcholine has been retained as a junctional transmitter from the earliest nervous system, although modifications have been introduced, particularly among the arthropods. Catechol and indol amines have appeared many times in different animal groups. Only in the vertebrates are there truly adrenergic nerves. Many mediators of nervous action remain to be discovered; probably they will turn out to be modifications of widely distributed compounds.

The hearts of some animals have intrinsic ganglionic pacemakers. Innervated myogenic hearts have evolved separately in molluscs and vertebrates. Neurogenic hearts occur in some annelids, crustaceans, and insects; apparently some larval hearts may beat myogenically before ganglionic control is established (*Limulus,* some *Diptera*). Myogenicity appears to have evolved secondarily in crustaceans, sometimes without central nervous regulation, as in certain entomostracans; *Daphnia* has an innervated but myogenic heart, the only known instance of this in crustaceans.

NUTRITIONAL PATTERNS

The evolution of nutritional patterns is rich with examples of loss of synthetic capacity. Presumably the first "organisms" were heterotrophic, using preformed organic compounds as nutrients. As the food sources were used up, selective advantage accrued to those animals or plants which could synthesize organic substances for themselves and for other organisms. Thus the most primitive of present organisms are probably the photosynthetic flagellates and algae. Large groups of organisms lack the capacity for photosynthesis, and these rely on green plants for organic food. Some of the flagellates have lost various specific synthesizing steps. For example, all require thiamine in their metabolism; many can synthesize it, a few can synthesize the pyrimidine, a few, the thiazole portions of the molecule, and some can synthesize neither, but must get their thiamine from the medium. Similarly many micro-organisms must get vitamin B_{12} from the environment. With nutritional specialization the ability to synthesize essential intermediates or coenzymes was lost with resulting economy to the organism. The ciliate *Tetrahymena* requires a purine; most insects require choline; the genus *Tenebrio* requires carnitine; vertebrates require fat-soluble substances known as vitamins A, D, E, and K. All animals have need of a few essential amino acids—and the list of these is nearly uniform from *Tetrahymena* to fruit fly and man. Thus those amino acids required for their carbon skeletons must have been established very early in animal evolution. Some substances, for example the B-vitamins as co-enzymes, have retained essentially the same function throughout evolution. Others, such as the sterols, have been modified and have been used for very different functions in different groups of animals.

There has been, therefore, loss of synthetic ability by whole large groups of animals, and single species have lost specific capacities. The most striking examples of loss of enzymes are found among parasites. Blood trypanosomes require exogenous heme for manufacturing their cytochromes while other trypanosomes make their own. Many parasitic helminths live well in the absence of oxygen or at low oxygen pressures; they fail to accumulate oxygen debts but instead excrete the acids they form in intermediary metabolism; they appear to have lost the usual enzymes for degrading these acids. Some parasites excrete acids unknown in the anaerobic metabolism of other animals, and some have lost common oxidative enzymes.

PROTEIN SPECIFICITY

Much attention has been give in recent years to protein specificity as revealed by serological techniques and amino-acid composition. In a way, serum-protein differences are a sort of morphological character, much like pigment color patches on an animal. Many degrees of specificity exist, from tissue specificity to quantitative differences between blood proteins of individuals (man), races, and species. Maximum serological reactions are considered to occur between the most distantly related animals, and the intensity of precipitin reaction has been taken as a measure of distance of relationship. Protein specificity is probably non-adaptive in respect to the physical environment, but it may be important in parasite-host relations. It may limit interbreeding between species, and in man it is linked to genes for certain chronic pathological states. Precipitin states have, in general, confirmed relationships as established anatomically in the higher taxonomic categories. For example, the Acanthocephala appear to be related serologically to the Platyhelminthes, not to the Nemathelminthes. Molluscs are closer serologically to annelids than to arthropods. The genera *Amphiuma, Siren,* and *Necturus* are more closely related to one another than to *Cryptobranchus*. Amino-acid analyses of corresponding proteins are not yet sufficient to provide a basis for evolutionary comparisons, but this technique may be expected to be of considerable future value.

VARIETIES OF VISUAL PIGMENTS

The visual pigments of animals are carotenoids known as "retinenes" combined with proteins called "opsins." Even in flagellates and higher plants carotenoids are the photosensitive pigments for photo-orientation. The retinenes of honeybees, squid, and vertebrates are similar. Two forms occur in the vertebrates—$retinene_1$, predominantly in marine and land forms, and $retinene_2$ in fresh-water forms. However, the opsins are variable and often characteristic of particular photoreceptor cells. In squids, for example, the metarhodopsin formed by the action of light is stable, but in vertebrates it readily breaks apart. In deep-sea fish the maximum light absorption is toward the blue end of the spectrum in contrast to the absorption by rhodopsin of surface fish. In the course of evolution the carotenoid part of the molecule has remained relatively unchanged while the protein or opsin has varied and has been selected.

In summary, comparative physiology contributes much, as do comparative anatomy and embryology, with respect to similarities and differences between animals at the higher taxonomic levels. Some characters run through many phyla, others show extreme degrees of specialization. The identification of specific compounds associated with given functions is so far from complete, even in a few kinds of laboratory animals, that the taxonomic usefulness of physiology and biochemistry is still limited. As more kinds of animal are studied with respect to molecular mechanisms, it is probable that many relations will be found which strengthen or weaken accepted views of phylogeny. Certainly the evolutionary viewpoint unifies the complex picture of different substances serving similar functions in various animals.

PHYSIOLOGICAL FACTORS IN SPECIATION

At the lower end of the taxonomic scale, namely speciation, functional analysis can provide crucial evidence concerning the mechanisms of natural selection. To a physiologist, studying the adaptedness of natural populations of plants and animals is more important than setting the limits of characters as to where one species ends and another begins.

CRITERIA FOR DEFINING SPECIES

Many papers and many symposia have attempted to define "species." Certainly no single definition is all-inclusive for both asexual and sexual reproduction in all organisms. Within a biological species there is, or can be, exchange of genes. Between two species, although they are similar and sometimes indistinguishable morphologically, gene exchange does not normally take place. We may refer to three ways of understanding biological species.

Morphological.—The simplest approach and the one used with the majority of organisms is species description by morphological characters. The taxonomist who examines and maps the sources of many specimens of similar animals is in the best position to decide arbitrarily but objectively which belongs in one species category and which in another. As a physiologist, I am grateful for the taxonomic keys which make identification possible, but I would urge that the name of an animal for which a large experimental literature has been built up should be changed only when strictly necessary. It is as important for taxonomists to be aware of experimental work on organisms of their specialty as for experimentalists to know the current names of their organisms. It is hoped that morphological taxonomy corresponds with phylogeny, yet it has much practical value quite apart from such correspondence.

Reproductive isolation.—The criterion of reproductive isolation can be tested for relatively few kinds of organism. The occurrence of hybridization in the laboratory is not an adequate reason to disclaim natural isolation. The causes of isolation may be many—genetic, behavioral, anatomical, hormonal, spatial, and other. These have been extensively discussed elsewhere in this volume (see Mayr, Dobzhansky). But the mechanisms of isolation are known for only a few species, and it is surprising to find relatively few systematists who are concerned with the means by which their species remain isolated.

Physiological adaptation.—An approach to species not much tried is a physiological one. Ecological separation is indicated in two general ways: (a) No two related species can successfully occupy the same ecological niche (possibly excepting a few overlaps which are isolated by breeding behavior). (b) No two species have identical distribution ranges. Hence, if all of the microclimatic and biotic features of an ecological niche and distribution range are known, a description of the distinctive physiological adaptations to the niche and range should describe a species. A critical assessment of the functional adaptive features (including behavior) should describe the unique fitness of a species to its environment. Morphological characters may be adaptive in themselves or they may be genetically linked to adaptive physiological characters.

The physiological description of species has scarcely been attempted; it requires a combination of field and laboratory tests and can be done for relatively few organisms. First, there must be a description of physiological variation in natural populations with respect to critical characters, that is, a statistical analysis of adaptive capacity. Second, such variation as is found must be analyzed for that component which is genetic and that which is environmentally determined. This can be done by cross acclimation, by transplantation, and ultimately by breeding experiments. Third, physiological analysis may reveal the mechanisms underlying the variant characters.

A number of criteria of physiological variation can be used. The most practical of these are tests under environmental stresses, since what is important for survival over long periods in nature is the extreme, not the mean, of an environmental condition. These tests have been described in previous reviews (Prosser, 1957 *a, b*) and may be enumerated as follows:

(1) Survival data at environmental limits, for example, median lethal values for heat, cold, salinity, oxygen supply, etc. Critical survival data are useful only if the acclimation state is known and if measurements are made over a time such that the cause of death is the same. The lethal level of an environmental parameter may well be plotted as a function of acclimation level, providing what Fry (1947) has called a "tolerance polygon."

(2) Environmental limits for reproduction or completion of a life cycle. This is possible only with those organisms which can be reared under controlled conditions; however, it comes nearer than other tests to what really matters in nature. Too few stress studies have been done at developmental stages.

(3) Internal state as a function of the environment. Some animals change internally with the environment; these are called "conformers," e.g., poikilotherms. Others maintain relative internal constancy in a changing environment, that is they are "regulators," e.g., homeotherms. Measurements of conformity or regulation can be extended to all the physical components of the environment.

(4) Recovery from deviation from a mean physiological state. All animals, whether conformers or regulators, exercise some homeostasis or compensation which tends toward survival even though the internal state is deviated; the patterns of response are distinct for the animal.

(5) Identification in regulators of the critical limits beyond which homeostatic controls fail and within which they are activated. Description of the sequential steps in regulation during stress.

(6) Rate functions, for example rates of energy-yielding reactions, as a function of the environmental stress. A familiar example is the measurement of temperature characteristics for metabolic rates.

(7) Behavior. This includes taxic responses, selection of "optimal" environments in gradients, also complex behavior, such as courtship, mating, and rearing of young. Identification of the neurological basis of behavioral differences presents a challenge to neurophysiologists and to ethologists.

Wide-ranging species with many subspecies, ecotypes, or local races, with varying amounts of interspecific hybridization must be described statistically. Morphological key characters are basic to the description. Degree of reproductive isolation can be deduced by comparing large numbers of individuals of nearby species. Complete description in terms of unique adaptedness requires more physiological information than is available for most organisms.

EXAMPLES OF PHYSIOLOGICAL ISOLATION

Many students of natural populations recognize different species on the basis of morphological and biological characters but fail to identify isolating mechanisms. Such properties as protective coloration, genetic linkage of non-adaptive characters with tolerance differences, chromosomal arrangements, and embryological abnormalities are recognized. However, survival is based on subtle physiological differences, and more attention needs to be given to functional isolation.

In discussions of isolating factors, a distinction must be made between primary or initial isolation in speciation and secondary or subsequent means of isolation. When two strains become established as races or ecotypes in separate ecological niches or at the ends of a cline, they usually differ in adaptive capacity with respect to some physical factor in the environment, that is, they have different selective advantages. These adaptive differences constitute primary isolating mechanisms which can be discovered by stress tests.

Spatial separation *per se* is not enough to result in speciation; there must be physiological adaptation to the environmental differences. During the period of separation, which may last for many generations, differences appear which are unrelated to the physical environment but which make for reproductive isolation; these differences may be anatomical, physiological, behavioral, or psychological incompatibility. Secondary isolating mechanisms may also appear in spatially separated small populations without primary isolating adaptations (as in drift), but true ecological separation must always be accompanied by primary adaptations. Frequently species become established because of primary adaptations and then develop non-adaptive reproductive isolation; later, with geologic or climatic change, they may become sympatric and remain isolated by the secondary means, while the primary adaptations are no longer important. Thus, the current means of isolation of two species need not be the same as that which led to the initial speciation.

Primary adaptations.—The curves relating high and low lethal temperatures to acclimation temperature in fresh-water fish describe polygons which are characteristic of different species. That is, the mortality curves corrected for acclimation are genetically determined. Comparison of the temperature tolerance curves of populations of fourteen species of fish from Ontario, Tennessee, and Florida showed no differences in eleven species, even though in two of these the northern and southern populations are considered as subspecies; in three species, genetic differences in the temperature-tolerance curves were found, and in two of these the populations are classed on morphological grounds as subspecies (Hart, 1952).

Several similar examples are known for the effects of temperature on rate of embryonic development. In general, eggs of aquatic poikilotherms develop more rapidly at a given temperature when they come from a cold climate than from a warm climate. Embryos of *Rana pipiens* from the northern United States (Wisconsin to Vermont) develop at such different rates from the embryos from Louisiana-Texas-Mexico that hybridization between the two is impossible. The populations at the two ends of the cline are clearly so different physiologically that they are true biological species, yet the entire cline is considered taxonomically as one species (Moore, 1949). That the genetic system responsible for these clinal differences must be relatively labile is indicated by the fact that *Rana pipiens* from the high and cool Costa Rica mountains resemble those from the northern states in the effect of temperature on development (Volpe, 1957). Similar differences exist for the development of certain marine snails in California and Alaska, but the cross-breeding experiments have not been performed (Dehnel, 1955). Oysters (*Crassostrea virginica*) from Virginia, where normal spawning occurs at 25°C., failed to spawn during two years in Long Island Sound, where the temperature failed to reach 25°C., although the local oysters spawned at the lower temperature (Loosanoff, 1951).

Two of the mating types (natural species) of *Paramecium aurelia* are distinguished by the temperature optima for their growth and reproduction (Sonneborn, 1957).

The stickleback of Belgium, *Gasterosteus aculeatus,* occurs in two subspecies, one of which (*gymnurus*) is predominantly a fresh-water fish, whereas the other (*trachurus*) tolerates higher salinities and lives in estuaries. Correlated with salt-water tolerance are low number of vertebrae, larger body size, and greater number of lateral plates, The interaction between the effects of temperature and salinity in affecting the number of dorsal fin rays differs in the two forms. Despite the fact that the two subspecies produce fertile hybrids, natural selection favors the two extremes, one in rivers, the other in salt estuaries (Heuts, 1947).

Many insect populations are isolated according to the plants on which they feed. The choice of food plant is largely by taste or food preference, which may or may not have a genetic basis (Fraenkel, 1959). Two recent species of the butterfly *Colias* can hybridize but are normally separated by food choice. *C. philodice* feeds on red clover, while *C. eurytheme* feeds on alfalfa. Transfer of the caterpillars from one food plant to the other results in some sterility of the adults, hence there must be differences other than taste preference (Hovanitz, 1949).

Two closely related species of *Drosophila*, *D. persimilis* and *D. pseudoobscura*, and two *Anopheles* mosquitoes, *A. homunculus* and *A. bellator*, occupy slightly different niches in their respective forests. *D. persimilis* tends to occupy colder, moister woodlands than *D. pseudoobscura*, is more prone to desiccation, less restricted to moist hours for emergence, and is photopositive. *D. pseudoobscura* is less permeable to water, emerges only in moist periods, and is photo-negative. Local races show marked differences in behavior correlated with local microclimates. Similar behavioral differences keep the two species of *Anopheles*, *A. homunculus* and *A. bellator*, in slightly different zones of the tropical forest (Pittendrigh, 1958).

Many more examples of ecotypes are known for plants than for animals. These include altitudinal, north-south, and saline-tolerance clines. For example, a number of races from several species of the grass *Poa* show adaptive differences to night temperature which correlate well with their native habitats (Hiesey, 1953).

The preceding examples represent isolating differences which have arisen in adaptation to different environments at the extremes of the range for a species. They are, therefore, primary adaptations.

Secondary adaptations.—Much more is known about mechanisms of isolation of sympatric species, the secondary adaptations of reproductive isolation. The mating behavior of each of six species of the *willistoni* group of *Drosophila* is so characteristic that no interspecific mating occurs. Diurnal rhythms of activity, precisely timed, may serve to keep overlapping species apart. In many fish, the recognition of mates of their own species is by color patches which provide recognition signs. Olfactory cues may be important in recognition of members of the opposite sex, especially in such insects as Lepidoptera.

In insects, anurans, and birds, production of specific sound patterns also provides secondary isolation. This has been demonstrated experimentally for several species of crickets, mosquitoes, for overlapping species of frogs, and for numerous birds.

Frequently similar species remain isolated while living together in what appears to be the same micro-habitat. The isolating mechanisms are not apparent for some leaf hoppers and terrestrial snails (*Achatinella*), of which several species live together on the same tree branches. It is probable that slight behavioral differences keep them isolated.

In summary, a complete description of a species must ultimately include the means by which it is isolated from closely related species. Considerable arbitrariness must be exercised in deciding whether two populations which differ genetically in some adaptive character are true species, particularly in clines and circles. However, a description in terms of functional adaptations, both primary and secondary, gives some understanding of how species arise and remain isolated.

Environmentally Induced Variation

The genotype of an organism fixes the limits within which an individual can vary with developmental and environmental influences. Animals which are reared under rigidly controlled conditions are much more uniform than those living in nature. When natural populations are examined for their physiological variability and individuals are cross-acclimated, one is impressed by the extreme lability of some physiological characters. Environmentally induced variation permits animals with similar genotypes to adapt to slightly different environments. At the limits of the range of a species, such phenotypic adaptation provides one basis for natural selection. A genetic change in the direction of a phenotypic, environmentally induced variation at the species limit, is more likely to become fixed than the same change in a dissimilar population at the opposite end of the range.

Many more examples are available of environmentally induced physiological differences between populations of a species than of genetic races.

Reference was made earlier to the changes which some animals show in their nitrogen excretion according to availability of water (e.g., the lungfish). *Mytilus* from the Baltic (salinity, 15 p/1000) have a higher metabolism and higher rate of pumping water than do specimens from the North Sea (salinity, 30 p/1000) (Schlieper,

1957). Both groups are isosmotic with their environment; upon transfer from one salinity to the other, a population takes on the metabolic rate and other rates corresponding to the new salinity. *Asterias,* on the contrary, have a lower oxygen consumption in the dilute salinity; they tend to take up water and are less successful than *Mytilus* in the Baltic; their compensatory mechanisms are poorly developed (Schlieper, 1957).

Callinectes, from the upper portions of an estuary, are able to regulate their blood osmotic concentration to a lower salinity than can individuals from the mouth of a river. On retention in normal sea water, the crabs from the dilute region become similar to those collected at the higher salinity. Fish like salmon or eels which migrate between fresh and saltwater have to reverse the direction of active transport of salts from active outward secretion when in sea water to active absorption in fresh water.

The hemoglobin content of the blood of alpine mammals is higher than the content at sea level, and men in acclimating to altitude require a month or more to alter the oxygen-transporting capacity of their blood. Similarly, many invertebrates, e.g., *Daphnia,* synthesize hemoglobin and also cytochrome when reared in low oxygen. Hence, the color of *Daphnia, Artemia,* and some copepods is red or pale, according to the oxygen in their environment (Fox, 1955).

Most fish maintain relatively constant oxygen consumption when the environmental oxygen is reduced to a critical partial pressure. Goldfish kept for several days in low oxygen had lower critical oxygen pressures, also lower standard metabolism, than goldfish from air-saturated water (Prosser *et. al.,* 1957).

Many examples of differences in temperature tolerance, in metabolic rate, in heart and breathing rates, are correlated with temperature differences associated with seasons or latitude. These have been summarized in recent monographs (Precht *et. al.,* 1955; Bullock, 1955; Prosser, 1955, 1958). In goldfish the lethal temperature (high or low) changes about one degree for every three degrees in acclimation, with the limits set genetically. In general, poikilothermic animals, particularly aquatic ones reared in a cold climate have a higher metabolism than those reared at higher temperatures when the measurements are made at an intermediate temperature. *Mytilus californianus* from latitude 48°21′ pumped water at the same rate at 6.5°C. as those from 38°31′ at 10°C. and those from 34°0′ at 12°C. Animals from colder waters are also less affected by temperature, i.e., their Q_{10} is lower than for individuals from warmer regions (Rao, 1953). Similarly limpets (*Acmaea limulata*) from the high intertidal zone have lower heart rates at given temperature than those from the low intertidal zone, an effect due to temperature acclimation. Transplantation from one zone to the other reverses the heart rate effect within a few weeks (Segal, 1956).

Homeothermic animals become adapted to cold by alterations in insulations and vascular reflexes. The temperature of the extremities of an aquatic bird or mammal may differ from that of the body by ten or more degrees and still maintain functional activity under different conditions of acclimation.

Environmentally induced variation or individual adaptation permits survival of animals over a wide range of external conditions without genetic change. Once a population is adapted phenotypically to an environmental extreme, a genetic change in that direction is favored for fixation.

TIME COURSE OF PHYSIOLOGICAL RESPONSE
TO ENVIRONMENTAL CHANGE

Perhaps the most important contribution comparative physiology can make to evolutionary theory is to increase understanding of natural selection by accounting for the action of the environment on organisms. The effects of an environmental stress must be considered in the appropriate time sequence. A general pattern of response applies to all sorts of environmental change. The generalized pattern described in Figure 1 is for a rate function (for example, metabolic rate) under a familiar stress, such as temperature.

The first stage in the response of an animal to a change in some environmental parameter has been variously called a "shock reaction," an "overshoot," or stimulation. Overshoots in oxygen consumption following a sudden rise in temperature, or an undershoot on sudden cooling, have been seen in many kinds of organisms. The first effect

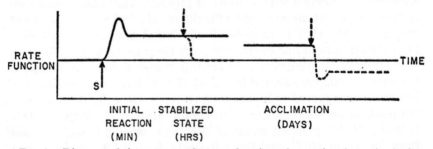

FIG. 1.—Diagram of time course of a rate function of a conforming animal after transfer at time S to an altered environment, such as elevated temperature. Initial reaction ("overshoot") is followed by stabilized state. Return to initial environment (*first broken arrow*) shows that the rate returns to original level. However, after some days of acclimation, a return to initial environment (*second broken arrow*) shows that the rate falls below initial value. The organism has become changed physiologically.

may be stimulation of sensory endings, and a sudden change in frequency of sensory impulses is noted. In many organisms, including those lacking sensory mechanisms, as yeast, there is initial brief stimulation (or depression) of oxygen consumption (Grainger, 1958). The magnitude of the early response varies with the intensity and rate of environmental change. This first stage is usually measured in seconds or minutes.

There follows a stabilized state, which is usually the period of constancy in which rate functions are measured. In conforming organisms (e.g., poikilotherms) the rate settles down to that of the altered internal state. Temperature characteristics are usually obtained from rates measured during this period. In regulating organisms a variety of feedback mechanisms, often nervous and/or hormonal, tend to restore the organism to normal. To maintain constancy of the internal state, some functions, such as metabolic rate, become stabilized at a new level. In homeotherms vasomotor and pilomotor reflexes are the first means of regulation to cold, with elevated heat production a second line of defense. Thus the nature of the stabilized state varies according to whether an animal is a conformer or a regulator. This stabilized state is usually measured in hours or days. The alterations produced in embryos in direct response to an environmental stress may persist into adulthood even after the stress is removed.

The initial shock reaction and the stabilized state constitute the direct or immediate responses of an organism. If the environmental change persists for days, weeks, or months, most organisms enter a state of compensation, shown to the right in Figure 1. This is the process of acclimation or compensation to a single environmental factor, as in controlled experiments, or of acclimatization to a complex of environmental factors, as in seasonal or climatic changes. Many of the examples of environmentally induced variation cited above are the results of acclimation.

Acclimation.—Acclimatory responses tend to restore an organism, even a conformer, toward a "normal" state. The metabolism of many poikilotherms acclimated to low temperature is higher than when they are acclimated to a high temperature, with the result that they tend to produce energy at approximately their original undeviated rate, that is, they compensate for reduced body temperature. Swimming rate may be higher in cold-acclimated than in warm-acclimated fish when measured at an intermediate temperature. In perfect acclimation the rate function at one body temperature is the same as at another. In the absence of acclimation there is no difference between the initial stabilized state and the acclimated or long-term rate. The most common response of conformers is a rate intermediate between the initial stabilized state and perfect acclimation; occasionally overcompensation or undercompensation has been observed (Precht, 1955).

Another type of acclimation is enzyme induction, extensively studied in microorganisms which are shifted from one nutrient to another. Quantitative changes in enzyme synthesis occur, according to the need for these enzymes. This phenomenon has been well established for higher animals and is probably present in all living things; it may be, as we shall see later, the basis for most environmentally induced variation. Among other chemical changes are those of winter hardiness in insects. In man acclimation to heat leads to increased capacity for sweating and lower skin temperature at a given air temperature.

A third kind of acclimation has been widely observed in both plants and animals—morphological adaptive change. In reduced oxygen, tadpoles have larger gills, and many kinds of animals synthesize more hemoglobin. In the cold, homeothermic animals grow thicker fur and their pattern of peripheral blood flow becomes altered; they may develop conditioned vasomotor reflexes. Plants may change their leaf form according to water supply, and may synthesize various pigments according to illumination. Within genetically fixed limits, embryonic changes may be considerable in different environments.

The time required for acclimation changes, whether by physiological compensations, enzyme adaptations, or morphological changes, varies with the organism, but it is usually within the range of 0.1 to 10 per cent of the life span.

Non-genic transmission of change.—Over still longer periods— several generations—adaptive variations in populations may be maintained and even transmitted by non-genic means. One type of non-genic transmission of isolating characters is by animal behavior. Some stereotyped direct responses to sensory stimulation are based on innate nervous patterns, particularly in insects and lower vertebrates, but other complex behavior patterns are often acquired by early experience and may be transmitted by conditioning from one generation to the next. Insects tend to deposit their eggs on the same kind of plant on which they fed as larvae; if unfamiliar food is offered through several generations, the larvae may accept it with increasing readiness. The complex feeding behavior of many birds and mammals may be compounded from innate direct responses but is "learned" as a total pattern. The importance of imprinting in some birds has been emphasized by modern ethologists. In man social evolution, which progresses much faster than organic evolution, is based on non-genetic transmission of behavior through culture patterns from generation to generation.

A second type of non-genic inheritance is by the cytoplasm. Microorganisms and plants provide many examples of cytoplasmic transmission from one generation to the next. Cytoplasmic particulates may thus be transmitted, e.g., the granules for the kappa factor in *Paramecium;* the plastids in some plants. Cytoplasmic factors are involved in the inheritance of serotypes in ciliates. The depressing effect of constant night-day temperature (no drop at night) on growth of peas was cumulative during five generations (Highkin, 1958); the sixth generation failed to grow at all. A pseudo-genetic effect in bacteria is the alteration of the cell membrane by a "permease" so that it becomes more permeable to some substances through a series of cell divisions (Novick and McCoy, 1958).

Selection.—One type of transmission of response to environmental stress is the "canalization" of developmental processes under strong selection as described by Waddington elsewhere in this volume. This uses normal genic mechanisms.

Finally, in the time span of many generations, the process of evolutionary adaptation involves the selection of genetically adapted types of organisms. This is the sequence of allopatric speciation where genetic mutants or rearrangements are selected as strains or races. Spatial isolation of races is eventually followed by speciation. The first step in this long process must be the environmentally-induced variation in natural populations; fixation is by natural selection from the random genetic variants. Natural selection is more than mere survival or death, reproduction or failure to reproduce. It favors the continuance of all the adaptive functions of an organism: nutritional, metabolic, and sensori-motor adjustments.

It is evident from the preceding summary that the physiological responses to the environment are many, that they depend on the intensity and rate of application of a stress, that they also vary according to the time elapsed since an environmental change. The specific interactions between organisms and their environments are limited genetically, but these interactions provide the basis for natural selection. Just as genetic "preadaptation" keeps an organism "ready" for a new environmental situation, conversely, phenotypic variation permits organisms to live at their range limits where genetic change in the direction of the environmental limit may become fixed.

MECHANISMS OF LONG-RANGE INTERACTION BETWEEN ORGANISMS AND ENVIRONMENT

Independence of the environment is of the essence of life; by definition no living organism is equivalent chemically to its environment. Maintenance of organismic independence or homeostasis requires energy; it requires a selective body surface. It can be mainly at the cellular level, as in microorganisms, plants, and some simple animals; and it may also involve the tissues and organ systems of the organism as a whole, as in higher animals. Even conforming organisms, such as poikilotherms or those which are poikilosmotic or oxygen-dependent, are not completely at the mercy of the environment. They have compensatory adaptations—biochemical and behavioral—which impart some independence of such stresses as extremes of temperature or salinity or reduced oxygen concentration. The automatic self-regulating processes provide a remarkable physiological lability which is the basis of environmentally-induced variation. The recognition of biochemical and physiological lability at the molecular level is a major biological advance of the present generation.

ENZYME INDUCTION

Perhaps the best known examples of biochemical lability come from enzyme induction. Bacteria, yeasts, molds, and to a lesser extent protozoans, may be grown on certain organic substrates which are their sole energy source. When transferred to a new nutrient, they may not at first have the necessary enzymes with which to break down the food, but they can synthesize the appropriate enzymes, provided they have the genetic capacity for the synthesis. For example, *Escherichia coli* cultured on glucose is unable to use β-galactose, but if transferred to a β-galactose medium, the β-galactosidase is formed. Various controls show that the effect is not selection of mutant bacteria but is actual enzyme synthesis from amino acids. The cells can be stimulated to synthesize the new enzyme by a specific substrate or by closely related compounds.

The phenomenon of enzyme induction has proven very useful for the study of protein synthesis. Cytoplasmic particles, particularly reticular granules, rich in RNA (ribose nucleic acid) seem essential for protein synthesis. Constitutive enzymes, that is, the enzymes normally present in a cell, such as the oxidative ones, can be formed under the influence of RNA already present in the cytoplasm although these enzymes can also increase or decrease. Induced enzymes require the formation of new RNA, apparently under the influence of specific nuclear DNA (deoxyribose nucleic acid). Genic material is DNA-protein which controls RNA synthesis and this in turn is used in protein synthesis. Enzyme proteins are specific for the multitude of adaptive functions of living cells. Induction of enzyme synthesis has been demonstrated in animals, for example, the formation of tryptophane peroxidase-oxidase in the liver of mammals (Knox, 1956) and of glucose-6-phosphatase in liver of rats on a high sucrose diet (Freedland and Harper, 1958). Thus, to some extent, substrates in the environment control the quantity of enzymes for attacking the substrates.

The concept of enzyme induction has been extended from organic substrates to physical factors in the environment. Reference has been made above to the higher metabolic rate in cold-acclimated fish and many other poikilotherms at a given temperature than in non-adapted ones. Precht, Christophersen, and their associates (1955) have found similar phenomena in yeasts. In these unicellular organisms the activity of certain oxidative enzymes is increased in low temperature; other parallel paths may be decreased. Tissues from goldfish acclimated to 10° are more sensitive to cyanide than those from goldfish acclimated to 30°; the converse is true for iodoacetate, hence certain oxidative paths are enhanced at low temperature, others at high (Ekberg, 1958). Similar increases in O_2 consumption have been found, not only in intact animals but in tissue homogenates and even in isolated mitochondria. With increased oxygen consumption, there is decreased P/O ratio in the cold (Kanungo, 1959). In mammals the same sort of effect is noted in cold-adaptation; a decoupling of phosphorylation from electron transfer is indicated (Smith *et al.*, 1958). Various parallel pathways of energy liberation are well known; some of these are cross-linked by common enzymes and coenzymes. It is postulated that the activation energies, as measured by temperature coefficients, are different and that if one path is slowed relative to another the chemical equilibrium will shift so that the substrates of the retarded path may accumulate. If these intermediates can be used as substrates by a cross-linked or parallel system, they will serve as enzyme inducers for that system. In this way a physical factor in the environment—temperature—may result in changes in intracellular enzymes by an induction mechanism.

That other physical factors can act similarly to temperature has been indicated but less well established. In goldfish acclimated to low oxygen, the metabolism of whole fish and of isolated tissues is reduced. It is probable that some of the metabolic effects of adaptation to various salinities, e.g., in *Mytilus edulis,* are by changes in enzyme activities.

Phenomena similar to enzyme induction probably lie at the basis of many morphological changes in response to environmental stresses and even in differentation in growing organisms. Enzyme induction and de-adaptation may underlie normal growth and development (Gordon, 1956).

Many of the behavioral responses to environmental extremes, for example, changes in selected or preferred temperatures or salinities, or cold and heat block of nervous reflexes, may be altered by acclimation. It is probable that the molecular properties of axon membranes and of synapses are labile. A well-known example is the ability of metatarsal nerve fibers of a sea-gull adapted to swimming in ice water to conduct at lower temperatures than the femoral portion of the same nerve fibers (Lyman and Chatfield, 1952).

Microbial physiologists have been concerned mainly with enzyme changes in response to substrates; animal physiologists are more concerned with adaptations to physical factors. It now appears that microorganisms can adapt enzymatically to physical factors and that animals also show biochemical changes much as do microorganisms. In both kinds of organism there is good integration by the internal fluid environment involved. In both—particularly in microorganisms—there are also genetic strains adapted to environmental extremes (e.g., thermophilic bacteria). In these specialized strains, the entire gamut of constitutive enzymes is adapted toward the environmental extreme; for example, temperatures for inactivation are elevated. The deep-sea bacteria have enzymes which normally function at (and may even require) hydrostatic pressures of some thousand atmospheres, pressures which quickly denature the corresponding enzymes of surface bacteria. Higher plants show many direct stabilized-state responses to environmental stresses—changes in pigment concentration, in leaf structure, in growth orientation. However, plants rarely show the compensatory type of response after prolonged exposure, that is, an altered internal state that approaches the original norm. Most known variations in plant populations are genetic, and much of modern agronomy is based on selection of adapted strains. Mutants which have undergone adaptation constitute the well-known ecotypes of the plant geneticist and ecologist (for example, strains of grass: Hiesey, 1953). It may be that the more complete chemical integration of microorganisms and higher animals provides more opportunity for biochemical adaptation, whereas in plants the individual cells are more independent of one another. It is recognized, of course, that the differences among microorganisms, animals, and plants are relative and that one can find some genotypic and some environmentally-induced variation in all three groups. Knowledge of the means by which environmentally induced variation occurs is the first essential step toward understanding natural variation, which is at the basis of speciation.

PROSPECT FOR THE FUTURE

Natural selection—"survival of the fittest"—is usually considered in terms of life and death, reproduction and failure to reproduce, or, in more precise analysis, in small differentials in reproductive capacity.

Actually there is much more to natural selection than this; it permeates the total biology of the organism. Physiological adaptation of various kinds is important in many phases of adaptational biology. The comparative physiologist may go far toward an understanding of the physicochemical basis of adaptation, toward a molecular analysis of evolutionary processes.

Biological progress has been characterized by a series of great generalizations. During the first quarter of this century the outstanding advance was the chromosome theory of inheritance and the understanding of chromosomal behavior. Toward the end of that period important advances were made in embryology by the discovery of the principle of embryonic induction, but this discovery has yet to be put in terms of specific chemical entities. During the thirties and forties the most outstanding advance in biology was the elucidation of intermediary metabolism: the understanding of how energy is made available for biological work. In the current decade the most important advance seems to me to be the identification of genic material with DNA-protein and the recognition—as yet poorly known—of the control by DNA of the synthesis of RNA and the control by RNA of protein synthesis. I venture to predict that the next area of breakthrough will be in learning how environmental stresses interact with cellular components to initiate the sequence of adaptive reactions.

Apparently substrate can, in some way, initiate the synthesis of specific RNA, which then facilitates the synthesis of specific proteins. This may be by a feedback system following mass-action kinetics. Three ways have been suggested in which induction might occur: inducers may act directly on the RNA template of protein synthesis (Spiegelman, 1956); they may act via the cytoplasm on nuclear DNA, and hence lead indirectly to formation of specific RNA (Gale, 1956); or they may remove the inhibition by one gene on another or by cytoplasmic suppressing compounds, and thus may release a synthesizing reaction. Cytoplasm can influence nucleus as well as the converse. For example, ultraviolet irradiation of only the cytoplasm of tissue-culture cells of heart can result in chromosomal damage (Bloom and Zirkle, 1955). Treatment of amoeba cytoplasm with nitrogen mustard or X-irradiation causes changes which then result in damage to untreated nuclei transplanted to the treated cytoplasm (Ord and Danielli, 1956). RNA from a penicillinase-containing strain of bacteria can cause the production of the enzyme in a strain which normally lacks it in the absence of the inducer (Kramer and Straub, 1956). Niu (1958) has shown that RNA from frog kidney can transform undifferentiated ectoderm of frog gastrulae into kidney; the RNA of other tissues is also specific. It is entirely possible that the feedback may extend via the cytoplasm to quantitative changes in the activity of specific DNA. Knowledge of how an inducer causes specific DNA to lead to the formation of template RNA and thence to protein synthesis will bring an understanding of the chain of reactions by which physical stresses induce cellular change.

Since the discovery by Avery of the transformation of one pneumococcus into another under the influence of transforming nucleotides, other examples—particularly in microorganisms—have been found of one DNA becoming incorporated into and transforming another cell type. There have even been suggestions that transfer of DNA from one higher plant to another (perhaps by sucking insects) might cause nuclear transformation. The possibility of introducing a specific DNA fraction from one cell type into another has revolutionary implications. This does not mean that mutation can be induced but rather that the environment may interact via the cytoplasm with nuclear synthesis of RNA, which is necessary for formation of adaptive enzymes. These adaptive responses apply to somatic cells, not germ cells, except insofar as generalized reactions involve all tissues. However, it is on such environmentally induced variation that natural selection operates. What is selected is not the changed state per se, but the capacity for change. Genetic change is random, and evolution is non-directed in the sense of orthogenesis; yet natural selection is full of direction, and by understanding the environment–cell interaction, the physiologist may provide important clues to the molecular mechanisms of natural selection.

REFERENCES

BALDWIN, E. 1939. *Comparative Biochemistry.* Cambridge: Cambridge University Press.

BLOOM, W., R. E. ZIRKLE, and R. B. URETZ. 1955. "Irradiation of Parts of Individual Cells," *Ann. N. Y. Acad.,* LIX, 503.

BULLOCK, T. H. 1955. Compensation for Temperature in the Metabolism and Activity of Poikilotherms," *Biol. Rev.,* XXX, 311.

DEHNEL, P. A. 1955. "Rates of Growth of Gastropods as a Function of Latitude," *Physiol. Zoöl.,* XXVIII, 115.

EKBERG, D. R. 1958. "Respiration in Tissues of Goldfish Adapted to High and Low Temperatures," *Biol. Bull.,* CXIV, 308.

FOX, H. M. 1955. "The Effect of Oxygen on the Concentration of Haem in Invertebrates," *Proc. Roy. Soc. London,* B, CXLIII, 203.

FRAENKEL, G. S. 1959. "The *raison d'etre* of Secondary Plant Substances," *Science,* CXXIX, 1466–70.

FREEDLAND, R. A. and A. E. HARPER. 1958 "Metabolic Adaptations in Higher Animals." IV, *J. Biol. Chem.,* CCXXXIII, 1041.

FRY, F. E. J. 1947. *Effects of the Environment on Animal Activity.* ("University Toronto Studies," Biol. Ser. No. 55.)

GALE, E. F. 1956. "Nucleic Acids and Enzyme Synthesis," p. 49 in *Enzymes: Units of Biological Structure and Function,* ed. O. H. GAEBLER. New York: Academic Press.

GORDON, M. W. 1956. "Role of Adaptive Enzyme Formation in Morphogenesis," p. 83 in *Neurochemistry,* H. H. JASPER, *ed.* New York: Academic Press.

GRAINGER, J. N. R. 1958. "First stages in the Adaptation of Poikilotherms to Temperature Change, p. 79 in *Physiological Adaptation,* ed. C. L. PROSSER. Washington, D.C.: American Physiological Society.

HART, J. S. 1952. *Geographic Variations of Some Physiological and Morphological Characters in Certain Freshwater Fish.* ("Publ. Ontario Fish Res. Lab.," Vol. LXXII.)

HEUTS, M. J. 1947. "Experimental Studies on Adaptive Evolution in *Gasterosteus aculeatus,*" *Evolution,* I, 89.

HIESEY, W. M. 1953. "Growth and Development of Species and Hybrids of Poa under Controlled Temperatures," *Amer. J. Bot.,* XL, 205.

HIGHKIN, H. R. 1958. "Temperature-induced Variability in Peas," *Amer. J. Bot.,* XLV, 626.

HOVANITZ, W. 1949. "Increased Variability in Populations Following Natural Hybridization," in *Genetics, Paleontology, and Evolution,* ed. JEPSON, MAYR, and SIMPSON. Princeton, N. J.: Princeton University Press.

KANUNGO, M. S. 1959. "Physiological and Biochemical Adaptation of Goldfish to cold and Warm Temperatures." Ph.D. dissertation, University of Illinois.

KNOX, W. E., V. H. AUERBACH, and E. C. C. LIN. 1956. "Enzymatic and Metabolic Adaptations in Animals," *Physiol. Rev.,* XXXVI, 164.

KRAMER, M. and F. B. STRAUB. 1956. "Role of Specific Nucleic Acid in Induced Enzyme Synthesis," *Biophys. Biochem.* Acta, XXI, 201.

LOOSANOFF, V. L. and C. A. NOMEJKO. 1951. "Existence of Physiologically Different Races of Oysters, *Crassostrea virginica,*" *Biol. Bull.,* CI, 151.

LYMAN, C. P. and P. O. CHATFIELD. 1952. "Adaptation to Cold in Peripheral Nerve in the Leg of the Herring Gull," *Anat. Rec.,* CXIII, 23.

MILLER, S. L. 1955. "Production of Some Organic Compounds Under Possible Primitive Earth Conditions," *J. Amer. Chem. Soc.,* LXXVII, 2351.

MOORE, J. A. 1949. "Geographic Variation of Adaptive Characters in *Rana pipiens,*" *Evolution,* III, 1.

NIU, M. C. 1958. "Thymus Ribose Nucleic Acid and Embryonic Differentiation," *Proc. Nat. Acad. Sci.,* XLIV, 1264.

NOVICK, A. and A. McCOY. 1958. "Quasi-genetic Regulation of Enzymatic Level," p. 140 in *Physiological Adaptation,* ed. C. L. PROSSER. Washington, D.C.: American Physiological Society.

ORD, M. J. and J. F. DANIELLI, 1956. "Site of Damage in Amoebae Exposed to Methyl di-(B-chloroethyl)-amine (a Nitrogen Mustard) and to X-rays," *Quart. J. Mic. Sci.* XCVII, 17 and 29.

PITTENDRIGH, C. S. 1958. "Adaptation, Natural Selection and Behavior," p. 390 in *Behavior and Evolution,* ed. ROE and SIMPSON. New Haven, Conn.: Yale University Press.

PRECHT, H. 1958. "Concepts of the Temperature Regulation of Unchanging Reaction Systems of Cold-blooded Animals," p. 50 in *Physiological Adaptation,* ed. C. L. PROSSER, Washington, D.C.: American Physiological Society.

PRECHT, H., J. CHRISTOPHERSEN, and H. HENSEL. 1955. *Temperatur und Leben.* Heidelberg: Springer.

PROSSER, C. L. 1955. "Physiological Variation in Animals," *Biol. Rev.,* XXX, 229.

―――. 1957a. "A Species Problem from the Viewpoint of a Physiologist," p. 339 in *The Species Problem,* ed. E. MAYR. Washington, D.C.: American Association for the Advancement of Science.

―――. 1957b. Proposal for Study of Physiological Variation in Marine Animals," *L'Ann. Biol.,* XXXIII, 191.

―――. 1958. "The Nature of Physiological Adaptation," p. 167 in *Physiological Adaptation,* ed. C. L. PROSSER. Washington, D.C.: American Physiological Society.

PROSSER, C. L., L. M. BARR, R. D. PINC, and C. Y. LAUER. 1957. "Acclimation of Goldfish to Low Concentrations of Oxygen," *Physiol. Zoöl.,* XXX, 137.

PROSSER, C. L., F. A. BROWN, D. W. BISHOP, T. L. JAHN, and V. J. WULFF. 1950. *Comparative Animal Physiology.* Philadelphia: W. B. Saunders Co.

RAO, K. P. 1953. "Rate of Water Propulsion in *Mytilus californianus* as a Function of Latitude," *Biol. Bull.,* CIV, 171.

SCHLIEPER, C. 1957.: "Comparative Study of *Asterias rubens* and *Mytilus edulis* from the North Sea (30 per 1,000 S) and the Western Baltic Sea (15 per 1,000 S)," *L'Ann. Biol.,* XXXIII, 117.

SEGAL, E. 1956. "Microgeographic variation as Thermal Acclimation in an Intertidal Mollusc," *Biol. Bull.,* CXI, 129.

SMITH, R. E. and A. S. FAIRHURST. 1958. "A Mechanism of Cellular Thermogenesis in Cold-adaptation," *Proc. Nat. Acad. Sci.,* XLIV, 705.

SONNEBORN, T. M. 1957. "Breeding Systems, Reproductive Methods, and Species Problems in Protozoa," p. 155 in *The Species Problem,* ed. E. MAYR. Washington, D.C.: American Association for the Advancement of Science.

SPIEGELMAN, S. 1956. "On the Nature of the Enzyme-forming System," p. 67 in *Enzymes: Units of Biological Structure and Function,* ed. O. H. GAEBLER. New York: Academic Press.

VOLPE, E. P. 1957. "Genetic Aspects of Anuran Populations," *Amer. Nat.,* XCI, 355.

WALD, G. 1952. "Biochemical Evolution," p. 337 in Modern Trends in Physiology and Biochemistry, ed. E. S. G. BARRON. New York: Academic Press.

N. TINBERGEN

BEHAVIOUR, SYSTEMATICS, AND NATURAL SELECTION

Several review articles have been published recently on the general topic of behaviour, classification, and evolution (see J. M. Cullen, 1959; Hinde, 1959; Lorenz, 1958; Roe and Simpson, 1958). The present paper will therefore deal with a slightly different subject and discuss, with some selected examples, the extent to which taxonomic characters must be assumed to be due to natural selection. Some questions of method will also be raised. While most examples will be taken from birds, some data on other animals will also be given, providing a phylogenetic analysis of behavioural data.

TAXONOMIC USE OF BEHAVIOUR CHARACTERS

It will be useful to consider, first, which behaviour characters can be used for taxonomic and systematic purposes, how they can be used, and what exactly are the phenomena which require an evolutionary explanation.

ANALYSIS OF BEHAVIOUR "MACHINERY"

It is now almost a commonplace to say that there *are* behaviour characters helpful to the taxonomist. Mayr (1958) has given a useful review. Behaviour always involves complex "machinery." A sequence of events leading to a certain behaviour usually involves sensory reception; always consists of an extremely complicated series of internal events involving the nervous system and often other systems; and ends in co-ordinated muscle activity. As the analysis of this machinery proceeds (as it does with increasing speed), the characteristics of species, or taxa of any level, can be described in increasing detail. Today behaviour characters of many different kinds are known. The

N. TINBERGEN is University Lecturer in Animal Behaviour at Oxford University and a Fellow of Merton College. A foremost proponent of the ethological school of animal study, he has written *The Study of Instinct* (1951), *Social Behaviour of Animals* (1953), and *The Herring Gull's World* (1953). The present paper originally appeared in *Ibis*, CI (1959), 318–30.

most striking of these, and hence the best known, are motor patterns, particularly those of the "fixed-pattern" type, which can be seen directly and described without elaborate analysis. Many investigations deal with differences or similarities between two or a few species. Thus Morris (1954) described how the song thrush, *Turdus ericetorum,* differs from the blackbird, *Turdus merula,* in its ability to smash shells of snails; Klomp (1954) described differences in the way lapwings, *Vanellus vanellus,* and black-tailed godwits, *Limosa limosa,* move their feet in walking. There are now also a number of more comprehensive reports, dealing with many species of a group (see, e.g., Crane, 1941, 1957, on fiddler crabs, *Uca;* Hinde, 1955, on finches Fringillidae; Lorenz, 1941, 1958, on ducks, Anatinae; Tinbergen, 1959, on gulls, Laridae; for more references see Hinde and Tinbergen, 1958); and these more extensive studies also concentrate mainly on motor patterns. We also know something about intertaxa differences in responsiveness to stimuli; thus the sparrow hawk, *Accipiter nisus,* and the goshawk, *A. gentilis,* while hunting in much the same way, select different prey (Lack, 1946); the alarm call of the kittiwake, *Rissa tridactyla,* is not very different from that of other species of gulls, but it has a much higher threshold to stimulation by predators (E. Cullen, 1957); the courtship of the males of *Drosophila simulans* responds to visual stimuli to a larger extent than do the males of the related *D. melanogaster* (Manning, 1959); the oystercatchers of the Faeroes show distraction displays more readily than do those of the mainland (Williamson, 1952); British starlings, *Sturnus vulgaris,* respond to day-lengthening more readily than do Continental starlings (Bullough, 1942).

Other behaviour characteristics concern some property of the internal machinery; naturally, reports on such characters are scarce and fragmentary. Beach (1958) concludes from comparative studies of androgens and their effects on reproductive behaviour that the responsiveness of "target systems" rather than the chemical composition of the hormones has changed in vertebrate evolution; Vince (1956) describes differences in ability to haul up food by means of a string between the goldfinch, *Carduelis carduelis,* and the chaffinch, *Fringilla coelebs;* Armstrong (1952) reports that the Shetland wren, *Troglodytes troglodytes zetlandicus,* is monogamous, in contrast with the polygamous wrens in more southerly latitudes. The tendency to learn in many species is confined to certain situations or internal conditions, and these may be very different in different species. The feeding behaviour of honeybees, *Apis mellifica,* can be conditioned to some, but not all, of the scents which their sense organs can receive (Von Frisch, 1956). Kittiwakes have no tendency to respond selectively to their own young, which other gulls learn to do in a few days (E. Cullen, 1957). Several species of gulls smash shell by dropping them from the air; the same behaviour is shown by carrion crows, *Corvus corone;* but, unlike crows, gulls very rarely learn to drop them over a hard substrate, although gulls are capable of many feats of learning, such as learning to select updraughts over hilly country, which helps them to travel along convenient flight lines under varying wind conditions (Tinbergen, 1953*a*). Honeybees condition themselves to feeding sites by performing a "locality study"; bumblebees do this only with certain flowers, not with others (Manning, 1956). As I will argue below, the study of such behaviour characters is not only important for its own sake, but, since many characters are functionally interrelated, the student of evolution has to extend his studies over as many characters as possible.

TRUE AND APPARENT BEHAVIOUR CHARACTERS

Behaviour is known to be subject to phenotypic change to a much greater extent than are morphological characters. Learning processes may even keep changing the behaviour throughout the life of the individual. It is therefore of special importance, when dealing with behaviour characters, to investigate whether observed differences are genetically determined or merely reflect differences in the environment. Although phenotypic changes may foreshadow genetical changes, as long as an observed difference is due merely to environmental effects it is not an innate difference and therefore does not offer an evolutionary problem. Several instances are known of species-specific differences which are induced by the environment and are species-specific only because the environment is constantly different for the two species compared. The selective responsiveness of turnstones, *Arenaria interpres,* to the alarm call of their species is species-specific; nevertheless, as Bergman showed (1946), turnstone chicks hatched under redshanks, *Tringa totanus,* did not respond to the notes of their own species but did respond to those of their foster parents. On the other hand, Goethe showed (1955) that the responsiveness of young herring gulls to the alarm call of the parents is not learned. Environmental effects have even been demonstrated in some motor patterns. Since Thorpe (1958) proved that the songs of individual chaffinches, *Fringilla coelebs,* can vary as a result of exposure to adults singing different songs, even striking differences in song between two chaffinch populations cannot, without analysis, be considered evidence of a true difference between them. Nicolai (1959) has described how an abnormal, acquired song pattern of an individual male bullfinch, *Pyrrhula pyrrhula,* was handed on almost unchanged through four

generations. Just as many mammals have developed special "exploratory behaviour" in order to get conditioned to their home area and
several Hymenoptera have developed "locality studies" which serve to
learn the layout of the environment of their burrow, hive, or food
source, so the bullfinch has a special "listening attitude" in order to
learn song; Nicolai shows that this listening is a response to the individual parent or foster parent, and this may be the reason why such
species learn the song of their own father selectively, even if many
other species are singing. The innate basis of this character would
then not be a tendency to learn the song of the own species but to
learn the song of the father. Again, these findings must not be gen-
eralised; Sauer showed (1954) that the song of blackcaps, *Sylvia
atricapilla,* is not acquired.

We therefore have to be cautious in the interpretation of observations like those reported by Williamson (1952) on the behaviour
differences between the oystercatchers of the Faeroes and those of the
British mainland. Whatever the precise causation of distraction displays is, it can safely be said that a state of conflict in which aggres-
sion, fear, and broodiness take a part is involved. Since the intensity
of escape is easily changed by conditioning, such differences in the
readiness to perform distraction displays could very well be induced,
for instance, by a different predator situation in the localities compared. Or the fact that kittiwakes do not learn to confine their parental
care to their own young may or may not be due to the fact that young
kittiwakes stay in the nest; it is conceivable that, if they roamed about
as the young of other gulls do, the parents would become conditioned
to them.

Of course, this problem is different from that whether a certain
behaviour *trait* is "innate" or not; we are now concerned with the
question whether behaviour *differences* between taxa are innate or not.
Each character may well develop under partial control of the environment, but what matters here is whether two species would still be
different if they were raised in exactly the same environment. This
is a matter of the extent of resistance of the ontogenetic development
against changes in the environment; in particular, in comparing two
species, the relevant question is whether species A, when raised in the
environment of species B, would still be different in the characters
studied.

Fortunately, those behaviour characters which are most easily observed and are therefore of the greatest use, viz., certain motor patterns, such as displays and other "fixed patterns," are exactly the type
of behaviour features which are most environment-resistant. This has
been pointed out repeatedly by K. Lorenz (1941, 1953, 1958), and

this resistance is, of course, the reason why they are so constant through entire populations.

The taxonomist is continually tempted, particularly in difficult groups, to rely for classification on one or a few characters of a large complex to the exclusion of the others. This temptation is particularly strong when a new category of characters is brought into play. Mayr has, I think, convincingly argued (1942) that there are no a priori reasons why one type of character should be more reliable than another, and, although the taxonomist does a great amount of "weighting," morphological, physiological, and behavioural characters have to be given equal weight for classificatory purposes, and they have to be used in conjunction. The use of behaviour characters to the taxonomist is not that they should be more reliable for classification but that they add to the total number of characters that can be used. Their addition may be helpful in separating species that are morphologically extremely similar, such as the digger wasps, *Ammophila campestris* and *A. adriaansei* (Adriaanse, 1947), or they may be of use in uniting species that have radiated morphologically; thus pigeons and sand grouse (Pteroclidae) are remarkably constant in the way they drink, viz., by pumping. Yet this alone would not justify the view that they must be related; the behavioural character merely adds strength to the morphological evidence. In general, it can be said that where behaviour characters have been used for purposes of classification, the results have been very similar to the classifications already developed by museum taxonomists on the basis of morphological characters (see, e.g., Andrew, 1956, for Emberizinae; Crane, 1941, 1957, for *Uca;* Hinde, 1955, for Fringillidae; Jacobs, 1950, for Acrididae; Moynihan, 1955, for Laridae; Spieth, 1952, for *Drosophila*), although minor modifications have been necessary; these, however, were usually based on a reconsideration of all characters.

It is, of course, only after completion of a taxonomic study that one can distinguish between more conservative and more changeable characters, and a priori each character, however trivial it may seem to be, has to be given the benefit of the doubt.

PHYLOGENETIC INTERPRETATION OF BEHAVIOUR DATA

THE BASIS OF INDUCTION

Compared with the morphologist, the ethologist aiming at evolutionary interpretation has a very narrow and restricted inductive basis to operate from. The morphologist can use historical (paleontological) and also to a certain extent embryological data to supplement the comparative facts, and often the conclusions derived from these three sources conform to and thus reinforce each other. Although, by extrapolating form-function relationships known in contemporary animals, some conclusions can be drawn about the behaviour of fossil forms (see Romer, 1958), these conclusions are only of a very general nature. A direct observation of changes in time is possible only where mutants are observed to arise in genetically known stock; by the very nature of a mutation as a disturbance of normal development, such changes are very small (Caspari, 1958). Direct experimental data on the effect of selection are still both extremely rare and expressed as *effects* of behaviour (viz., reproductive isolation) rather than in terms of behaviour itself (Koopman, 1950; Knight, Robertson, and Waddington, 1956). So far, the only method applied to any extent is the comparative method. The basic assumption of this method is that differences between contemporary related forms are consequences of divergent changes in time and, conversely, that similarities between non-related forms are the consequences of convergent change. This method, of course, depends on the possibility of deciding whether the forms compared are truly related, i.e., derived from common stock, or not. This is done by over-all likeness, and this implies the use of as many characters as possible. The most promising groups for this type of study are those which encompass forms which "share" (are similar in) a great number of characters and yet are different enough to offer many differences for study. The classifier and the evolution student therefore begin by traveling along the same road; both begin by judging the affinity of the taxa compared on the basis of their over-all likeness.

It is fortunate for the ethologist that the classification of many groups has already been worked out statisfactorily. Although the addition of new characters, among them behaviour characters, sometimes leads to revisions of the existing classification, it can be said that, on the whole, the ethologist can assume that taxonomists can be relied on when they consider a given group monophyletic. Yet, in view of the fact that the addition of behaviour characters has sometimes changed the classification, the ethologist should always use his behaviour characters to check up on the existing classification.

ORIGIN OF BEHAVIOUR CHARACTERS;
DERIVED MOVEMENTS AND DERIVED ORGANS

In order to translate differences between contemporary forms into changes of time, one further step is required: an interpretation of the direction of the change. Without knowing whether behaviour character a of species A is more primitive than behaviour character b of species B (or whether a or b is nearer the character o of the original ancestor O), no pronouncement about the direction of change can be made. As in comparative anatomy, however, it is often possible in comparative ethology to trace the origin of a set of homologous movements. This has been done with what seems a fair degree of success in the so-called "derived movements," movements which have undergone adaptation to a new function. Just as the comparative anatomist can conclude that the claws of lobsters, *Homarus* spp., are derived from the first pereiopod which has acquired the new function of seizing and crushing of prey, so the comparative ethologist can conclude, for instance, that some courtship signals of ducks have been derived from preening and have been newly adapted to the function of sending out a signal. In order to draw this kind of conclusion, it is essential, as in comparative anatomy, to combine data derived from the comparison of species with data about the functions of both the original and the derived character (Tinbergen, 1959). The most convincing examples of evolutionary changes of function have been found in signaling movements, and the particular process of adapting to the signaling function is usually called "ritualisation."

HOW DOES THE BEHAVIOUR MACHINERY CHANGE IN EVOLUTION?

Comparative data obtained in this way can be used for two different purposes: (1) we want to know how behaviour machinery can change in evolution, and (2) we try to understand why the changes have been in the directions observed.

With regard to the first question, the differences between taxa (which of course must be supposed to be the result of long-continued mutation and selection combined) are often such that the compared characters cannot be measured on the same yardstick; the differences strike us as "qualitative." Examples are the species-specific claw-waving movements of fiddler crabs (Crane, 1941, 1957), the courtship movements of ducks, Anatidae (Lorenz, 1941, 1958), the agonistic and pair-formation displays of gulls, Laridae (Tinbergen, 1959), the songs of songbirds; in fact, the differences that can at once be described as "quantitative" are extremely rare. Changes in behaviour due to mutation and many differences between closely related populations, subspecies, and even species, on the contrary, can often be recognised after a preliminary analysis as simple quantitative shifts: a little more of this, a little less of that. Thus certain mutations in rats effect increased tameness; another is known to increase the inclination to fight; a third results in a reduced aggressiveness (Keeler and King,

1942). The *y*-mutant of *Drosophila melanogaster* spends more time in the preliminary part of courtship and less time "vibrating" and copulating (Bastock, 1956). It is therefore essential to attempt to reduce the "qualitative" ("new") differences to accumulations of "quantitative" changes. Often a formal analysis of the complex differences can pave the way for this. Thus many differences in the waving movements of *Uca* species are combinations of changes in amplitude, in direction, and in speed of the single components of the total movement (Crane, 1957); displays of gulls have radiated by the combined effects of such simple changes as increase or decrease of the amplitude, speeding up or slowing down, changes in thresholds, and incorporation or disappearance of single components (Tinbergen, 1959); similar elementary changes have been suggested by Blest's analysis of the antipredator displays of emperor moths, Saturnoidae, and hawk moths, Sphingidae (Blest, 1957). Of course, such a formal analysis should ultimately be accompanied by a physiological analysis in order to establish beyond doubt that what appears to be a quantitative shift is really not a misleadingly simple effect of a more complex inner reconstruction perhaps due to convergence; but a comparison of the scale of differences caused by single mutations with those observed between more or less closely related forms strongly suggests that our interpretation must be correct in principle and that "qualitative" differences between closely related forms are merely more complex than the basic small quantitative steps.

EVIDENCE OF NATURAL SELECTION

The second purpose of comparative studies is to find out why evolution has led to the results we observe in present-day animals. This task really amounts to an assessment of the relative importance of the contribution made by random variation, on the one hand, and by adaptation directed by selection, on the other. Since randomness is, per definition, detectable only by elimination of every conceivable directedness, it is natural that this approach should lead to a quest for directedness. In comparative studies (where the effect of selection cannot be demonstrated directly) this again leads to the study of the survival value of behaviour characters. Although, fortunately, the study of survival value is no longer scientifically suspect, critical work on this aspect of behaviour—as distinct from more or less happily inspired guesswork—is still rare, and one of the principal aims of my paper is to call attention to what I think is one of the major, and often neglected, tasks of comparative studies, behavioural or morphological.

Further, if it is our aim to understand the adaptive aspects of evolution, we cannot be satisfied with the investigation of the survival value of single characters, but we shall have to consider the adaptedness of the animal as a whole. Where this is being attempted, numerous characters which at first glance do not seem to "make (functional) sense" are seen to be adapted, because their functional significance lies in their interrelationship with other characters.

The two most fruitful types of approach are (*a*) the study of divergent forms derived from common stock and (*b*) that of distantly related convergent forms.

CONVERGENCE

Von Haartman (1957) has listed a number of characters which have convergently been developed by small birds of various groups which breed in holes. He showed that they share the following characters: (1) they tend to defend a nest hole rather than a larger territory; (2) the males have a special ceremony by which they attract females to the nest hole, and some bright colour patterns are employed in this ceremony; (3) the eggs are of a uniform, light colour (the few exceptions are argued, on good grounds, to be due to evolutionary inertia which prevents egg colour from changing as rapidly as some other characters); (4) the young gape in response to darkening of the nest entrance; and (5) the young develop slowly. He argues that these peculiarities are all functionally related to nesting in holes, which is itself an antipredator device (hole-nesting species raise a higher proportion of fledgling than do open nesters). The separate characters are all really components of one major character.

DIVERGENCE

A still more detailed study has been made by E. Cullen (1957) of the adaptive aspects of divergence. The following is a list of 24 peculiarities of the kittiwake, *Rissa tridactyla,* in which this species differs from the other gulls:

1. Nests on narrow ledges on steep cliffs	
2. Tame while on cliff	
3. Alarm call rare	Relaxation of
4. Predators are not attacked	other means
5. Chicks are not camouflaged	of antipredator defense
6. Defecation on nest's rim	
7. Egg shell is not carried away	

8. Strong claws and foot musculature	
9. Female squats during copulation	
10. Deep nest cup	Precautions
11. Two eggs	against falling
12. Immobility of chicks	off cliff
13. Chicks face "wall"	
14. Facing-away in chicks, black neck band	

15. No upright posture
16. Special fighting technique ("twisting") } Fighting

17. Choking acts as song
18. Upward choking at the end of meeting ceremony } Pair formation

19. Mud is collected and trampled down to form a nest platform
20. Stealing of nest material
21. Guarding the empty nest } Nest building

22. Incomplete regurgitation } Nest sanitation

23. Parents lack food-call
24. Chicks lack "pumping"
25. Parents do not know chicks individually } Parent-chick relationships

At first glance, some of these peculiarities do not seem to be adaptive at all. Without a careful consideration of functional aspects, it would, for instance, be obscure why the egg shells are not carried away; why the movement of facing away, which in other species is shown only by the adults, should appear here in the chicks; why the species lacks the characteristic upright posture which all other species have; or why the empty nest should be guarded. Cullen argues that most, if not all, characteristics of the kittiwake are corollaries of one major adaptation: nesting on very narrow ledges on perpendicular cliffs. This is undoubtedly a successful antipredator device; kittiwake broods are much less subject to predation than those of other gulls. The first six characters are really the outcome of relaxation of other ways of defense. Characters 8 through 14 are protections against falling off the cliff. Facing away in the chicks fits in here, since it inhibits attacks by nest mates and others and takes the functional place of running out of harm's way, which is more usual in other gulls. The absence of the upright (15) is correlated with the absence of the habit, common in ground-nesting gulls, to peck down at an opponent from above; since the upright is considered to be derived from the intention movement of this type of attack, its absence in the kittiwake is not surprising. The twisting movement (16) often succeeds in throwing an intruder off the cliff. The use of choking as song (17) is related to the fact that the male kittiwake's territory is really nothing more than the nest site. The mud platform (18) serves to broaden the foundation for the nest and to offer a horizontal substrate even on a slanting ledge. Scarcity of nest material on the cliffs has put a premium on stealing (20), and this has enhanced guarding even of the empty nest (21). Since kittiwakes are nidicolous birds, nest fouling has to be avoided, hence the incomplete regurgitation (22): neither males nor parents drop food in the nest; in the rare cases when food is spilled, it is painstakingly collected. Since the chicks are always on the nest, the parents need not call them to the food (23), nor need the chicks attract the parents' attention by vigorous up-down head movements (pumping) (24), nor is there any need for the parents to recognise their brood by any other means than nest site (25).

Thus a consideration of function reveals the adaptedness of all these peculiarities and also shows that they are interrelated.

ADAPTED FEATURES ARE SYSTEMS

These studies demonstrate that adapted features are systems composed of many functionally related "characters." Moreover, it is impossible to separate functionally behaviour characters from "morphological" or "physiological" characters: egg coloration and growth rate of hole-breeding birds are just as much parts of the adapted system as a nest-showing ceremony; the black neck band of the young kittiwake (which is alleged to enhance the signaling effect of facing away) is just as much a part of the kittiwake's adapted system as the tameness of this species or its movements of trampling down mud on the nest plat-form.

Apart from such comprehensive adapted systems, which, so to speak, ramify and affect a great many characters, species may differ in systems with fewer components. The kittiwake differs from other gulls not only in its cliff-nesting habits but also by its pelagic feeding and by possessing a bright orange mouth. The first character may be linked with cliff nesting; there are indications that pelagic life may make a species particularly loath to settle on the land, and the conflict be-tween the demands of individual safety (which makes all gulls prefer wide-open spaces) and those of a suitable breeding ground may well have been shifted in the kittiwake toward an increased fear of the land, with its abundance of predators, and thus have forced it to select the safest possible nesting habitat. The orange mouth, however, seems to be an entirely independent character, a brightly coloured releaser which supports the effect of the threat postures, for it is striking that all threat postures of the kittiwake involve a wide opening of the mouth (even in those postures in which other gulls keep the bill closed), whereas "friendly" postures (such as the food-begging movements) involve closing of the bill. It is clear that even in this less comprehen-sive system morphology and behaviour are functionally linked.

Lorenz (1949) described a similar, relatively limited system in the starling, whose habit of boring the bill into the soil, then "prizing" upper and lower mandible apart and looking down into the crack thus formed, is correlated with such characters as the position of the eyes (in line with the bill slit), lateral compression of the skull in front of the eyes, the ability to flatten the plumage anterior to the eyes, and a high growth rate of the bill. The correlation between behaviour and morphology has, of course, been established in many cases, particularly in feeding and in signaling systems.

INTERACTION OF SELECTION PRESSURES

The conclusion that adapted features are systems leads to some further considerations. Once one is interested in studying the function of behaviour (or of any life-process) and tries to discover in particular cases what type of selection pressures could have been involved, one cannot help seeing that selection pressures must often be in conflict with one another. But the recognition of the system character of adapted features then shows that, apart from conflicts, there are many other interactions. One ends up by discovering that each character not only has been improved with regard to its own particular function but has also undergone *indirect* effects, which, when considered alone, appear to be due to random change but are recognised as effects of selection when seen as parts of systems. I will not try to classify the many types of interaction which one can recognise but will give some examples to show the great variety of indirect effects of selection.

In many cases there is a conflict between demands on one particular character. The legs of geese are not ideal swimming legs or ideal walking legs, but they are an excellent compromise between both. Similarly, in many camouflaged animals there is a conflict between immobility (without which camouflage does not work) and mobility in the interest of, e.g., feeding or mating. Different animals have arrived at different compromises: either immobility by day and mobility by night, or stealthy movement or very rapid movement and sudden cessation. Each species may "have its own reasons" for having gone in for one or another of these solutions.

On the social level, there is a clash of interest between the demands of spacing-out of breeding pairs, which in territorial animals is safeguarded by a balanced attack-escape system (Tinbergen, 1957), and the demands of pair formation and mating; the compromise has given rise to the courtship of such species (Hinde, 1953; Morris, 1956; Tinbergen, 1953*b*, 1954, 1959). If there were no conflict between those two systems, there would be no reason why such highly complicated, conspicuous, and therefore dangerous elaborations of courtship should have evolved. The results of these conflicts have themselves become the subject of new direct selection pressures: improvement in their signal functions.

Of particular interest are the conflicts between the demands of individual safety and survival and those of the survival of the family, between short-term and long-term survival. All gulls and terns select an open, flat habitat, which allows them to see an approaching predator in time, and they are very reluctant to alight between high tall structures such as trees or buildings, although conditioning can overcome this reluctance. In spring the requirements of reproduction force them to select a breeding habitat of which they are individually afraid. Many species show repeated "dreads" or panics when they first arrive at their breeding haunts; these panics subside only gradually (Kirkman, 1937; Tinbergen, 1953a). Without knowledge of the two selection pressures involved, one would be tempted to consider these dreads as totally unadapted; yet they are the outcome of a conflict between two adapted systems. The development of conspicuous signals, whether colours or calls or movements, must be supposed to have been curtailed continually by the demands of individual safety. Marler (1955) has shown convincingly that these latter actually mold the signals: warning calls of small songbirds have certain qualities which render them very difficult to locate for predators of the size that normally prey upon them, and this has led to striking convergences. The compromise between camouflage and bright signal colours is, of course, too well known to need elaboration here.

There are further numerous other relationships which cannot be readily listed under the heading "conflict." As has been pointed out repeatedly since Lorenz (1935), it is of advantage to species which employ social signals to make each of them unambiguous, so that disrupting misunderstandings are avoided. There is evidence suggesting that this mutual relationship is true not only between whole categories of signals, such as appeasement postures, on the one hand, and agonistic postures, on the other, but even within the set of agonistic postures which each species of gull has at its disposal there is evidence of selection pressure toward interdisplay distinctness (Tinbergen, 1959).

Pressure toward distinctness has also been traced in interspecific differences of displays. F. W. Blair (1955) reported that the mating calls of two *Microhyla* species are more distinct in the area where they overlap than in the other parts of their ranges. Perdeck (1958) has shown that the main difference between two sibling, sympatric *Chorthippus* species is in their mating sounds, and he has experimentally demonstrated that this is the main factor in reproductive isolation between the two. Of course, it must not be supposed that all differences in mating calls are due to the direct selection for interspecies difference; the mating call of the kittiwake is very different from that of other gulls, yet this is probably the *indirect* outcome of nesting on cliffs rather than of selection for interspecies distinctness.

Interrelations between characters can also be of a quite different kind; the signals of each species have developed in conjunction with the responsiveness of the reactor; what has been favoured by selection has been the signal response system as a whole. Neither signal nor response would be of any survival value in itself, although each of them is, of course, the elaboration of something already present. A comparative review of signaling systems leads to the conclusion that in some cases the responsiveness of the reactor has molded the signal, while in other cases the signal-producing effector (the releaser) has developed from the start, together with the specific responsiveness; in other cases, again, the movement must have been primary. The fact that insect-pollinated flowers are usually yellow, blue, or ultraviolet and that bird-pollinated flowers are predominantly red is no doubt a reflection of the sensory equipment of the two animal groups concerned. Species with good visual receptors (which are used in many functional contexts such as feeding, escape from predators, etc.) have also developed visual signals, and those with good auditory receptors also have developed auditory signals. In other cases the sense organ may have evolved exclusively in the service of intraspecific communication: it certainly seems plausible to assume that locusts and grasshoppers have developed their sound-sensitive organs primarily for this purpose.

Many characters have also been enhanced one-sidedly by indirect pressure exerted in other functional spheres. For instance, the sparrow hawk, *Accipiter nisus,* and some other raptors collect twigs for their nest by swooping down on dead twigs still attached to trees and breaking them off with their talons (Bal, 1950). There can be little doubt that this is a consequence of the development of talons and of the swooping and seizing methods in the service of feeding. The use of this rather than the more usual methods of collecting nest material is therefore an indirect effect of selection; the fact that when the bird is in nest-building condition these movements are elicited by the sight of twigs rather than prey and that the collecting movement is successively integrated with carrying and building rather than with killing and eating is, of course, due to direct selection toward perfection of the nest-building system for its own sake.

These few examples must suffice to show that it is simply impossible to judge the part played by selection in the evolution of a certain character unless all its functional contexts, including its relations with other functional systems, have been investigated. The keys to a full understanding of the effects of selection, therefore, are (1) functional study, (2) study of all functional systems an animal possesses, and, last but not least, (3) study of interactions of all kinds. Such comprehensive functional studies are still extremely rare, and I am convinced that whenever they are undertaken they will show that the indirect effects of selection are much more far-reaching than we are aware of now.

We see, then, that a study of function and an awareness of the system character of adapted features are forcing the behaviour student to an attitude of healthy respect for the all-pervading power of selection. Consequently, he is less inclined to attribute characters to random change than are most museum taxonomists. It could, of course, be asked whether this high degree of adaptedness is perhaps typical of behaviour rather than of morphological characters. I am firmly convinced that this is not so but that we have to do with differences between scientists. The behaviour student is, by inclination and by opportunity, much more in touch with the live animal than most museum taxonomists. Those taxonomists who do study the live animal are likewise acquiring the same healthy respect for selection.

BEHAVIOUR CHARACTERS AND TAXONOMY

The conclusion that adapted features are systems of functionally related components forces us to reconsider once more the question What is a taxonomic character? The answer is, of course, that it depends on the aims which the scientist has in mind. The classifier is fully entitled to use, e.g., the tameness of the kittiwakes, their nest-building behaviour, the black neck band of their young, and their nidicolous habits as four separate characters. But the evolutionist is not entitled to treat them as four independent characters. To him, the correct description of the characteristics of the species would be in terms of adapted systems, such as (1) cliff breeding; (2) pelagic feeding; (3) orange inside of the mouth and related characteristics of posturing; and a few other characters such as the shape of the black wing tip and the underdeveloped fourth toe. The character "cliff nesting" characterises the list of 25 characters mentioned separately above. The classifier can use all 25 characters to show how different the kittiwake is from other gulls; the evolutionist concentrates them into a few systems. Unawareness of the difference in aims between classifiers and evolutionists could give rise to endless disputes between splitters and lumpers. However, when the real aim of comparative studies is not to classify, but when classification is merely a means toward an understanding of the evolutionary history, then there is no question of an annoying or confusing dispute; what emerges as positive gain is a better description of how and why species have diverged the way they have.

CONCLUSIONS

1. When behaviour characters are used in systematics, extra caution is needed to distinguish between true differences and immediate environmental effects.

2. Apart from small mutational steps and extremely fragmentary evidence on the effect of selection, no direct evidence about evolutionary change in time is available, and the argument is based on the assumption that differences between related contemporary forms and similarities between non-related contemporary forms reflect changes in time.

3. Behaviour characters are, in principle, neither more nor less useful than morphological or other characters; they merely add characters to the total by which over-all likeness is judged.

4. Comparative data can be used for two purposes: (*a*) a description of the behaviour changes which have happened in evolution, with the ultimate aim of describing how the behaviour machinery has changed, and (*b*) an assessment of the relative importance of selection versus random change.

5. The description of behaviour changes aims at reducing "qualitative" differences between taxa to accumulations of small quantitative steps.

6. Critical studies of survival value, applied to total behaviour patterns, are needed to assess the effects of selection. Where this has been done, either by studying convergence or by comparing divergent related species, it has been found that many characters are interrelated components of adapted systems. These systems are complexes of morphological, physiological, and ethological features.

7. There are numerous relationships between the various functional systems an animal has, and many characters have therefore been subject to indirect effects of selection pressure.

8. There is no reason to suppose that behaviour characters have been subject to selection to a greater extent than any other character; the ethologists' high regard for the influence of selection is due to his characteristics rather than to those of the material.

BIBLIOGRAPHY

ADRIAANSE, A. 1947. *"Ammophila campestris* Latr. and *Ammophila adriaansei* Wilcke," *Behaviour,* I, 1–35.

ANDREW, R. J. 1956. "The Aggressive and Courtship Behaviour of Certain Emberizines," *Behaviour,* X, 255–308.

ARMSTRONG, E. A. 1952. "The Behaviour and Breeding Biology of the Shetland Wren," *Ibis,* XCIV, 220–42.

BAL, C. 1950. "De Nestbouw van Sperwers, *Accipiter n. nisus* (L.) in Nederland," *Ardea,* XXXVIII, 19–35.

BASTOCK, M. 1956. "A Gene Mutation Which Changes a Behaviour Pattern," *Evolution,* X, 421–39.

BEACH, F. A. 1958. "Evolutionary Aspects of Psychoendocrinology." In *Behavior and Evolution,* ed. ROE and SIMPSON, pp. 81–103. New Haven.

BERGMAN, G. 1946. "Der Steinwälzer *Arenaria i. interpres* (L.) in seiner Beziehung zur Umwelt," *Acta zool. Fenn.,* XLVII, 1–151.

BLAIR, F. W. 1955. "Mating Call and Stage of Speciation in the *Microhyla olivacea–M. carolinensis* Complex," *Evolution,* IX, 469–80.

BLEST, A. D. 1957. "The Evolution of Protective Displays in the Saturnoidea and Sphingidae," *Behaviour,* XI.

BULLOUGH, W. S. 1942. "The Reproductive Cycles of the British and Continental Races of the Starling (*Sturnus vulgaris* L.)," *Phil. Trans. Roy. Soc., B,* CCXXXI, 165–246.

CASPARI, E. 1958. "Genetic Basis of Behavior." In *Behavior and Evolution,* ed. ROE and SIMPSON, pp. 103–28. New Haven.

CRANE, J. 1941. "Crabs of the Genus *Uca* from the West Coast of Central America," *Zoologica,* XXVI, 145–208.

———. 1957. "Basic Patterns of Display in Fiddler Crabs (Ocypodidae, genus *Uca*)," *ibid.,* XLII, 69–82.

CULLEN, E. 1957. "Adaptations in the Kittiwake to Cliff-Nesting," *Ibis,* XCIX, 275–302.

———. 1959. *Behavior as a Help in Taxonomy.* Sust. Assoc. Publ. 3, 131–40.

FRISCH, K. VON. 1956. "Lernvermögen und erbgebundene Tradition im Leben der Bienen," In M. Autuori, *L'Instinct,* pp. 345–87. Paris.

GOETHE, F. 1955. "Beobachtungen bei der Aufzucht junger Silbermöwen," *Zeitschr. Tierpsychol.,* XII, 402–33.

HAARTMAN, L. VON. 1957. "Adaptation in Hole-nesting Birds," *Evolution,* XI, 339–48.

HINDE, R. A. 1953. "The Conflict between Drives in the Courtship and Copulation of the Chaffinch," *Behaviour,* V, 1–31.

———. 1955. "A Comparative Study of the Courtship of Certain Finches (Fringillidae)," *Ibis,* XCVII, 706–46.

———. 1959. "Behaviour and Speciation in Birds and Lower Vertebrates," *Biol. Rev.,* XXXIV, 85–128.

HINDE, R. A., and TINBERGEN, N. 1958. "The Comparative Study of Species-specific Behavior." In *Behavior and Evolution,* ed. ROE and SIMPSON, pp. 251–68. New Haven.

JACOBS, W. 1950. "Vergleichende Verhaltensstudien an Feldheuschrecken," *Zeitschr. Tierpsychol.,* Beiheft, I, 1–228.

KEELER, C. E., and KING, H. D. 1942. "Multiple Effects of Coat Color

Genes in the Rat, with Special Reference to Temperament and Domestication," *Jour. Comp. Psychol.,* XXXIV, 241–50.

KIRKMAN, F. B. 1937. *Bird Behaviour.* London & Edinburgh.

KLOMP, H. 1954. "De Terreinkeus van de Kievit, *Vanellus vanellus* L.," *Ardea,* XLII, 1–140.

KNIGHT, G. R., ROBERTSON, A., and WADDINGTON, C. H. 1956. "Selection for Sexual Isolation within a Species," *Evolution,* X, 14–22.

KOOPMAN, K. K. 1950. "Natural Selection for Reproductive Isolation between *Drosophila pseudoobscura* and *D. persimilis,*" *Evolution,* IV, 135–48.

LACK, D. 1946. "Competition for Food by Birds of Prey," *Jour. Anim. Ecol.,* XV, 123–29.

LORENZ, K. 1935. "Der Kumpan in der Umwelt des Vogels," *Jour. Ornithol.,* LXXXIII, 137–213 and 289–413.

———. 1941. "Vergleichende Bewegungsstudien an Anatinen," *ibid.,* LXXXIX, 194–294 *(Festschrift O. Heinroth).*

———. 1949. "Die Beziehungen zwischen Kopfform und Zirkelbewegung bei Sturniden und Ikteriden." In E. MAYR and B. RENSCH (eds.), *Ornithologie als biologische Wissenschaft: Festschrift E. Stresemann,* pp. 153–58. Heidelberg.

———. 1953. "Psychologie und Stammesgeschichte." In G. HEBERER, *Die Evolution der Organismen,* pp. 131–72. Stuttgart.

———. 1955. "Morphology and Behavior Patterns in Closely Allied Species," *First Conf. Group Proc. Macy Foundation,* pp. 168–220.

———. 1958. "The Evolution of Behavior," *Scient. American,* CXCIX, 67–83.

MANNING, A. 1956. "Some Aspects of the Foraging Behaviour of Bumble-Bees," *Behaviour,* IX, 164–202.

———. 1959. "Comparison of Mating Behaviour in *Drosophila melanogaster* and *D. simulans,*" *Behaviour,* XV, 123–146.

MARLER, P. 1955. "The Characteristics of Some Animal Calls," *Nature,* CLXXVI, 6.

MAYR, E. 1942. *Systematics and the Origin of Species.* New York.

———. 1958. "Behavior and Systematics." In *Behavior and Evolution,* ed. ROE and SIMPSON, pp. 341–63. New Haven.

MORRIS, D. 1954. "The Snail-eating Behaviour of Thrushes and Blackbirds," *Brit. Birds,* XLVII, 33–49.

———. 1956. "The Function and Causation of Courtship Ceremonies." In M. AUTUORI, *L'Instinct,* pp. 261–87. Paris.

MOYNIHAN, M. 1955. *Some Aspects of Reproductive Behavior in the Blackheaded Gull (Larus r. ridibundus L.) and Related Species.* (*Behaviour* Suppl., No. 4, pp. 1–202.)

NICOLAI, J. J. 1959. "Familientradition in der Gesangsentwicklung des Gimpels (*Pyrrhula pyrrhula* L.)," *Jour. Ornithol., C,* 39–47.

PECKHAM, G. W., and PECKHAM, E. G. 1898. *On the Instincts and Habits of the Solitary Wasps.* (Eisc. Geol. Nat. Hist. Survey Bull. No. 2, pp. 1–245.)

PERDECK, A. C. 1958. "The Isolating Value of Specific Song Patterns in Two Sibling Species of Grasshoppers (*Chorthippus brunneus* Thunb. and *C. biguttulus* L.)," *Behaviour,* XII, 1–76.

ROE, A., and SIMPSON, G. G. 1958. *Behavior and Evolution.* New Haven.

ROMER, A. S. 1958. "Phylogeny and Behavior with Special Reference to Vertebrate Evolution." In *Behavior and Evolution,* ed. ROE and SIMPSON, pp. 48–77. New Haven.

SAUER, F. 1954. "Die Entwicklung der Lautässerungen vom Ei ab schalldicht gehaltener Dorngrasmücken," *Zeitschr.* Tierpsychol., XI, 10–23.

SPIETH, H. T. 1952. "Mating Behavior within the Genus *Drosophila* (Diptera)," *Bull. Amer. Mus. Nat. Hist.,* XCIX, 401–79.

THORPE, W. H. 1958. "The Learning of Song Patterns by Birds, with Especial Reference to the Song of the Chaffinch, *Fringilla coelebs,*" *Ibis,* C, 535–71.

TINBERGEN, N. 1953a. *The Herring Gull's World.* London.

———. 1953b. *Social Behaviour in Animals.* London.

———. 1954. "The Origin and Evolution of Courtship and Threat Display." In A. C. HARDY, J. S. HUXLEY, and E. B. FORD (eds.), *Evolution as a Process,* pp. 233–51. London.

———. 1957. "The Functions of Territory," *Bird Study,* IV, 14–27.

———. 1959. "Comparative Studies of the Behaviour of Gulls (Laridae): A Progress Report," *Behaviour,* XV, 1–71.

VINCE, M. A. 1956. " 'String Pulling' in Birds," *Brit. Jour. Anim. Behaviour,* IV, 111–16.

WILLIAMSON, K. 1952. "Regional Variation in the Distraction Displays of the Oystercatcher," *Ibis,* XCIV, 85–97.

DARWINISM, MICROBIOLOGY, AND CANCER

Darwinism has always been, and still is, a great stimulant to the development of profitable ideas in comparative biology and comparative pathology. Fifty years ago, on the occasion of the celebration of the fiftieth anniversary of the publication of Darwin's great work, *Origin of Species,* Ilya Metchnikoff in his speech in Cambridge explained how the idea of evolution stimulated the discovery of phagocytosis and the development of the comparative pathology of inflammation. Observations on amoeboid cells of some hyaline lower invertebrates devouring inert particles contributed to the understanding of the role of leucocytes in the defense of the human body against the invasion of bacteria.

In the same famous speech Metchnikoff went as far as to suggest that Darwin's theory of evolution could also help in the attack upon the problem of cancer, one of the most difficult tasks of modern medicine. It is not altogether fortuitous that one of the leading Darwinists today, Sir Julian Huxley, in his remarkable book on *Biological Aspects of Cancer,* published in 1958, strongly defends the idea that cancer is not merely a medical problem: it is a biological phenomenon, and its elucidation is closely connected with advances in a number of key branches of present-day biology. How near we now stand to what Huxley called the biochemical "kernel" of cancer, none can confidently say; but there is no doubt that the wide "biological" approaches he advocated are the ones most likely to get at it quickly.

In these studies, microorganisms should not in any way be neglected. The possible malignant alterations in the cells of certain Protozoa have attracted the interest of biologists in the course of the last thirty years, and more recently considerable attention has been paid to "equivalents" of cancer cells in yeast, fungi, and bacteria.

At first sight, the search for "equivalents" of cancer cells among microorganisms is devoid of any serious foundation. In fact, how could one imagine cancer cells in the world of the free-living unicellular microbes? The malignant growth, by its very nature, could arise

G. F. GAUSE is Scientific Director of the Institute of Antibiotics of the Academy of Medical Sciences, Moscow.

only in multicellular organisms, where cells acquiring malignancy multiply without limit, disturb the regulatory mechanisms, and penetrate into the surrounding tissues.

Nevertheless, some observations in the field of comparative biology of cancer stimulated an altered attitude toward this subject. For example, Thomas, Evans, and Hughes (1956) have induced striking tumors, cytologically similar to animal tumors, in basidiomycete fungi (among them, the cultivated mushrooms *Psalliota*) by diesel-oil vapor and by tar fumes. Similar cytological effects can be induced in multicellular and unicellular fungi by the action of carcinogenic substances. In the former case real tumors develop. In the latter case malignancy is acquired by the free-living cells of microscopic fungi, which could be considered as the "equivalent" of cancer cells among microorganisms.

But before embarking into any search for possible equivalents of cancer cells among microorganisms, one should take into consideration some fundamental biochemical issues, without which the whole venture is doomed to failure. The focal point of our interest should be an analysis of specific metabolic differences among various strains of microorganisms, which may be similar to those distinguishing cancer cells from their normal ancestors.

DEFICIENCY OF RESPIRATION IN CELLS OF MALIGNANT TUMORS

Biochemical studies made by O. Warburg (1926, 1956) in the course of the last thirty years—and confirmed in many other laboratories— have shown that the transformation of a normal cell into a malignant one may be considered the result of injury to the cellular respiratory mechanism. A more detailed analysis of this transformation brings us to the following conclusions:

1. The formation of cancer cells may depend upon *the irreversible damage to respiration*. The latter can be brought about by chronic intermittent oxygen deficiency due to the action of respiratory poisons, by various carcinogenic substances, by radiant energy, and by the action of viruses.

The injury to respiration may consist in the irreversible damage of the intracellular self-perpetuating respiratory mitochondrial elements or grana. The respiring grana can be destroyed by X-rays, carcinogenic hydrocarbons, and many other means.

2. A cell with injured respiration remains alive only in rare cases. Most of the cells with damaged oxidation perish. But when the re-

spiratory injury is not lethal, there may occur a transformation of the cell into the malignant state. Such cells are the ancestors of tumors, inasmuch as they acquire an opportunity for unlimited multiplication in the living body.

Further, cancer cells possess increased capacity for fermentation as compared with normal ones, as judged by the increased production of lactic acid under aerobic and anaerobic conditions. However, the increase in glycolysis does not occur in all cases; some examples are known when, in malignant cells of man, fermentation and oxidation are both diminished as compared with normal cells.

3. The injury to respiration, peculiar to cancer cells, brings about, according to Warburg, a very important consequence—the dedifferentiation of cancer cells, which lose many specific cellular structures. It is well known that cancer cells can originate from cells of different tissues and that in nature there exist various types of malignant tumors. Nevertheless, all of them are unique in impaired respiration and the consequent dedifferentiation of cells.

The conclusion reached by Warburg concerning the injury to respiration in cancer cells was criticized (Weinhouse, 1955). Nevertheless, this conclusion is supported by numerous measurements. The injury to respiration in cancer cells can also be demonstrated by various observations, in addition to direct manometric measurements. For example, according to Lettré *et al.* (1957), the mitochondrial fraction with which respiration is connected is strongly decreased in cancer cells as compared with the normal ones.

The impairment of the respiratory mechanism of tumors may be related to the defects in their cytochrome system. Malignant tissues, in comparison with normal tissues, are characterized not only by possessing the lowest concentrations of cytochrome *c* but also by possessing the greatest disparity between the components of the cytochrome oxidase—cytochrome *c* system. In relation to the activity of cytochrome oxidase, malignant tissues have the lowest proportion of cytochrome *c*, as can be concluded from manometric measurements (see Greenstein, 1954). These observations point to the functional disturbance in the cytochrome system of human solid tumor cells, which may be directly related to the deficiency of their respiration.

Somewhat different results were obtained by Chance and Castor (1952) in the direct spectroscopic study of the respiratory pigments of the intact, freely suspended ascites tumor cells of mice. No significant differences in the contents of cytochromes *a*, a_3, and *c* in normal and cancer cells were detected. However, the cytochrome *b* in cancer cells was almost undetectable, whereas it was always present in normal cells. In this way spectroscopic studies revealed a deficiency in cytochrome *b*, pointing to the functional insufficiency of the cytochrome system in malignant cells.

More recent studies by Chance and Hess (1959) indicate that it may be the "metabolic control" rather than the absolute concentration of cytochrome that plays an important role in the low respiration of tumors.

One has to notice, however, that Greenstein (1954) observed with the aid of the manometric method the deficiency of cytochrome *c* in the cells of various solid tumors of man, whereas Chance and Castor (1952) recorded spectroscopically the deficiency of cytochrome *b* in the free-living ascites tumor cells of mice. Whether these observations reflect actual differences between free-living cells of mice and solid tumors of man or differences in the experimental techniques of spectroscopy and manometry is not clear at the present time (Greenstein, 1954).

Modern biochemistry relative to some features of metabolism in tumor cells, although still very incomplete, should be taken into account in the search for anticancer substances (Gause, 1958). If cancer cells possess hereditary impairment of their respiratory systems, could one not obtain some equivalents of cancer cells in microbiology? That is, could one not obtain biochemical mutants of microorganisms with hereditary impairment of their respiratory system and, most important of all, utilize these mutants as tests in the screening for antibiotics and other substances that selectively inhibit malignant growth?

The Equivalents of Cancer in Yeast and Fungi

The impairment of respiration characteristic of cancer cells arises in consequence of the irreversible damage to cytoplasmic respiratory grana under the action of carcinogenic substances, radiations, and viruses and can, under similar conditions, be induced in the cells of microorganisms. Meisel and Zavarzina (1947) clearly expressed this idea in a study of the action of carcinogenic hydrocarbons (benzpyrene and methylcholanthrene) upon yeast cells. Unfortunately, these two hydrocarbons, strongly carcinogenic for cells of laboratory animals, are relatively inefficient in yeast. It was later found that trypaflavine (3,6-diamino-10-methylacridine-chloride) is much more efficient and easily induces mutants with deficient respiration in yeast belonging to different species (Ephrussi *et al.,* 1949). These mutants possess small colonies on the nutrient agar. The parent culture of yeast, *Saccharomyces cerevisiae,* under aerobic conditions metabolized 92 per cent of glucose by oxidation and 8 per cent by fermentation, whereas the trypaflavine-induced mutant oxidized 12 per cent and fermented 88 per cent of the glucose (Tavlitzki, 1949). High aerobic glycolysis of the mutants is the cause of the small size of their colonies on agar plates, because fermentation yields less energy than oxidation (Slonimski, 1949).

The yeast mutants with small colonies possess impaired respiration and high aerobic glycolysis—i.e., just those features of metabolism which distinguished malignant cells from their normal ancestors in the experiments of Warburg. The metabolic similarity between these biochemical mutants of yeast and cancer cells has recently been discussed by Lindegren and Hino (1957), particularly in relation to the degeneration of the oxidative mechanism as a possible cause of dedifferentiation which might lead to cancer.

Lindegren and Nagai (1958) have also shown that respiratory deficiency in yeast can be induced by manganese, copper, cobalt, and nickel. These observations have led them to some considerations of a general character, which we quote:

Respiratory deficiency in yeast may be the result either of destruction or inactivation of a cytoplasmic granule or mutation of a gene. It has been shown that this condition may be induced with high frequency during growth by different organic poisons. The inorganic ions manganese, copper, cobalt and nickel induce respiratory deficiency in yeasts with high frequency. The high frequency of induction and the relative independence of ploidy suggests that most of the respiratory deficiencies induced by those ions are due to the destruction or inactivation of cytoplasmic granules rather than to effects on the genome. . . .

It is commonly said that most mutagens (meaning agents which cause gene mutation) are carcinogens, and it has been inferred that the problem of cancer is related in some way to the structure of the deoxyribonucleic acid. This inference rests on the assumption that gene mutation is an important factor in carcinogenesis. Many of the effects, however, which are ascribed to gene mutation may be due to the damage to the autonomous cytoplasmic granules, and such carcinogens as ultraviolet and X-rays have often been demonstrated to produce stable variations in the extra-chromosomal apparatus. Re-evaluation of ideas relating gene mutation to carcinogenesis may be in order [p. 448].

It has been shown that in the trypaflavine-induced mutant of yeast studied by Ephrussi and Slonimski the impaired respiration results from the deficient cytochrome system: cytochromes a and b are lacking, whereas the content of cytochrome c is increased as compared with the parent culture. These characteristics of the mutant culture are fixed by heredity and do not change in the course of numerous passages on agar slants.

Further studies in this field were published by Gause, Kochetkova, and Vladimirova (1957), who studied eleven different mutants of yeast (*S. cerevisiae*) with impaired respiration induced by trypaflavine, camphor, and ultraviolet radiation.

In all eleven mutant strains there was a strong hereditary injury to the respiration; the oxygen consumption in various mutant strains decreased to one-tenth to one two-hundredth of that of the parent cells. It is interesting to record in this connection that in some mutants the injury to respiration was accompanied by an increase in aerobic glycolysis; in others aerobic glycolysis was only slightly enhanced; and, finally, in one of the mutant cultures the aerobic glycolysis was decreased as compared with the value characteristic of the parent culture. In other words, in biochemical mutants of yeast with impaired oxidation, aerobic glycolysis can change in different directions, in the same way as can the aerobic glycolysis of malignant cells belonging to different strains.

In cultures of *Neurospora crassa*, biochemical mutants with impaired respiration were also observed; in many respects they resembled the yeast with deficient respiration (Haskins *et al.*, 1953; Tissieres *et al.*, 1953, 1954).

The Equivalents of Cancer in Bacteria

Heretofore we have been concerned with the respiratory impairment in the cells of mutant cultures of yeast and fungi. Could one not obtain similar mutants in bacteria under the action of carcinogenic agents?

Studies in this field were made by Gause, Kochetkova, and Vladimirova (1957). Six different strains of *Staphylococcus aureus* were used in these investigations. Suspensions of *S. aureus*, strain 209 and other strains, were plated upon the nutrient agar and immediately irradiated by ultraviolet light so that about 99 per cent of the bacteria were killed; subsequent incubation revealed the appearance on these plates of a few mutant colonies. The mutants grew slowly on nutrient agar, producing small colonies which differed from the parent strain in being orange (Nos. 1 and 2) or orange-rose (No. 3) in color. These characteristics of the mutant strains have proved stable through numerous subcultures over a period of several years.

In different strains of mutant staphylococci the consumption of oxygen is decreased to 40–65 per cent of that of the parent culture. The decrease in oxygen consumption in the biochemical mutants of staphylococci is not so great as it is in the biochemical mutants of yeast, in which oxidation may sometimes decrease to one two-hundredth of that of the parent culture—that is, it is practically abolished under aerobic conditions. As is well known, the consumption of oxygen in cancer cells may often decrease to half the value characteristic of normal cells. In other words, the impairment of the respiratory system of cancer cells is quantitatively more like that of biochemical mutants of staphylococci than it is like the respiratory deficiency in the mutant strains of yeasts.

The respiration of mutant strains of staphylococci is much less sensitive to cyanide than is the respiration of the parent cultures. This observation points to a deficiency of the cytochrome system as a cause of impaired respiration in the mutant strain. Spectroscopic studies confirmed these expectations. Whereas in the parent strain three a bands of cytochrome are distinctly visible (b_1, a, and a_2), in both mutant strains of staphylococci band b_1 is altered.

Further studies by Gause, Ivanitskaia, and Vladimirova (1958) have shown that in *Bacterium coli* and *B. paracoli* biochemical mutants with impaired respiration can also be obtained. They are induced by ultraviolet radiation and especially by urethan, which, as is well known, has a strong carcinogenic action upon the cells of higher animals and inhibits cytochrome electron transport. It is probable that the carcinogenic action of urethan is due to the fact that it is concentrated in the cell on the respiring surfaces but, in contrast to alcohol, is not itself burned up on those surfaces (Warburg, 1956).

We have, finally, to discuss a difficult but important question— To what extent can biochemical mutants with impaired respiration in yeast, fungi, and bacteria actually be considered equivalents of cancer cells among microorganisms? It is well known that radiant energy and certain chemical substances induce characteristic alterations in the cells of multicellular organisms, which bring about their malignant growth. These alterations are associated with the injury to the respiratory system of the cell, localized in the intracellular grana. Some changes in the cytochrome system are also observed, which are still controversial and may concern cytochromes b and c. Many different types of cancer cells are known, with various deficiencies of respiration, which differ in their morphology and physiological characteristics.

A similar picture can be observed among microorganisms. In the cells of yeast, fungi, and bacteria under the action of radiant energy and of such a universal carcinogenic agent as urethan there may occur stable hereditary impairments of respiration. These may be expressed in different degree in various mutants, inasmuch as many different kinds of defects may lead to respiratory deficiency. Various changes in cytochrome spectra are also recorded in biochemical mutants of yeast, fungi, and bacteria, which are associated with the damaged respiration and usually involve the band of cytochrome *b*.

It is clear that there is much biological similarity in these two series of observations. There is indeed some justification for drawing an analogy between the biochemical mutants of microorganisms with impaired respiration and cancer cells, as far as such an analogy can contribute to a better analysis of the cancer problem in the light of general biology. It has rightly been pointed out recently that cancer research can prosper only if it is broadly based.

THE EQUIVALENTS OF CANCER CELLS IN PROTOZOA

An interest in the study of possible equivalents of cancer cells among Protozoa has been shown sporadically by various investigators during the course of the last thirty years. In 1928, Metcalf published a paper entitled: "Cancer in Certain Protozoa?" pointing out that, in cultures of the Opalinids, abnormal cells can be observed occasionally that are cytologically reminiscent of malignant tumors. He wrote:

In the Opalinids we have cytological conditions corresponding to those in mammalian cancer: (1) enlarged cells with enlarged nuclei arising by division of the chromosomes without division of the nucleus or by fusion of nuclei. Such nuclei have too many chromosomes; (2) unequal division of such enlarged nuclei causing still further distortion in kinds as well as number of chromosomes present; (3) amitotic division of the chromatin without division of the nucleus; (4) degeneration of nucleus and of cell. . . . We may say that the phenomena in the Opalinids are as fundamentally cancerous as they are in mammalian cancer. If cancer is at its foundation a distortion of the chromosome complex it may occur as readily in a protozoan as in a metazoan [pp. 554–56].

These observations concerning the cytological peculiarities of cancer cells are entirely substantiated by modern cytology, but their interpretation is different nowadays: the chromosomal changes in cancer cells may not represent the cause, but the consequence, of alterations in the cytoplasmic nucleoproteins (Biesele *et al.*, 1956).

The problem of possible equivalents of cancer cells in Protozoa is considered in greater detail in a small book by J. C. Mottram (1942), dealing with the application of blastogenic agents to ciliates. He studied the action of carcinogenic hydrocarbons, ultraviolet radiation, radioactivity, and heat upon the Infusoria *Colpidium* and occasionally observed the appearance of abnormal cells. Comparing the abnormal cells of ciliates arising in the culture under the action of carcinogenic agents with the cells of malignant tumors in vertebrates, Mottram noticed a significant similarity between them in the following respects:

Tumors in Vertebrates	*Abnormal Cells in Infusoria*
1. Induced by blastogenic agents	1. Produced by the same agents
2. Occur among actively dividing cells	2. Occur only in dividing cells
3. Occur in punctate manner, only very few of cells become tumor cells	3. Are found only in small numbers in treated cultures
4. Once produced, will continue to grow in the absence of blastogenic agent	4. Will produce populations of abnormal cells in the absence of the agents
5. Can be propagated indefinitely by grafting, without loss of ability to form tumors	5. Can be cultivated indefinitely without loss of capacity to produce populations of abnormal cells
6. Consist of cells of wide morphological variation	6. Produce populations of cells varying widely from normal to monstrous forms

If the abnormal cells in Infusoria, induced by the action of carcinogenic agents, could actually be considered as some equivalents of cancer cells, this generalization would be of great significance for cancer research. Unfortunately, the weak point in the considerations of Metcalf (1928), as well as of Mottram (1942), consists in the fact that there is actually no firm basis for considering the morphological abnormalities arising in the cultures of Infusoria under the action of various agents as true "equivalents" of cancer cells. It is clear that, under the action of carcinogenic substances and of radiation, hereditarily abnormal polymorphic cells do appear in the cultures of Infusoria. But as long as we do not know anything about the respiration and other biochemical characters of these monstrous forms, any comparison of them with tumor cells has no firm basis. It is not impossible that among various morphological abnormalities there may occur some cells worthy of a more detailed investigation from the viewpoint of the biochemical aspects of malignancy. The primary objective, therefore, is to learn to recognize the possible equivalents of cancer cells among Protozoa by their biochemical characteristics.

The advances in biochemistry and physiology of Protozoa attained in recent years point to the possibility of realizing these ends. In the search for possible equivalents of cancer cells in Protozoa, the colorless flagellates are of particular interest. In accordance with current views, the colorless flagellates may represent the possible ancestors of Metazoa: the first multicellular organisms might have originated as the consequence of non-disjunction of the dividing unicellular flagellates (Zachvatkin, 1949). If the colorless flagellates are actually the ancestors of the higher forms of living beings and are nearer to Metazoa than to bacteria, this similarity should extend not only to gross morphology but also to biochemistry. It is well known, for example, that the flagellates, as well as other Protozoa, resemble multicellular animals in their resistance to various antibacterial antibiotics and differ sharply from bacteria. It is also possible to speculate that the equivalents of cancer cells among these organisms might be more akin to tumor cells of animals than the corresponding equivalents of cancer cells in the bacterial world.

There is also another purely technical reason to pay particular attention to colorless flagellates. Some of these, as, for example, *Polytoma uvella,* grow excellently upon the solid nutrient agar media in pure cultures similar to the growth of bacteria (Pringsheim, 1924, 1954). This feature greatly facilitates the utilization of these organisms in the study of the biochemical mutants with impaired respiration. In this group one is concerned with the ancestors of multicellular organisms which can be handled as easily as the cultures of bacteria.

Gause, Kochetkova, and Vladimirova (1959) isolated several new strains of *P. uvella* from infusions of peaty soils and obtained them in pure cultures without bacteria by selecting single colonies from agar media.

Inasmuch as *P. uvella* belongs to Protozoa and not to bacteria, the prospect of its undergoing malignant transformation by carcinogenic hydrocarbons is more promising. We therefore added to the liquid and solid *Polytoma* media a very efficient carcinogenic hydrocarbon (9,10-dimethyl-1,2-benzanthracene) and maintained one of the strains of *P. uvella* in these media for 3 months at 28° C., re-inoculating the cultures every 48 hours from the solid to the liquid medium and vice versa. At the very beginning of this experiment, the carcinogenic preparation stimulated the rate of growth in *P. uvella* and induced the appearance on the solid medium of unusual rose-colored colonies. After numerous isolations and subsequent cultivation of cells from such colonies in the presence of hydrocarbon, we finally obtained a strain of *P. uvella* which constantly formed, on the agar media without hydrocarbon, colonies of small size and orange-rose color. Another strain of *P. uvella* which was not exposed to the action of carcinogenic hydrocarbon formed on agar media larger, white, colonies.

In the mutant culture of *P. uvella* the consumption of oxygen is only 62 per cent of that of normal respiration. These differences are fixed by heredity and were maintained for a long time during numerous passages on the common nutrient media. The impairment of respiration in this case is quantitatively similar to that observed in some strains of cancer cells.

The induction of biochemical mutants with the impaired respiration in Protozoa, which was earlier attained in the yeast, fungi, and bacteria, demonstrates the expanding frontier of investigation of the equivalents of cancer cells in the world of microorganisms. The utilization of these biochemical mutants for the study of the problem of malignant transformation of the living cell testifies to the potential power of modern microbiology for the elucidation of some aspects of cancer. It is hoped that many important problems of the malignant transformation of the cell which in the past were unsuccessfully attacked by frontal assault may in the future be outflanked, where they cannot be stormed, by studies using the equivalents of cancer cells among microorganisms.

THE SEARCH FOR ANTICANCER SUBSTANCES

We have been concerned heretofore with biochemical mutants of microorganisms with impaired respiration as possible biological equivalents of cancer, whose study could contribute important comparative material to the problem of malignant transformations of the living cell. At this point, we would like to concentrate on another aspect of these investigations and attempt to utilize these mutants for practical purposes as possible tools for the detection of anticancer substances. It would be interesting to use these mutants as sensitive detectors in the search for new antibiotics and synthetic preparations selectively inhibiting cells whose metabolism is altered in the "cancer" direction. In this special case, one can visualize a tendency of the last hundred years: the transformation of the philosophy of nature into technology.

The first step in an attempt to utilize mutants with impaired respiration for any screening work should consist of an investigation of the action on these mutants of the already known anticancer substances, whose selective effect on neoplasms has been proved experimentally or even clinically. Do these substances with the already recognized anticancer properties actually produce any selective inhibition of the biochemical mutants of microorganisms with impaired respiration?

Experiments made in this direction by Gause, Kochetkova, and Vladimirova (1959) with such anticancer preparations as degranol (a combination of nitrogen mustard with mannite), actinomycin C, as well as antimetabolites of nucleic acids (6-mercaptopurine and 6-azauracil riboside), have shown that these substances possess selective inhibitory action upon biochemical mutants of staphylococci and *B. coli* with impaired respiration. At the same time, such antibiotics as penicillin and streptomycin, possessing no antitumor action, inhibit the growth of the parent culture of staphylococci as well as that of the biochemical mutants derived from it to the same degree. On the other hand, the antibiotic albomycin does not at all inhibit the growth of mutant cultures with impaired oxidation and possesses bacteriostatic action only upon the parent culture with normal respiration. Albomycin contains iron in its molecule, and it inhibits the growth of bacteria only in the presence of oxygen; the impairment of the respiratory mechanism in the bacterial cell makes this substance no longer effective. One has to conclude, therefore, that the selective inhibitory action of anticancer substances on bacterial mutants does not depend upon some general physiological weakness of the latter but is due to the mechanism of action of the substances under study. Common antibacterial antibiotics inhibit the growth of the parent cultures and of their biochemical mutants to the same degree, and, finally, there are substances entirely ineffective against the mutants.

Similar results were obtained also in the testing of some anticancer substances upon the cultures of the flagellate, *P. uvella*. Actinomycin C, possessing some anticancer action, preferentially inhibits the mutant culture of *Polytoma* with the impaired respiration, whereas quinine and atabrine, devoid of any anticancer properties, inhibit the growth of the normal and mutant cultures of *Polytoma* to the same degree (Gause, Kochetkova, and Vladimirova, 1959).

Inasmuch as some already known anticancer preparations exhibit selective inhibitory action upon the biochemical mutants of microorganisms with impaired respiration, the latter acquire some significance as possible detectors in the search for new anticancer substances. One can use these biochemical mutants for the screening of substances which selectively inhibit the growth of cells with impaired oxidation. This procedure could be helpful for the detection of possible antitumor substances in the cultures of microorganisms. The biochemical mutants give us an opportunity to select substances with definite mechanisms of inhibitory action instead of carrying out purely empirical search for new antibiotics.

It is sometimes said that biochemical mutants of microorganisms with impaired respiration might be of some interest in the screening work for anticancer substances only if the hereditary respiratory damage in cancer cells represents the cause and not the consequence of their malignancy. But, fortunately, this is not justified. If the primary cause of cell malignancy is intimately related to some disturbance in the nucleic acids or elsewhere and if the respiratory damage represents only the consequence of this still unknown primary effect, it is immaterial for the present purpose. It is the cell that gives us the proper answer in the screening work. One induces malignancy by carcinogenic agents and searches for the selective inhibitions of cells altered in this particular way. It is therefore perfectly irrelevant for the screening work whether the respiratory damage represents the primary or the secondary alteration in the metabolism of the malignant cell. We have already noted that the antimetabolites of nucleic acids that were tested in the expectation of their interference with nucleic acid metabolism are, in fact, producing selective inhibition of the growth of biochemical mutants of microorganisms with impaired respiration.

Another point which concerns the general problem of chemotherapy and should be taken into consideration is the relation between the action in vitro and in vivo. The selective action upon the cells with impaired respiration represents an in vitro test, which may or may not be accompanied by the selective action in vivo. It is always necessary, therefore, that the substances detected in the in vitro test should be subjected to trial on laboratory animals inoculated with various tumors.

CONCLUSION

The search for possible equivalents of cancer cells among microorganisms may be considered as an answer to the plea, made by Ilya Metchnikoff fifty years ago, in which he insisted on the urgent need of a broad biological approach to problems of pathology. The study of evolution has proved that all living beings on earth are related to one another through origin from common ancestors. It represents an obvious basis for suggestion that certain pathological processes may appear in their most primitive forms in lower organisms, where their expression is particularly favorable for analysis. It is this idea which inspired Metchnikoff to work on the comparative pathology of inflammation more than fifty years ago. One can hope that at the present level of development of cancer research a broad biological approach aimed at the discovery of possible equivalents of cancer cells among microorganisms and an elucidation of the problem of malignant transformation of the living cell could also be helpful.

In his paper, "On Darwinism," originally delivered at the 1909 Darwin Celebration in Cambridge, Metchnikoff (1943) explains how Darwin's work stimulated the development of his ideas in the field of comparative pathology. It does not seem that Darwin's biological philosophy incorporated much concern with microbial life or that he ever mentioned cancer cells. But it is quite clear that the Darwinian doctrine, or at least the climate of opinion in which it evolved, in the course of the last hundred years has influenced and is still influencing the very mode of approach to the practical problems of pathology.

BIBLIOGRAPHY

BIESELE, J., GREY, C., and MOTTRAM, F. 1956. "Some Early Effects of Carcinogenic Hydrocarbons on Mouse Skin," *Ann. New York Acad. Sci.*, LXIII, 1303.

CHANCE, B., and CASTOR, L. 1952. "Some Patterns of the Respiratory Pigments of Ascites Tumors in Mice," *Science*, CXVI, 200.

CHANCE, B. and HESS, B. 1959. "Spectroscopic Evidence of Metabolic Control," *Science*, CXXIX, 700.

EPHRUSSI, B., HOTTINGUER, H., and CHIMENES, A. 1949. "Action de l'acriflavine sur les levures. I. La Mutation petite colonie," *Ann. Inst. Pasteur*, LXXVI, 351.

GAUSE, G. F. 1958. "The Search for Anticancer Antibiotics: Some Theoretical Problems," *Science*, CXXVII, 506.

GAUSE, G. F., IVANITSKAIA, L. P., and VLADIMIROVA, G. B. 1958a. "On Cytochrome System in Biochemical Mutants of *Bacterium coli* and Staphylococci with Imparied Oxidation," *Doklady Acad. Sci. USSR*, CXVIII, 189.

———. 1958b. "On Biochemical Mutants in Bacteria with Impaired Respiration," *Isvest. Acad. Sci. USSR*, ser. biol., VI, 719.

GAUSE, G. F., KOCHETKOVA, G. V., and VLADIMIROVA, G. B. 1957a. "On Biochemical Mutants in Yeast Cells with Impaired Oxidation," *Doklady Acad. Sci. USSR*, CXVII, 138.

———. 1957b. "Biochemical Mutants of Staphylococci with Impaired Oxidation as Tests in the Search for Anticancer Antibiotics," *ibid.*, p. 720.

———. 1959. "On the Action of Some Anticancer Substances upon the Biochemical Mutants of Microorganisms with Impaired Respiration," *ibid.*, CXXIV, 3.

GREENSTEIN, J. P. 1954. *Biochemistry of Cancer*. 2d ed. New York: Academic Press.

HASKINS, F., TISSIERES, A., and MITCHELL, H. and M. 1953. "Cytochromes and the Succinic Acid Oxidase System of Poky Strains of *Neurospora*," *Jour. Biol. Chem.*, CC, 819.

HUXLEY, J. 1958. *Biological Aspects of Cancer*. London: Allen & Unwin; New York: Harcourt, Brace & Co.

LETTRÉ, H., and SACHSENMAIER, W. 1957. "Trockengewichte der Fraktionen von normalen und malignen Zellen," *Naturwiss.*, XIV, 335.

LINDEGREN, C., and HINO, S. 1957. "The Effect of Anaerobiosis on the Origin of Respiratory-deficient Yeast," *Exper. Cell Res.*, XII, 163.

LINDEGREN, C., and NAGAI, S., and H. 1958. "Induction of Respiratory Deficiency in Yeast by Manganese, Copper, Cobalt, and Nickel," *Nature*, CLXXXII, 446.

MEISEL, M. N., and ZAVARZINA, N. B. 1947. "The Action of Carcinogenic Hydrocarbons upon Microbial Cell," *Zhur. Gen. Biol.* (Moscow), VIII, 37.

METCALF, M. N. 1928. "Cancer in Certain Protozoa?" *Amer. Jour. Trop. Med.,* VIII, 545.

METCHNIKOFF, I. 1943. "On Darwinism." In *Collected Papers.* Moscow.

MOTTRAM, J. C. 1942. *The Problem of Tumours: The Application of Blastogenic Agents to Ciliates: A Cytoplasmic Hypothesis.* London: Lewis.

PRINGSHEIM, E. 1924. "Algenkultur," *Handb. biol. Arbeitsmeth.,* Abt. XI, Teil 2, p. 377.

———. 1954. *Algenreinkulturen: Ihre Herstellung und Erhaltung.* Jena: Fischer.

SLONIMSKI, P. 1949. "Môde d'utilisation du glucose par les mutants petite colonie," *Ann. Inst. Pasteur,* LXXVI, 510.

TAVLITZKI, J. 1949. "Étude de la croissance des mutants petite colonie," *Ann. Inst. Pasteur,* LXXVI, 497.

THOMAS, P. T., EVANS, H. J., and HUGHES, D. T. 1956. "Chemically Induced Neoplasms in Fungi," *Nature,* CLXXVIII, 949.

TISSIERES, A., and MITCHELL, H. 1954. "Cytochromes and Respiratory Activities in Some Slow Growing Strains of *Neurospora,*" *Jour. Biol. Chem.,* CCVIII, 241.

TISSIERES, A., MITCHELL, H., and HASKINS, F. 1953. "Studies on the Respiratory System of the Poky Strain of *Neurospora,*" *Jour. Biol. Chem.,* CCV, 423.

WARBURG, O. 1926. *Über den Stoffwechsel der Tumoren.* Berlin: Springer.

———. 1956. "On the Origin of Cancer Cells," *Science,* CXXIII, 309; CXXIV, 269.

WEINHOUSE, S. 1955. "Oxidative Metabolism of Neoplastic Tissues," *Adv. Cancer Res.,* III, 269.

ZACHVATKIN, A. A. 1949. *The Comparative Embryology of Lower Invertebrates.* Moscow.